The Great Ideas

Man
Mathematics
Matter
Mechanics
Medicine
Memory and Imagination
Metaphysics
Mind
Monarchy
Nature
Necessity and Contingency
Oligarchy
One and Many
Opinion
Opposition
Philosophy
Physics
Pleasure and Pain
Poetry
Principle
Progress
Prophecy
Prudence
Punishment
Quality
Quantity
Reasoning
Relation
Religion
Revolution
Rhetoric
Same and Other
Science
Sense
Sign and Symbol
Sin
Slavery
Soul
Space
State
Temperance
Theology
Time
Truth
Tyranny
Universal and Particular
Virtue and Vice
War and Peace
Wealth
Will
Wisdom
World

Among Greeks of the classical period, the paradigm of science was mathematics and mathematical astronomy. In this detail from Raphael's "The School of Athens," Euclid is surrounded by a group of eager followers as he explains some rare mathematical truth.

The Great Ideas Today

1983

Encyclopædia Britannica, Inc.

CHICAGO
AUCKLAND • GENEVA • LONDON • MANILA • PARIS • ROME • SEOUL • SYDNEY • TOKYO • TORONTO

Library of Congress Number: 61-65561
International Standard Book Number: 0-85229-411-5
International Standard Serial Number: 0072-7288
Printed in the U.S.A.

A NOTE ON REFERENCE STYLE

In the following pages, passages in *Great Books of the Western World* are referred to by the initials '*GBWW*,' followed by volume, page number, and page section. Thus, '*GBWW*, Vol. 39, p. 210b' refers to page 210 in Adam Smith's *The Wealth of Nations*, which is Volume 39 in *Great Books of the Western World*. The small letter 'b' indicates the page section. In books printed in single column, 'a' and 'b' refer to the upper and lower halves of the page. In books printed in double column, 'a' and 'b' refer to the upper and lower halves of the left column, 'c' and 'd' to the upper and lower halves of the right column. For example, 'Vol. 53, p. 210b' refers to the lower half of page 210, since Volume 53, James's *Principles of Psychology*, is printed in single column. On the other hand, 'Vol. 7, p. 210b' refers to the lower left quarter of the page, since Volume 7, Plato's *Dialogues*, is printed in double column.

Gateway to the Great Books is referred to by the initials '*GGB*,' followed by volume and page number. Thus, '*GGB*, Vol. 10, pp. 39–57' refers to pages 39 through 57 of Volume 10 of *Gateway to the Great Books*, which is James's essay, "The Will to Believe."

The Great Ideas Today is referred to by the initials '*GIT*,' followed by the year and page number. Thus '*GIT* 1968, p. 210' refers to page 210 of the 1968 edition of *The Great Ideas Today*.

Contents

Preface

This year again, as for several years past, we omit the symposium discussion of a topic of current interest with which issues of *The Great Ideas Today* used to begin—omit it for the reason, among others, that as the contents of the book have to be determined many months in advance of publication, in order that contributors may have the time they need to write the sort of articles we request of them, we can no longer be confident, given the pace of change in this rapidly spinning world, that any topic selected for discussion will actually be current by the time the book appears. So we now leave such currency to publications that are more quickly assembled and more frequently printed than is possible with an annual such as ours.

If we seem nevertheless to have landed in the very midst of a timely controversy with the first of two essays that comprise our review of developments in the arts and sciences—an essay on evolution by Steven M. Stanley of the Johns Hopkins University—it is because any consideration of that subject is likely to suggest a response to the Creationist teachings that were enacted into law in certain parts of the country not long ago as curricular requirements, before the courts threw them out. In fact, Professor Stanley has little if anything to say about such teachings. His essay is evidence rather of the continuing revision of Darwinian theory which is going on in science, a revision not in Darwin's basic hypothesis, of which there can be no doubt (evolution is perhaps the most overwhelmingly substantiated theory that empirical science has ever come up with), but in the manner and the pace according to which the emergence (and disappearance) of species has been accomplished. The correction of our understanding of this which now seems possible is set forth with great clarity and persuasiveness by Professor Stanley.

A second article in this section of the volume provides at long last what readers of *The Great Ideas Today* have more than once indicated they would like to see, which is an account of mathematics in our time. The problem with such an undertaking, which is that any serious discussion of mathematics must to some extent be mathematical, and that, if it is, it will be too difficult to grasp, has happily been overcome by Felix Browder, who is chairman of the department of mathematics at the University of Chicago. Professor Browder discusses his subject in a manner that, if not always easy to follow, is no harder than it requires, and as in addition he has conceived his task in terms that justify a lengthy survey of the history of mathematics, readers will find themselves doubly informed.

Two essays that will serve as rereadings of the Great Books follow these articles. One is a discussion of Galen by Douglas Buchanan, himself a physician and longtime reader of Great Books, who was invited by the editors to become a contributor on the strength of an earlier paper he had written on Galen as a physiologist, which is incorporated into the longer essay that appears here. A second piece devoted to Great Books authors is Owen Gingerich's account of the astronomers who are to be found in volume 16 of *GBWW*—that is, Ptolemy, Copernicus, and Kepler— whose writings Professor Gingerich, a contributor to previous issues of *The Great Ideas Today,* has taught for many years in his classes at Harvard. Readers who feel intimidated by the scientific works in the *GBWW* will be reassured by the discussion of these writings, which is intended by Professor Gingerich for the nonspecialist, and which may serve for anyone as the ideal introduction to the materials with which it deals.

This year's issue also offers an editorial essay, the work of the staff of the Institute for Philosophical Research, working with the Institute's Director, Mortimer J. Adler, on the subject of civil police. These are the only kind of police which are appropriate to a civil society, and although arguably they are indispensable to the maintenance of any civil government, by curious omission they did not exist until recent times.

In addition, there are two essays that may be regarded as special features. One is a discussion by Otto Bird, our consulting editor, of the relation between poetry and philosophy as they appear in *The Divine Comedy.* The other is an essay by Clifton Fadiman on children as readers of books—that is, on the character of children's imagination, their taste, and their literary perception. Mr. Fadiman, who is as near an authority on the subject as anyone who is not a child can presume to be, has added a list of children's books which have established themselves as favorites since they first appeared, and endeavors to suggest why that is so.

In still another part of the volume, two recent books which have been thought of interest to readers of *The Great Ideas Today* are discussed by contributors both of whom have appeared in previous issues. First is Charles Van Doren, who wrote last year on *The Mind's I,* edited by Douglas R. Hofstadter and Daniel C. Dennett; on *Brainstorms,* by Daniel C. Dennett; and on *Mind Design* edited by John Haugeland. Mr. Van Doren is here concerned with Fernand Braudel's depiction of the Mediterranean world in the age of Philip the Second, a massive work by one of the most celebrated and, Mr. Van Doren suggests, among the greatest of living historians. Braudel's is not history as most people understand the term, however, but something by comparison very rich and strange, and those who have not yet made the acquaintance of his works will be tempted to do so, we think, by this account of him.

A second review essay is by Ramsey Clark, the former United States Attorney General, now a practicing lawyer much concerned with public issues, who discusses a volume of essays by Scott Buchanan, one of which appeared in an earlier *Great Ideas Today* (*GIT* 1972, pp. 4–21). Buchanan, who served on the editorial advisory board of *Great Books of the Western World*, wrote most of these essays while a fellow of the Center for the Study of Democratic Institutions in Santa Barbara, California. This collection of his papers on law and politics is the first of several volumes that his friends and former students intend to bring out of his writings, which have long been out of print.

Three works that may be regarded as additions to the Great Books library which *The Great Ideas Today* has accumulated over the years finish out this issue of the annual. The first consists of the introduction and a number of samples from Kepler's *New Astronomy*, a work of 1609 in which Kepler demonstrated the ellipsoid pattern of the planets' motion around the sun, in particular that of Mars. His marvelous introduction to this book, as well as certain sample chapters from it, are offered here in a new translation, portions of which are by Professor Gingerich and others by William Donahue.

Kepler's work is followed by what is generally considered the best, as it was also the last, of the tragedies written by Racine during the great period of French classical drama, his *Phaedra*. Based on the *Hippolytus* of Euripides (*GBWW*, vol. 5, pp. 225–236), it is a play that recounts the guilty passion of Phaedra, queen of Athens, for Hippolytus, the son of Theseus, king of the city and her husband. Racine makes Phaedra the central figure of the story, whereas for Euripides, as for the Greeks generally, it was rather Hippolytus, if not Theseus himself.

And finally, for the first time in *The Great Ideas Today*, there is a book by Nietzsche, *The Birth of Tragedy*. This is an essay on the drama of the Greeks which is celebrated for its analysis of the conflict between what it calls Apollonian and Dionysian elements in Greek culture and its perception of the harsh character of the Greek tragic vision (as distinct from the serenity that Matthew Arnold, for example, believed the plays contained). *The Birth of Tragedy* remains an essay of great power and interest, although its thesis is no longer accepted as wholly adequate or even entirely correct. It was Nietzsche's first book, and one that, given its development, is easier to read than his subsequent writings, which are set in his more familiar aphoristic style, can ever be.

PART ONE

Current Developments in the Arts and Sciences

Evolution of Life: Evidence for a New Pattern

Steven M. Stanley

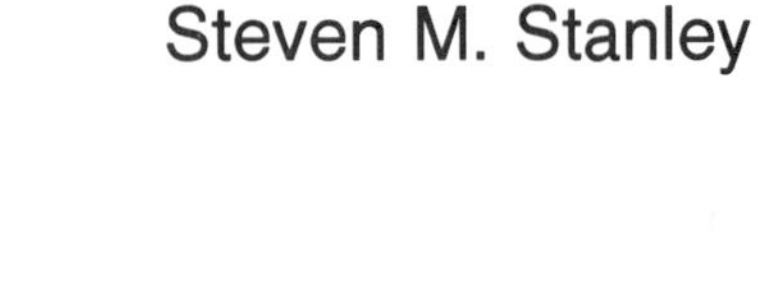

Steven M. Stanley is a professor of paleobiology at the Johns Hopkins University. He did his undergraduate work at Princeton University and received his Ph.D. from Yale in 1968. He began his scientific career studying living organisms—bivalve mollusks—and later applied his conclusions to the interpretation of their evolution as recorded in the fossil record. In the early 1970s he began to undertake more general studies, interpreting trends, rates, and patterns of evolution from the fossils he studied. This further led him to explore ways of testing the punctuational model of evolution and examining its consequences. Recently he has been interested in patterns of extinction, especially the causes of mass extinctions of marine life.

In 1973 Professor Stanley received the Maryland Academy of Science's Allan C. Davis Medal for the outstanding young scientist of the year. He was also awarded the Schuchert Award by the Paleontological Society in 1977 for contributions to teaching and research before the age of forty.

He has written many scientific articles in his field as well as two recent books: *Macroevolution: Pattern and Process* (1979) and a less technical volume, *The New Evolutionary Timetable: Fossils, Genes, and The Origin of Species* (1981).

For decades, most evolutionary biologists have assumed that the many species populating the world around them are in a process of slow but substantial evolutionary change. The prevailing idea has been that species continually evolve to meet changes in the environment, and that this evolution, over long intervals of time, produces large-scale restructuring of most species. This traditional view of large-scale evolution has become known as the gradualistic view, and it can be traced back to Charles Darwin. Darwin expressed the gradualistic view many times and in many different ways in his great book *On the Origin of Species.* Perhaps his most eloquent expression of the view is in the following passage (Darwin, 1859, p. 84; cf. *GBWW,* Vol. 49, p. 42):

> It may metaphorically be said that natural selection is daily and hourly scrutinising, throughout the world, the slightest variations; rejecting those that are bad, preserving and adding up all that are good; silently and insensibly working, *whenever and wherever opportunity offers,* at the improvement of each organic being in relation to its organic and inorganic conditions of life. We see nothing of these slow changes in progress, until the hand of time has marked the lapse of ages. . . .

Natural selection was, of course, the mechanism that Darwin proposed to account for evolution. It amounts to a difference among the individuals of a population in contribution of descendants to future generations. The kinds of individuals that, in time, come to predominate in a population are those that, by virtue of long life or high reproductive rate, produce relatively large numbers of fertile offspring. Darwin asserted that as long as new kinds of individuals appear in each generation of an established species, there is raw material available for the biological transformation of the species in a slow but ultimately profound way.

Also conveying this gradualistic view of evolution is the only illustration to be found in *On the Origin of Species* (reproduced here as figure 1). This diagram represents a tree of life, and in presenting it, Darwin established a metaphor for evolutionary branching that has become familiar to all educated people of the Western world. Actually, what Darwin plotted was not so much a tree as a bush, whose branches had grown diagonally upward in many directions. Each branch represents what is known as a lineage, or a line of evolutionary descent. On a graph such as this, the

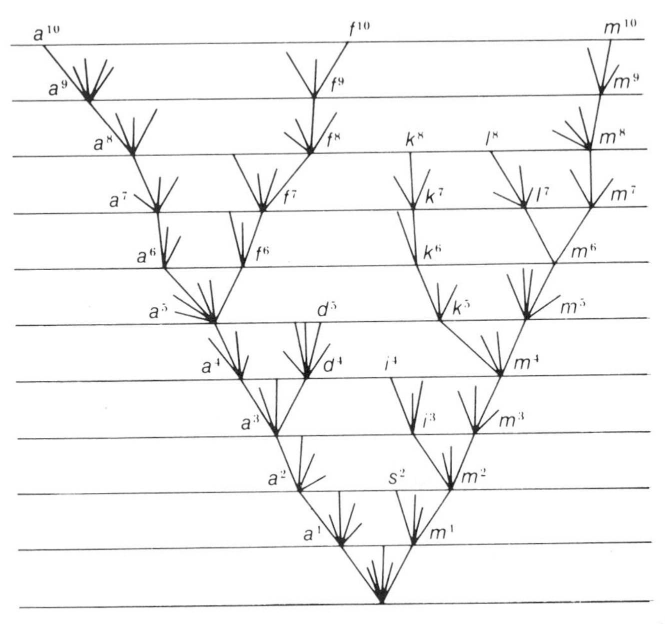

Figure 1. The only illustration that Darwin published in *On the Origin of Species.* This is the first portrayal of the "tree of life" in the era of modern evolutionary biology. The diagonal lines represent biological lineages, or lines of evolutionary descent, with the vertical axis representing time and the horizontal axis representing one or more biological traits. Note that the origin of a new lineage is not associated with rapid evolutionary divergence (a new lineage does not branch from its ancestral lineage at an especially low angle on the graph).

vertical axis represents time and the horizontal axis, one or more biological traits that are evolving—often one or more aspects of size or shape. Thus, the angle of a branch depicts the rate of evolution within that branch: the more horizontal the branch, the more rapid the evolution.

An important aspect of Darwin's hypothetical tree of life is that its branches did not originate by means of unusually rapid evolutionary change. No branch departed suddenly from its parent branch along a nearly horizontal path and later bent upward to record a subsequent history of much slower change. This point relates to a major source of controversy in the field of evolutionary biology today.

Many evolutionists, particularly ones specializing in the study of fossils, now argue that most evolutionary change is associated with the rapid origins of species. There are two facets to this so-called punctuational view of evolution. One is the idea that most evolution occurs when one species buds rapidly from another; the second is the idea that once a species has budded from another and taken firm hold of a place in nature—once it is populous and widely distributed—it experiences relatively little further evolution. The budding of one species from another is known as speciation. The occurrence of speciation has, of course, long been recognized. At issue is what it actually achieves in the evolutionary history of a group of animals or plants. Does speciation simply add a new lineage that departs slowly in some new evolutionary direction? Or does it often entail sudden evolutionary change?

The persistence of Darwin's gradualistic view, which downplays the role of speciation, can be seen in the writing of prominent evolutionists of the twentieth century. The modern synthesis emerged in the 1940s, after three decades of controversy about the mechanism of evolution, as a reaffirmation of Darwinism in the context of modern genetics. The new movement took its name from the title of a book, *Evolution, The Modern Synthesis,* written by Julian Huxley in 1942. Here Huxley wrote:

> Species-formation constitutes one aspect of evolution; but a large fraction of it is in a sense an accident, a biological luxury, without bearing upon the major and continuing trends of the evolutionary process.

Theodosius Dobzhansky, the foremost experimental geneticist of the mid-twentieth century, likewise attributed little importance to rapidly divergent speciation. In an article published in 1972, he finally began to see the matter differently, and in this article he described the slow, rather than rapid, divergence of new species from their ancestors not as the certain but merely as the "usual, and by now orthodox, view."

Other biologists and paleontologists had occasionally expressed skepticism of the orthodox view—some in mild ways and some with radical alternatives. The radical claims were rejected out of hand, and even the mild views were crushed beneath the weight of the gradualistic establishment.

A crucial issue in the emergence of the gradualistic view of evolution related to the quality of the fossil record. When Darwin formulated his gradualistic view during the middle part of the last century, he was quite naturally compelled to look to the fossil record for confirmation. When he did so, he was sorely disappointed. His hope had been to find laid out before him in the stratigraphic column sequences of populations documenting the gradual transformation of species. What he encountered instead were discrete species that showed virtually no change in shape between their first and last appearances. Darwin responded to this situation by challenging the quality of fossil evidence. He devoted many pages of *On the Origin of Species* to arguments that the fossil record was woefully incomplete. Among his passages on this subject was the following:

> The noble science of Geology loses glory from the extreme imperfection of the record. The crust of the earth with its embedded remains must not be looked at as a well-filled museum, but as a poor collection made at hazard and at rare intervals.

It is notable that Darwin did not reach this conclusion by careful scrutiny of the fossil record. On the other hand, careful scrutiny by a lone scientist in Darwin's day would hardly have yielded the detailed picture that we are developing at the present time. Not only are we reaping the harvests of thousands of expert paleontologists whose collective efforts have spanned many decades; we have at our disposal good estimates of the absolute ages of fossils, based on measurements of the radioactive decay of naturally occurring chemical elements. Darwin was quite honest in admitting that he had not shown the fossil record to be incomplete on the basis of independent evidence but had deduced the poor quality of the record from its failure to support his gradualistic picture of evolution. In *On the Origin of Species,* he wrote:

> But I do not pretend that I should ever have suspected how poor was the record in the best preserved geological sections, had not the absence of innumerable transitional links between the species . . . pressed so hardly on my theory.

That Darwin devoted so much of his book to a negative evaluation of the quality of fossil evidence testifies to his great concern about the problem. He confessed that the failure of the fossil record to document gradual evolution was "probably the gravest and most obvious of all the many objections which may be urged against my views."

There was, in fact, a way of resolving the difficulty that Darwin chose not to pursue. This would have been to propose that most evolutionary change has been concentrated in sudden branching events within the tree of life—to accept the idea that species have formed rapidly and then have experienced relatively little evolutionary change, even if they have survived for millions of years thereafter.

The new challenge

It is, in fact, increased faith in the fossil record that has led to the challenge that during the past decade has been leveled at the gradualistic view of evolution. "Faith" is perhaps a poorly chosen word, because the new ideas have an empirical foundation. They are rooted in fossil data.

In 1954, Ernst Mayr suggested that the sudden appearance of evolutionary novelties in the fossil record might reflect the actual pattern of evolution rather than the extreme imperfection of the record.

Mayr, a biologist, did not arrive at these ideas by studying the fossil record, however. His ideas were based on observations of living species of birds. Mayr noted that many species of birds seemed to have evolved rapidly and recently from small populations of parent species—populations situated near the peripheries of the geographic ranges of the parent

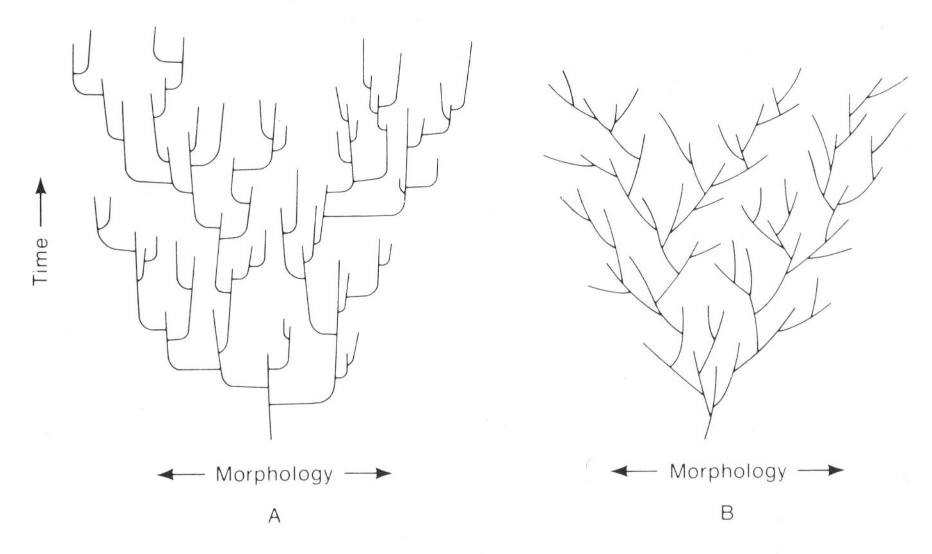

Figure 2. Idealized trees of life depicting the punctuational model of evolution (left) and the gradualistic model (right). The gradualistic tree resembles the tree published by Darwin, in that branching events do not characteristically accelerate evolution; they merely establish new pathways for gradual evolution. The punctuational tree, in contrast, depicts a pattern in which many branching events are associated with accelerated evolution, whereas once established, new branches (species) evolve very slowly; the result is that most evolution is associated with branching events.

species. Mayr reasoned that, in general, local speciation events might be the source of most major evolutionary transitions.

More recently, the idea that most evolution is concentrated in speciation events (branching events by which the tree of life grows) has been formalized as the *punctuational model* of evolution. The alternative view, that most evolution takes place by the slow transformation of well-established, populous species, represents the *gradualistic model.* The two models entail quite different shapes for the tree of life (figure 2). In effect, the punctuational view transforms the traditional tree into something resembling a saguaro cactus.

It is primarily paleontologists who, during the past decade, have tested this idea, championed it, and explored its consequences. While their case rests in part on biological arguments, like those of Ernst Mayr, paleontological data form its primary foundation. Most compelling is evidence that large numbers of species have existed for vast stretches of geologic time. This and other lines of evidence will be outlined below, but first, three points about the punctuational model deserve mention.

First, the punctuational view of the fossil record sees that record as being much more complete than Darwin and many others have envisioned, but still not perfect. The record is faithful enough to demonstrate that very minor evolutionary change is the rule for large, well-established species; on the other hand, the record is generally not good enough to document geologically rapid change—change accomplished in less than a few tens of thousands of years—within a small population restricted to a local area. Fossil evidence that well-established species are stable forces us to conclude that small populations must be the sites of most evolution. This constitutes almost total reliance on negative evidence, but many scientific tests are similarly based. If there are only two alternatives (in this case, that most change occurs in populous species or that most change occurs in small populations), then the elimination of one alternative renders the other almost certainly valid. Actually, there is a third alternative for the pattern of evolution, which entails the sudden transformation of an entire large species—a sort of rebirth, but arguments will be advanced below to the effect that dramatic events of this type are unlikely to play a major role in evolution.

Second, it should be understood that not all speciation events produce marked change. We have clear evidence that many species have budded off from others with little alteration. Pairs of species known as sibling species, for example, consist of two nearly identical members, one of which has usually evolved from the other. The punctuational view simply holds that *some* speciation events accomplish major changes and that such changes account for most evolution in the history of life.

Third, the punctuational view does not rule out a dominant role for natural selection as the agent of evolutionary change. Natural selection, as proposed by Darwin, has two aspects. What the process amounts to is the contribution of different kinds of individuals to the genetic composition of future generations. One aspect has to do with survival through the reproductive period of life: the longer an individual lives, the more offspring it is likely to engender. The other aspect has to do with rate of production of offspring: even an individual having only an average life span can contribute a disproportionately large number of offspring to the next generation if it produces them at a high rate. The best of both worlds in natural selection is living an unusually long time and being unusually fecund in the process. Of course, processes other than natural selection could still play major roles in the rapid emergence of new species within small populations. The point is simply that the punctuational model by no means demands that we abandon traditional Darwinian natural selection as the prevailing mechanism of change.

The test of adaptive radiation

One way of investigating whether the gradual transformation of established species can have been responsible for most evolution in the history of life is to look to the place where most evolution has occurred: adaptive radiation. Adaptive radiation is the rapid proliferation of new taxa (species, genera, and groups of higher rank) from some ancestral group. "Radiation" is an apt metaphor for the expansion of many new forms of life from a common source. The fossil record provides clear evidence that most major evolutionary transitions occur within adaptive radiations. One of the most spectacular of these took place not long ago, by geological standards, and its relatively recent occurrence leaves its history well displayed in the fossil record. This large-scale event is also of interest to us because we are one of its most conspicuous products. It is the adaptive radiation of the class Mammalia, which gave the most recent geological era, the Cenozoic, its nickname—the Age of Mammals.

Before primitive mammals began their great adaptive radiation, they had been in existence for about 150 million years—a long stretch of time even to a geologist. They had, however, remained small and inconspicuous; the largest were no larger than a house cat, and many species may have been nocturnal. There is little question that during this long interval before their modern radiation the mammals' great evolutionary potential was held in check by the remarkable success of the dinosaurs. The dinosaurs had got off to an evolutionary head start on the mammals, and during their reign on Earth they undoubtedly suppressed the mammals through both competitive interference and predation. But about 65 million years ago, for reasons that are still debated, the dinosaurs disappeared, and the mammals inherited the Earth.

The ensuing adaptive radiation of the mammals accomplished a great deal in a very short interval of geological time. Within about 12 million years—by the end of Early Eocene time—there existed most of the orders of mammals that have ever come into being (figure 3). Most striking in their degree of evolutionary divergence from the ancestral forms, which generally resembled small rodents, were the order that includes the whales and the order that includes the bats. In fact, it appears that each of these two groups evolved from small terrestrial ancestors in much less than 12 million years.

The test of adaptive radiation asks a simple question: During an interval when major evolutionary changes were wrought in the history of a group (during an adaptive radiation), how long were individual species in existence? If a species was gradually remodeled by evolution, it might have accumulated enough changes before extinction to deserve a new name. Because such an evolving lineage represents a continuum, its division by a scientist into two or more species is a matter of arbitrary judgment. What is important in the present context is simply that any set of populations that is grouped as a species encompasses only a small amount of variation in form. If a gradual transformation of species was responsible for most of the evolution that occurred in an adaptive radiation, like the great radiation of modern mammals, then many individual

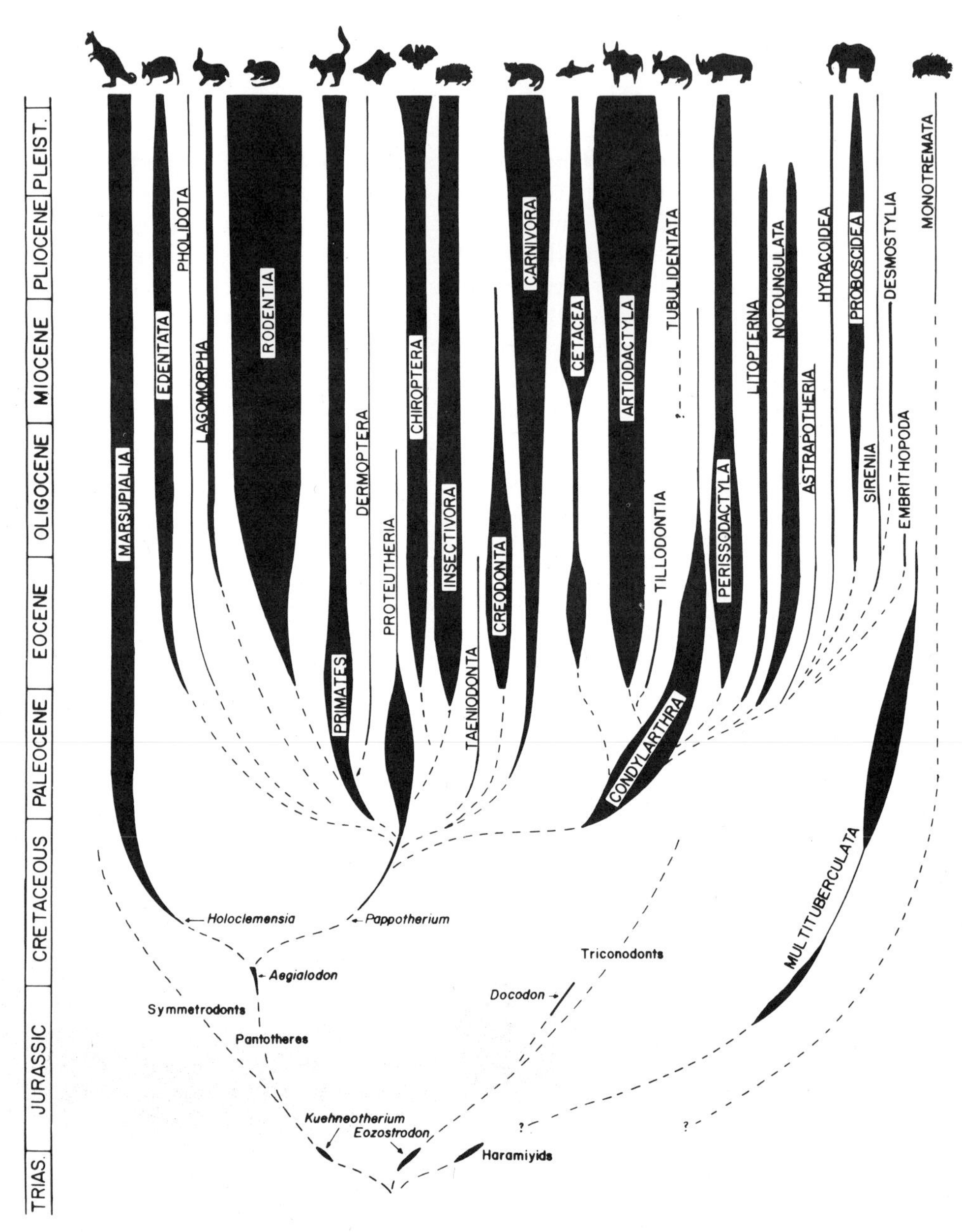

Figure 3. Diagram depicting the adaptive radiation of mammals during the Cenozoic era, or Age of Mammals. A number of groups of small mammals lived during the Mesozoic era, but it was not until the dinosaurs suffered extinction that the mammals began their major adaptive radiation. The vertical bars of the upper part of the diagram represent individual orders of mammals that existed during the Cenozoic era. The width of a bar indicates the number of genera within an order. Most Cenozoic orders were already present by Early Eocene time. (After P. D. Gingerich.)

species could only have existed for very short intervals in comparison to the span of time during which the major evolutionary changes of the radiation took place.

The enormous changes that ushered in the Age of Mammals were achieved in less than 12 million years. As it turns out, species were quite stable during this interval. The Big Horn Basin of Wyoming offers the best documentation of their stability. Here the arid climate of today leaves bare for our scrutiny thick sedimentary deposits of the Early Eocene age (figure 4). During Early Eocene time, the mammalian radiation was in full swing. Within this interval, which lasted no longer than about 5 million years and perhaps as little as 3.5 million, more than a score of new families appeared on Earth, and hundreds of new genera (a genus—plural, genera—is the taxonomic category below the family and above the species). Deposits of the Big Horn Basin accumulated in front of the newly forming Rocky Mountains, and the continuous supply of sediment from the mountains, resulted in an unusually complete stratigraphic record. The rich fossil faunas here represent life of moist, well-vegetated habitats within a subtropical climatic zone.

How long were individual species surviving in the Big Horn Basin region during Early Eocene time, when so many new kinds of mammals were appearing on Earth? Figure 5 reveals that large numbers of species lived for one or two or even three million years without evolving enough to deserve new names. Each of the species represented in this diagram is known from many successive stratigraphic intervals, and yet, as each is traced upward through time, its preserved teeth and bones undergo changes so minor as to be undetectable by experts.

The species whose stratigraphic ranges appear in figure 5 form the Willwood fauna, named for the Willwood Formation, which is the sequence of sediments in which the species have been fossilized. The Willwood fauna must represent a large portion of the Early Eocene fauna of North America. In other words, it constitutes a good statistical sample of what species were doing, in an evolutionary sense, while many new kinds of mammals were appearing on Earth.

Thus, it appears that we must appeal to rapid evolution within small, localized populations whose history is not to be found in the fossil record if we are to account for the major evolutionary transformations of the great mammalian adaptive radiation. Once formed, species were quite stable—far more stable than a decade ago almost any reputable paleontologist or biologist would have predicted. The story told by the Big Horn Basin fossils, whose record is unrivaled in quality by faunas elsewhere in the world, offers strong testimony in favor of the punctuational model of evolution.

Though lacking fossil records as complete as the record of the Willwood mammal fauna, many other groups of animals and plants offer similar evidence of great geological stability.

Figure 4. Early Eocene sediments exposed in badlands of the Big Horn Basin of Wyoming. These sediments, which accumulated under warm, moist conditions, contain what may be the finest readily accessible record of ancient mammal species in the world, and these species survived for long stretches of geologic time without undergoing appreciable evolutionary change. (Photo courtesy of the American Museum of Natural History.)

Figure 5. The recognized stratigraphic ranges of sixty-nine species of fossil mammals in the central part of the Big Horn Basin of Wyoming. Time runs horizontally in the diagram, and the bar at the top of the diagram shows the time scale, with uncertainty indicated by the dashed portion. The entire interval depicted here represents the Early Eocene Age, which lasted at least 3.5 million years and at most 5 million years. The range of each species is shown by a horizontal bar, along which vertical ticks indicate occurrence at particular levels. Arrows at the ends of some bars indicate known occurrence of a species in older or younger sediments at other localities. Species known from only one or two samples are not included in the diagram, but the many species that are plotted might all exhibit substantial evolutionary change and yet none does. In fact, virtually no evolution can be detected in any of the species lineages, even though most span between one and three million years. (After D. Schankler and R. T. Bakker.)

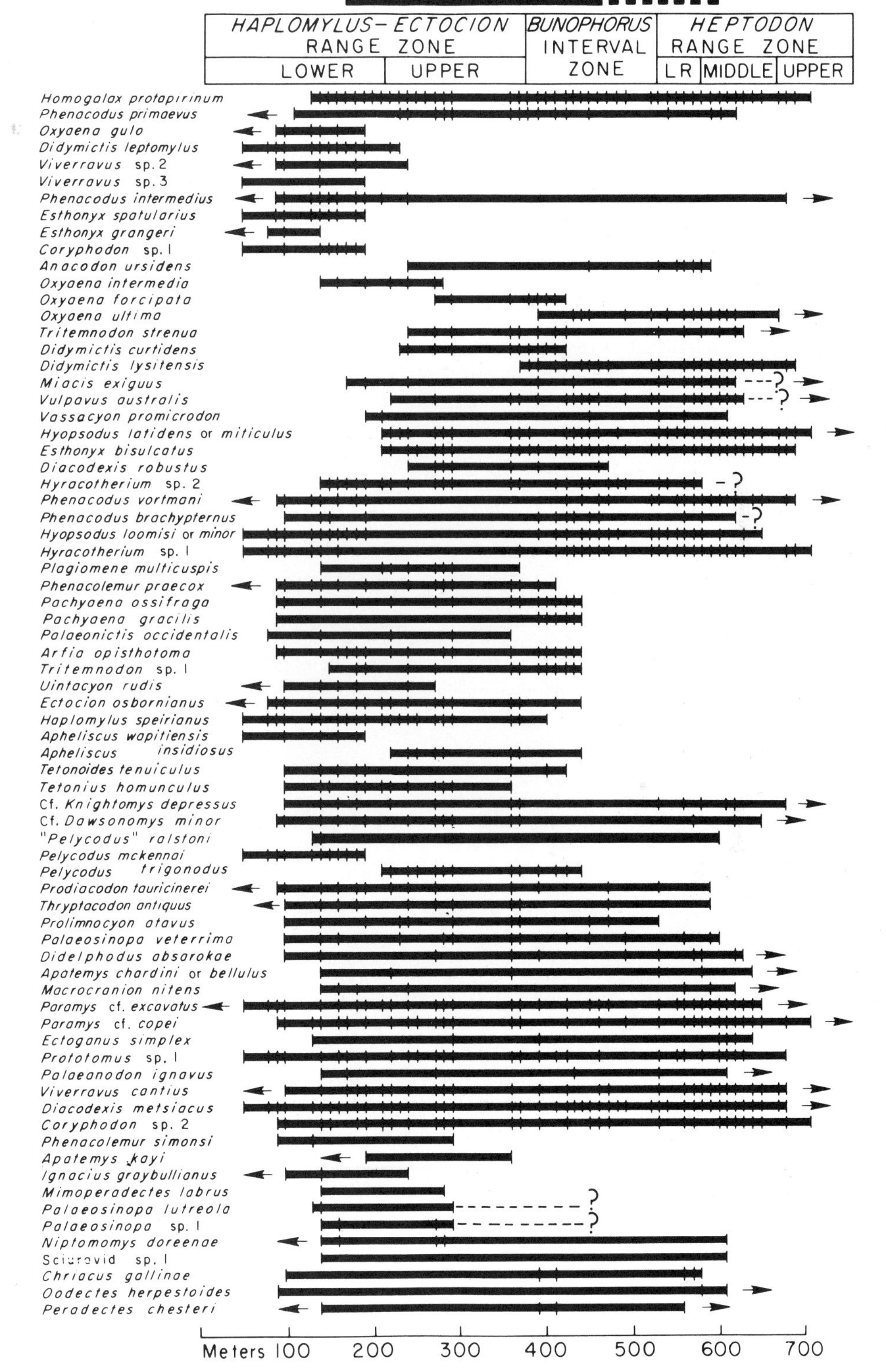
2 MILLION YEARS
HAPLOMYLUS–ECTOCION RANGE ZONE
LOWER
UPPER
BUNOPHORUS INTERVAL ZONE
HEPTODON RANGE ZONE
LR
MIDDLE
UPPER
Homogalax protapirinum
Phenacodus primaevus
Oxyaena gulo
Didymictis leptomylus
Viverravus sp. 2
Viverravus sp. 3
Phenacodus intermedius
Esthonyx spatularius
Esthonyx grangeri
Coryphodon sp. 1
Anacodon ursidens
Oxyaena intermedia
Oxyaena forcipata
Oxyaena ultima
Tritemnodon strenua
Didymictis curtidens
Didymictis lysitensis
Miacis exiguus
Vulpavus australis
Vassacyon promicrodon
Hyopsodus latidens or miticulus
Esthonyx bisulcatus
Diacodexis robustus
Hyracotherium sp. 2
Phenacodus vortmani
Phenacodus brachypternus
Hyopsodus loomisi or minor
Hyracotherium sp. 1
Plagiomene multicuspis
Phenacolemur praecox
Pachyaena ossifraga
Pachyaena gracilis
Palaeonictis occidentalis
Arfia opisthotoma
Tritemnodon sp. 1
Uintacyon rudis
Ectocion osbornianus
Haplomylus speirianus
Apheliscus wapitiensis
Apheliscus insidiosus
Tetonoides tenuiculus
Tetonius homunculus
Cf. Knightomys depressus
Cf. Dawsonomys minor
"Pelycodus" ralstoni
Pelycodus mckennai
Pelycodus trigonodus
Prodiacodon tauricinerei
Thryptacodon antiquus
Prolimnocyon atavus
Palaeosinopa veterrima
Didelphodus absarokae
Apatemys chardini or bellulus
Macrocranion nitens
Paramys cf. excavatus
Paramys cf. copei
Ectoganus simplex
Prototomus sp. 1
Palaeanodon ignavus
Viverravus cantius
Diacodexis metsiacus
Coryphodon sp. 2
Phenacolemur simonsi
Apatemys kayi
Ignacius graybullianus
Mimoperadectes labrus
Palaeosinopa lutreola
Palaeosinopa sp. 1
Niptomomys doreenae
Sciuravid sp. 1
Chriacus gallinae
Oodectes herpestoides
Peradectes chesteri
Meters 100 200 300 400 500 600 700

The angiosperms, or flowering plants (plants with conspicuous flowers and also grasses and hardwood trees and shrubs), exhibit great species longevities and offer another opportunity for us to conduct the test of adaptive radiation. For decades, the sudden appearance of this group in the fossil record representing the Cretaceous period was a great source of perplexity to evolutionists. The problem was that a wide variety of flowering plants were found to be represented by fossil remains in rocks that seemed to be virtually as old as the oldest flowering plant fossils. This problem was apparent even to Darwin, who, in a letter to a friend, the botanist J. D. Hooker, described it as "an abominable mystery" and somewhat desperately suggested:

> I have fancied that perhaps there was during long ages a small isolated continent in the S. Hemisphere which served as the birthplace of higher plants—but this is wretchedly poor conjecture.

During the 1970s, paleobotanists studying fossil leaves and pollen of the Atlantic coastal plain between the District of Columbia and Baltimore uncovered evidence of what really happened. They found fossils of leaves

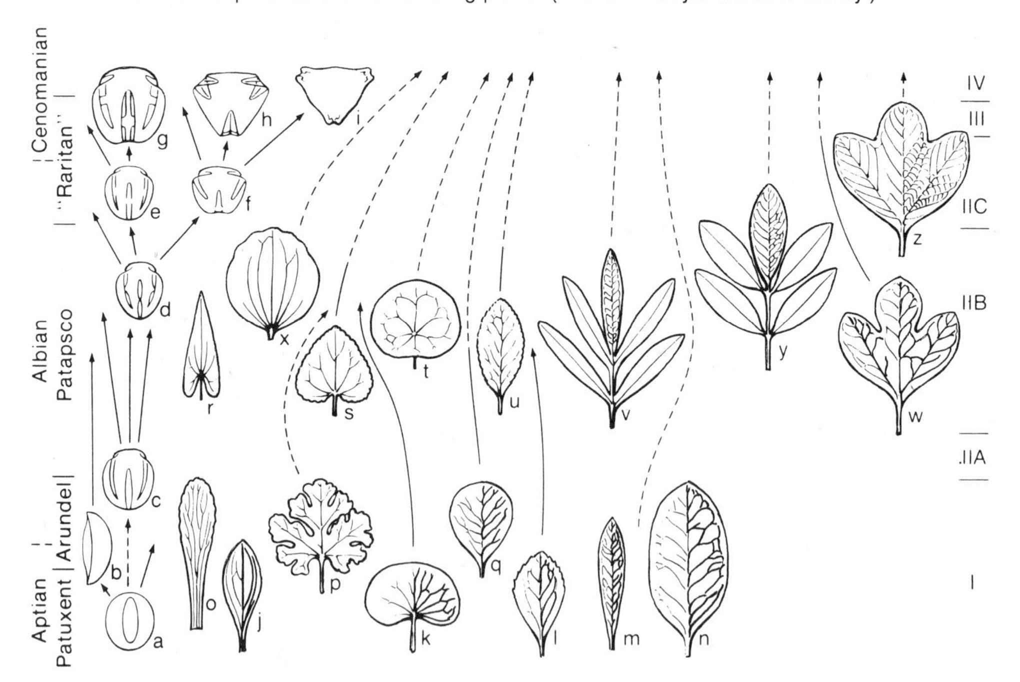

Figure 6. Increase in the variety and complexity of pollen (a to i) and leaves of early flowering plants in Cretaceous deposits of the Atlantic Coastal Plain. The sediments that yield these plant remains are assigned to four successive geological formations (the Patuxent through "Raritan") and represent the time interval from about 110 million to 100 million years ago. The pattern of evolutionary expansion here represents a very early stage in the initial adaptive radiation of flowering plants. (After J. A. Doyle and L. J. Hickey.)

and pollen that reveal not the instantaneous appearance of many different types of angiosperms but an adaptive radiation that began about 100 million years ago, in mid-Cretaceous time, and can be traced through about 10 million years at this East Coast study site. The earliest fossil leaves here are simple in form, having smooth margins and irregular veins (figure 6). Higher in the stratigraphic record, the leaves increase in variety and complexity. More shapes are present and many of the leaves are compound or have jagged margins. In addition, the younger leaves display veins arranged in neat geometric patterns. The pollen preserved with the leaves reveals a similar pattern of evolutionary expansion and complication. The first pollen grains to appear in the stratigraphic section are simple forms, with a single germination furrow. Collections made at progressively higher stratigraphic levels yield a greater variety of pollen shapes and are dominated by species that have three germination furrows.

These flowering plant remains of the Atlantic coastal plain reveal net changes that were clearly adaptive—properly spaced veins add strength to leaves and multiple germination furrows increase the likelihood that a pollen grain will germinate—but of greater importance, perhaps, is the rate of adaptive radiation that is documented. Despite decades of searching, paleobotanists have encountered no fossils of angiosperms that are appreciably older than those just described. The coastal plain fossils offer us a view of the initial adaptive radiation of the angiosperms, a radiation that brought a wide variety of new plant groups into being within just 10 million years.

Just how brief is 10 million years in the evolution of flowering plants? Although leaves and pollen are not highly reliable for the identification of plant species, seeds are, and study of fossil seeds representing the latter part of the Age of Mammals reveals that species of flowering plants have survived on the average for the better part of 10 million years. In the western United States, where species were not trapped in inhospitable regions by continental glaciers of the recent Ice Age, average geological duration has been even greater. We do not have estimates of the durations of angiosperm species during the Cretaceous adaptive radiation described above, because the fossil record for this early interval is imperfectly known. It is nonetheless a remarkable fact that a substantial amount of radiation was achieved in about 10 million years, which approximates the duration of an average species of angiosperms during the Cenozoic era.

Gastropod mollusks (snails) and marine bivalves have been characterized by average species durations in excess of 10 million years. This can be seen simply by examining fossil occurrences of extinct species (figure 7), but it is demonstrated even more compellingly by the nature of fossil faunas just a few million years old—faunas that include species still alive today. As it turns out, in an average bivalve fauna 7 million years old, half of the species survive in modern seas, having experienced hardly any measurable change in shell form. For gastropods, the percentage is only slightly lower. Within both groups, most of the fossil species that are not recognized in the modern world are not overlooked because they have undergone evolutionary change. Rather, they are species that have suffered extinction.

Foraminifera—single-celled creatures with shells—display even greater longevity. An average species of the families of this group that occupy the seafloor has survived for more than 30 million years! The test of adaptive radiation again manifests itself. Many of the modern families of Foraminifera made their appearance shortly before the Age of Mammals got underway, during an interval not exceeding 30 million years—the duration of an average species.

It might seem unlikely that such small and fragile animals as insects would have left a fossil record substantial enough to bear on the issue of punctuational evolution. As it turns out, however, one group of insects offers quite valuable evidence. This is the beetles, a group in which structures of the genitalia serve to distinguish one species from another. Beetle genitalia, it happens, are also extremely durable when preserved in sediments that are largely devoid of oxygen. As a result, many nonmarine sediments deposited during the recent Ice Age harbor excellent faunas of identifiable beetle species. The Ice Age spanned the better part of two million years, and, as it turns out, all of the beetle fossils found within it belong to living species.

Some paleontologists have remained skeptical of the validity of the fossil data that have been alleged to document the general stability of species. One of their arguments has been that only species that do not change much will be recognized at two widely separated positions in the fossil record. In fact, for many groups of species for which comprehensive data are now available, this criticism has no bearing. The Willwood mammal fauna represent a prime example. Here large numbers of species have been sampled at stratigraphic levels separated in age by only about fifty thousand years. The fossil record of any of these mammal species is so complete that it would document slow but substantial evolution, had such evolution occurred, yet no such evolution is revealed.

Another criticism that has been leveled at the punctuational arguments of paleontologists relates to sibling species—pairs or larger groups of species that are nearly identical. The criticism is that sibling species are so similar in form (often being distinguishable only by minor differences in shape or behavior) that they will never be distinguished from one another in the fossil record, which includes only fragmentary evidence of body

Figure 7. Stratigraphic ranges of fossil species of bivalve mollusks in rocks of New York State representing Late Devonian time, which began about 360 million years ago. Note that the excellent fossil record here shows an average species to have survived with little change for at least 10 million years. (After A. L. McAlester.)

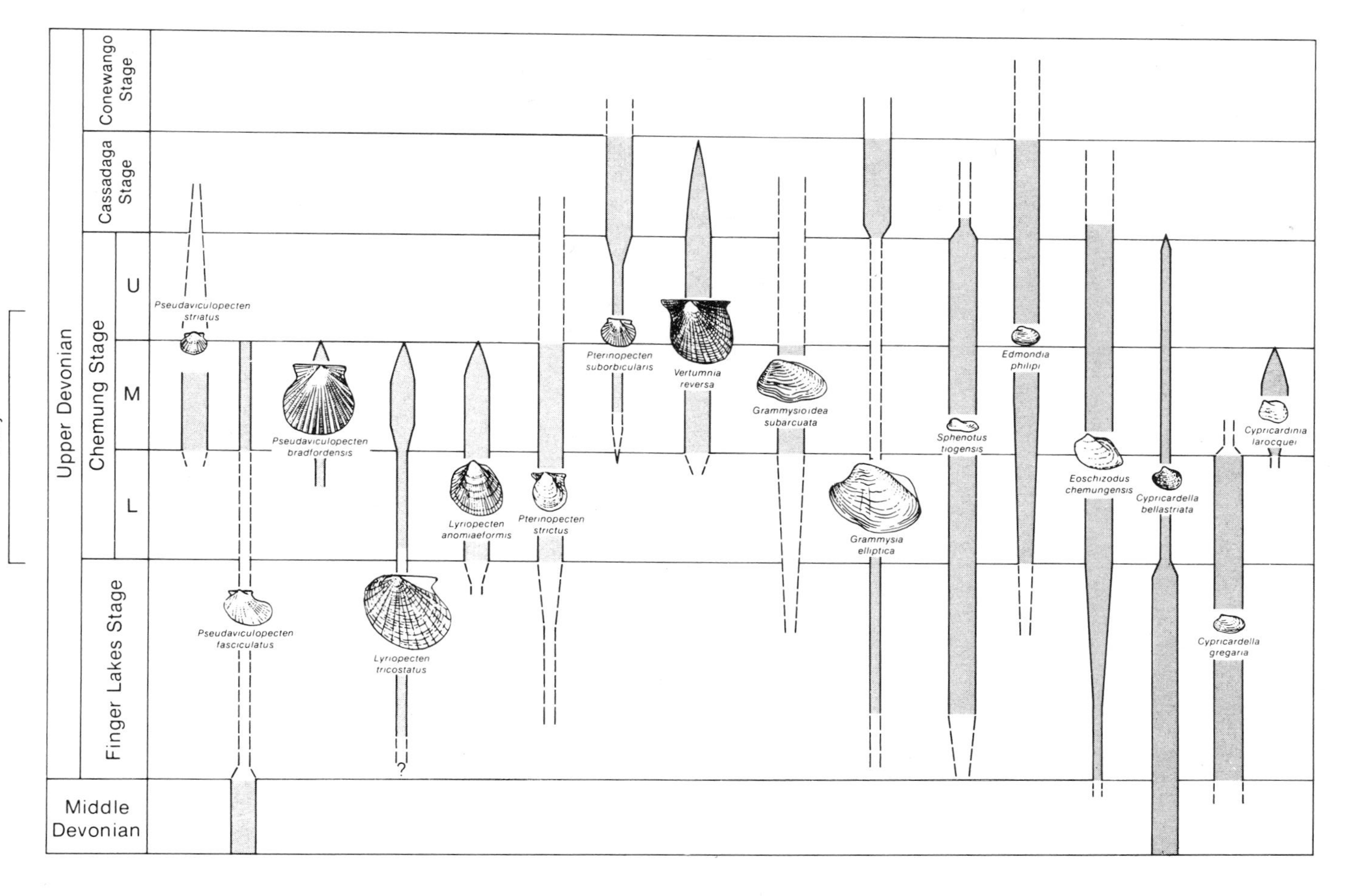

5 My
Upper Devonian
Middle Devonian
Chemung Stage
Finger Lakes Stage
Cassadaga Stage
Conewango Stage
L
M
U
Pseudaviculopecten striatus
Pseudaviculopecten bradfordensis
Pseudaviculopecten fasciculatus
Lyriopecten tricostatus
?
Lyriopecten anomiaeformis
Pterinopecten strictus
Pterinopecten suborbicularis
Vertumnia reversa
Grammysioidea subarcuata
Grammysia elliptica
Sphenotus tiogensis
Edmondia philipi
Eoschizodus chemungensis
Cypricardella bellastriata
Cypricardella gregaria
Cypricardinia larocquei

form. There is no question that a pair of sibling species will ordinarily be erroneously united as one, when known only from fossil evidence. This, however, is of no relevance to the debate about punctuational evolution. If a group of nearly identical fossil populations spanning 10 million years in the fossil record are assigned to a single species but actually represent three sibling species, each spanning a fraction of 10 million years, then the stability that these sibling species collectively represent argues against the efficacy of gradual species transformation just as strongly as would the comparable stability of a single species. In neither case has 10 million years of opportunity for gradual change accomplished anything to speak of.

Another test

It is important to appreciate that abundant fossil evidence showing stability for species over long stretches of geological time does not necessarily imply that events of branching (speciation) are the sites of most evolutionary change. An alternative possibility is that entire species, after long intervals of little evolution, are occasionally transformed suddenly into quite new forms of life—that species are periodically "reborn."

This idea can be tested by a second test of the gradualistic model of evolution. The test recognizes that the gradualistic and punctuational models offer very different predictions about how evolution should proceed in a certain kind of segment of the tree of life. This is a long, narrow segment, one that spans a considerable interval of time but includes few branches. The presence of few branches means that few speciation events will have occurred. If, as the punctuational model asserts, speciation is the site of most evolution, then the model predicts that long, narrow segments of the tree of life should encompass little total evolutionary change: Their youngest representatives should look very much like their oldest representatives.

The gradualistic model offers no such prediction. It asserts that species evolve at varying rates, but rates that over long stretches of time often produce substantial biological restructuring. Thus, according to the gradualistic model, long, narrow segments of the tree of life, like other segments, should often encompass substantial evolutionary change.

What, then, has been the history of long-existent but sparsely branching groups of animals and plants? As it turns out, virtually every group of this type has experienced very little change from the beginning of its evolutionary history to the end. A group of animals that illustrates this point especially well is the bowfin fishes, which constitute the family Amiidae (figure 8). The bowfins came into being during the Cretaceous period, millions of years before the Age of Mammals began. Their fossil

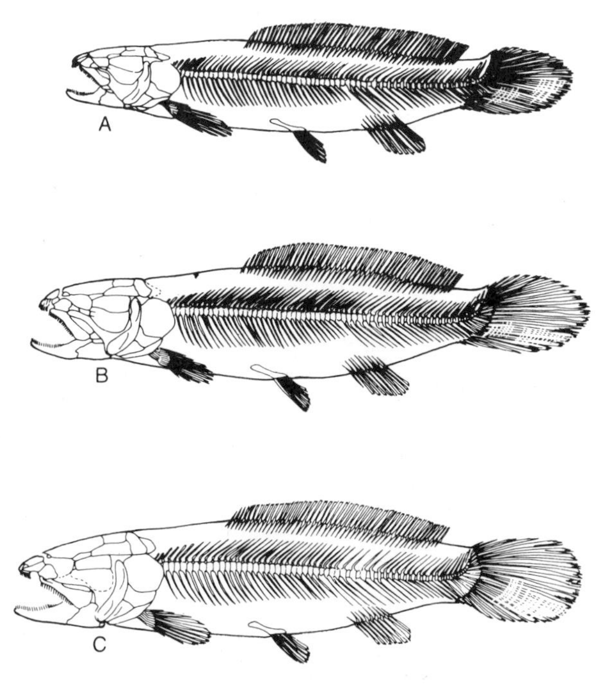

Figure 8. Close similarity among a 65-million-year-old bowfin fish species (bottom), a mid-Cenozoic species (middle), and the living species. Very few bowfin fish species have ever existed, and in the absence of many speciation events, the bowfin family has experienced evolutionary stagnation. The living species is a "living fossil." (After J. R. Boreske.)

record is of particularly high quality for the past 70 million years or so, and it reveals the presence of only four species during this interval, which means that the family has experienced very few speciation events. Inasmuch as only a small percentage of speciation events, in general, produce substantial amounts of evolutionary change (most speciation events cause only minor divergence), the punctuational model predicts that the bowfin fishes should have experienced little total evolutionary change, despite having existed for many millions of years. What has happened to body shape in the group? Very little. The species that were alive about 70 million years ago are very similar to the single living species.

To test the gradualistic model further, we cannot include in our compilation examples for which we have only fossils of great antiquity that resemble living species. We must include only examples for which we have a reasonably continuous fossil record. Otherwise, we would be excluding from our compilation any ancient fossil groups that had experienced major changes without leaving a fossil record in younger sediments to connect them with living descendants. When we conduct the test fairly, we indeed find that great evolutionary stability is the rule. The surviving members of all long, slender segments of the tree of life represented by a good fossil record are what we call "living fossils," a label that Darwin coined. Among the more familiar examples are the sturgeon, garfish, snapping turtle, alligator, and ardvaark. The living ginkgo tree, which is widely cultivated in North America, is a botanical example; the single living species is virtually identical with ginkgos that lived some 60 million years ago.

When the gradualistic model of evolution dominated evolutionary thought, living fossils represented an enormous puzzle. Thinking that all forms of life that survived for long stretches of time should undergo gradual change, evolutionists sought vainly for a solution. Some suggested that living fossils were so well specialized that they had no need to change. Others postulated, on the contrary, that they were so broadly adapted that they had no need to change. There was no factual support for either of these allegations, and living fossils remained a mystery. Not only is the punctuational model, unlike the gradualistic model, compatible with the presence of living fossils at the ends of all long, narrow segments of the tree of life; it actually predicts that they should exist.

Stability: A message to geneticists

The abundant evidence that species of animals and plants have remained quite stable in form while the groups to which they belong have experienced substantial evolutionary change can be translated into the simplest language of population genetics. It is now apparent that, barring its extinction, a typical established species of mammals, marine invertebrates, land plants, or insects has undergone little measurable change in form during at least one hundred thousand generations, and often a million or 10 million generations. "Little" here can be taken to mean that a competent taxonomist will assign the oldest and youngest populations to the same species or to very similar species. This generalization holds even if the family, order, or class to which the species belonged experienced many evolutionary changes during the species' evolutionary lifetime. Thus, although each generation afforded the opportunity for natural selection to operate on this typical species, the form of the species for some reason resisted restructuring.

The reasons for the newly discovered stability of species are by no means fully understood. One potentially fruitful way to uncover them is to investigate how major evolutionary changes are achieved where they do occur, in small populations of animals and plants. Examples of recent speciation events that have produced marked evolutionary divergence thus deserve our careful scrutiny.

Evidence of rapid speciation

If, indeed, fossil data demand that species form rapidly in small, localized populations, we must inquire whether this demand is compatible with biological observations. It is patently evident that biological data gathered so far have not forced the punctuational model upon us; but do they oppose the idea, leaving us with a conflict between the branch of science that deals with fossils and the branch that concerns living things? The essential question is whether there is evidence that some living species that are quite distinct from their parent species have formed very rapidly on a geological scale of time. Such evidence would be comforting in showing that the fossil data that support the punctuational model are not demanding something that is biologically impossible. Rapidly divergent speciation has been called quantum speciation, with reference to the sudden evolutionary step that is taken, but this label should not be taken necessarily to imply that such an event entails any novel genetic mechanism.

There is, in fact, evidence that new species have sprung up in the recent past. "Recent" here is a term in need of definition. The fossil record even at its most complete, as in the Lower Eocene strata of the Big Horn Basin, fails to offer temporal resolution for fossil occurrences on a finer scale than about fifty thousand years. The record of species stability over intervals longer than this tells us what happens to well-established species having large populations. It tells us nothing about how much time evolutionary divergence in the formation of a new species may require when that divergence is achieved within a population too small to leave a fossil "trackway" of evolution. All we can reasonably suggest, perhaps, is this: It is unlikely that any population could remain for more than a few thousands or a few tens of thousands of years at a size too small to be likely to leave a fossil record. In other words, most interbreeding populations either expand from small size or suffer extinction rather quickly. What we can do more profitably is to examine just how rapidly divergence has, in fact, produced some living species. As it turns out, some of the examples are quite striking.

Hawaii harbors several moths of the genus *Hedylepta* that feed only on banana plants (figure 9). Other species of the genus feed on other Hawaiian plants, and similarities of form demonstrate that one of these that feeds on palms is the ancestor of the banana-feeding species. Each of the banana-feeding species is restricted to high mountain forests on only one or two islands, and the reason they must bear a descendant rather than ancestral relationship to the palm-feeding species is that, while palm trees are native Hawaiian plants, banana trees are not. In fact, Polynesians first introduced the banana plant to the Hawaiian Islands only about a thousand years ago. This sets an upper limit for the evolution of the new banana-feeding insect species. For all we know, they evolved in a small fraction of this interval.

Figure 9. Two Hawaiian banana-feeding species of the moth genus *Hedylepta*. These species originated from moths with other feeding preferences during the past thousand years, when Polynesians introduced the banana plant to Hawaii.

At the margin of Lake Victoria, in Uganda, there sits a small body of water called Lake Nabugabo that has an areal extent of some fifteen miles. The smaller lake obviously formed from the larger one when a sand spit grew across a channel that formerly united the two bodies of water. Radiocarbon dating of fossil plant material in the spit shows that Nabugabo was separated from the parent lake approximately four thousand years ago. Within Lake Nabugabo are five species of cichlid fishes unknown from Lake Victoria or any other locality in the world. Each of these species obviously evolved from a similar species that still lives within Lake Victoria. Each of the daughter species differs from its evolutionary parent species in minor traits, including the coloration of male animals. This divergence in color is especially notable because in cichlid fishes male

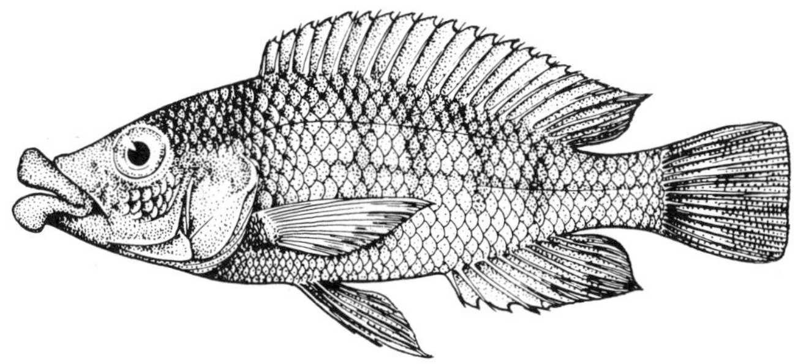

Haplochromis chilotes, a specialized insectivore (× 2/3).

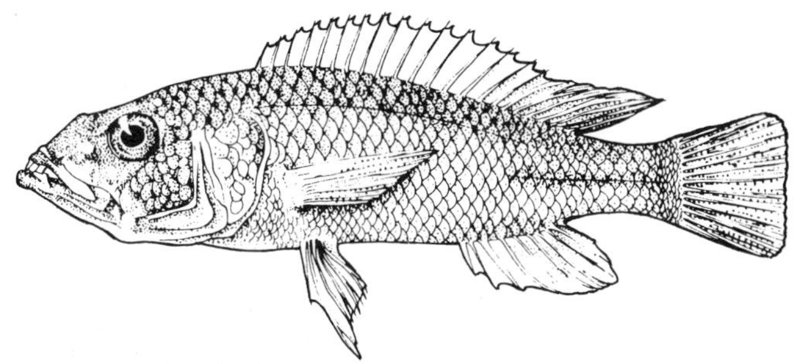

Haplochromis estor, a piscivore (× 1/3).

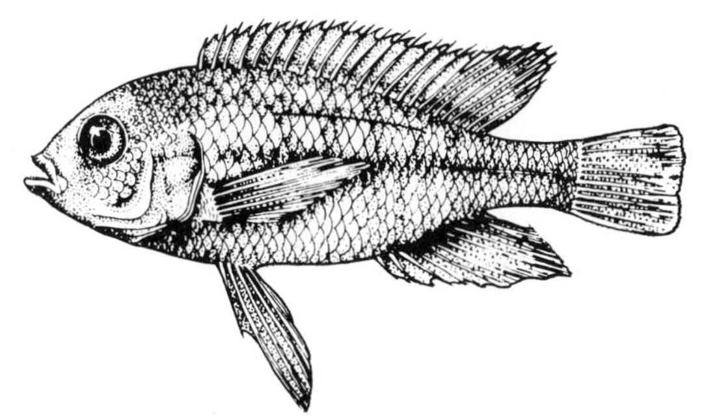

Haplochromis sauvagei, a mollusk eater (× 2/3).

Figure 10. Three species of very different cichlid fishes that evolved within Lake Victoria, Uganda, within the last three-quarters of a million years. An average species of freshwater fish normally survives with little evolutionary change for 3 million years or more. (British Museum of Natural History.)

color patterns serve as badges of recognition within species for mating; thus, there is no question that the Nabugabo populations represent true endemic species that are, in effect, trapped in their cradle of origin.

Lake Victoria itself offers evidence of evolutionary divergence on a much larger scale. This lake is at most 750,000 years old, which makes it quite young on a geological scale of time, and yet it contains about 170 species of cichlid fishes, all but three of which are unknown to any other locality. Among the many endemic species of Lake Victoria are several with quite unusual adaptations (figure 10). Some feed on insects, some specialize on mollusks, some graze on plants, and some eat other fishes (but among these are species that devour only fish larvae and embryos, and one species sustains itself largely by eating the scales of other fishes!). Most of these feeding specialists display special adaptations that fit them to their particular habits. Virtually all of these numerous endemic species must have evolved within Lake Victoria.

There exist within the lake, however, a few species that, on the basis of their primitive form, are believed to represent the ancestral species of the localized adaptive radiation that produced the many other species. Interestingly, relict streams of the river system that produced Lake Victoria harbor a species that closely resembles the putative ancestral species within the lake. This species may be the one that contributed the initial colony of fishes to the lake; at least, it must be a close relative of the colonizing species. The presence within the lake today of a small number of primitive species that seem to have changed little since evolving early in the history of the lake conforms to the punctuational model. While the gradualistic model would find unusual the evolutionary stagnation of primitive species, the punctuational model predicts that they would undergo little evolution, however long they survive after giving rise to descendant species within the lake.

In fact, the so-called species flock of cichlids in Lake Victoria provides us with a test of adaptive radiation in miniature. It does so because we can show that, in general, freshwater fish species survive an average of about 3 million years without experiencing more than a trivial amount of evolutionary change. This is several times the total length of time that has been available for the evolution of the many quite distinctive new kinds of fishes in Lake Victoria, and many of these may have formed during a tiny fraction of the available time. Is the fossil evidence of average species duration reliable? Indeed it seems to be, because experts in the recognition of living fish species have shown that skeletal structures, which constitute the most common fossil remains of fishes, provide an adequate basis for species recognition.

A small freshwater fish of the Death Valley region, near the border between California and Nevada, offers evidence of quantum speciation

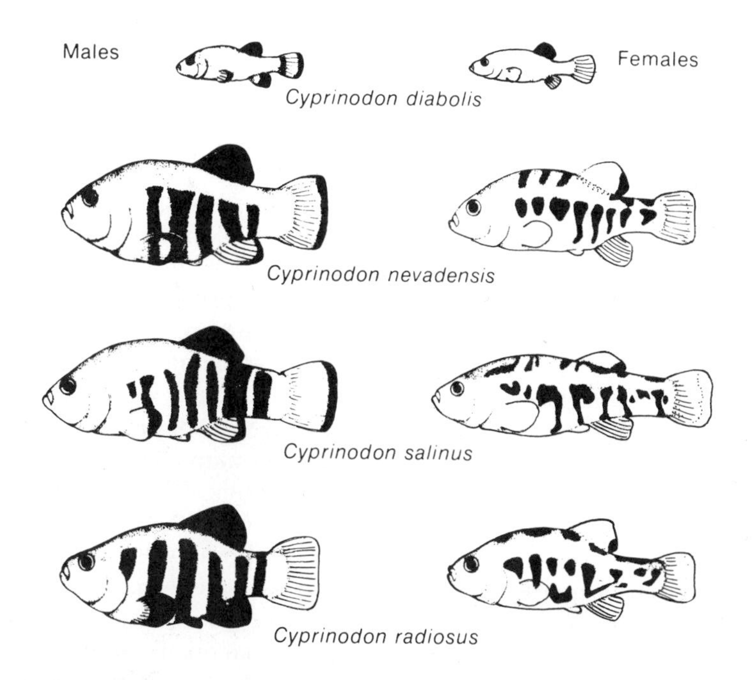

Figure 11. Four species of pupfishes that evolved in streams and thermal springs of the Death Valley region within the last twenty or thirty thousand years. The devil's pupfish (above) occupies a tiny thermal spring and is so distinctive that, although currently assigned with the other species to the genus *Cyprinodon,* actually deserves its own generic name. (After J. H. Brown.)

for which tighter time constraints can be demonstrated. This is the species known as the devil's pupfish, which lives as a tiny population isolated in a small hot spring in which the water temperature remains at about 92 degrees Fahrenheit (figure 11). The devil's pupfish is a highly unusual, dwarf form that has reduced pelvic fins or none at all. It certainly deserves placement in a genus of its own, yet it cannot have evolved more than ten thousand to thirty thousand years ago, when glaciers receded from western North America and left previously moist regions to the south hot and arid. The tiny thermal spring that is the home of the devil's pupfish became isolated at this time, as what amounted to an aquatic oasis in a newly formed desert. Here its population has probably never grown beyond about three hundred individuals. The devil's pupfish is only one of several pupfish species living in isolation in small springs within Death Valley. Had any of these existed before the postglacial desiccation of the region, it would be expected to occur now in many springs because large numbers of springs should have served as refuges for species that had been distributed over areas encompassing thousands of square miles, as fish species normally are.

Insular adaptive radiations

It is notable that all of the examples of recent speciation described above have taken place on islands or in lakes, which amount to "islands" of water in a "sea" of land. There are two reasons for this situation. One is that when island-like habitats form they are often devoid of life; they are barren for colonization. When the first species of a particular group of animals or plants arrives in the vacant habitat, its populations are confronted with exceptionably favorable opportunities to diverge into new species that exploit the habitat in different ways. It is not simply the absence of potential competitor species that affords this opportunity, but also the absence of potential predators. Both competition and predation normally stand in the way of speciation.

It is quite startling to realize that an average species of any sort gives rise to only about one other species before becoming extinct. Such an estimate is based on the observation that the number of species in the world changes rather little during a typical interval of 5 or 10 million years. This means that during such an interval an average species will bud off approximately one new species. Thus, speciation is a rare event. The fact that many speciation events produce little adaptive divergence (many parent and daughter species are very similar) means that quantum speciation, or speciation that achieves marked adaptive divergence, is extremely rare. Most species suffer extinction without giving birth to a single new species by quantum speciation. This situation contrasts sharply with the rapid proliferation of species in newly formed insular settings.

The second reason why we frequently find the products of adaptive radiation in island-like regions is that these are discrete areas bounded by ecological barriers. Short-lived island-like regions have probably served as sites of important adaptive radiations in the recent geological past, but the elimination of their boundaries by such things as geological and climatic changes have left these sites largely unrecognizable, and the events within them undecipherable. In times past, large continents and ocean basins have undoubtedly served as sites of enormous insular adaptive radiations. When the dinosaurs vacated the Earth through their extinction at the close of the Mesozoic era, the entire world, in effect, became a vast island available for the adaptive radiation of the mammals, which had been waiting in the wings.

We can actually identify today broad regions of continents that have recently served as sites of adaptive radiation but now have less discrete borders than have lakes or true islands. One of these is the large drainage area of the Mekong River System of Southeast Asia. Here there now exist in the various rivers approximately a hundred small aquatic snail species of the family Hydrobiidae. The entire drainage system came into existence about 10 million years ago, when the Himalayan Mountains were raised up. This great mountain-building event was a result of the northward movement against Asia of the landmass that now constitutes the peninsula of India. India was rafted northward aboard a great "plate" of the Earth's crust, and when it reached the southern margin of Asia, it was forced beneath the Asian crust, which it elevated to form the tallest mountain range on Earth. Riding as passengers were a few species of hydrobiod snails that colonized Asia when India made its landing. Interestingly, the ancestry of these snails can be traced to Africa, to which India had been attached when both lay farther to the south. Not only did the collision of India with Asia "inoculate" Asia with the snails, it simultaneously created environments for the snails' spectacular adaptive radiation by raising up Southeast Asia and thus producing the great river system that drains this region.

Thus, small insular and regional adaptive radiations for which we can see evidence in the modern world serve as useful models for much larger episodes of the past for which we cannot reconstruct detailed geographic histories.

Genetics and the time-scale dilemma

While there is no question that the debate about punctuational evolution was initiated by paleontologists, the implications of the debate for certain areas of biology have been the source of much controversy as well. At issue, in particular, is the way in which genetic change brings about radical morphological change. Historically, this subject has represented one of the greatest battlegrounds in all of twentieth-century biological science. Adding to the intensity of debate today is the fact that, by the 1950s, it was widely believed that all basic issues were settled and that the future would bring only refinements and embellishments. In fact, the modern synthesis of evolution was in large part a collective movement on the part of modern geneticists that was meant to unite their branch of science with Darwin's essential concept of evolution. Gradualism was certainly one of the components of the modern synthesis, and the question that must be addressed today is whether abandonment of evolutionary gradualism necessitates an abandonment of the genetic underpinnings of the modern synthesis.

Some of the older living biologists are clearly disturbed by their sense of *déjà-vu.* Early in their careers, they witnessed widespread disagreement about the nature of evolution, and as time passed, they felt fortunate to see dissension replaced by broad-based consensus. What had most severely threatened the Darwinian concept of evolution early in the twentieth century, and had left its mark until the 1930s, was the claim that single mutations of large effect—so-called macromutations—accounted for most evolutionary change.

It was, perhaps, natural that such an idea would emerge as it did, immediately after the birth of modern genetics at the turn of the century. Not only did biologists suddenly appreciate that there exist discrete units of inheritance (genes); they recognized that mutations of such units implied that on some scale evolution must take place by discrete steps. Led by Hugo de Vries, who observed the dramatic effects of mutations on the external forms of many plants, the so-called macromutationists cast aside natural selection altogether. Why resort to the piecemeal restructuring of a species by the accumulation of many infinitesimal changes over long stretches of time, was their question? Why rely on the unlikely occurrence of many successive mutations when a distinctive new species might form from a parent species by a single jump? To the macromutationists, this idea seemed to follow from the Principle of Parsimony, whereby of two or more cogent hypotheses that might explain a scientific phenomenon, the simplest is to be favored over the others. To Darwinians, the idea that a single large accidental step could be advantageous seemed absurd. They followed Darwin in believing that change could only be achieved by the addition of small steps that maintained the species in adaptive equilibrium with its environment.

It was largely the success of experimental genetics between 1920 and 1950 that brought victory to the Darwinians, or Neodarwinians, as they came to label themselves. One critical set of observations here were those of Dobzhansky who, after immigrating to the United States from Russia, showed that natural populations of the fruitfly *Drosophila* undergo seasonal changes brought about by natural selection in a changing environment. Though oscillating with the seasons, these changes seemed to illustrate the power of the selective process in nature. Strengthening the case for selection by small steps were numerous experiments by Dobzhansky and others that produced change by artificial selection in the laboratory.

In the light of the turbulent history of evolutionary biology earlier in this century, it is not surprising that many geneticists have viewed the punctuational model as an unwelcome specter from the past. The analogy distorts the punctuational model, however. This model actually says nothing about genetic mechanisms. Rather, it is a description of a pattern of change. It asserts that large, widespread species tend to evolve very sluggishly and that small, narrowly distributed populations are the sites of most evolutionary change. It also holds that the small populations in which evolution tends to be concentrated are populations that are budding off from parent species. In other words, most evolution is associated with speciation. Adherence to the punctuational model requires modification, not total rejection, of the tenets of the modern synthesis. In particular, although the new model does not require that we cling to the genetic underpinnings of the modern synthesis, neither does it necessarily undercut them.

There is one remarkably puzzling aspect of the traditional wedding of genetics to gradualism in the modern synthesis. This is the simple fact that the strength of natural selection required to produce changes of form that are documented by numerous fossil data, if applied uniformly, would have to be so weak that it could not realistically be sustained. As a concrete example, one can consider the evolution of the modern horse from an ancestor that roamed the Earth some 50 million years ago and was no larger than a fox terrier. Whether we consider what seems like a large evolutionary increase in body size, a substantial lengthening of the neck, an increase in the complexity of the molar teeth, a disappearance of most of the toes, or any other of the net changes of form that separate the modern horse from its ancestor, simple calculations yield the same result. Given the normal amount of variation found in such bodily features within a single species, natural selection would produce the observed net change from the ancestral condition to the modern one by the occurrence of something like one selective death per million in every generation. So weak a causal mechanism could never sustain itself against the effects of random fluctuations in the mortality of animals of various body types.

In other words, there are many accidents in nature, and for natural selection to overcome them in a consistent way (by causing body forms of a particular type to be consistently favored) it must be a much stronger force than one that accounts for one death in every million. This kind of calculation, which yields the same result for example after example of net evolutionary change, is of enormous consequence.

First, we must note that evolutionary changes for which calculations have been made have often quite obviously been adaptive. Many features found in modern horses but not their ancestors, for example, improve horses' ability to live on grasslands, which were absent from the Earth when the earliest horses lived. Complex molars serve to grind up harsh grasses that contain silica; a single hoof sustains pounding on hard turf better than several toes; and a large body improves endurance for long-distance running from predators on open plains.

Net evolutionary changes that have yielded adaptive changes like these must have a causal explanation. They cannot have developed accidentally, by chance genetic changes. What we must call on, then, is a concentration of adaptive change in brief intervals. Natural selection strong enough to overcome chance genetic changes must operate sporadically, and the rest of the time a typical species must undergo little modification. While this conclusion does not specify that the change must usually be concentrated in small populations, it is nonetheless quite compatible with the punctuational model. Strangely, it was not until recently that calculations leading to this conclusion were undertaken.

Similarly ignored for decades was the impossibility of reconciling strong selection pressures that were created in the laboratory with rates of evolution documented by fossil data. Laboratory experiments that were alleged to mimic what happens in nature actually entailed so many selective deaths per generation, and such rapid changes in body form, that comparable selection pressures operating in nature would produce enormous evolutionary changes (ones yielding new classes of animals and plants) during what would amount to brief instants of geological time. The implication, which was completely overlooked, is that something is usually stifling the effective operation of natural selection in nature. Geneticists were no more at fault than paleontologists in failing to note this problem of temporal scale. Perhaps someday historians of science will explore the reasons for this oversight and the one described in the previous two paragraphs.

Mechanisms of quantum speciation

A more detailed look at small-scale insular radiations offers clues to the ways in which quantum speciation is accomplished. As background for understanding these clues, it is important to comprehend the traditional view of the geography of speciation. According to this view, a new species normally forms from a geographically isolated population of a preexisting species. The geographic isolate, as it is called, is often positioned in an environment that is unusual for the parent species. Partly as a consequence of this and partly as a consequence of the accidental nature of genetic mutations, upon which natural selection operates, an isolated population that survives for some time normally undergoes evolutionary divergence from the parent species.

Within the modern synthesis, geographic speciation was not generally seen as being the site of particularly rapid evolution. This splitting process simply served to establish a new direction for the normally slow but powerful process of evolution. In fact, it was widely believed that an isolated population required a long period of time to attain reproductive isolation from its parent species—that is, to become a full-fledged new species. The punctuational view, of course, grants a much more important role to the branching process, seeing it as often occurring rapidly and as contributing the bulk of all evolutionary change.

Some controversy still surrounds the notion that isolation is necessary for speciation—a notion that is by no means essential to the punctuational model. Some biologists, especially those who analyze the genetics of populations mathematically, argue that a new species can form without complete isolation. A certain amount of misunderstanding also stems from the employment of the term *geographic*. In fact, the word *spatial* would seem to be more appropriate. The problem with *geographic* is that it is wedded to a human scale of distribution. For a colony of insects living beneath a large rock, a second colony beneath another rock just a few meters away might, from the standpoint of genetic communication, be just as distant as one population of prehistoric humans living in Britain was from another living in France before the invention of the boat.

With regard to adaptive radiation in small insular environments, the spatial question is whether there is sufficient opportunity for isolation to play a role in speciation. Does evidence that adaptive radiations have taken place in confined areas argue against a role for isolation? The recognition that spatial barriers measured in meters rather than kilometers may suffice eliminates the problem in most cases, but often there is still no proof that spatial isolation has actually occurred. The difficulty is that speciation events are generally too rare and localized for us to witness them. Furthermore, the completion of most of these events probably requires intervals of time so long as to exceed the lifetime of a human observer. Despite these problems of documentation, there remains a consensus of opinion that most speciation events are dependent on spatial isolation.

Several models have been designed to explain certain aspects of speciation within adaptive radiations in the light of observations made in nature. One of these models has already been alluded to. It asserts that adaptive radiation entailing quantum speciation often follows from the absence of the sorts of competitor and predator species that normally prevent small populations from expanding into successful new species. An artificial experiment conducted in southeastern California in a body of water called the Salton Sea offers support for this kind of model.

Until 1905, the basin in which the Salton Sea now sits was a salt flat that was periodically flooded by the Colorado River. Between 1905 and 1907, the Colorado's waters flowed into the basin at an abnormally high rate, after breaching an irrigation gap in the river's levee. The basin was filled to a depth of sixty-seven feet, and the Salton Sea was thus born. This body of water, which has shrunk slightly in areal extent but still measures about ten by thirty miles, was named for its high salinity, which developed as salts of the lake floor dissolved in the ponded waters. In 1950 and 1951, scientists introduced a species of small, silvery fish into the lake. This species, known as the bairdiella, is a marine animal that dwells in the Gulf of California. The early history of the Salton Sea population of the bairdiella was quite remarkable.

The bairdiella first spawned successfully in its new environment in 1952, but a proportion of the hatchlings estimated at between 13 and 23 percent were deformed in one way or another. Some had one blind or abnormally small eye; others were afflicted with strangely deformed lower jaws or had none at all; still others had snub-nosed heads; and some displayed malformed spines or anal fins. These freakish traits remained within the population for some time, but in 1953, after a second spawning, the population began to experience food shortages. The competition that resulted led to a decline in the proportion of deformed individuals, and by 1954 they constituted only 2 or 3 percent of the total population.

The first bairdiellas born in the Salton Sea emerged in a world devoid of competitors and predators. In an already populated habitat, nearly all animals with comparable deficiencies would be excluded from use of essential resources like food and space or would quickly be caught and eaten by predators. Unfortunately, we do not know what percentage of the deformed individuals in the Salton Sea had genetically based defects that would have been inherited by their offspring and what percentage were afflicted with nongenetic defects resulting from errors in the normal sequence of development. What we can do, however, is imagine what would happen in a much larger lake or ocean basin that was newly formed and available for occupancy.

If, indeed, we extrapolate the implications of the bairdiella experiment in the small Salton Sea to the scale represented by continents and ocean basins, we can anticipate that a larger number of colonizing species in a much larger number of habitats would experience the same phenomenon, which might be referred to as a release from stabilizing selection. Stabilizing selection is natural selection that tends to maintain the adaptive status quo. It amounts to a weeding-out process that eliminates deviant individuals—ones that differ from the modal, or most common, kinds of individuals within the population. If even minor deviants are selected against through early death or low fecundity, then the properties of the population will not shift through time: evolutionary stagnation will result. When the dinosaurs became extinct, the entire world represented a series of islands made available to small mammal species. Of the myriads of mammalian populations, many must have suddenly been released from the stabilizing selection pressures which had previously constituted an evolutionary straight jacket for the mammalia as a whole.

Hampton Carson has introduced the concept of the "population flush" to explain more fully what may happen under the circumstances just described. A population flush is the release of an unusually large amount of variability in form and behavior within a population founded in a new environment by a small number of individuals, or even a single pregnant female. The flush is presumed to be followed by a population crash, so that after a few generations only a few individuals survive. Exactly which kinds of individuals survive is in part a matter of natural selection and in part a matter of chance. Chance enters in, both as a determinant of the particular individuals that found the population before the flush and as a partial determinant of the kinds of individuals that survive the castastrophic crash. One or more of the variants may come, through further evolution, to represent a well-adapted new kind of species.

Harlan Lewis has proposed a somewhat different mechanism known as catastrophic selection. This concept is based on the observation that some plant species, adapted to drier conditions than their parent species, seem to have formed when a severe drought decimated nearly all individuals of a population of the parent species. The ancestors of the daughter species existed within the parent species as genetically distinctive individuals capable of withstanding unusually dry conditions. They alone survived the drought and, under the unusual new conditions, quickly evolved into a new species.

Thus, while the punctuational model does not demand that we reject the most fundamental elements of modern genetics, it does challenge a number of the subsidiary ideas. It appears that most adaptive change is not only concentrated in relatively brief periods of time but is achieved by a relatively small number of genetic changes. One fact suggestive of this is that within many taxonomic groups of animals and plants there is a very poor correlation between the genetic differences and the differences in form separating individual species. This situation is brought home to us humans quite effectively when we are forced to contemplate the fact that we share about 99 percent of our genes with chimpanzees. On the other hand, there are groups of species in other vertebrate families that are nearly identical to each other in form but that differ substantially in genetic constitution. During the 1960s,this lack of correspondence was not well recognized. The invention of gel electrophoresis seemed to show such promise for evolutionary analysis that enthusiasm for the technique led some workers astray. Electrophoresis is a procedure that allows proteins to be separated from one another, and when these are proteins (often enzymes) that are under genetic control, they are, in effect, genetic markers that permit a partial genetic comparison of two individuals or two species. Some workers believed that to understand evolution all that was needed was an assessment of genetic differences among species.

It is now quite clear that wholesale genetic comparisons are of limited value. Many genetic changes are of trivial adaptive significance, whereas others have a substantial impact on body form, physiology, or behavior. Another complicating factor is that individual genes do not act in isolation. Often a particular adaptation is under the control of more than one gene, and often a single gene exerts influence over more than one adaptation. Many fish that live only in caves are blind, and some birds that are restricted to small islands have stunted wings and are flightless. What these facts reveal is that if a particular structure that was functional loses its adaptive value—if it is no longer sustained by natural selection that favors its retention—then it will be selected against. Almost certainly, what happens is that the structure is linked by certain genes to other, still-functional features of form, physiology, or behavior, and that as natural selection has caused these other features to change, the useless eyes or wings have been "dragged" passively along. Such passive alteration will almost always lead to loss of function, because it constitutes change that is incidental with regard to function.

Not only do genes interact with each other through their joint, and often opposing, effects on the structures and processes that they control; genes also interact more directly with each other. Some function differently or fail to function in the absence of others. Genes that control others have been loosely termed regulatory genes, but they are unfortunately quite difficult to study because most do not yield chemical products that are detectable by means of electrophoresis.

The many complications that have beset the science of genetics since the emergence of electrophoresis, with its false hope for simplification, have created much uncertainty. Many molecular geneticists are searching for new mechanisms of inheritance that geneticists who study the evolution of populations find unlikely and unnecessary. There is even debate about the possible role of changes in the arrangements of genes on chromosomes. Are such changes incidental, or are there instead "position effects"? In other words, does the way in which genes function relate to their physical position with respect to one another on a chromosome? Especially within the rodent order, many examples have been found of species that are nearly identical except in number of chromosomes. In 1966 Harlan Lewis, speaking of chromosomal number in plants, wrote in the magazine *Science*:

> The significance of basic numbers is twofold: . . . they are very conservative, particularly among woody plants where one frequently finds the same chromosome number throughout a family, subfamily, or other large taxonomic group. . . . It seems clear that change in basic chromosome number is not a normal consequence of gradual differentiation, but a rare event resulting from unusual circumstances.

Whether change of chromosome number or configuration is occasionally expressed in form or behavior is uncertain. In many cases it may serve simply to isolate one population from another reproductively (causing hybrid offspring to be nonviable or nonfertile, for example), thus allowing other more fundamental genetic changes to cause divergence of form or behavior.

Whatever the details of quantum speciation turn out to be—and they may prove to vary greatly from example to example—the punctuational model of evolution, in stressing the role of quantum speciation in evolution in general, differs from the modern synthesis largely in emphasis. It places far more weight on what happens within small populations, where accidental change in gene frequencies (genetic drift) plays its biggest role. This is not to say that the punctuational scheme relies primarily on genetic drift. Almost certainly, natural selection among individuals, operating generation-by-generation, is the dominant process of change. On the other hand, the change is rapid, and, thus, the punctuational model lays greater importance on selection that operates upon pronounced and discontinuous variation of form, behavior, and physiology. In a brief speciation event that causes marked evolutionary divergence, there is not time for innumerable small steps of change.

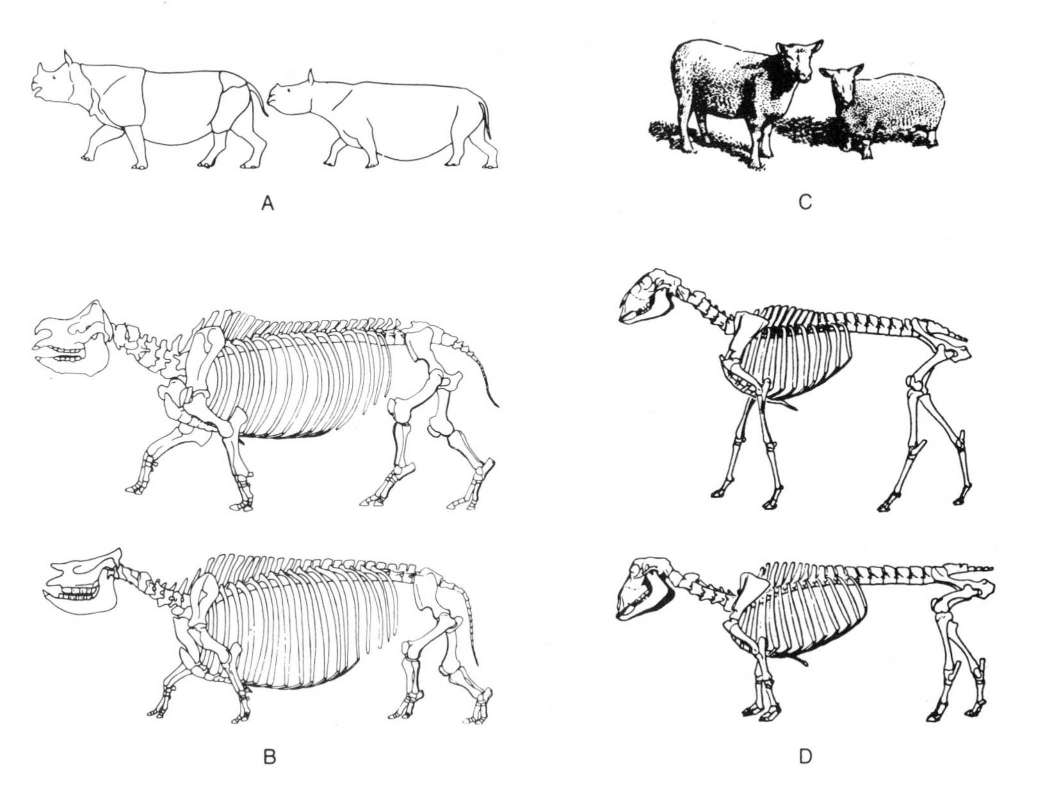

Figure 12. Effects of achondroplasia, a genetically based growth abnormality. Achondroplastic animals are dwarfs in which limb bones grow normally in girth but fail to lengthen properly. In drawing A, the extinct achondroplastic rhino *Teleoceras* is depicted walking behind a modern Indian rhino. Drawing B contrasts the skeletons of the two animals. Drawing C shows an achondroplastic sheep, known as an ancon, standing alongside a normal sheep, and drawing D contrasts the skeletons of these animals. A single mutation forms an ancon sheep, and presumably very few genetic changes produced the distinctive rhino genus *Teleoceras*.
(A and B drawn by G. S. Paul; C and D after H. Grünberg.)

Morphogenetic questions

Morphogenesis is the progressive unfolding of an individual animal or plant—the development of the adult animal from a fertilized egg. Evolution is, in effect, a remodeling process. Whatever it produces must somehow be derived from what existed before. This means that evolution can often be viewed as a morphogenetic change—as a change in the pattern of growth and maturation.

In the middle part of the twentieth century, this idea was carried to an extreme. Richard Goldschmidt, though a great geneticist and an important innovator in the union of morphogenesis and evolution, went so far as to suggest that the world's first bird might have hatched from a reptile egg. In part, his ideas harked back to the macromutationist era of the early part of the century. For an unusual new kind of individual—one quite different from its parents or other members of its population—Goldschmidt coined the label "hopeful monster." The word *hopeful* alluded to the creature's prospects of surviving and becoming the progenitor of a large and distinctive new group. The implication was that, at birth, the monster represented an entirely new family or order or class of animals or plants.

The concept of the hopeful monster has been much derided, and one biologist has even renamed the hypothetical animal a "hopeless monster." The difficulty with the original concept is that it presumed that somehow a single genetic change could yield numerous changes in form and behavior that allowed the animal or plant possessing them to function as an integrated unit. It is not so easy to rule out, a priori, the establishment of less severe changes in the course of a small number of generations.

Teleoceras is a strange extinct form that may shed some light on the possibilities for rapid origin of new kinds of animals that, though not truly monstrous, are quite unusual in comparison to their parent species. *Teleoceras* was a dwarf rhinoceros, which had a body much like that of a typical rhinoceros but extremely short legs (figure 12). This curious animal evolved in Europe during the Miocene epoch and, despite its short stature, made its way into North America. Here its abundant fossil remains indicate that the animal enjoyed great ecological success on flat plains, to which it was probably restricted by its short legs.

It seems quite evident how an evolutionary change in the developmental sequence of a normal rhinoceros led to the origin of *Teleoceras.* At least twice during the last two hundred years, sheep with unusual features resembling those of *Teleoceras* have appeared in domestic flocks and had their traits perpetuated by artificial inbreeding because farmers valued the sheep's inability to jump fences. The sheep's abnormality, which also occurs in other animals, is known as achondroplasia. In an achondroplastic animal, bones grow normally in width but are stunted in longitudinal growth. This condition normally results from a single mutation.

By analogy, we can suppose that the major morphological change that was associated with the origin of *Teleoceras* was accomplished by a single genetic change. This does not mean that the genus owed its existence to such a solitary genetic change. In all likelihood other mutations were required to offset unfortunate side effects of the mutation that produced achondroplasia. Domestic strains of achondroplastic sheep have not survived for many generations because the sheep are vulnerable to certain kinds of hoof disease. Most genes of large effect are deleterious, and the rare example that is manifested in some useful way (as we must assume happened in *Teleoceras*) must nearly always introduce harmful side effects.

Thus, not only is an achondroplastic evolutionary transformation not a wholesale restructuring, as was implied in Goldschmidt's idea that the first bird might have hatched from a reptile egg, but, to have been successful, it probably required more than a single genetic change.

A different kind of rapid evolutionary change that has quite drastic consequences gained appreciation even when gradualism dominated evolutionary thinking. This is called progenesis. It is the evolutionary pattern in which a particular kind of animal or plant becomes juvenilized: what was previously a juvenile stage of development suddenly becomes the adult stage. In effect, the species ceases to "grow up" because what was the juvenile form becomes reproductively mature and the animal ceases to develop further.

The classic example of progenesis is the evolutionary origin of an amphibian known as the axolotl. This animal fails to live up to the name "amphibian" because, unlike a normal salamander species, it does not metamorphose from a tadpole-like aquatic stage to an adult terrestrial stage. Instead, its development stops at the tadpole-like stage, which becomes sexually mature. What is particularly remarkable about the axolotl is that its failure to mature in the normal fashion can be traced to a developmental deficiency. The animal's pituitary gland simply fails to stimulate the thyroid gland in the normal fashion with a hormone. This condition is the apparent product of a single genetic mutation, and there can be little doubt that the transformation from the salamander ancestor to the axolotl took place by means of a localized speciation event, during which the causal mutation was fixed within a small population. To be sure, although the geologically sudden occurrence of progenesis represents quantum speciation, an entirely new kind of animal does not emerge. Except in its attainment of sexual maturity, the axolotl is nearly identical to juvenile individuals of its parent species.

An evolutionary change of much greater consequence was probably achieved largely by quantum speciation in the origin of the giant panda. For many years it was debated whether this animal had its ancestry in the raccoon family or the bear family, but detailed anatomical comparisons have now confirmed the derivation of pandas from bears. The panda is essentially a bear that has been highly modified in taking up the habit of feeding largely on bamboo. So coarse is this kind of food that the animal requires an enormously strong chewing apparatus. Thus, in the evolutionary origin of the giant panda, the jaws and related masticatory structures were greatly enlarged. In contrast, postcranial features were weakened and otherwise altered in such a way as to yield the clumsy "teddy bear" appearance and awkward locomotory pattern of the panda that endears the animal to zoo-goers.

It seems evident that, in the evolution of the giant panda, effective operation of the hindquarters was, in effect, sacrificed for the enlargement of the head region. The bulldog, which was developed by domestic breeders for clamping its jaws onto other animals in dog fights, displays similar pelvic abnormalities to those of the giant panda, and, like those of the panda, the bulldog's hindquarters are quite weak. In the case of the panda, this weakening illustrates how evolution in nature often moves forward with adaptive compromise. It appears that the giant panda evolved by a change in growth gradients such that an increased amount of material and energy was directed toward the front of the animal. The resulting locomotory deficiency was tolerated because the animal evolved at high, mountainous elevations, where the threat of predation was greatly reduced. It has been estimated that a very small number of genetic changes could have produced the basic anatomical transformation from bear to giant panda—perhaps just three or four. In terms of form and adaptation, however, the profundity of the transformation is illustrated by the long-unresolved taxonomic debate as to whether the panda evolved from bears or raccoons.

Unfortunately, the fossil record of giant pandas is only now coming to light and has not yet revealed much about the family tree of the single modern species. What we might reasonably envision, however, is that the basic transformation from bear to panda took place by way of a single speciation event, involving a very small population of bears isolated from others in a high Himalayan bamboo forest.

Complex animals like bears may be less likely to experience drastic but successful anatomical reorganizaton than are simple animals. Probably no group of vertebrate animals formally recognized as a class has ever been transformed into another class by means of a single speciation event (the amphibians, reptiles, birds, and mammals each constitute a class of vertebrates). Among the lowly mollusks, however, there is a good chance that one speciation event did achieve a class-to-class transition. The evolutionary event in question here is the origin of the class Gastropoda, which contains all species of snails.

Snails are characterized by the anatomical feature known as torsion. Torsion is a twisting of the body (not to be confused with coiling of the shell) such that the digestive tract assumes the shape of a "U," with the anus positioned above the head. Probably the chief advantage of this configuration in the long run has been that it has permitted the animal to seal its shell with a trapdoor-like operculum, which is attached to the upper surface of the animal's foot. The fundamental question about snail evolution is how torsion evolved.

Long ago a remarkable fact caught the attention of students of molluscan evolution. This is the fact that, in some primitive archaeogastropods, torsion is accomplished in just two or three minutes by an anatomically simple mechanism. This mechanism involves the pattern of development of the muscles that attach the larval snail to its shell. The right-hand muscle passes diagonally from the shell to the animal's head. By contracting during torsion, this muscle twists the body of the animal through a loop of about 180°. The left-hand muscle, which develops secondarily, then assumes the function of attaching the animal to its shell in the new orientation, and in most snails this orientation is sustained throughout the life of the snail.

So simple and quick is the development of torsion that many decades ago it was suggested that the process was initiated in evolution by a single genetic mutation. The principle of parsimony, which is a fundamental tenet of scientific testing, favors this idea: why invoke more than one genetic change when a single change could easily accomplish the event? Further support for this idea comes from the mode of development of snails that do not retain torsion into the adult stage but lose it, becoming bilaterally symmetrical, like the ancestors of snails. In the group of snails that undergo "detorsion," a variety of anatomical conditions can be found. In different species, different organ systems have become detorted to varying degrees. Obviously, many different genetic changes have been entailed in the evolutionary process of detorsion. Had torsion evolved in a similar fashion, we would expect to see the primitive groups of snails that survive today exhibiting varying degrees of torsion, but this pattern is not observed.

In the 1960s the idea that torsion came into being by a single mutation was derogated as being incompatible with the modern synthesis of evolution. The modern synthesis was seen as requiring that so drastic an anatomical change be wrought by many small, sequential evolutionary steps. Consideration of the probabilities involved, however, seems to eliminate objections to the single-mutation hypothesis.

Presumably the first snails differed from their immediate ancestors, which might be termed "presnails," in no major way except in being torted. We can imagine that, within the ancestral population, a female experienced a mutation that caused her to give birth to torted offspring. Any of a number of conditions might have caused these unusual offspring to become a new species—that is, to become reproductively isolated from the parent population. The most extreme condition one might imagine would be immediate reproductive incompatibility conferred by the change that yielded torsion. Less extreme scenarios entail (1) mating between the torted and untorted forms, but depressed fitness of the resulting hybrids, leading to natural selection favoring additional mutations that produced complete reproductive incompatibility or (2) chance geographic isolation of two or more torted individuals, leading to evolutionary divergence and, ultimately, loss of potential to interbreed with the parent population.

To consider the probabilities of a speciation event of this kind, we can make several conservative numerical estimates. "Presnails" must have existed for at least 10 million years before snails evolved, and we can assume that, at any time during this interval, at least a hundred species of "presnails" occupied the oceans of the world. Finally, we can assume that an average species of these animals at any time included at least 100 million females that bred annually. These numbers allow us to calculate that, as a minimal estimate, there were 100,000,000,000,000,000 broods of pre-snails (a hundred million billion) in which torsion might have occurred by way of a single mutation and become genetically fixed. Given this astronomically large number of possibilities, it is impossible to say that such an evolutionary change is unlikely.

Torsion is the anatomical feature that biologists use to define a snail, which is to say the class Gastropoda. Although this class may have arisen by means of a simple genetic change and a single speciation event, its origin was nothing like the hypothetical example of the first bird hatching from a reptile egg. Presumably the first snails moved and reproduced and fed in virtually the same way as their untorted predecessors. Perhaps they were no more ill-adapted than the members of some modern snail populations that have been found to have bodies coiled in what is conventionally termed a left-handed fashion resting within a right-handed shell. Because of spatial separation or an abundance of food and space, many pairs of nearly identical species of animals in the modern world do not experience ecological competition with one another. Thus, the first torted snails might easily have survived even if they were slightly less adept at moving or feeding than were their untorted ancestors, some of which must have survived after the snails evolved. Most of the advantages that have given the snails their great success as a class of animals, including the advantage conferred by the lid-sealing operculum, evolved long after torsion was in place. Snails may have arisen by means of a quantum speciation event, but they were by no means hopeful monsters of the sort that Goldschmidt envisioned.

Quantum speciation events of the sort just described are exceedingly rare in the history of life. Why is this? If, indeed, a single mutation, or two or three, accounted for the bulk of the morphological change in these examples, these mutations nonetheless almost certainly failed to produce a new animal that was well adapted in all respects. Like the domestic ancon sheep, they probably suffered from deleterious side effects that could only have been eliminated by the acquisition of additional genetic changes. The probability that appropriate mutations will arise before the population suffers extinction must be very low. In this context it is easy to see why insular habitats, with their low pressure of competition and predation, are the sites of many quantum speciation events.

Why are species such stable entities?

Although we by no means fully understand the process of quantum speciation, the knowledge that we do have of the process is of great value in our efforts to understand why, during the history of life on Earth, an average species has undergone little evolution in the course of a million generations or so. In other words, a clear view of one side of the coin—a partial understanding of why a small population occasionally succeeds in undergoing rapid modification—must help us to fashion an image of the other side of the coin where, seeing that large, well-established species are resistant to change, we wonder why that, too, is so.

One kind of insight comes from the evidence that a speciation event involving a change of development of growth gradients very often entails the generation of nonadaptive side effects in addition to the production of one or more useful adaptations. For example, it is quite evident that, in the origin of the giant panda, modification of the hindquarters was not itself selected for but was a by-product of other change. There is little chance that the genes yielding this kind of change of form could survive and spread throughout all populations of a large, widespread species. To do so, they would have to supplant genetic features that function well without harmful side effects. Missing here are factors of potentially great significance to the fixation of new features in small, isolated populations—factors like inbreeding, spread of genetic features by chance, and weakened selection pressures in the absence of predators and competitors. Thus, the morphogenetic complexities of many kinds of potentially useful evolutionary change must be one factor that obstructs evolution in large, well-established species.

A second important factor may be the way in which species are normally deployed in nature. A typical large, well-established species is represented by many partly isolated populations among many of which only limited gene flow takes place. This gene flow takes place by migration or transport of reproductive propagules, like gametes that float through water or pollen that moves through air. There is more than one level of inhomogeneity in the spatial distribution of a typical species. In other words, there are often clusters of individuals within larger clusters. At any level, each cluster will experience a unique set of environmental circumstances (exposure to a unique set of predators, competitors, food options, and physical conditions). Almost always at some level there will be forces of natural selection tending to move different populations in different evolutionary directions, but enough gene flow between populations to prevent any of the populations from diverging appreciably. Furthermore, selection pressures within individual populations will fluctuate with time. As a result of these conditions, it may be virtually impossible for the entire species to undergo substantial evolutionary change in any particular direction. Looking back to the other side of the coin, we can recognize another condition conducive to successful evolution in small populations: small populations, in occupying small geographic areas, are likely to be subjected to consistent selection pressures without disturbance by gene flow from other populations that are experiencing different selection pressures.

The idea that large species divided into partly isolated populations should be unable to evolve easily is diametrically opposed to one of the popular ideas of the modern synthesis. This is the shifting balance theory, according to which large species of this type have been judged to provide unusually favorable opportunities for evolution. The contention of the shifting balance theory has been that the populations of a species occupy what are known as adaptive peaks, which they climb by natural selection. A small population can move down from a peak by chance changes in its genetic composition and then, by natural selection, can move to a new peak.

The second important component of the shifting balance theory is the idea that there is selection among the individual populations. If one moves to a particularly high peak (evolves especially useful adaptations), eventually it will be likely to bud off new populations of the same type. These will tend to accumulate, while less well adapted populations will dwindle in number. The net result is supposed to be the continual evolutionary modification of a large, widely deployed species, and this puts the shifting balance theory very much at odds with the punctuational model of evolution. The conflict is especially evident when we note that the adaptive landscape, of which adaptive peaks form a part, should be constantly changing with changes in the environment.

In summary, the fossil data indicating that large, well-established species evolve quite sluggishly points to the presence of one or more sources of stability. These include morphogenetic constraints and sufficient gene flow among neighboring populations of the individual species to stymie long-term directional evolution.

Is human evolution punctuational?

Nowhere is the gradualistic tradition of the modern synthesis more evident than in the study of human evolution. The convention among physical anthropologists has been to view modern humans as the product of a single line of evolutionary descent. This putative line of descent passed from somewhat apelike australopithecines through early members of our genus (first *Homo habilis* and then *Home erectus*) to our species, *Homo sapiens*. When few fossil data are available, as was long the case for the human family, it often remains possible for paleontologists to assert the presence of a gradual trend by, in effect, connecting the dots. As knowledge of the fossil record improves, this procedure can be rejected if it turns out that supposed ancestral and descendant species overlapped in time. Temporal overlap implies evolutionary branching, but that alone does not eliminate the possibility of a gradualistic pattern. As illustrated in figures 1 and 2, much branching can occur within a gradualistic tree of life, as long as most evolutionary change is not associated with this

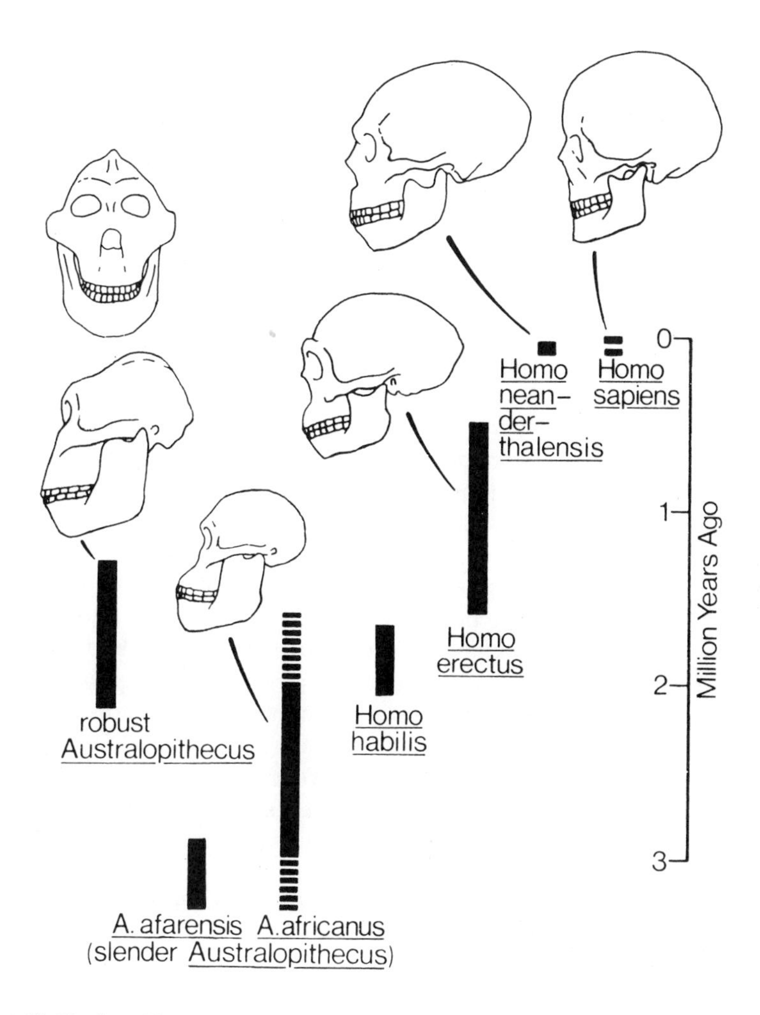

Figure 13. Stratigraphic ranges established to date for species of the human family (broken portions of bars indicate uncertain occurrences). Four of the five oldest species existed for intervals in the order of a million years. The two younger groups, Neanderthals and modern humans, have fossil records spanning only a few tens of thousands of years, but in neither group is evolutionary change of form noticeable.

branching. The second kind of evidence necessary to refute an alleged example of gradualism is evidence of the stability of species.

The question of branching poses a problem in the analysis of human evolution. For many years, a concept known as the single species hypothesis has served as a basic tenet in the study of human evolution. The hypothesis asserts that competition for such things as food, shelter, and food-gathering territory should have prevented more than one species of humans from existing on Earth at any time. This idea has gone hand-in-hand with the idea that gradual evolution within a single line of descent has led to our species.

There is no question that the single species hypothesis is not strictly valid. An australopithecine skull of the robust type has been found with a skull of *Homo erectus* at an African collecting site about 1.6 million years old. This is not a startling discovery, however, because the robust kind of australopithecines (perhaps all assignable to the species *Australopithecus robustus*) have for some time been recognized to represent a side branch of human evolution—an evolutionary dead end. *Australopithecus* had enormous jaw and cheek teeth (figure 13) and probably differed from *Homo erectus* in diet.

Within the genus *Homo,* it is debatable whether there has been temporal overlap of species. A strong argument can be made that Neanderthal did not belong to our species, where it has traditionally been placed. If this is true, then the single species hypothesis is violated, but only minimally, because there is evidence of temporal overlap of Neanderthals and humans of the modern type in Europe for the geologically brief interval of only about ten thousand years.

What are the differences between Neanderthal skeletons and those of the modern type? Both the pelvis and the shoulder blade differ between the two groups and the skulls are quite distinct. Neanderthal is, in fact, characterized by several features that are strongly reminiscent of *Homo erectus:* a strongly prognathous jaw; prominent ridges around the eye socket; a low, sloping forehead; and a long, low skull. There is also in Neanderthal a unique gap between the rear molar tooth and the rear portion of the jaw. One of the reasons that Neanderthal has traditionally been assigned to our species is that its brain was, on the average, slightly larger than ours. Another factor has been the popularity of the single species hypothesis. A prevailing belief that the evolution of the genus *Homo* has almost inexorably produced gradual increase in brain size within a single line of evolutionary descent has traditionally led to the assumption that Neanderthal must belong to our species.

Ironically, the single species hypothesis may be supported by the history of Neanderthal without strengthening the gradualistic model. There is evidence that Neanderthals and modern humans coexisted in Europe during the brief interval between about forty thousand and thirty thousand years ago. At the end of the interval, Neanderthal was extinct and modern humans remained alive, apparently populating all of Europe that was habitable by them. Thus, there is good circumstantial evidence that modern humans eradicated Neanderthal, and such behavior would strengthen the skeletal evidence that the two groups were distinct species: their populations remained discrete rather than merging through widespread interbreeding.

The interaction of Neanderthals and modern humans may serve as a model for earlier interactions between species of the genus *Homo.* A newly formed species may quickly have eliminated its predecessor, having evolved in geographic isolation and then quickly spread back into the predecessor's territory. This kind of pattern represents a slight variation on the single species hypothesis, but maintains the essential idea of the hypothesis.

The problem that results is that we have little chance of finding in the fossil record evidence of such brief temporal overlap. We can only say that the failure of the fossil record to demonstrate overlap between early species of *Homo* fails to establish a case against the punctuational model. What remains for consideration is the question of species stability, which is tending more and more to support the punctuational model.

An example of species stability relatively early in the history of the human family relates to *Australopithecus afarensis,* the species to which the famous skeleton named Lucy belongs. Remains of this species are known from the Afar region of northeastern Africa and also from farther south, in Tanzania. "Afarensis" was a small creature by modern human standards, standing less than four feet tall, but with a brain about as large as that of a gorilla, which is a much larger animal.

There is no question that "afarensis" stood upright. Its pelvis was not shaped like the elongate pelvis of an ape but like a human pelvis, which serves for support of the body in an upright posture. Furthermore, the small australopithecine left bimodal trackways in volcanic ash that closely resemble the tracks of modern humans. These tracks and associated fossils found by Mary Leakey have been dated by radiometric methods, and range back to about 3.6 million years in age. In contrast, the Lucy skeleton and associated bones have been assigned a revised age of about 2.9 million years. Thus, the species *Australopithecus afarensis* lived for the better part of a million years, and, in fact, during this interval underwent so little evolution that none has yet been demonstrated from preliminary studies of bones and teeth.

Another humanoid species that we know survived for a long interval of time is *Homo erectus,* which is an especially interesting creature because it was our evolutionary parent or grandparent. Skulls assigned to this species range in age from about 1.6 million years to about 400,000 years. There has been much debate as to whether *Homo erectus* experienced appreciable evolution during this long interval. Its brain may have increased in size somewhat, but the several specimens available exhibit no evidence of appreciable change in skull shape. The skull remained robust, with heavy brow ridges and a prognathous jaw.

The distinctive features of the modern human skull include the variable but generally prominent chin, the flat face, and the highly vaulted forehead and round skull. None of these features is approached in the youngest *Homo erectus* skulls or by skulls of Neanderthal. The oldest unquestionably modern human remains are found in Europe and the Middle East in deposits about 40,000 years old. Fragmentary remains of skulls that may be of the modern type have been found in Africa, in deposits ranging back to about 100,000 years, but the true nature of these has yet to be discerned. Whether our species arose about 40,000 years ago or earlier than 100,000 years ago, and whether it evolved from *Homo erectus,* from Neanderthal, or from some other as yet unknown species derived from Neanderthal, its origin represented a striking departure from what existed before. This departure was achieved quite rapidly on a geological scale of time, and there is a good chance that it was achieved by a quantum speciation event.

The biological transition from a species with a more robust skull to our species almost certainly entailed the retention of certain juvenile features from the anatomy of the ancestral species. In fact, the evolutionary retention of juvenile features has been one of the hallmarks of human evolution in general. It is apparently the mechanism by which members of the human family evolved a large skull with a large brain. (A baby ape's skull is bigger in relation to body size than is an adult ape's skull.) Increase in brain size was under way long before our species formed, but other features unique to our species also reflect evolutionary juvenilization. Among these are our flat face and our highly vaulted forehead and rounded skull. Hauntingly similar features are, in fact, evident in baby chimpanzees.

In sum, there is a strong likelihood that our species evolved from a more robust, slightly more apelike ancestor by a speciation event in which evolution shifted a number of juvenile features to the adult stage. There is no question that during the past forty thousand years, which may represent most of our species' stay on Earth, our anatomy has undergone extremely little change in Europe. Here the modern population has a skeletal configuration that is virtually indistinguishable from that of the earliest known Cro-Magnon people, who may have been the very first members of our species.

Large-scale evolutionary trends

The evidence that species of animals and plants are relatively stable entities raises the important question of how long-term evolutionary trends develop within large segments of the tree of life. If, for example, a modern horse did not arise by the slow, persistent modification of a diminutive ancestor with multiple toes, what kind of punctuational evolutionary pattern led to the modern animal?

A simple kind of pattern that we might choose to invoke would be one consisting of several successive steps of speciation in a particular evolutionary direction. For a small segment of the tree of life, such a pattern may indeed develop, but when we comtemplate a segment of phylogeny like that of the horses, in which dozens of species have existed, we must envision a more complex pattern. Quite often during the past 50 million years there have existed horses of many sizes and many differing anatomical traits. There is no way that one can say that there is an ideal shape for a member of the horse family. Horses can live in herds on open plains or they can move in small groups through forests. They can graze on harsh grasses or browse on soft leaves. The diversity of opportunities explains the diversity of species in the history of the horse family. Many speciation events have occurred within the family, and not all have moved in the same adaptive direction.

We see more than one direction of evolution even within much smaller segments of the tree of life. The evolutionary pathway from early australopithecines to modern humans entailed only a few speciation events. Some evolutionary changes along the way may have been unreversed, but at least one conspicuous change did undergo a marked reversal. This was the change in robustness of the skull. It is almost universally agreed that the genus *Homo* evolved from a slender australopithecine, like the forms that have been variously assigned to *Australopithecus afarensis* and *africanus.* These were creatures with moderately strong brow ridges, but they are commonly referred to as slender or gracile forms. The younger species *Homo erectus* is also, almost without question, a more recent ancestor of modern humans, and this species possessed a more robust skull. Modern humans, however, represent a return to a more gracile condition: our facial bones are relatively thin and our jaw muscles relatively weak.

The back-and-forth trend in robustness within the human family illustrates an important point. The directions of speciation events are often unpredictable. The direction of a particular event may be largely under the control of natural selection driven by environmental conditions, but when we stand back and look at a species at any moment, we cannot predict what population may participate in the next speciation event, if any, to issue from that species. We do not know what the environmental conditions will be or what genetic changes will crop up to be tested by natural selection.

With such uncertainty, how does phylogeny undergo a net shift over a long period of time from one average adaptive condition to another? Most large-scale trends may develop by a process illustrated in figure 14. In this hypothetical example, a trend moves toward the biological condition represented on the right-hand side of the diagram. This trend develops even though as many speciation events move to the left as move to the right. Thus, a bias in the direction of speciation does not account for the trend. Furthermore, the total amount of evolutionary change produced by speciation events moving to the left equals the total amount produced by events moving to the right. What, then, yields the trend?

Two factors contribute. The first is a tendency for species positioned toward the right-hand side of the diagram to survive slightly longer (exhibit lower extinction rates) than those positioned toward the left.

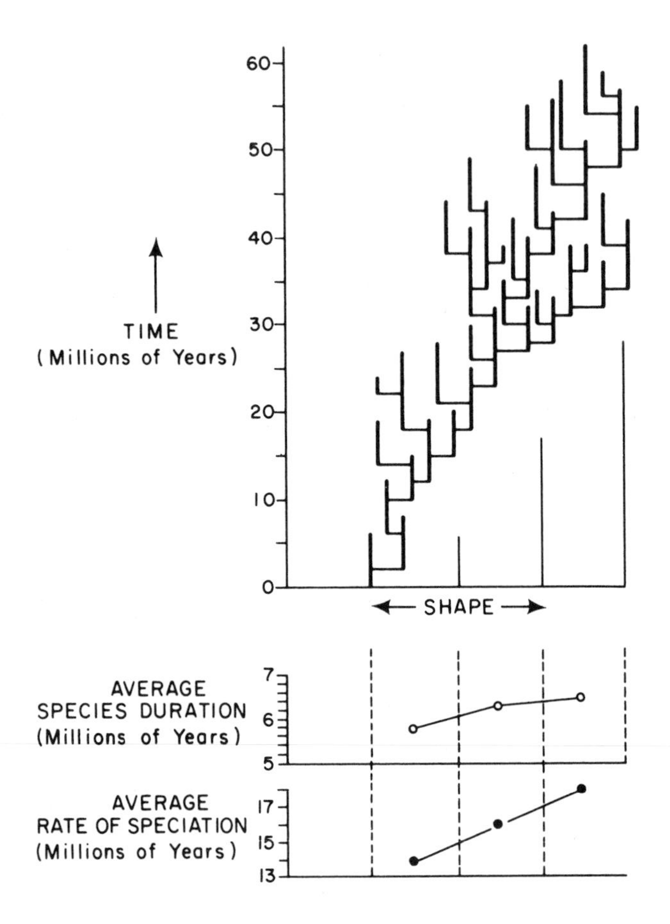

Figure 14. A large-scale trend within a hypothetical segment of the tree of life. For simplicity, all evolutionary change here is shown as being associated with speciation (an exaggeration of the real situation). The trend, which changes the average shape toward the condition represented on the right-hand side of the diagram, is produced by species selection. This is a process dependent upon differences among species in rate of speciation and/or extinction. In this particular example, rate of speciation and rate of extinction work together to yield the trend. Average rate of speciation decreases toward the right-hand side of the diagram (this is the reciprocal of average species duration), and average rate of speciation (number of speciation events per unit time within a lineage) increases. The result is a progressive dwindling of species on the left-hand side of the diagram and an accumulation of species on the right-hand side. In some real segments of the tree of life, rate of extinction and rate of speciation have worked against one another, but one of the two has dominated, to produce a trend.

Comparison of species selection and natural selection within a population of individuals.

	Natural Selection Among Individuals	Species Selection
Unit of selection	Individual	Species
Souce of variability	Mutation and shuffling of genetic material by sexual reproduction	Speciation
Mode of selection	A. Survival against death B. Rate of reproduction	A. Rate of extinction B. Rate of speciation

This causes species positioned toward the right, on the average, to speciate more times before they become extinct than do species positioned toward the left.

The second factor has to do with individual species' rate of speciation per unit time. Here again there is a gradient favoring species positioned toward the right-hand side of the diagram. The diagram is constructed so that, on the average, the number of speciation events per million years of existence is higher for species positioned toward the right. What these circumstances yield is a progressive shift of the tree of life toward the biological condition represented by the right-hand side of the graph.

In the mechanism of large-scale trend formation illustrated in figure 14, speciation, moving to the left and to the right, represents the raw material of change. The process operating on this raw material to produce change is called species selection. As illustrated in the table, this process is analogous to selection among individuals within a population. In species selection, however, species take the place of individuals as the units of selection, and rate of speciation per unit time and survival against extinction take the place of fecundity and of survival against death.

It is important to understand that species selection can be the predominant source of a large-scale trend even if natural selection among individuals accounts for the origins of individual species. The crucial point is that the origin of a species at one small locality and in one small population is no guarantee that the species will fare well in a broader environmental context—that it will survive for a long time or produce descendant species at a high rate.

It is also important to understand that a low rate of extinction (long survival) of species of a certain kind will not always work hand-in-hand with a high rate of speciation to produce a large-scale trend. Within many segments of the tree of life, the two factors will work against one another and a trend will result from the prevalence of one of the two factors.

Ultimately, several different agents and conditions must be responsible for species selection. Among the most important are what ecologists call limiting factors—environmental factors that control population sizes of animals and plants. These factors, which include food supply, predation, competition, and conditions of the physical environment, as well as chance factors, determine whether species decline rapidly to extinction, and they also determine whether small populations are able to emerge as large, full-fledged new species. Thus, they govern both rates of extinction and rates of speciation.

Another unrelated factor also yields species selection by way of differential rates of speciation. This is an inherent tendency to speciate. In fact, we can observe that certain kinds of species have speciated at a high rate compared to others that belong to the same family or order, but that are characterized by certain critical biological differences.

For example, certain families or orders of marine mollusks include some species that produce larvae that drift great distances in the ocean and other species that produce larvae that remain on the seafloor close to their parents. The latter species tend to speciate at unusually high rates because their limited powers of dispersal make it relatively easy for small populations to become geographically isolated from the other populations of their species. In terms of species selection, there is a trade-off, however. Species that do not disperse easily tend to suffer high rates of extinction because they are narrowly distributed and vulnerable to local environmental changes. Fortunately, we can often assess the larval history of a family of marine mollusks by examining the larval segments of shells of individual species. When we see evidence that a living family that consists largely of weakly dispersing individuals has attained this state by transition from a former state in which species with floating larvae predominated, we have evidence that the trade-off has not been an even one. If we assume, reasonably, that few individual species have undergone transformation from having floating larvae to having nonfloating larvae, we must conclude that species selection has favored nonfloating larvae. In other words, the high rate of speciation of species with nonfloating larvae has more than offset the attendant high rate of extinction, and these species have tended to accumulate in the course of time.

We are only now beginning to assess patterns of species selection in the fossil record. One of the difficulties here is that thorough documentation of the process requires that we possess detailed information about the temporal distributions and biological properties of a large percentage of the species within a particular segment of the tree of life. The fossil record does not readily yield comprehensive data of this sort for long intervals of time. Nonetheless, case studies like the molluscan example described above are beginning to come to light.

Imperfections and gaps in the ecosystem

If the punctuational view of evolution is valid, the ecosystem has a very different character than the one traditionally envisioned. In a world dominated by gradualistic evolution, species would constantly be adjusting to environmental change. Not only have gradualists assumed that such change occurs, they have tended to assume that there are strong evolutionary pressures tending to fill gaps left by extinction. Darwin, in fact, believed nature to be essentially saturated with species. He inherited this idea from his intellectual predecessors, who had actually adopted it from theology. The *scala naturae,* or great chain of being, had been considered to represent a perfect creation of life. The idea here was that species covered the Earth to form a perfect ecosystem without gaps. Plenitude was the formal name given to this concept, and although the name was abandoned in the course of the nineteenth century, the concept remained and, with some modification, became formalized within the niche theory of ecology during the twentieth century.

Until the 1960s the primary focus of theoretical and experimental ecology was upon how species partitioned the environment into discrete niches. For some communities of species this kind of analysis has merit, but for others it turns out to be inappropriate. We now recognize that where predation or other forms of disturbance are prevalent, competition is not severe. Populations remain at such low levels that resources like food and living space are in ample supply, and no species of superior competitive ability is able to thrive to the degree that it pushes out others.

The punctuational model does further damage to the concept of competitive saturation of the environment. Particularly important here is the haphazard nature of speciation, which, according to the punctuational model, is the site of most evolutionary change. Speciation is dependent upon the vagaries of environmental change, and, if species do not easily change once they have formed, millions of years may pass before a niche or set of niches vacated by extinction happens to be filled by speciation. Today, for example, there is a scarcity of large mammal species, owing to extinctions during the recent Pleistocene epoch of large forms like rodents the size of hippos, ground sloths twenty feet tall, and bison with six-foot horn spans. Since the extinction of these forms, surviving species of mammals have passed though thousands of generations without replacing the extinct giants by evolving to large size.

The implication of the punctuational model, then, is that there is not universally present on Earth a tightly integrated balance of nature. Some species are intimately related to others, but the decline or disappearance of one species does not usually cause other species to evolve substantially in some new direction. Furthermore, a long interval of time is sometimes required for speciation to fill the void.

Why was Darwin a gradualist?

There is no question that Darwin's view of evolution imparted great momentum to the gradualistic framework that emerged within the modern synthesis of the present century. When we stand back and view the historical context of Darwin's work, his gradualistic position seems almost inevitable. There was not just one reason for Darwin's view that evolution moves slowly but powerfully to transform well-established species. Rather, there seem to have been several factors that contributed significantly to his position.

One factor that perhaps influenced Darwin without his awareness was the natural tendency that we all have to push a new idea toward an extreme in differentiating it from previously recognized alternatives. For Darwin, the competing idea was the theological one of special creation. While the geologically sudden (punctuational) evolution of a new species entails more time than an instantaneous event of divine creation, the temporal patterns involved must have seemed dangerously similar to Darwin as he contemplated trying to convince his contemporaries to accept the heterodox option of evolution. Darwin may unconsciously have staked out a position as far from special creation as possible. How could he have expected other scientists to have accepted the idea that an unfamiliar process (natural selection) was responsible for producing life in the modern world by operating sporadically and locally, under the very conditions that might make it almost impossible to distinguish it from special creation?

Related to the special creation problem is another that pertained to the difficulty of making a convincing case in favor of a shocking new idea. Certainly, if one intends to argue strongly for the operation throughout the world of a previously unrecognized process, the most persuasive approach is to suggest that the process moves with almost imperceptible slowness.

One of the most obvious influences on Darwin's thinking was the gradualistic world view embodied in the newly developing uniformitarian approach to geology. While on the voyage of HMS *Beagle,* Darwin read Charles Lyell's new treatise, *Principles of Geology,* which argued forcefully for uniformitarianism, or the interpretation of the origins of ancient rocks in terms of processes that could be seen to be operating in the modern world. Certainly the idea that the Earth's surface was undergoing continuous change by natural processes opened the door to the idea that life might also be transforming gradually.

There were also two false ideas about the natural world that moved Darwin in the direction of gradualism. Both were rooted in theology but persisted as widespread misconceptions within biological science in Darwin's day. One of these was the previously mentioned concept of plenitude, or the fullness of nature. Darwin's writings reveal that he believed the world to be fully packed with species, so that there was virtually no space for a new species without the disappearance of one that had existed before. This was, in fact, an aspect of the uniformitarian system of Lyell, who believed that species, like physical materials, were cycled through environments of the Earth's surface without any substantial net change in the physical or biological world. In short, Lyell believed in a kind of global dynamic equilibrium, in which the plenitude of life was never lost.

The prevailing idea of plenitude gave Darwin great difficulty in conceiving of natural selection. This can be seen in his notebooks, which seem to record the moment when the idea of natural selection finally came to him. Here he wrote of "a force like a hundred thousand wedges trying [to] force every kind of adapted structure into the gaps on the economy of nature, or rather forming the gaps by thrusting out the weaker ones." As he jotted down his thoughts here, Darwin altered his idea in mid-sentence because he realized that there were supposed to be no gaps in nature. He was forced to propose a kind of subtle domino effect, in which if a single species were able to change just a little, then this would make room for a minor change in some other species, and so on. Clearly, not recognizing that there are, in fact, many gaps between species in nature, Darwin had been obstructed in trying to envision room for evolution of any sort.

The second misconception with which Darwin was saddled was the remarkable idea that species do not vary appreciably in form. Like the notion of plenitude, this one derived from the theological concept of a perfect creation. Natural selection was supposed to operate on variability among individuals, and yet biologists gave scant recognition to this necessary raw material.

Certainly under these circumstances the sluggish pace for natural selection was most reasonable to Darwin and would have been more palatable to his contemporaries as well. His great concern with the question of variability is revealed in the enormous amount of time that, before writing *On the Origin of Species,* he spent in documenting the existence of variability in both domestic and wild species of animals and plants. Darwin observed the existence of occasional "sports" in domestic populations—individuals that we might now refer to as strange mutants—but he believed that while they could survive under human protection, similar forms in nature would suffer early death under conditions of plenitude, in which competition would be severe.

Finally, Darwin accepted the observation of domestic breeders that inbreeding would inevitably result in poor adaptation. We now recognize that only a small infusion of genetic material is necessary to overcome serious inbreeding depression and that, in fact, pure inbreeding is not always highly deleterious. For Darwin, however, the "evils" of inbreeding, to use his word, seemed to require that only large populations, in which outbreeding is the rule, could survive in nature and evolve effectively.

Fair consideration of all of these factors can only lead to the conclusion that Darwin had little choice but to favor a gradualistic pattern for the evolution of animals and plants in nature. Like other great thinkers, no matter how creative they may be, he was in part the product of his environment.

* * * * * *

The tenets and consequences of the punctuational model of evolution are summarized in *The New Evolutionary Timetable: Fossils, Genes, and the Origin of Species,* by Steven M. Stanley (New York: Basic Books, 1981). *Darwin to DNA, Molecules to Humanity,* by G. Ledyard Stebbins (San Francisco: W.H. Freeman & Co., 1982), provides an up-to-date, authoritative summary of organic evolution. More advanced treatments can be found in three popular textbooks. Ernst Mayr, who contributed many of the elements of the punctuational model, has summarized his views in *Populations, Species, and Evolution* (Cambridge, Mass.: Harvard University Press, 1970). Two other general textbooks are *Evolution,* by Theodosius Dobzhansky, Francisco J. Ayala, G. Ledyard Stebbins, and James W. Valentine (San Francisco: W.H. Freeman & Co., 1977), and *Evolutionary Biology,* by Douglas J. Futuyma (Sunderland, Mass.: Sinauer Associates, 1979). An interesting collection of essays about evolution can be found in *Evolution: A Scientific American Book* (San Francisco: W.H. Freeman & Co., 1978). Two or three essays that relate to the punctuational model can be found in Stephen J. Gould's delightful collection of essays, *The Panda's Thumb* (New York: W.W. Norton, 1980). Of the many biographical sketches of Darwin and his contemporaries, Loren Eiseley's *Darwin's Century* (New York: Anchor Books, 1961) remains one of the most appealing. A good account of Darwin's historic voyage around the world, with beautiful illustrations, can be found in Alan Moorehead's *Darwin and the Beagle* (New York: Harper and Row, 1969). A recent work of general interest is Roger Lewin's *Thread of Life: The Smithsonian Looks at Evolution* (Smithsonian Expo, 1982).

Mathematics in Our Time

Felix E. Browder

Born in the U.S.S.R. in 1927, Felix Browder came to America at the age of five. Educated in New York, he did his undergraduate work at the Massachusetts Institute of Technology and received his Ph.D. in mathematics from Princeton. Since then he has taught and done research at universities all over the world and is at present chairman of the department of mathematics at the University of Chicago.

Professor Browder has also served as chairman of committees in several mathematical societies. He addressed the International Congress of Mathematicians at Nice in 1970 and has lectured at various mathematical conferences across the country.

Partial differential equations and nonlinear functional analysis have been his particular areas of expertise; he is the author of more than 200 books and articles dealing mainly with those two topics. Professor Browder has also written general treatises on mathematics including "The relevance of mathematics" for the *American Mathematical Monthly* and "The Stone Age of mathematics on the Midway" for the *University of Chicago Magazine.*

Introduction

Of all the domains of intellectual activity, mathematics is the most difficult to present to the general educated public. Readers abound for a variety of books on black holes, on the first three minutes of the universe, or on the Grand Unification Theories of elementary particle physics, all of which involve a highly intricate mathematical structure in their inner machinery. But this inner machinery is never exposed to public view, and for good reason. One knows as a practical matter (and this is the wisdom of every experienced science editor) that the explicit presentation of a mathematical argument or worse still of a mathematical formula is enough to chill the heart of the most stoical reader. Say, for example, that I were foolish enough (and perverse enough) for the sake of illustration to present the reader of these lines with the age-old formula for the solution of a quadratic equation, which the Babylonians knew in operational terms some thousands of years B.C. and which is written in the algebraic notation invented in late Renaissance Italy. What a shock! We may well ask why.

To turn the matter around, the liberally educated reader may recall that in the most celebrated philosophical work of all time, Plato's *Republic* (see *GBWW,* Vol. 7), Plato suggests (or rather Socrates does, who we may regard as Plato's spokesman) that the unique proper foundation for a genuine philosophical education for the rulers of his ideal State is mathematical study. Why does he make that rather remarkable suggestion? Many contemporary students of Plato, or even would-be disciples, find it hard to answer this question, though Plato himself provides an explicit answer in the text. His answer is simple and can be used as the starting point of our present discussion. Plato says that his ideal ruling class must study mathematics for two principal reasons: It is the most generally practical and useful subject of study, on the one hand. On the other hand, it is the most difficult in conventional worldly terms and forces the learner to confront his own powers of thought in the most explicit and philosophically taxing way.

Educational doctrines like Plato's are of course no longer very fashionable (even though, in the nineteenth century, they caused future bishops of the Church of England educated at Cambridge to take mathematics degrees and examinations). Indeed, they have never been dominant in the educational tradition that comes down from the Greco-Roman world continuously to the present day. The reason is not hard to find. Any concept of knowledge or general education that is based upon forcing the mind to reach its highest powers indeed seems Utopian to the extreme. Even at the time when Plato wrote in Athens—the fourth century B.C.— a completely different tradition was much more popular in education. This was the tradition of Isocrates based upon rhetoric, the art of persuasive speech (and persuasive writing). No matter how brilliant or original the mathematicians and philosophers of the Greek and Hellenistic worlds may have been (and some compare most favorably with anything that came after them), their lack of power to affect the consciousness of *their* educated public is reflected in the most famous anecdote about Euclid. The latter was asked by a royal pupil to give him a quick recipe for learning his mathematics. Euclid's reply is celebrated. There is no royal road to geometry.

Given this historically authenticated tradition going back two thousand years, on what basis can one presume that anyone who is not professionally dedicated to mathematical study ought to have any knowledge of mathematics or any insight into its nature and accomplishments? The question is a tricky one and deserves a clear and candid answer.

For most periods of human history (and the Europe of the eighteenth-century Enlightenment may be a partial exception), the educated public tended to regard mathematical ideas and mathematical research as a very esoteric though possibly very useful business. It was to be left in the care of a handful of zealous devotees, to be regarded with awe on some occasions, disdainfully on others. In the latter connection, I think of a well-regarded president of an Ivy League university several decades ago who announced in his annual report that his university had purchased its first major computer, "putting"—in his words—"several dozen mathematicians out of work." The image his words conjure up is indeed comical; a large roomful of medieval clerks or Egyptian scribes in long rows adding up columns of figures. This learned gentleman, whose university had an excellent mathematics department (and still has), must have thought of these members of his faculty as occupied with running hand calculators. The amount of intellectual contact between him and them was obviously nil. Given such a relationship (or lack of one), it is not very surprising that many mathematicians have accepted the state of affairs in reverse and argue (often very dogmatically) that it is neither possible nor desirable for them to explain themselves or their activities to the educated public.

The nature of mathematics

One of the most important reasons for not accepting the happy complacency of mutual ignorance and disdain is the simplest: Mathematics is the principal instrument we use to understand the world and manage our affairs in it. In terms of understanding the physical world, this has been obvious since the seventeenth century, when it was discovered, to paraphrase Galileo, that numbers and geometrical shapes are the language of Nature. In terms of the practical life of civilization, the idea goes back much further, indeed as far as we can see beyond the edge of written records. In the passages from the *Republic,* Plato ridicules Homer for suggesting that one of his Greek heroes invented numbers. How are we to believe, Plato asks, that the generals of the Greek army were able to muster their soldiers or their ships without counting them? Or how, we might ask in a similar vein, can any reasonably organized agricultural society carry on its activities without that most basic of all applied mathematical instruments, the calendar? To go to the other extreme, how did our Ivy League president expect his newly purchased digital computer to function in meaningful intellectual tasks without mathematically trained people to program it?

We can say it in much more general terms: Every reasonably complex human society functions in terms of deeply ingrained mathematical elements and tools. Think for example of money, or of votes. The only distinctive features of our present situation are the increasingly sophisticated nature of the mathematics that is imbedded in social practice, the specialized human disciplines which serve that practice, and the rapidity with which it develops and changes.

Let us focus the discussion more precisely. If we want a general characterization of mathematics, it would be the following: Mathematics is the science of order, structure, and relation. It tends to study stable ordered structures of relations; by so doing it also studies change, disorder, and the breakdown of structure (though Plato would be horrified at the thought). The three systems of order with which mathematics begins (and with which it obviously began historically) are those of number, in the sense of counting and calculating, of geometrical shape, and of their mixture in the form of measuring.

Among the Greeks of the classical period with whom the concept of science arose, the paradigm of science was mathematics (in the form primarily of geometry) and mathematical astronomy. The Greek philosophers and mathematicians discovered a stable structure of order in geometry whereby, from simple and relatively obvious principles, one could obtain an immense body of highly unobvious truths by a reliable method, that of *logical deduction.* It was in consciousness of this achievement going on before his eyes that Plato set forth the motto over the door of the Academy: *Let no one ignorant of geometry enter here.* An extension of this principle in the

Platonic dialogue *Timaeus* (see *GBWW*, Vol. 7) led him to the formulation of a "myth," the myth of the geometrical creation of the physical cosmos. Though some of Plato's philosophical successors like Aristotle criticized and rejected his pan-mathematical enthusiasms, this side of the Platonic tradition lived on in various forms. It was transmitted through the Middle Ages, for example in the concept of the seven liberal arts: the trivium of grammar, logic, and rhetoric, and the quadrivium of the four mathematical sciences, number, geometry, music, and astronomy. More important still, the gigantic achievements of Greek mathematicians like Eudoxus, Archimedes, and Apollonius and the greatest of all scientific books, Euclid's *Elements* (see *GBWW*, Vol. 11) and Ptolemy's *Almagest* (see *GBWW*, Vol. 16), were transmitted to Western Europe a thousand years later as the foundation stones of modern mathematics and science.

The beginnings of modern mathematics

Modern mathematics and the characteristically mathematical form of modern physics arose together in Western Europe during the sixteenth and seventeenth centuries. The late Middle Ages and the early Renaissance in Italy had seen the translation of the major works of the Greek tradition from Greek and Arabic into Latin but had also seen the translation of Arab mathematical works that represented a different mathematical thrust than the Greek deductive and geometrical tradition. This new thrust, based presumably upon influences from Babylonia and from India, emphasized *calculation* rather than *logical deduction.* The author of the most prominent of these works, al-Khwārizmī, gave his name to the term *algorithm* (i.e., procedure for calculation) and the title of his book became *algebra.*

The emphasis upon calculation, especially in the solution of polynomial equations involving powers higher than two in the unknown, gave rise to the prototypical achievement of this stage of mathematical activity, namely the discovery of algorithms for finding roots of equations of third and fourth degree which was made by a constantly feuding group of Italian savants. It gave rise as well to a number of features now considered characteristic of mathematical practice in all its varieties. To make calculations easier and more efficient, problems and steps in their solution had to be formulated in *symbols* rather than words. The characteristic use of letters and other symbols to represent unknown or unspecified quantities became fixed, as did the use of standard symbols for algebraic operations on such quantities, the use of exponents, as well as the equality sign.

Behind all of these innovations lay an innovation so fundamental that it almost passed unnoticed. This was the introduction of Arabic numerals, which intrinsically involve the use of *zero* as a place-holder. The greater sophistication in algebraic problem-solving involved not only the decimal system of notation and the use of negative numbers but, much more dramatically, the first appearance of that most remarkable of elementary mathematical creatures, $\sqrt{-1}$, the imaginary square root of a negative number. *Number,* itself, the result of counting or of measuring, had been freed from the constraints and inhibitions of Greek tradition. The positive whole numbers, or as we should say today, the positive integers, had been given an autonomous existence by the Platonic school, so that you could uninhibitedly speak of *three* and its properties rather than just three apples or three sheep. No such dispensation was accorded to fractions in the Greek tradition, which could only be considered as ratios of whole numbers and never given an independent existence. The results of measurements in the geometrical context were always tied in their categorical nature to the context. A length, strictly speaking, could not be directly compared to an area or a volume; dimensional analysis held sway in this primitive form.

The beginnings of algebra and analytic geometry

In the thrust of the *algebraic* or more properly *analytic* movement of the sixteenth and early seventeenth centuries, these inhibitions were swept away. A number became something you calculated with, regardless of context or philosophical predisposition. *Analysis* was the term derived from Greek writers like Pappus to describe a procedure which reversed the customary direction of *deduction.* Given a problem, an equation to solve, you analyzed it into problems or equations whose solution implies the solution of the original problem. In place of deducing unquestioned truths from previously known unquestioned truths, the analytic movement proposed to derive new problems from old problems, the chain of problems finally coming to rest in a problem you know how to solve.

The most remarkable variant of this approach arose in the formula for the solution of the cubic equation published by Jerome Cardan. One case of that solution involved *numbers* of an unusual type, complex and imaginary numbers of the form $a + b\sqrt{-1}$, with a and b standing for two of the "real" numbers familiar from the usual dealings with numbers. Such expressions appear already in the formula for the solution of a quadratic equation, $ax^2 + bx + c = 0$, but can be neutralized in that context by considering that their appearance simply indicates that no real solution of the equation exists. In the case of the cubic equation $ax^3 + bx^2 + cx + d = 0$, where the numbers a, b, c, and d which appear (and are called the coefficients of the equation) may all be real numbers, there may be a "real" solution x of the equation, but paradoxically the formula for the solution is given in terms that use the "imaginary" $\sqrt{-1}$. The full naturalization of these "imaginary" numbers did not come till the latter part of the eighteenth century when J. R. Argand and Carl Gauss showed that they had a representation not as points on a line like the real numbers but as points of a geometrical plane.

The naturalization just mentioned was itself part of another decisively important process strongly linked to the new concepts of number and the concept of analysis. This was the development—at the hands of François Viète, Pierre de Fermat, and René Descartes—of the new kind of geometry, the *analytical geometry.* Two paradigms existed for mathematics up to this point, the rigorously deductive *synthetic* geometry of Euclid's elements and the pragmatic algebraic problem-solving of the analytic movement. What the analytical geometry proposed to do was to solve problems (or more specifically to prove theorems) in the context of the classical framework of the geometry of Euclid by reducing those problems to algebraic equations which could be attacked in the analytic style.

The technique for doing this more than slightly impious deed involves an identification of a point on the geometric plane or in space with a collection of numbers, its *coordinates* in a particular representation. For points on the line, the representation is reasonably straightforward once a unit of length on the line has been chosen, as well as an origin of coordinates. To all points on the right of the origin of coordinates, one assigns their distance from the origin in terms of the unit of length; while to points on the left, one assigns the negative of their distance from the origin of coordinates. For points in the plane, one takes a pair of perpendicular intersecting lines, chooses the origin of coordinates on each line as the point of intersection, and a common unit of length. Then the coordinates of a planar point are the coordinates of its perpendicular projections on each of the lines. Each point corresponds uniquely to a pair of real numbers, and each pair of real numbers to a point. *Analytic geometry,* the study of the properties of loci of algebraic equations involving the coordinates of geometric points, provides an alternative *model* to the deductive processes of Euclidean geometry.

The systematic vs. the historical approach to mathematics

Before proceeding further, we ought to look more explicitly at the mode of exposition which we have begun to follow. Our object in the present discussion is to survey the contemporary state of mathematics both as an intellectual discipline in its own right and in its vital relations with science and the social process. We have begun by talking about the Babylonians, the Greeks, and the sixteenth century. Is there a method in this apparent contradiction? We should like to assure the reader that there is, and point out the essential reasons for this method.

The standard way of presenting a mathematical subject matter is by didactic exposition, presenting formal definitions and their deductive consequences. A variation on this style presents informal and intuitively attractive examples, but without venturing at least tentatively into definitions and their consequences, you cannot explicitly present the mathematical process itself. Mathematics, like all the sciences, is not a body of truths given ready-made or to be picked up without effort like shells at the seashore. It is a process and an art in which the "artist," the practitioner of the research art, is changed and has his consciousness of the world changed by the results of his practice. He sees in new perspectives, and because he sees through new eyes, he is able to see things that he could not see before. What I have proposed to do in the presentation of contemporary mathematics is to make this process more obvious to the reader's eyes by viewing mathematics in the context of its historical background. What we see in that background are the roots and motives that underlie the most basic concepts of the mathematics of the present, and I believe they appear in a much more transparent form than they would in a didactic exposition.

The form is more attractive, too, especially when we apply it to those parts of the basic subject matter of mathematics which contemporary practice finds boring or trivial. In terms of contemporary intellectual interests, there seems to be nothing worthwhile to be said of *commercial arithmetic,* for example, and yet, from the historical point of view, it was one of the decisive moving forces (almost certainly one of two decisive moving forces) behind the Babylonians' innovative use of numbers and the development of algebra. Moreover, it can be argued very persuasively that the whole development of the economic processes of commerce and credit, and the laying of the roots of capitalism in Renaissance Italy and throughout Western Europe would have been impossible without the upsurge of an effective commercial arithmetic based upon the introduction and use of Arabic numerals.

To take another case, there is a very persistent prejudice against Euclidean geometry reflected in numerous efforts in mathematical education to eradicate its influence and replace it with some other kind of geometric education more suitable for the modern world. The most extreme form of this kind of thinking is the explicit slogan "Á bas Euclide" (*Down with Euclid*), which became associated with the dogmatic viewpoint of one influential French mathematician. But whatever we may judge the value of these dogmas to be, it is not possible to see the mathematical world straight if we systematically ignore the fact that Euclid's *Elements* provided the unquestioned foundation for two thousand years of what mathematicians and all varieties of mathematical practitioners believed to be *rigorous mathematical deduction.* Nor can we doubt that when the French consortium of mathematical writers who go under the name of *Nicolas Bourbaki* (and among whom the critic of Euclid was once conspicuously numbered) began writing their *Éléments des mathématiques,* they had it as their ambition to play the same role for future mathematical generations that Euclid had played for past millennia.

To take a final case, similar reforms in mathematics teaching at American universities have almost completely eliminated the teaching of analytic geometry as an autonomous part of the basic mathematical curriculum and have minimized it as a subsection of the teaching of calculus. It is not my purpose here to complain of the nature of this change, nor even of the damaging effects that eliminating most explicit consideration of geometrical topics may have on the capacities of students who learn through a curriculum which has been impoverished in this particular way. What I should like to emphasize (and certainly not only for the benefit of mathematicians) is that we can gain a great deal of perspective on our present prospect by viewing it in the context of its historical development.

The argument just presented is not an argument for mathematical history or for the history of science in its technical sense, though explicit arguments for these disciplines can indeed draw some support from this viewpoint. Rather it justifies a procedure whereby we attempt to see major trends in our contemporary situation, not as something that erupted yesterday, but as the culmination of long-based historically authenticated processes. It is the culmination, let me stress, not the validation. There is no mathematical argument and no scientific theory whose validity is based upon its having been employed or believed several hundred or a thousand years ago.

Nor would I argue that the significance of contemporary mathematical achievements should be judged exclusively or even primarily in terms of their relationship to the mathematical past. There exist spokesmen for this point of view, and I tend to disagree with their conclusions, finding for myself that the real test of the significance of mathematical achievements lies in the future, in broadening and deepening the thrust of the immanent development of mathematical ideas and techniques. From this viewpoint, the argument may seem paradoxical, but we can put it in a reasonably persuasive form, it is only this: Any meaningful perspective on the development of mathematics in the present-day world and on the relationship of mathematics to science, technology, and society can avoid dogmatism of one form or another only by recognizing that the past, present, and future of the mathematical enterprise are inextricably connected. The relation between the past of mathematical experience, the present of problems, prospects, and efforts, and the future in which these efforts have their goals is a complex one. We must, however, take it into account.

The mathematization of physical science

The forms of mathematics

Before turning back to pursue the historical thread of the role of mathematics and mathematical ways of thinking in the great scientific revolution of the seventeenth century in Western Europe, let me append another methodological note. In a paper which I wrote a number of years ago about the role of mathematics in the world, I suggested that a great deal of clarity could be achieved in discussions of the subject if one separated out four different guises under which mathematics appears in the world.

They show mathematics as:

(1) an element of general social practice;

(2) a tool in various intellectual disciplines;

(3) a self-conscious intellectual discipline in its own right pursuing its own self-generated intellectual goals;

(4) an ideal of human knowledge.

By making separations of this sort, I did not mean to suggest that those areas of mathematical practice or influence are totally distinct or without interaction. The degree and nature of the interaction is sometimes difficult to assess in a precise way, though it is of importance to attempt such an assessment in terms of the contemporary situation. What I do suggest (and meant to suggest when I first put forward this division) is that, by recognizing these four meanings of the word *mathematics,* we also recognize that all of them have a valid claim to existence. Certainly, the first three of these categories are embodied in enormously different spheres of human practice in the present-day world, and we shall insist in our later discussion upon the usually unrecognized omnipresence of the two first bodies of practice in the contemporary world. But the terms on which the different spheres of mathematical practice interact have varied considerably in different periods of human history and are in a process of change even today.

Mathematics and society: historical examples

The assumption of a certain kind of "sociologizing" view of the development of mathematics and other intellectual disciplines is that the natural path of development and influence should go down the ordered list we have given; social practice should give rise to specialized intellectual disciplines which use mathematics and these in turn should give rise to mathematics as an autonomous discipline which formulates mathematical ideals. But the major facts of mathematical history belie this assumption, at least in its most naive form.

Since the assumption involved seems to be a deeply rooted part of contemporary common sense, the reader is entitled to be presented with some major examples and a reasoned justification for why such examples exist. Let us begin with the latter. Mathematical practitioners, like other human beings, live in some human society, are educated in that society, and react in a meaningful way to the social heritage which they receive from it of knowledge, interests, and goals. In all societies except possibly the most primitive, this heritage is usually received by the individual through the medium of relatively stable institutions such as family, church, school, and the state. The goals which these institutions foster may go far beyond the naive utilitarian goals of food, shelter, and sex; in almost all cases, they embody symbolic goals deemed essential to the stable existence of that institution and of the social practices which it fosters.

These symbolic goals, once embodied in a relatively stable institutional form, take on a life of their own and often give the individual participants in the institutional practice an important sense of the "meaningfulness" of their social involvement and of their own existence as individual human beings.

To give these generalities a more concrete flavor, let us consider the Babylonians, who of all the great long-lived Asiatic civilizations developed the highest mathematical culture. Babylonian mathematical practice, at least in its higher phases, had two main purposes: commerce, and astronomical observation for the sake of astrological prediction. Both these purposes were implemented through the central institution of their society, namely, the temple household operated by a priestly clerical staff. To maintain the operation of this institution, an important stable subinstitution had to exist—the school. The mathematics of the Babylonians was a *scholastic* mathematics derived from the structure and practice of a long-lived and extremely conservative educational routine. We may generalize from this particular example that in some contexts, at least, the social practice which most clearly influences and shapes mathematical practice in its various forms is *educational* practice.

In classical Greek civilization, matters were considerably different. During the crucial period of creativity from the sixth to the fourth century B.C., in which the concept of mathematics as a self-conscious intellectual discipline first arose, parallel to but distinct from the sister discipline of philosophy, it was not identified with any stable institution. It was not fostered by family, church, school, or state.

Greek mathematicians lived a self-conscious existence as intellectual practitioners, as individuals or in small groups. They operated within the framework of small philosophical schools (what we would call institutes for advanced study), like Eudoxus in the Platonic Academy, or operated their own schools for their disciples, as Eudoxus did in his native city of Cnidus. They were noted for their extensive travel as individuals, sometimes journeying far from the Greek world to Egypt or Babylon to look for insight or inspiration. All this, of course, they did in the context of the Greek city-states in which, to some observers, it seemed that family, church, school, and state were all in a process of dissolution. The basic ingredient which made this sphere of activity possible for the Greek mathematicians, philosophers, and all the other varieties of professional intellectuals for which Greece became celebrated was the existence of a social form, the existence of *leisure.* As Aristotle tells us very explicitly, without the existence of a leisured class, supported either by private resources or by patrons, Greek intellectual life would not have been possible.

This seems in drastic contradiction to the sociological generalization put forward above, that the intellectual interests and goals of society are mediated to individuals by stable social institutions like family, church, school, or state. The Greek case is in obvious, even dramatic contradiction to the apparent thrust of this generalization. We can reconcile ourselves to this fact, if we wish, in the style endorsed by the great Danish theoretical physicist Niels Bohr. We can call the generalization about the indispensability of stable institutions a deep truth in the Bohrian sense, that is, one whose negation is also a deep truth. Less paradoxically, we can say that, most of the time, the generalization is true. It only fails in the most interesting cases.

Mathematics as the science of the changeless

There is a more important lesson to be learned from this contrast than the failure of this sociological generalization to cover all cases. The Greeks themselves, or at least some of their most influential intellectual figures, were conscious of the contrast. The Greek world of the city-states was gripped by conflict, social strife, and social change. It was in part a melancholy sense of this and its destructive consequences that made Plato think of mathematics as a paradigm of human knowledge, because the knowledge it involved did not alter with time. Mathematics could be added to (and Plato himself in the *Republic* formulates a new mathematical research program in solid geometry), but the achievements of mathematical discovery were permanent. That permanence and the transparency of mathematical concepts were what Plato treasured and wished to extend to a universal ideal of genuine knowledge. This was the first and almost certainly the most important defense of mathematics as having such human importance.

The mathematical ideal propagated by Plato and his disciples had a significant effect in fostering the development of mathematics as a self-conscious discipline. One can measure the potential of such influence by the names of important Greek mathematicians of this period associated with the Platonic circle. Mathematics as a tool in mathematical astronomy also received a major impetus. The same Eudoxus who formulated the theory of ratios put forward in Euclid's *Elements* was also the first to give a serious mathematical model for the movement of the planets.

Even without a conscious dedication to Plato's metaphysics or his social ideals, mathematics and the mathematical sciences continued to flourish into the Hellenistic period, chiefly at the Museum in Alexandria. This was a significant social innovation, a royally sponsored research institution in the pure sciences and the humanities which fostered the flowering of the highest achievements of the Greek intellectual spirit within a Greek-ruled state governing an Egyptian population.

The concept of mathematics endorsed by Plato was mathematics as an ideal science of the changeless. Though Plato himself formulated the hypothesis of a mathematical physics of matter in the *Timaeus,* Aristotle, his successor, declared it to be inapplicable to the changeable and highly unstable phenomena of the sublunary sphere.

Geometry and physical reality

The great achievement of the "Platonists" of the seventeenth-century Scientific Revolution—Galileo, Descartes, Kepler, and Newton—was to bring the superlunary mathematical physics down to earth, to unite the Earth and planets in the Copernican spirit in a single mathematical physics which applied to earthly phenomena as well as to the heavens. This achievement left us with a paradigm of a mathematical natural science which, for better or worse, is as permanent an achievement of human knowledge as any theorem of geometry. It had two principal components of a mathematical nature. Of these, the first was that involving the relationship between physics, conceived as the science of moving bodies, and Euclidean geometry.

In contrasting the Greeks with the moderns (and especially the latter after the discovery of non-Euclidean geometries), it has often been said that the Greeks conceived geometry as an objective science of space, whereas the moderns have thought of geometry as the creation of logically consistent models for a possible science of space. If we consider only the Greek side of this comparison, there is an ambiguity involved, at least if we take Aristotle as a possible spokesman for Greek concepts. It is not so obvious that Aristotle's physics take place in a homogeneous Euclidean space, both because the cosmos is finite for Aristotle and because there is a preferred direction, up and down. The latter is an empirically observed preferred direction in our earthly affairs. It was the great achievement of Galileo (among his many achievements) to abolish this preference in science—and to replace the experienced inhomogeneous physical space of earthly affairs with the idealized homogeneous Euclidean space of geometry. If we combine this intellectual tour de force with Galileo's formulation of the Law of Inertia—that a moving body acted on by no external forces moves in a straight line—we see the principal underpinnings of the Scientific Revolution. Its revolutionary aspects in terms of its effect on human thought in Western Europe at large focus primarily on the vindication of Copernicus's heliocentric theory of the heavenly bodies. Its revolutionary effect on scientific thought arose from the mathematization of nature.

Descartes attempted to carry the relation of physics to geometry to a still more radical point, by identifying the two. His attempt was not successful, though it clearly influenced Newton, if in part only by reaction. It was Newton's achievement to fulfill the program conceived by his predecessors to create a mathematical physics of moving bodies. His *Principia* (see *GBWW,* Vol. 34) encompasses both the celestial physics of planetary motions (in the sophisticated form discovered by Kepler) and terrestrial physics. To carry through this massive program, Newton had to participate in another great achievement of a mathematical nature, the creation of the differential and integral calculus.

Calculus and infinite processes

The word *calculus* has a flavor similar to the word *algorithm* and refers to an instrument of calculation. The mathematical discipline to which the word refers does indeed contain many devices for calculation as well as many conceptual problems that took several centuries to resolve. The central common feature of the varied techniques that comprise the calculus is the use of *infinite processes.*

An eminent mathematician once defined mathematics as the *science of the infinite.* Though the definition may leave something to the imagination, it has an essential kernel of truth. From its beginnings as a self-conscious discipline among the Greeks, mathematics has been concerned with the infinite. The infinite begins with the counting process, and the realization that there is no largest whole number. No matter what the count, you never reach completion, and you can always go further. In the language of philosophy, this is the potential infinite. On the geometric line, you find two kinds of infinity of different types. One is obtained by extending the line, one unit at a time, and is analogous to the potential infinite. If you envision the line as a completed whole, the whole process being carried through to its end, you have the actual or completed infinite. Similarly, if you take a finite line segment and divide it in half, take one of the pieces and divide it in half, and continue an indefinite number of times, then for each whole number n, you obtain a piece which has a ratio of $1{:}2^n$ with the original segment. The question arose whether there is a completed end to the process, something which is infinitely small as opposed to the completed line which is infinitely large.

One of the most celebrated of Greek philosophers, Parmenides of Elea, had argued—against the Atomists and the Pythagoreans who broke up reality into pieces, either material or mathematical—that reality as a whole must be rational and to be rational must be indivisible, unstructured, and unchanging. His disciple Zeno has attained a permanent celebrity in the history of thought by proposing arguments against multiplicity and change, propounding a family of paradoxes based upon the completed infinite. The impact of Zeno's paradoxes upon the development of Greek mathematical thought is hard to establish unambiguously, but it is clear from the evidence that it left infinite processes and the completed infinite in bad repute. However, even at the earliest stage of Greek geometric research, it was clear that many of the most basic geometric problems (particularly problems involving finding areas of plane figures and volumes of solids) could not be resolved without invoking an infinite process. The simplest and most basic such problem is finding the circumference of a circle of unit radius, or its area. In contemporary terms, this amounts to computing the celebrated constant π, which we now know is not a quotient of two whole numbers, nor even the root of an algebraic equation with whole numbers as coefficients. We can tabulate its decimal expansion to great lengths by computer, but we know by precise rigorous arguments that this decimal expansion will never stop no matter how far we compute, nor will it even repeat by blocks. Another slightly less famous example is the proof of the formula for the volume of a cone, first supposedly obtained by the philosopher Democritus.

In a philosophical form, the prejudice against the infinite was expressed by Plato who pitted the finite and structured as good against the unlimited or infinite as bad. Plato's favorite mathematical result was the theorem first established by the mathematicians in the Academy that there are exactly five regular solids, the last one having been discovered in the Academy itself. One of his collaborators, Eudoxus (who was actually the acting head of the Academy during one of Plato's celebrated trips to Sicily), made a more direct confrontation with the problem posed by Zeno's paradoxes for mathematical practice. He created his famous theory of ratios as expounded by Euclid with its method of exhaustion, an elaborate intellectual structure involving upper and lower bounds by which one could rigorously argue about the results usually obtained from infinite processes without having to invoke those processes explicitly in a completed form. The technical machinery has a strong formal resemblance (though it differs in its explicit logical nature) to the scheme introduced for a very similar purpose by the German mathematician Dedekind in the nineteenth century and known to the student of mathematics today as the method of Dedekind cuts.

In a strictly logical (or we might even say, Platonic) sense, Eudoxus's brilliant logical construction resolved the difficulties of the paradoxes of the infinite by reducing all the practical cases of interest to the potential infinite (a manageable kind of ogre for mathematical argument of a rigorous type) rather than the completed infinite. It could even be applied, at least by a genius like Archimedes, to resolve a variety of problems in computing perimeters of curves, areas of plane figures, volumes of solids, and to resolve other problems that we would characterize in modern times as problems in the integral calculus. There were at least two major drawbacks. One had to be as talented as Archimedes to do it at all in any nontrivial case, and nearly all cases were nontrivial. More important, even Archimedes had to admit that he could not discover the answer by this method; he could only verify its correctness after he already knew it. For finding the answers, he resorted on the sly to less reputable methods.

There the matter rested for nearly two thousand years. The intellectual and mathematical thrust of the Hellenistic world withered away during the period of Roman domination, and the destruction of the Western Roman Empire, together with religious struggles in the Eastern Empire, buried the long-lived remnants of the Greek intellectual flowering. Though infinity in a theological sense might be a fit subject for scholastic debate in medieval Europe, the mathematical problems of infinity lay on no one's intellectual agenda until the early seventeenth century.

The roots of the calculus

What brought the problem of infinity back into the forefront of the mathematical and scientific advance was a twofold set of problems. The first, chronologically, was of a relatively technical mathematical character in the new approach to geometry called analytic geometry. This, as we remarked earlier, had related problems concerning geometric loci to problems of solving algebraic equations corresponding to these loci. Conversely, if you let the algebraic variables x and y correspond to the coordinates of a point in the plane, and prescribe an algebraic equation to be satisfied by the two variables x and y, you obtain a locus in the plane of those points whose coordinates satisfy the given algebraic equation. In general, this is a curved line, and we may call it an algebraic curve. Curves

Figure 1 Equations for Conic Sections

Circle

Given center O, radius r

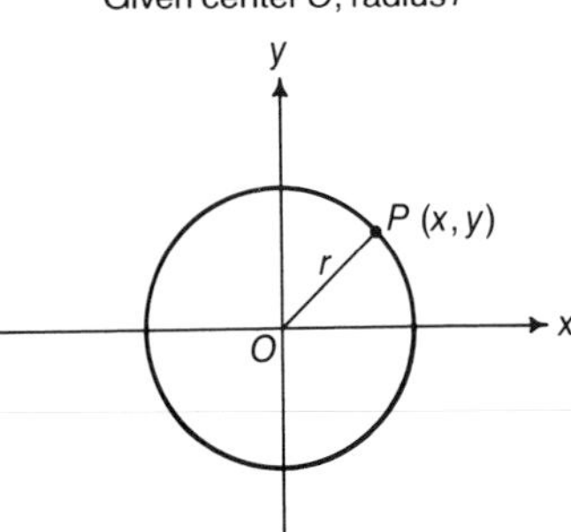

Definition: OP = radius r

Equation: $x^2 + y^2 = r^2$

Ellipse

Given foci F, F' and constant a

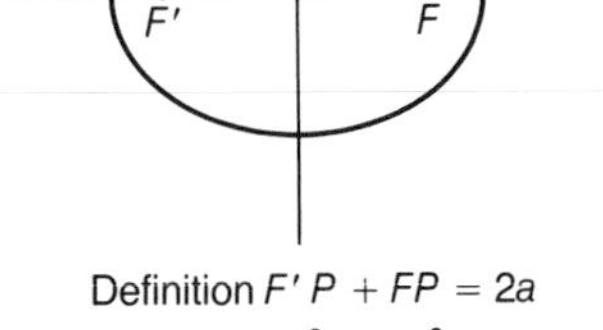

Definition $F'P + FP = 2a$

Equation: $\frac{x^2}{a^2} + \frac{y^2}{b^2} = 1$

Parabola

Given foci F, line DD'

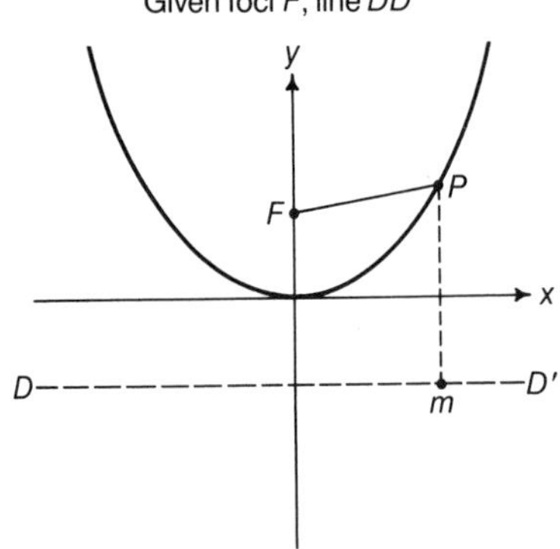

Definition: $PF = PM$

Equation: $y^2 = 2mx$

Hyperbola

Given foci F, F' and constant a

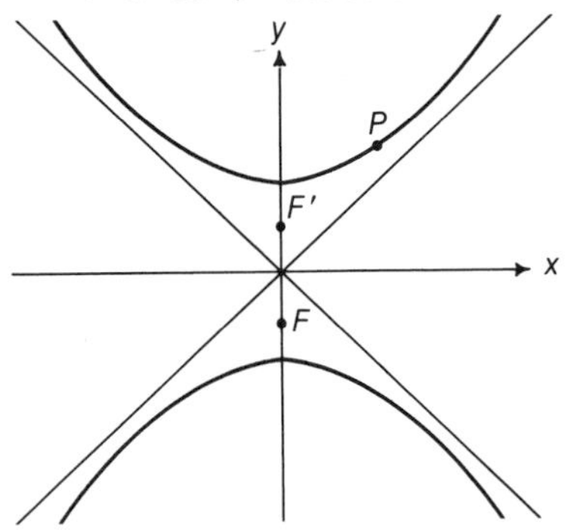

Definition: $PF - PF' = 2a$

Equation: $\frac{y^2}{b^2} - \frac{x^2}{a^2} = 1$

corresponding to algebraic equations of second degree give us the classical conic sections—the ellipse, hyperbola, and parabola—studied intensively in antiquity by Apollonius using synthetic methods (see figure 1). More general curves of degree higher than two began to be studied, and for a number of technical purposes it was important to find the equations of the line tangent to a given such curve at a given point.

Here was the first appearance of the class of problems and their solutions to be treated by the differential calculus. Intuitively, the problems had the following characteristics: One considered the given point on the curve and considered a nearby point on the curve. If the distance between the two points was small but the points were distinct, one could get an approximation to the chord joining the two points on the curve. If the second point was taken "infinitesimally" near to the given point, this chord should be the tangent line (see figure two). If the formulae for the chords turned out formally to simplify drastically for the infinitesimally near case, that should be the equation of the tangent line. But, is this a mathematical argument in the old, classical, rigorous Euclidean style? Obviously not.

The contribution of Newton and Leibniz (who spent a good deal of time fighting over who first made the discovery) was to construct formal machines which rode roughshod over the problem while ignoring the kinds of objections the Greeks would have made to the procedure. Both produced formal "calculi", i.e., engines of formal calculation, which systematically gave answers to problems of the kind involved in the integral calculus and to problems in the differential calculus. The most important discovery, which has always been called the fundamental theorem of the calculus in textbooks, although few bother to try to explain explicitly why

Figure 2

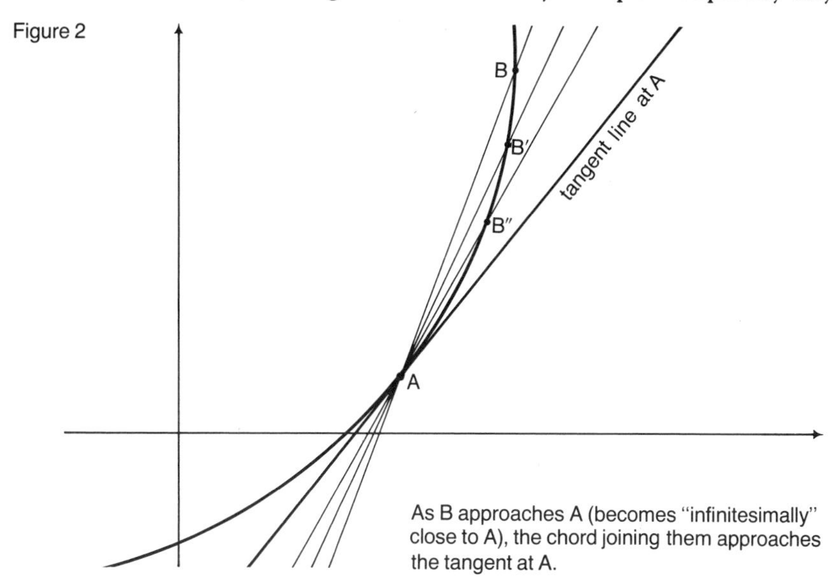

As B approaches A (becomes "infinitesimally" close to A), the chord joining them approaches the tangent at A.

it is so fundamental, is that the two classes of problems which arise in fundamentally different contexts from the point of view of intuition, once you bring them to the formal context of calculus, are basically the same. In an appropriate technical sense, the basic infinite process of differentiation in the differential calculus and the basic infinite process of integration in the integral calculus have a fundamental relation: one undoes the effect of the other.

The justifications offered by Newton and Leibniz for their formalisms are very different, though the formalism each offered is substantially the same. Leibniz based his justification explicitly upon an acceptance of the accomplished infinite, assuming the existence in some sense of infinitesimal quantities and calculating with these infinitesimals as if they were conventional real numbers. This was fully in the spirit of the algebraic formal style of the analytic movement and was as far as you could get in the given context from the rigorous geometry of the Greeks. Newton gave justifications for the infinite process of taking a limit by seeing the curve as a mechanical process of flow and using these flows or fluents to give him his fluxions. Leibniz's procedures have only been shown to be formally consistent in the past several decades in the development of the so-called nonstandard analysis by Abraham Robinson and others. This is a form of analysis which gets the same results as conventional limit arguments of the nineteenth-century type by using infinitesimals. Its advantages are as yet mainly hypothetical. Newton used his fluxions very much in the spirit of Archimedes, mainly to get the results; the verification he carried through by Euclidean methods.

Newtonian mechanics: mathematics as the science of change

The crucial point about the calculus in the seventeenth century we have left until last, and it is of decisive importance. The new mathematical physics of Newton and, in particular, the basic Third Law of Motion of Newton's mechanics could only be formulated in terms of the differential calculus.

$$F = m\frac{d^2x}{dt^2}$$

F = force, m = mass, x = distance, t = time

$\frac{dx}{dt}$ = instantaneous velocity

$\frac{d^2x}{dt^2}$ = acceleration = rate of change of velocity

Working out the consequences of these laws was a problem in solving differential equations, one that involved both the differential and integral calculus. Since then, the laws of nature have spoken in the language of calculus.

The reasons for this fact are of great conceptual importance. In Aristotelian mechanics, rest was fundamental and change a disturbance of rest, unless it was change toward a more stable state of rest. In the mechanics of Galileo and Newton the laws of change are fundamental, and rest is an epiphenomenon. In Newtonian mechanics the position of a moving body expressed in terms of its coordinates with respect to some inertial frame is no more fundamental than its instantaneous velocity, and in a sense less fundamental than the instantaneous rate of change of the instantaneous velocity, the instantaneous acceleration. The fundamental Third Law of Motion of Newton generalizes Galileo's Law of Inertia by describing what happens to a moving body when an external force acts upon it. The effect of the external force is expressed in terms of the instantaneous acceleration of the body.

Over the early years of the eighteenth century, Newton's mechanics and planetary cosmology as put forward in the *Principia* had an enormous impact upon the educated world of his age. It was hailed, and in a sense rightly so, as the single greatest intellectual achievement of all time, giving the fundamental answers to the basic questions about Nature. We know from our vantage point that even within the sphere of physics proper this was not literally true, and that both new questions and new types of answers to questions which went far beyond the Newtonian perspective were to appear in the nineteenth and twentieth centuries. Certainly, Newton's achievement was not to give the final answer to all questions, even in the restricted domain of mechanics. Yet Newton set the pattern by which advances in physical science would continue to be measured, achieving a synthesis of mathematically formulated physical theories expressed in terms of differential equations and descriptive of a significant range of physical phenomena.

Differential equations of the Newtonian type describe the rates of change of a physical system at a given time in terms of the state of the system at that time. Integrating the differential equation allows the description of the system at future times in terms of the state at an earlier time and, in principle at least, yields the possibility of verifying the predictions of any scientific theory. It was this model that Kant, a pious Newtonian, had in mind when he said that a satisfactory scientific theory had to be in mathematical form.

Mathematics and the eighteenth-century enlightenment

By the beginning of the eighteenth century, the achievements of the mathematicians and mathematical physicists of the seventeenth century had begun to have a decisive impact on the thought and world view of the educated public of the Western European states. Galileo had proclaimed a scientific revolution centered on the Copernican hypothesis and had been threatened with tortures and forced to recant by the Inquisition.

The principal result in the ensuing period was to dry up the scientific and intellectual life of Italy, and to thwart its beginnings in the southern Catholic countries. Descartes, frightened by Galileo's treatment, became cautious in publication and made a principle of residing only in Protestant countries. Nevertheless, the decisive thrust of his writings, which forcefully expounded an unconditional rationalism based upon the mathematical method, gained them an unrivaled acceptance among the thoughtful public of his time. When at the close of the seventeenth century Newton successfully constructed a mathematical model of the great World Machine, the prestige and influence of a mathematically oriented rationalism reached its greatest height.

Social influences upon mathematics

One can ask about the social influences and motives that may have led to the extraordinary intellectual flowering of seventeenth-century mathematical physics, which in its originality and long-term influence is probably rivaled only by that of the Greeks. It is very hard to determine a consistent pattern. True, the sixteenth and seventeenth centuries were the great ages of exploration and settlement in the New World and throughout the globe. Navigation was certainly one of the principal practical problems of the age, and astronomical observation, the construction of accurate navigational charts, and the invention of new instruments were the principal tools in the solution of this problem. This is surely the basic social motive that led to the foundation of the Greenwich Observatory in England, and the appointment of the Astronomer-Royal. In the early seventeenth century, Francis Bacon, the Lord Chancellor of England and the exponent par excellence of scientific supremacy, had furnished a broad rationale for science as a social instrument. His ideas were of considerable influence in the foundation of the Royal Society after the middle of the century, though the practical outcome was not as glorious as Bacon had envisioned. The French Académie des Sciences followed shortly after, and in the early years of the eighteenth century new academies of science were founded in Berlin and St. Petersburg at the instigation of Leibniz.

The motive force in all this was clearly not utility in the narrow sense of immediate practical advantages to be gained from mathematical and scientific applications. It was utility in the broader sense, prestige and publicity for the absolute monarchs and their ministers. Informal networks of communication through letters and personal contacts turned into a new network of formal publication through the *Proceedings* of the Academies and new journals of a scholarly type such as the *Acta Eruditorum* which Leibniz sponsored in Leipzig.

The new academies on the European continent gave both employment and social status to the leading figures of mathematical and scientific research. D'Alembert was the long-time secretary of the Académie Française, his protégé Condorcet was secretary of the Académie des Sciences; the greatest mathematician of the eighteenth century, Leonhard Euler was employed for thirty-one years by the St. Petersburg Academy and twenty-five years by the Berlin Academy. His successor at the Berlin Academy was J.-L. Lagrange, a native of Turin, who became the leading mathematician in France in the closing years of the century.

Euler, eighteenth-century analysis, and mechanics

Rapid development of research in mathematics and mathematical physics of the eighteenth century broadened and deepened the Newtonian paradigm. Though Newton had founded the paradigm in England, its continuation took place in large measure almost exclusively on the Continent at the hands of Leibniz's pupils and successors. The first book on the calculus was written by a French nobleman, G.-F.-A. de L'Hôpital, who was a pupil of Leibniz and got his name into all later calculus textbooks through L'Hôpital's Rule. The principal tradition of research was continued by the Bernoullis—Jacob, John, and Daniel, in particular—and by Euler, who was of the Basel school of Swiss mathematics. Euler was almost certainly the most prolific mathematician of all time. His writings cover the full range of mathematical disciplines and all conceivable mathematical sciences (including such practical arts as shipbuilding). He occupied most of the publication space for the *Proceedings* of his two academies for almost a century, and his *Collected Works* are almost eternally in the course of publication.

Euler founded a new paradigm of mathematical activity, that of *analysis,* in the eighteenth- rather than the sixteenth-century sense—a sense which, after the *rigorization* imposed by the nineteenth century, continues as a major subdivision of mathematical research to the present day. The content of this new paradigm of analysis can be stated in a short phrase: the mathematical and physical consequences of the calculus. Though Newton and Leibniz had invented the calculus, Euler was its accomplished master. The ingenuity of his attack, its power, penetration, and fertility were unrivaled. He applied the calculus and an endless algorithmic fertility in an unceasing flow of original accomplishments through an extremely long scientific lifetime.

A major point of concentration of Euler's work, and of the mathematical research of the century, was the extension of the ideas of Newtonian mechanics to the mechanics of continua, solid bodies, fluid flow, elasticity, and wave motion. This extension demanded a sharper insight into the Newtonian paradigm, and it also demanded a broader armory of mathematical tools in the calculus. Partial derivatives or differential equations (see box) replaced ordinary differential equations; techniques involving the use of infinite series were broadened and more critically scrutinized; and, most important of all, analytical techniques involving functions of a complex variable were introduced and used in important ways.

$$u = u(x,y)$$

$$\frac{\partial u}{\partial x} = \text{rate of change of } u \text{ with respect to } x \text{ with } y \text{ held fixed}$$

$$\frac{\partial u}{\partial y} = \text{rate of change of } u \text{ with respect to } y \text{ with } x \text{ held fixed}$$

$$\frac{\partial^2 u}{\partial x^2} = \frac{\partial}{\partial x}\left(\frac{\partial u}{\partial x}\right)$$

$$\frac{\partial^2 u}{\partial y^2} = \frac{\partial}{\partial y}\left(\frac{\partial u}{\partial y}\right)$$

The concept of function

One of the most crucial and most strategically important of the mathematical ideas that had to be understood and clarified in such investigations as the study of wave motion was the concept of *function.* Each age of mathematics can be characterized to a large degree by the nature of the entities on which it focuses its interest. For the Pythagoreans of early Greece, it was the individual whole numbers, to each of which (at least up to ten) they attached a broad range of mystical attributes. For Plato, the succession of integers took the place of the individual whole numbers (though he retained a firm belief in the magical power of such individual numbers as the Nuptial Number of the *Republic*). For the Greek geometers, it was geometric figures beginning with the circle and line and continuing with triangles, polygons, solids, conic sections, and such late oddities as Archimedes's spiral. For the algebraists of the late Renaissance, it was *number* in the generic sense as the possible range through which an algebraic *variable* could run. When algebra turned into analytical geometry and the tools of the analytic movement began to be applied to the problems of the physics of moving bodies, the crucial entities began to be *curves* or *fluents,* entities which in an implicit sense foreshadow the concept of *function.*

If a figure in the plane is described as the locus of points which satisfy an algebraic equation in two variables (say x and y, to use their conventional names), it is obvious in a relatively simple way in many cases that, if one of the two variables is prescribed, the value of the other variable for a point on the curve is automatically determined by the prescription of the first variable. Such a situation is called a *functional relationship,* and if, for example, giving the value of the x-variable at a point of the curve determines the y-variable for that point, we say that y is a function of x, usually written $y = f(x)$. The function, which we have written as f, is the relation or rule which determines for each x, which y is assigned to x. The entity which we call a *function* is the rule or relation, not a particular value of the variable y which corresponds to a particular value of the variable x.

The fluent of Newton is a corresponding mechanical notion corresponding to the representation of the movement of a mass point in the plane or on a line. As the time t varies, the position of the mass-point varies, but, for each prescribed time t, the point P (or its various coordinates) is determined by t. The fluent is the rule by which t determines P.

The calculus deals with functions, not numbers. Take, for example, the differential calculus, which is concerned with *derivatives* (to use a variant of the Leibnizian terminology) or *fluxions* (to use Newton's language). Suppose we consider a fluent in Newton's sense, e.g., let $x = f(t)$ be a function which for each value of the time t in a certain interval A assigns a position variable x which is a real number. What is the fluxion (derivative) of this fluent (function)? It is a new function of t, which we can describe by the following procedure:

> If $x = f(t)$, for a given value of t to find the derivative $dx/dt = \dot{x}(t)$: Add a small quantity h to t, calculate the change in x, the increment $\Delta x = f(t + h) - f(t)$ and divide it by h, which is the change in t: $\Delta x/h$. Let h tend to 0, and we obtain $\dot{x}$ (see figure 3).

If this process gives you a definite value when h becomes zero, this value $\dot{x}$, which of course depends on the original choice of t, is the value of the fluxion at t, $\dot{x} = g(t)$.

There are two principal problems here which have to be resolved before this definition is really meaningful. The first is of course how one can take h to be zero, since for $h = 0$, both the numerator Δx and the denominator h are zero, and division by zero is meaningless. As we noted earlier, this problem was brushed aside in different ways by Newton and Leibniz and was only resolved in a coherent way in the early nineteenth century by Bernhard Bolzano and A.-L. Cauchy.

The second problem is this: what are the rules or functions, f, to which such processes can apply? For a considerable time, a century or longer,

Figure 3 Derivatives

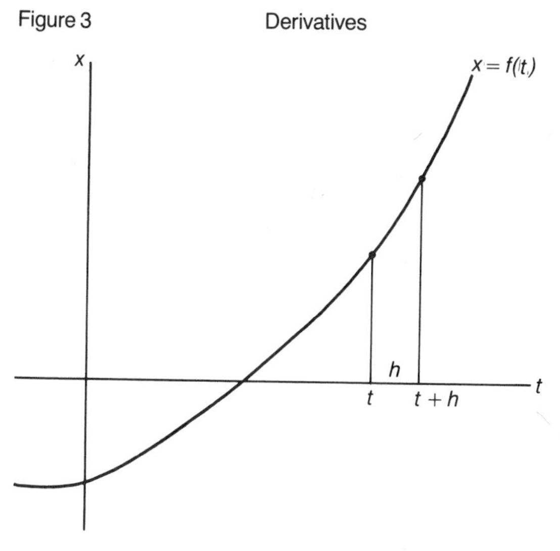

no firm answer was given to this question. There seemed to be no need to answer it in a precise way. The function or rule was assumed to be given by an algebraic expression, or in the case of more general functions, by very definite algorithms:

1. the trigonometric functions sin (x), cos (x), tan (x) and their reciprocals obtained by taking the ratios of the sides of a right triangle, with x denoting the radian measure of a given angle of the triangle;
2. the exponential function a^x, which generalizes the power function x^a by making the exponent of the power variable rather than the base; and
3. the logarithm function $u = \log_b(x)$ defined by inverting the relationship $x = b^u$.

Using these algorithms and their algebraic combinations, one obtains a wide variety of functions. More generally, one obtains functions by adding up infinite series of known functions $f(x) = f_1(x) + f_2(x) + \ldots + f_n(x) + \ldots$, where the final set of dots indicates that the process has no finite termination point though each step in the process of addition is explicitly prescribed. (Such a sum is usually written in the notation $\sum f_n(x)$.)

As in so many cases, it is the introduction of these very fruitful but potentially difficult infinite processes that brings the difficulty to a boil. For the concept of function, the first really interesting case was D'Alembert's discovery in connection with the study of the wave equation, the partial differential equation (i.e., equation involving derivatives taken with respect to different variables) which governs wave motion. D'Alembert observed formally that if the wave function u is governed by one space variable x and the time variable t, then every function $u(x,t)$ of the form $f(x + t) + g(x - t)$ is a solution of the wave equation for any pair of functions f and g of a single argument (see figure 4). Moreover, you could construct cases when f and g had corners and really did not have derivatives in the appropriate sense.

A more crucial difficulty arose in connection with the study of the heat equation by Fourier in the early nineteenth century. Fourier studied the flow of heat on the line and observed for heat flow on the interval from 0 to 1, that if one prescribed the temperature T to be 0 at both 0 and 1 for all positive time, t, and to be a prescribed function $f(x)$ on the interval at time $t = 0$, then the solution was given by an explicit infinite sum provided that the initial temperature distribution function $f(x)$ could be written in the form $f(x) = \sum_{n=1} a_n \sin(n\pi x)$.

Fourier then attempted to establish that every function $f(x)$ which vanishes for $x = 0$ and $x = 1$ can be written as an infinite sum of the form given above, what we now call a Fourier sine series. The difficulty of his argument was compounded by the fact that functions, f, which could be written in this form and in corresponding series involving cosines as well

Figure 4 The Wave Equation

$u = u(x,t)$ varies with a space variable x and a time variable t

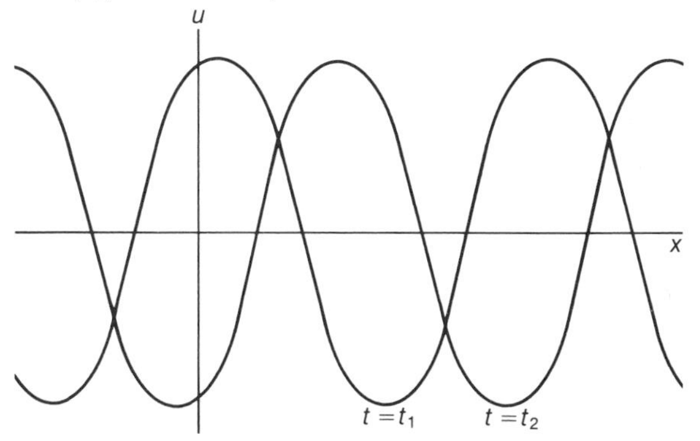

as sines—the general Fourier series—can be very odd from the point of view of the usual vague notion of function. For example, they may be *discontinuous,* by having breaks or jumps.

The task of sorting out these questionable analytic arguments and laying a firm foundation for analytical proofs and definitions led to the nineteenth-century movement for the *rigorization of analysis,* which in turn brought this flourishing mathematical sphere to a level of deductive rigor and precision equal to the classical achievements of Euclid's geometry.

The origins of the variational approach to mechanics

Euler did not spend much time or energy with questions of this type. He had too much to do on more concrete problems, whether in mathematical analysis, mathematical physics, the theory of numbers, combinatorics, or in founding the study of combinatorial topology. Together with Lagrange, Euler laid a systematic foundation for the calculus of variations, a branch of mathematical analysis which was to prove essential to the future development of mathematical physics.

The equations of Newtonian mechanics were differential equations which described the rates of change of a physical system in terms of the coordinates of its given state and provided a mathematical model of what might be called an immanent causal principle, the present determining the future. Leibniz and some of his followers (most particularly the Berlin mathematical physicist Pierre-Louis de Maupertuis) objected to this kind of physics on theological grounds, as when Laplace was asked by Napoleon where God appeared in his celestial clockwork and replied that he had no need of that hypothesis.

Leibniz and Maupertuis demanded a mechanics that spoke in terms of God's achieving some transcendent end by maximizing some good, represented by a physical quantity determined by the passage of the system to its final state. The French mathematician Fermat had already framed such a principle in the case of geometrical optics a century earlier. Using the techniques developed by Euler and himself, Lagrange was able to show that every mechanical system in the Newtonian sense had its course determined by an external principle in the Leibnizian sense. Whatever implications this may have had for theology, it proved of decisive importance as a intellectual tool in the future development of mathematical physics.

Number theory

Both Euler and Lagrange, as well as their French contemporary Legendre, were also concerned with questions arising from a completely different paradigm of mathematical research, the theory of numbers. The study of the properties of whole numbers, their additive and multiplicative properties, began with the Greeks in the classical period and clearly was motivated in its beginnings by the Pythagoreans, who regarded the whole cosmos as generated in some undefinable way by the whole numbers. (So absorbing was their concentration upon this topic that it has been facetiously suggested that Plato's motto over the door of the Academy—*Let no one ignorant of geometry enter here*—may have been directed at orthodox Pythagoreans, not at the mathematically ignorant in general). In Euclid's *Elements* one finds a sophisticated discussion of the elements of the theory of prime numbers—whole numbers whose only whole number divisor is either itself or one. The simplest and most striking elementary result is that there are an infinite number of primes. All primes after two are odd, since no prime other than two can be divisible by two. Some primes occur in pairs, n and $n + 2$, (e.g., 5 and 7, or 11 and 13). A problem which the Greeks could state and which has never been answered is the *twin prime problem: Are there an infinite number of such prime pairs* n *and* n + *2?* We do not know.

An important variant of number theory is the study of Diophantine equations. That name reflects the work of the Greek mathematician Diophantus, who formulated a large number of problems of this kind and solved a few. A Diophantine equation, to use the modern language of algebra, poses an algebraic equation in several arguments with coefficients which are whole numbers and asks for solutions in terms of whole numbers. The simplest example occurs in connection with the celebrated theorem of Pythagoras which states that if x and y are the lengths of the sides of a right triangle, and if z is the length of the hypotenuse, then $z^2 = x^2 + y^2$.

It is a very old question whether we can determine all such triples of lengths which are whole numbers. The Egyptians and Babylonians certainly knew the triple {3, 4, 5}, and judging from internal evidence, the Babylonians knew the Pythagorean theorem. The Greeks knew the general solution to this problem, and Diophantus studied a wide variety of others.

The study of the theory of numbers was brought back to life in a full-blooded way by Fermat, who studied the Latin translation of Diophantus's book and left a celebrated comment on the margin of one of its pages: "I have proved that there are *no whole number solutions of* $z^n = x^n + y^n$ *for any* n *greater than two.* However, the margin is not big enough to hold the proof." No further writings of Fermat exist on the subject, so that the assertion on Diophantus's margin has become the celebrated Fermat Problem. Intense efforts have been expended on its solution, special cases treated for *n* up to the seventies beginning with Euler, and sizeable prizes established for its solution. One such prize, which was never collected, was established at Göttingen before the First World War, and the proceeds from its fund were used to endow visiting professorships at Göttingen until the postwar inflation wiped it out. Recently, a foundation has been established in Dallas, Texas, centering on Fermat's problem. No one yet has solved it. But the substantial efforts to establish the result that Fermat could not prove in the margin has been a major influence in research in algebra, especially in the nineteenth-century development of ideal theories in algebraic number fields.

Fermat's other contributions to number theory are somewhat better documented, but, owing probably to the fact that he was a disciple of Viète and the analytic school, Fermat had a somewhat less than reverent attitude toward the notion of giving complete or formal proofs of his results. Many had to wait till Euler got to them for this kind of treatment. Legendre continued the number theoretic tradition in France in the eighteenth century and gave the first statement of the quadratic reciprocity law which Gauss was to treat so masterfully after the beginning of the nineteenth century.

The solvability of algebraic equations

One of the most interesting and fruitful lines of mathematical research was directed to the old problem inherited from the late Renaissance about the solvability of algebraic equations in terms of radicals or roots. As we noted earlier, the solution of the equations of third and fourth degrees (that is, with exponents as great as three or four) had been one of the great triumphs of the early history of algebra in Italy. Despite many sustained efforts, no progress had been made on the equation of fifth degree. This problem was taken up by Lagrange, who began a systematic study of the roots of algebraic equations with rational coefficients. That was to culminate in the early decades of the nineteenth century with the proofs by Abel and Galois that the fifth-degree equation could not be solved by radicals (i.e., by algebraic operations, and taking roots). This was the first great *impossibility theorem,* in which it could be shown in a completely convincing way that the solution of a particular problem could *not* be carried through. Yet, the significance of the theorem was even greater than that, for it was the thread of mathematical research that led to the discovery and first application of the concept of a *group,* one of the simplest and most fruitful concepts of modern mathematical and scientific thought.

Lagrange considered the roots $\{r_1, \ldots, r_n\}$ of an algebraic equation $p(x) = 0$, with p a polynomial of degree n whose coefficients are rational numbers (i.e., quotients of integers). If you have a set of n objects for a given whole number n, you can consider their permutations, where a permutation is simply an interchange of these objects, or, if you wish, a change in the order in which they are listed. Thus, if the n objects are simply the whole numbers from 1 to n, a permutation, m, is given by a list of the whole numbers from 1 to n in a (possibly) different order $\{m_1, \ldots, m_n\}$ with the operational meaning that you replace 1 by m_1, 2 by m_2, 3 by m_3, and so on, ending with the replacement of n by m_n. The simplest permutation, e, is the one which leaves each element alone, so that $e = \{1, 2, \ldots, n\}$. Of course, any permutation can be applied to the roots of the equation $p(x) = 0$, in which case it will reorder the roots themselves. Lagrange considered the family of rational functions of n arguments, i.e., $f(x_1, \ldots, x_n)$, where f is the quotient of two polynomials in n-arguments with rational coefficients, and he then studied the solvability properties of the algebraic equation in terms of the behavior of these functions when you permuted the roots.

Some decades later, Galois continued and completed Lagrange's attack on the problem. The permutations have an algebraic operation you can perform on them, the operation of composition. Given two permutations, m and r, you can form a new permutation, $m \cdot r$, by first applying m and then applying r. The result is usually different if you take them in reverse order, so that most of the time, $m \cdot r \neq r \cdot m$. For this reason, it is called a *noncommutative* operation in general.

The concept of group

The permutations on n objects form an algebraic system called a *group* in a sense first made precise and explicit by Galois, where a group in the modern way of stating definitions is a set, S, on which there is defined a (binary) operation which assigns to any pair of elements s and s_1 of S, another element $s \cdot s_1$ which we call their product. No matter how this assignment is made, we call it a *group* if it satisfies three general conditions.

Axioms for a group:

1. For any triple of elements of S, s, s_1, and s_2, we can form $s \cdot s_1$ and then multiply the result by s_2 to obtain $(s \cdot s_1) \cdot s_2$. On the other hand, we can first form $s_1 \cdot s_2$ and then multiply s by it, to form $s \cdot (s_1 \cdot s_2)$. In every case, we require that $(s \cdot s_1) \cdot s_2 = s \cdot (s_1 \cdot s_2)$. This is called the *associativity* axiom.

2. There is a fixed element e of S, the identity element, such that for

every s of S, $s \cdot e = s = e \cdot s$.

3. For each element s of S, there exists another element written s^{-1} such that $s \cdot s^{-1} = e = s^{-1} \cdot s$.

You can generalize the group of permutations by taking an infinite set A rather than a set of n objects for a finite n, and forming the *group of transformations* of A. In this very general context by a transformation T of A we mean simply a rule or function which assigns to each element a of A, another element $T(a)$ of A with the sole requirement that for any b of A, b is assigned as $T(a)$ to exactly one element a of A. Permutations are simply transformations of a set A with n elements, but A can be infinite.

As an example, let Z be the set of all integers, positive, negative, and zero. Then the assignment T such that $T(n) = n + 1$ for every n in Z is a transformation of Z. If Z^+ is the subset of Z consisting of the positive integers (the whole numbers), then T is not a transformation of Z^+ because 1 which lies in Z^+ is only $T(0)$, and 0 does not lie in Z^+. For two transformations T and T_1 of A, we can form a new transformation $T \cdot T_1$ called their composition by letting $(T \cdot T_1)(a) = T_1 [T(a)]$. If we let $I(a) = a$ for every a, I is called the identity transformation. Similarly, for every transformation T, you can form its inverse transformation T^{-1} by the prescription that $T^{-1}(b) = a$ if, and only if, $T(a) = b$. With these definitions, the set of transformations T of a given set A always forms a group, which we may call the transformation group of A.

If S is a group with a given binary operation and with identity element e, and if S_1 is a part of S (a subset, to use the conventional language of set theory), then we say that S_1 is a *subgroup* of S if for each pair of elements s and s_1 of S_1, their product $s \cdot s_1$ also lies in S_1, if in addition e lies in S_1, and finally if for each s in S_1, its inverse s^{-1} also lies in S_1. Then S_1 with the same binary operation, the same identity element, and the same set of inverses forms a group and this group is called a subgroup of S.

Another relation between two different groups S and S_2 is that of *homomorphism* (which literally in the Greek means the "same structure"). By a homomorphism R of S into S_2, we mean an operation, R, which to each element s of S assigns an element $R(s)$ of S_2 and satisfies the following three conditions:

1. $R(s \cdot s_1) = R(s) \cdot R(s_1)$, for all s and s_1 in S.

2. $R(e) = e_2$, where e is the identity element of S and e_2 is the identity element of S_2.

3. $R(s^{-1}) = [R(s)]^{-1}$.

As an example, we can consider a subgroup S_1 of a group S as defined above and define the homomorphism R by letting $R(s_1) = s_1$ for each s_1 in S_1 where on the right we consider s_1 as an element of the larger group S. Then R satisfies the three conditions for a homomorphism.

Using these definitions, we can reinterpret Galois's argument for the nonsolvability by radicals of the general algebraic equation of fifth degree. To each algebraic equation of degree n with rational coefficients, Galois associates a group which is now called its *Galois group.* This is obtained as a subgroup of the transformation group of the set A which consists of all rational functions of the roots $r_1, \ldots, r_n$ of the given equation. For each permutation m of n objects, you define a transformation T_m of A by setting

$$T_m f(r_1, \ldots, r_n) = f(r_{m_1}, \ldots, r_{m_n}).$$

You verify that the family of transformations T_m as m ranges over the permutations m forms a subgroup of the transformation group of A. This is the Galois group of the equation. Galois then shows that the property of solvability by radicals is equivalent to a property of the Galois group, G, of the equation that is expressible just in terms of its group structure, subgroups, homomorphisms, and so forth. In technical language, what is being said is that the group G is *solvable.* Galois finally constructs an equation of fifth degree with rational coefficients whose Galois group is *not* solvable.

The existence of roots of algebraic equations

The perceptive reader may have noticed a peculiar characteristic of this argument as stated, namely its reliance upon constructions using entities which we do not explicitly know, namely the roots $\{r_1, \ldots, r_n\}$ of the given equation. That does not really matter here, since the conclusion is a negative conclusion, and if there *were* an explicit procedure to obtain the roots of the fifth degree equation, we could explicitly exhibit the roots. Moreover, the argument is hypothetical, for it asserts that if we *can* list the roots and there are n roots, then the argument proceeds. Nor is it weakened in its force if some of the roots are not distinct, for what is really meant by the roots is the existence of the factorization $p(x) = (x - r_1) \ldots (x - r_n)$. A more serious problem, which has been resolved in a very definitive way, is the existence of roots at all, and in particular of roots which are complex numbers.

If we are given an algebraic equation whose coefficients are rational numbers, or even integers, there is no guarantee at all that this equation has any real roots. Thus the simple equation $x^2 + 1 = 0$ has no real roots, since for any real number x, $x^2 + 1$ is always at least 1. We solve this problem by introducing the imaginary unit $i = \sqrt{-1}$, which is the solution of this equation. It follows immediately from the explicit formulae for their solutions that every algebraic equation of degree two, three, or four with rational coefficient or even with complex coefficients, has a complex root, x, of the form $a + bi$ with a and b real numbers. Following Argand and Gauss, we identify each such number with the point in the Cartesian plane which has the two coordinates (a,b). Thus the real numbers are identified with the points on the x-axis, the pure imaginaries, bi, with the points on the y axis (see figure 5).

Figure 5 Complex Coordinates

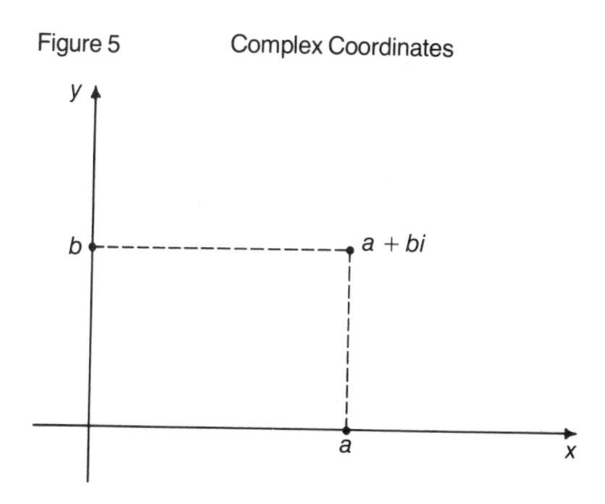

We now must face the question: For algebraic equations of degree at least five, does each such equation have a root in the complex plane? The assertion that it does was first stated by D'Alembert in the middle of the eighteenth century, but the first satisfactory proofs were given by Gauss toward the end of the century. Gauss gave a number of different proofs, as if the reader who was not convinced by one might well be convinced by another. What might nevertheless leave any possible reader of the proofs unconvinced was presumably their *nonconstructive* character, for none of these proofs actually tells us how to construct a root of an equation if we are asked to do so. In a very direct sense, Gauss in this work thus makes himself the founder of *nonconstructive mathematics,* the art of showing the existence of solutions for problems without explicit exhibition of their solution. These are the first general *existence theorems.*

We need not be too concerned, however, for in any particular case, we can set up a systematic procedure for finding all the roots. What Gauss's theorem (usually called the Fundamental Theorem of Algebra) really tells us is that this procedure will always be successful.

Nineteenth-century classical mathematics

When we speak either of classical mathematics or of classical physics, we almost always mean the mathematics or physics of the nineteenth century. As in politics and economics, so also in mathematics and physics, the theorists of the nineteenth century assumed that they had finally reached a stable satisfactory resolution of all basic problems from which it would never be necessary to move in any serious way. As in politics and economics, their solutions crumbled or were dispossessed by more adventurous and more imaginative perspectives even before the century was over.

Analytic functions of a complex variable

The central axis of classical nineteenth-century mathematics was the theory of analytic functions of a complex variable. Every important development in the creative process of the century's mathematics was either drawn from that or became strongly related to it before its development was complete. We have already referred to the *rigorization of analysis.* This was an indispensable prerequisite for building up the structure of what turned out to be the most perfect example of a coherent rigorous deductive system, one that satisfied the almost imcompatible characteristics of being at once ultimately flexible in application and at the same time fruitful in its relation to other mathematical paradigms.

We have already presented the problems posed by the precise delineation of the concept of function. The problem could be solved in two ways. One could define a function as any rule whatever that assigned to elements of one domain the elements of a second domain. This approach, derived from Bolzano and Dedekind, had the merit of conceptual clarity but left the mathematician with functions that had essentially no properties—which were, as one might say, purely abstract. One could restrict oneself to continuous or piece-wise continuous functions, but, if so, that required a precise formulation of the notion of limit and the related notion of continuity.

The result, due essentially to Cauchy, again proceeded by substituting the potential infinite for the actual infinite.

In the classical formulation of infinitesimals, a function $f(t)$ took on a limit value k at t_0 if $f(t_0 + h) = k$ for h an infinitesimal. In the limit definitions of Cauchy (foreshadowed rather loosely by D'Alembert in the eighteenth century), this was true if for any measure of smallness r, $f(t) - r$ was less than r in absolute value for $t - t_0$ sufficiently small. Thus a function, f, was continuous at t_0 if the limit of $f(t)$ at t_0 was $f(t_0)$ (see figure 6).

Figure 6

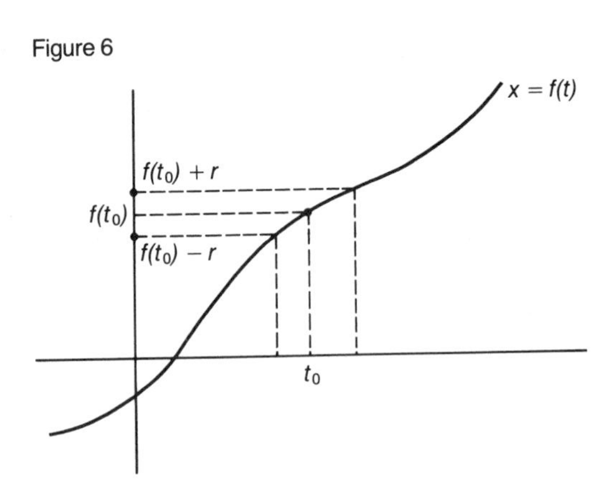

The merit of this type of definition became clear if it was applied to the problem of convergence of a sequence of functions, or the sum of an infinite series of functions. Did the limit function have the same properties as the terms of the sequence? Could you operate on the terms of the sequence in various ways and get, in the limit, the same operation applied to the limit? The answer to both questions was far from clear in many important cases, and negative in many others. This reflected the fundamental difficulty of the limit process when it was applied to repeated limits.

The first and paradigmatic type of simple positive answer came in such results as the theorem of Cauchy that the limit of a sequence of continuous functions is continuous, provided that the convergence is uniform. Here the uniformity was expressed easily and directly in terms of the limit notion as stated above. If $\{f_n: n = 1, 2, 3, \ldots\}$ is a sequence of functions on an interval $[a,b]$ containing t_0 in its interior, then for any t in the interval, $f_n(t)$ converges to $f(t)$ as n goes to infinity if, for any positive measure of smallness r, there exists an integer N which depends on r and, of course, on t such that for n larger than $N = N(r,t)$, we have $|f_n(t) - f(t)| < r$. The convergence is uniform if, for each positive r, we can choose $N(r,t)$ independent of t in the interval.

Suppose that a function f of a real variable, t, on an interval $[a,b]$ is continuous. Does it have a derivative? The French mathematical physicist Ampère published a proof in the early years of the century that it was differentiable except at a sequence of points in the interval. The proof was fallacious, and in the middle of the century the German mathematician Karl Weierstrass wrote down an example of such a function which did not have a derivative at any point of the interval. Suppose that f does have a derivative? Does it have a second derivative, i.e., does its derivative itself have a derivative? The answer to this question was seen to be negative also. One could apparently create scales of functions having as many of the niceness properties of functions as one pleased without having any others.

A particularly useful property of functions having at least k derivatives in an interval is their approximability in the neighborhood of a point t_0 by a sum of powers of $(t - t_0)$. This is expressed by Taylor's formula as

$$f(t) = f(t_0) + \frac{df}{dt}(t_0)(t - t_0) + \ldots + \frac{d^{k-1}f}{dt^{k-1}}(t_0)\frac{(t - t_0)^{k-1}}{(k-1)!} + R_k(t)$$

with $|R_k(t)|$ bounded by a multiple of $|t - t_0|^k$. Such a function, f, having derivatives of all orders is said to be *analytic* in the real domain if $R_k(t)$ approaches zero for each t as k goes to infinity. You can ask in the real domain if an indefinitely differentiable function f is analytic in that domain. The answer again is easily seen to be negative.

The much more interesting fact, one that was the foundation of the theory of analytic functions of a complex variable, is that all the answers to these questions became positive when applied in an appropriate way to complex valued functions of a complex variable.

The appropriate domain for such a function might be the interior of a circle C_R of radius R about a point z_0 in the complex plane. Here z_0 is the complex number $x_0 + iy_0$, and we are identifying z_0 with the point in the Cartesian plane with the coordinates (x_0, y_0). For all nearby points with coordinates (x,y), we obtain corresponding complex numbers $z = x + iy$. For two such points z and z_0, $[z - z_0]$ is the Euclidean distance in the plane $\sqrt{(x - x_0)^2 + (y - y_0)^2}$. We can say that the function f from the disk D_R with boundary C_R to the complex numbers has a derivative at the point z_0 if there exists a complex number w_0 such that $\left\{\frac{f(z) - f(z_0)}{z - z_0} - w_0\right\}$ has the limit 0 at z_0. We set $f'(z_0) = w_0$, where f' is the symbol used to denote the derivative function of f. If f is differentiable at each point z of D_R, then the derivative f' is itself a complex valued function of D_R.

We can ask the same questions as we did above in the case of real-valued functions of a real argument. The answers come back with an apparently miraculous reversal. If f is once differentiable at each point of the open disk D_R, then it has indefinitely many derivatives and is *analytic* in the sense that for every point z of D_R, $f(z) = \sum_{j=0}^{\infty} a_j(z - z_0)^j$ with the series convergent for each z in D_R and the coefficients a_j given in terms of the j-th derivative of f at z_0, as in Taylor's formula (see figure 7).

The uniform limits of analytic functions on D_R (above) are again analytic, not just continuous, and you can differentiate the convergent sequence to get a sequence converging to the derivative of the limit. Hence you have a very powerful and flexible tool for studying such functions, generating new functions, and investigating their properties. Moreover, most of the classical polynomial functions, rational functions, trigonometric functions, exponentials and logarithms can be extended in easily

Figure 7

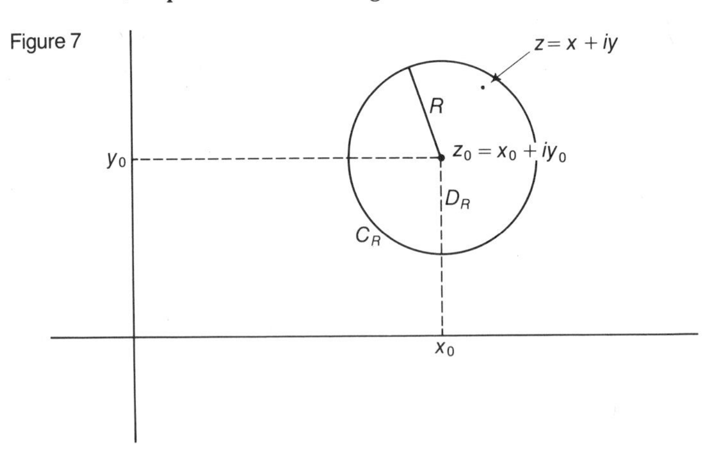

determined ways to become analytic functions on precisely defined domains. Complex integrals can be defined for such functions, and when such functions have a singularity at one point in a domain, the structure of the function in a neighborhood of the singular point can be described very precisely in terms of an infinite series of negative powers of $(z - z_0)$.

This theory was first constructed by Cauchy in France in the first half of the century and significantly strengthened and applied by Weierstrass and Riemann in the second part. It provided the mathematicians of the nineteenth century with an immensely powerful tool which functioned equally well both for rigorous proofs and for calculations. Never before had algorismic mathematics and deductive mathematics worked so closely hand-in-hand. Riemann in particular brought intimately into this framework the central problems of number theory in the distribution of primes and the central results of the theory of algebraic functions (i.e., functions of a complex argument z defined by solving for w the polynomial equation $P(z,w) = 0$, yielding w as a function of z). He used the newly developed theory of surfaces to represent multivalued analytic functions in terms of Riemann surfaces, and he developed an important attack upon some of the basic partial differential equations of mathematical physics in terms of significant new properties of analytic functions producing one-to-one correspondences between domains in the complex plane.

Analytic functions and number theory

Let us begin with Riemann's contribution to analytic number theory, the striking involvement of the theory of analytic functions of a complex variable with the theory of distribution of prime integers. The prime whole numbers are those, we recall, which have no proper divisor other than themselves or 1. There are an infinite number of prime whole numbers, but no systematic way to enumerate them explicitly or describe them by a formula.

The most important classical problems of the theory of numbers refer to the properties of primes, and in particular to their distribution.

The latter term refers to the function $\pi(x)$, the number of primes p which are less than, or equal to, x. No precise formula for $\pi(x)$ is known or even conjectured, but an unceasing attack has been made for two hundred years to try to find good approximations to $\pi(x)$ in terms of known and calculable functions.

One such approximation is $x/ln(x)$ where $ln(x)$ is the natural logarithm of x to the base e,

$$e = 2.7185 \ldots = \lim\ (1 + 1/n)^n \text{ (as } n \text{ goes to infinity).}$$

A second approximation is in terms of an integral

$$L(x) = \int_2^x \frac{du}{ln(u)}\ .$$

Gauss conjectured in the last years of the eighteenth century that $\pi(x)$ is *asymptotic* to $x/ln(x)$, i.e., $\pi(x)[x/ln(x)]^{-1} \rightarrow 1$, as x goes to infinity.

Gauss found no proof for his theorem, and though a heuristic argument was given by the Russian mathematician Tchebycheff in the 1850s, no proof was found until 1892, when J.-S. Hadamard and C.-J. de la Vallée Poussin proved the theorem independently using the structure of the ζ-function of Riemann.

The Riemann ζ-function is a function of the complex variable z, defined and analytic for $z \neq 1$. For the real part of z greater than 1, it is given by the infinite series

$$\zeta(z) = \sum_{n=0}^{\infty} n^{-z}.$$

Using the functional equation for the ζ-function which expresses $\zeta(z)$ $\zeta(1 - z)$ in terms of more elementary functions, Riemann extended the function to its full domain of definition. Euler had earlier considered this function and given an infinite product representation in terms of factors of the form $(1 - p^{-z})$ with one factor for each prime p. Riemann, using this fact, initiated a program of studying the distribution of the primes by studying the zeroes of the ζ-function, a program which was fulfilled by Hadamard and de la Vallée Poussin in their proofs of the Prime Number Theorem mentioned above.

Riemann's most audacious proposal is embodied in his celebrated *Riemann Hypothesis,* almost certainly the single most famous unsolved problem in mathematics, except perhaps for the *Fermat Theorem* which we mentioned above. This hypothesis concerns the zeroes of the ζ-function with $0<Re(z)<1$, the so-called critical strip, and asserts that for all such zeroes, the real part of the zero must equal $\frac{1}{2}$. The delicacy of the result can be seen from the following facts: 70 million zeroes have been found by computer, and the Riemann hypothesis is true for all of them. It has been shown that an infinite number of zeroes have real part $\frac{1}{2}$, and even that the density of these zeroes among all possible zeroes in the strip is at least $\frac{1}{3}$. Yet no really firm progress toward a proof of the hypothesis as such is evident.

To illustrate the dangers of using empirical evidence in connection with a property which says that *all* cases have a certain property, we might recall that Gauss also conjectured that $\pi(x)$ is at least $L(x)$ for all x on the basis of numerical computations up to 10^{10}. J. E. Littlewood showed that this conjecture is false, but it is not known whether there is a counterexample of an order of magnitude less than 10^{1166}. The original counterexample was of the order $10^{10^{10^{34}}}$.

Nineteenth-century geometry

Geometry flourished in the nineteenth century—not just *geometry* but *geometries.* Analytic geometry had already come into being two hundred years earlier, and with it algebraic geometry—the geometric properties of loci defined by algebraic equations in several variables. Projective geometry was intensively developed both on a *synthetic* basis (from axioms) and on an *analytic* basis in terms of the notion of projective coordinates.

This could best be described as the study of properties of geometric figures in the Euclidean sense which were unaltered under an oblique projection of one plane onto another in the three-dimensional space (in which, for example, circles are equivalent to ellipses). These geometries were not "infinite" in the sense that Euclidean geometry is, for they have points at infinity. One important result was the duality principle of Poncelet that in a valid theorem of plane projective geometry, if you interchange the terms *point* and *line* with the appropriate reversal of containment, you get another valid theorem of projective geometry, often strikingly different in intuitive content from the one with which you started.

Differential geometry. Differential geometry began and flourished as the study of properties of geometrical figures using the techniques and ideas of the differential calculus. This had been one of the original sources of interest in developing the calculus, but it was only after the work of Gaspard Monge and the French school at the turn of the century on the theory of curves in three-dimensional space, and Gauss's work on surfaces in the early part of the nineteenth century, that the field began to be an important focus of mathematical ideas and results. The curvature of a curve was defined at a point, and with it, the curvatures of the different curves passing through a point of a two-dimensional surface in three-dimensional space. With these, one can define the Gaussian curvature, the mean curvature and the lines of curvature of the surface. Considering the length of curves on the surface as defined by the encompassing space, you could define curves of shortest length, the *geodesics* of the surface. Gauss observed that many, though not all, of the quantities and objects of geometric interest were *intrinsic* or *internal* to the surface, i.e., they would be the same in any other surface which was obtained from the given one by a one-to-one correspondence which preserved the distance between points as measured along the geodesics.

Riemann extended these ideas to more general geometric objects which were not necessarily of dimension two but could be of arbitrary integer dimension *n*. He considered the possibility of sets of points which locally were described by *n* coordinate functions, and such that two overlapping descriptions fitted together smoothly. These were the *differentiable manifolds* in the terminology of a much later day.

On such sets, one could impose another kind of structure, the structure of a certain kind of measure of distance called a *Riemannian* metric, which was analogous to the metric induced on surfaces lying in a three-dimensional space. Using this metric, you could define curves of shortest length joining two points, again called *geodesics,* and define a distance between points in general as the length of the shortest geodesic joining these two points. Using the structure of these invariant metrics, later investigators defined the concepts of *parallelism*—moving a direction on the surface parallel to itself as you move along a curve—and related concepts like *affine connection* and *covariant differentiation.* It was this whole armory of concepts and techniques of calculation, especially the calculation of the *curvature tensor,* which was to furnish the mathematical language in which Einstein could express his general theory of relativity in the twentieth century.

Non-Euclidean geometry. One consequence of the development of ideas concerning surfaces was of decisive conceptual importance in the future development of both mathematics and physics. This was the discovery—independently by János Bolyai and Nikolay Lobachevsky—of the existence of *non-Euclidean geometries,* in fact several essentially different kinds of such geometries.

Even in the Hellenistic period, the Greek writers on geometry had distinguished between two parts of the structure of the geometry of the plane set forth by Euclid in his *Elements,* putting in a special category those which were derived from the *Parallel Postulate.* The latter asserts that, given a line and a point external to the line, there is exactly one line through the point which is parallel to the given line (i.e., that does not meet it, no matter how far both are extended). The fact that Euclid called this a postulate indicates a certain sort of caution, since a postulate indicates an assumption that a skeptical reader might be tempted not to assume, but which he should assume hypothetically in order to note the consequences. Some of the consequences are very familiar, including the homely theorem that the sum of the angles of a triangle is two right angles—or 180° in the familiar notation inherited from Babylonian astronomy.

Many leading mathematical writers in ancient times attempted to prove the parallel postulate from the other principles of geometry without any real success, including the astronomer Ptolemy and the neo-Platonic philosopher Proclus. The question of the indispensability of the parallel postulate remained a topic of occasional interest to a small group of devotees over the centuries, most particularly to the Jesuit mathematician Girolamo Saccheri and the German mathematician Johann Lambert, both in the eighteenth century. Saccheri's strategy in trying to prove the parallel postulate was to assume that it was false, either because there were no lines parallel to a given line, or because there were more than one. One then tried to deduce a contradiction. The intensive efforts applied to this task yielded a mass of results deduced from the contrary assumptions, but no contradiction.

What Bolyai and Lobachevsky essentially did was to show that this failure was not an accident. There could be no contradiction, since if you interpreted the Euclidean axioms aside from the parallel postulate as referring not to the familiar points and lines of the usual Euclidean plane but to the geodesics of an appropriate two-dimensional surface, then the parallel postulate in those cases could certainly fail in either direction. Gauss wrote in his notebooks, never published until long after his lifetime, that he had observed this much earlier but never had the courage to publish his observation for fear of ridicule.

What followed from these observations was important in two entirely different ways for the future course of mathematics and its applications to physics.

First, there could conceivably be different geometries each of which was logically coherent, and one different from Euclidean geometry might well apply to physical space. In fact, the sum of the angles of a triangle could be computed in each geometry from the formula of Gauss-Bonnet and depended in a relatively simple way on the curvature of the surface and the area of the triangle. Curvature properties thus played the essential role in determining how far the geometry deviated from being Euclidean.

Second, this was the first major example of an important mathematical discovery made by constructing a *model* of a set of mathematical axioms, in which you could test what could be deduced from a set of mathematical assumptions by writing down the assumptions in a formal way, thinking of the entities described by the assumptions as being essentially undetermined except insofar as the formal relations described by the assumptions held, and then finding an unintuitive interpretation of these entities in which the assumptions do hold, but other properties you are interested in testing may or may not hold. The most conspicuous use of this procedure since the discovery of non-Euclidean geometries has been its application to the axioms of set theory, in proving that important principles concerning the existence or nonexistence of certain kinds of infinite sets cannot be either proved or disproved from the usual axioms of set theory.

Riemann surfaces. One of the most important applications of the ideas of the theory of surfaces as defined intrinsically without reference to their being part of a three-dimensional space was the construction by Riemann of the Riemann surfaces as models for the behavior of multivalued analytic functions. Various kinds of reasonably elementary functions like $\sqrt{z}$ or $\log(z)$, when extended from their original definition as real-valued functions of a real argument to become analytic complex-valued functions of a complex argument, have the annoying tendency of becoming multivalued. You extend their definition in the most natural way (the method of analytic continuation), and you get too much, at least from the most simpleminded view. You get many values defined for a single value of the complex argument z. Rejecting the temptation to get rid of this phenomenon by various artifices of an artificial kind, Riemann made a blessing out of necessity by collecting all the possible values together and turning the collection into a two-dimensional surface, first plugging up holes at suitable points and putting a point at infinity. The result for each such function is a closed two-dimensional surface, and in fact each closed two-dimensional surface arises from some function in this manner. The study of Riemann surfaces asks for surfaces which are essentially distinct, in the sense of having different families of analytic functions defined on the surface.

Transformations and invariants. Riemann surfaces, non-Euclidean geometries—all the different varieties of geometry, as well as the basic concept of a group—were all brought together in a dramatic way around 1870 by the German mathematician Felix Klein in his celebrated *Erlanger Programm.* Klein observed that geometries could be treated systematically as an adjunct of the theory of groups of transformations. Given a set A, you can define the group of all transformations of A. If the elements of A are subject to some family of relations, if A has a *structure* defined on it, then one can restrict oneself only to those transformations T which preserve that structure. If A is itself a group, for example, one can consider transformations T of A which preserve the group operations. These are homomorphisms in the language we introduced earlier, and a homomorphism which is also a transformation (i.e., maps A one to one with itself) is called an isomorphism.

Another example of importance is the following: Suppose A is a vector space over the real space of complex numbers. This means that for any two elements of A, you have a notion of addition which is a binary operation written $a + b$, and for any real or complex number c and an element a of A, you have the operation of multiplying a by c yielding $c \cdot a$, and moreover that these operations have a number of simple properties:

(1) With respect to the binary operation A is a commutative group with identity element that we write as O and with inverses denoted by $(-a)$.

(2) $1 \cdot a = a$ for all a. For any pair of complex numbers c and c_1, $c(c_1 \cdot a) = (cc_1) \cdot a$, and $(c + c_1) \cdot a = c \cdot a + c_1 \cdot a$. For any pair of elements a and a_1 of A, $c \cdot (a + a_1) = c \cdot a + c \cdot a_1$.

The basic paradigm for this definition is that in which we take A to be the family of n-tuples of real or complex numbers

$$a = (a_1, a_2, \ldots, a_n)$$

where you add n-tuples by adding each component and you then multiply by a real or complex number, c, by multiplying each component by c. This example generalizes the representation of the plane or Euclidean three-dimensional space by coordinates and, in these two cases, gives us the so-called vector operations on the plane or in three-dimensional space.

For a vector space, A, and a mapping R of A into itself, you say R is *linear* if $R(ca) = c \cdot R(a)$, $R(a + b) = R(a) + R(b)$ for every c and every a and b in A. In other words, R respects the operations of the vector space. Thus, we can speak of *linear transformations,* and, if we wish, of *nonlinear* transformations.

The Erlangen program and structuralism. The Erlangen program was to reverse the relation we have just described. Instead of starting with a given structure and asking for all the transformations that preserve it, the Erlangen program starts with a given subgroup of the group of transformations of a set and asks for all properties left invariant under the transformations of the subgroup. Euclidean geometry from this perspective was the structure on the plane or in three-dimensional space obtained by taking as your subgroup of transformations the group of all rigid motions, which are all linear transformations that preserve distance. This includes translations (movements in a fixed direction by a fixed distance), rotations around a given axis in the three-dimensional case, rotations around a given point by a given angle in the plane, reflections in a given plane, etc. In projective geometry, you take a bigger group. In Riemannian geometry, take the group of transformations of your differentiable manifold which are differentiable and preserve distances.

The Erlangen program does not change the nature of the structures that are being studied, but it leads to a change of perspective through what it emphasizes. For example, in the case of Riemann surfaces, it was observed by Klein and the French mathematician Poincaré that if you impose a suitable metric on the unit disk in the complex plane (the Poincaré metric), the resulting two-dimensional Riemannian manifold, the hyperbolic plane, is the simplest possible model for the kind of non-Euclidean geometry in which there are many parallel lines to a given line passing through an external point. Taking suitable groups of transformations of the hyperbolic plane which preserve this distance, and identifying any two points a and b of the surface such that $T(a) = b$ for all the transformations of the subgroup, you get a Riemann surface. It was shown that the surfaces obtained include all Riemann surfaces.

Historically, we can see the Erlangen program as the starting point of a broad mathematical movement which attained its greatest influence in the twentieth century. We may call this movement the *structuralist* movement, since its essential characteristic is to see in any particular mathematical object, or in any particular property of an object, an example of a structural or defining property of all objects or groups of objects of no matter what kind, and which can be identified one to one with the given ones so as to preserve the relations in view.

An abstract group, from such a viewpoint, is not a given set with a group structure defined on it, but the class of all sets having a group structure which can be placed in a one-to-one correspondence with the given set by a relationship which preserves all the group operations. An abstract vector space is not a given set on which we have defined a vector space structure but the class of all such concrete vector spaces which can be identified with the given one by linear one-to-one correspondences. Or, to take another example which became extremely important in the twentieth century, if we have a correspondence between two sets on the plane or in three-dimensional space, we can say that this correspondence is continuous if for any sequence of points $\{x_j\}$ in the first set which has the limit x, the corresponding sequence $\{T(x_j)\}$ in the second set has limit $T(x)$—in other words, T respects limits. A correspondence is said to be bicontinuous if T and the transformation T^{-1} going in the opposite direction are both continuous. The topological space defined by a given set is then the class of all sets which can be placed in a bicontinuous one-to-one correspondence with the given set.

The Bourbaki movement in France, which is one of the most influential loci of the structuralist viewpoint, has emphasized that the central theme of mathematical research should be the varieties of structures defined by mixing three types: algebraic structures obtained from various kinds of binary operations, topological structures, and order structures (which use a relation $a < b$, like the relationship of inequality for real numbers, or a being to the left of b on the number line).

Nineteenth- and twentieth-century algebra

Algebra, too, quite aside from group theory, flourished in the nineteenth century—not just *algebra* but *algebras.* Here again the most significant general idea was the observation that there was more in the concept of algebra than just the algebraic operations on the familiar body of the real numbers. The sixteenth century had already extended these algebraic operations to the complex numbers $a + bi$ with a and b real. If $c + di$ is another complex number (and we recall that i denotes the $\sqrt{-1}$), then we add them to obtain $(a + c) + (b + d)i$, and we multiply them to obtain $(ac - bd) + (ad + bc)i$. The results of addition and multiplication are independent of the order of the terms, and all the familiar rules of elementary algebra are valid. The result is what in modern algebraic notation is called a *field.*

Many efforts were made to extend the complex numbers to bigger systems of *numbers* in some general sense which maintained all their algebraic properties. In each case, some significant property had to be altered.

> One example was the *quaternions,* in which you take elements of the form $a + bi + cj + dk$, with a, b, c, d real and $i^2 = j^2 = k^2 = -1$. If you want to keep the property of associativity of multiplication, you are led to the definition of multiplication of the complex units as *anti-commutative*: $ij = -ji = k; jk = -kj = i; ki = -ik = j$. Other, even bigger systems were invented, like the Clifford numbers in which even the associativity of the multiplication was abandoned.

The interest of all these unusual number systems, from the point of view of their inventors, was that they were supposed to do for you in three dimensions what complex multiplication did for you in two dimensions, in the sense that they seemed to provide an algebraic machine for dealing with problems in geometry and physics. A long controversy persisted for many decades of the nineteenth century over the relative virtues of the quaternions versus other algebraic systems for dealing with the properties of vector products in three dimensions (see figure 8). A more general

Figure 8 The Quaternions

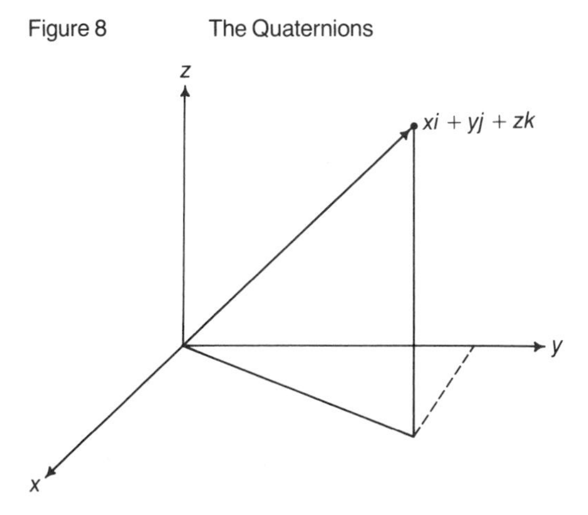

system of products in three (or even higher) dimensions had been given by the German mathematician Hermann Günther Grassmann in his book *Die lineale Ausdehnungslehre,* but Grassmann's conceptual system was incomprehensible to most of the mathematicians of his time. Its most assimilable part, the *Grassmann* or *exterior algebra,* which developed the consequences of anti-commutativity systematically, was taken over by Élie-Joseph Cartan in France and used as the basis of his theory of *exterior differential forms.* Other systems of a semi-algebraic kind, designed for the purposes of differential geometry, were introduced by the Italian school of differential geometers in their development of the *tensor calculus.*

Another algebraic system which had a broad impact was the *matrix algebra* introduced by the English mathematician Arthur Cayley in the early 1850s and studied intensively for many decades. The entities forming the algebraic system were square or rectangular arrays of numbers, but in the perspective that became dominant in the twentieth century, matrices were representations of linear transformations of finite dimension given in coordinate form.

Matrices of a given dimension can be added and multiplied by scalars, while for square matrices, composition serves as an operation of multiplication. These algebraic systems deviate even further from the classical ideals of algebra, for not only is multiplication noncommutative, and you fail to have inverses, but zero divisors appear, i.e., you have non-zero matrices M such that $M^2 = 0$.

Matrix algebras were eventually incorporated into a broader algebraic subject, the theory of *rings,* and in the latter area, which was developed in a very thorough fashion in the twentieth century, the matrix algebras appear as a basic building block of more general kinds of rings.

More on group theory

As we remarked earlier, in terms of its applications group theory came to play an increasingly important role in various areas of mathematics. Galois's work was basically ignored for several decades after his early death, but the concept of group and its basic properties were popularized by the French mathematician Camille Jordan after the middle of the century.

The structure of groups was intensively studied, with two particular extreme varieties serving as the primary foci of attention. One of these foci was the subject of finite groups, i.e., groups having only a finite number of elements. Commutative finite groups had already been studied by Gauss (though not under that name) in his fundamental work on algebraic number theory, where he considered groups made up of complex roots of unity, and it was shown very early that they were products of cyclic groups of prime power (i.e., groups of the form $\{e, g, g^2, \ldots, g^{-1}\}$ for p a prime and with all the elements distinct). Attempts were begun to find structure theorems for noncommutative finite groups, and attention centered on the basic building blocks for more general finite groups, the finite simple groups. A group in general is called *simple* if it has no nontrivial images under homomorphisms. These efforts came to an impasse toward the end of the nineteenth century and were only resumed with a triumphant conclusion in the past two decades.

Another class of groups, whose study led to a broad and fruitful attack upon many deep mathematical problems (and furnished the principal tools for the theoretical physics of elementary particles of our own day), was the class of *Lie groups* introduced and studied by the Norwegian mathematician Sophus Lie for several decades after 1870.

Lie groups combine in their definition two kinds of structure, the algebraic structure of a group and the structure of a differentiable manifold. In the combination you require that the group operations are indefinitely differentiable, i.e., that if you take the coordinates of two group elements g and h, then the coordinates of the group product $g \cdot h$ should be differentiable functions of the coordinates of the two pieces. Lie studied the structure of such groups, and he and his pupils showed that the analysis of this structure could be reduced to the analysis of quite a different kind of algebraic object, the *Lie algebra* of the group. This algebra has some resemblance to a matrix algebra, but its multiplication is anticommutative ($AB = -BA$). In addition, it fails to satisfy the condition that the multiplication is associative. The associativity is replaced by another identity, the *Jacobi identity*.

An algebraic study of these algebraic structures was begun in the 1890s by Killing in Germany and Cartan in France. Its success created a very effective instrument not only for the study of the groups themselves but also of their *representations*. The latter term denotes simply the homomorphisms of the given group into groups of linear transformations of some vector space, usually but not always of finite dimension. The decomposition of such representations into simple pieces corresponds to a generalization of the analytic process of decomposing a function into its Fourier series.

The beginnings of functional analysis

Another kind of decomposition studied both for linear transformations T of a finite dimensional vector space V and for linear differential operators L, is a decomposition of the vector space into *characteristic* or *eigenfunctions*. These are elements v of the vector space V such that $T(v) = cv$, for some real or complex number c called the eigenvalue. In the case of differential operators L, C.-F. Sturm and Liouville had considered such decompositions for a vector space consisting of functions f defined and differentiable on an interval of the line and satisfying a boundary condition on each end of the interval. The question as to the existence of such eigenfunctions had first been raised by Lagrange in his celebrated work on mechanics, *La méchanique analytique*, in connection with the study of small vibrations of mechanical systems. To find such decompositions, L had to be assumed to be linear, i.e., to satisfy the superposition principle $L(cf + c_1 f_1) = cL(f) + c_1 L(f_1)$.

The study of such eigenvalue problems was the first example of a class of mathematical problems and concepts that developed to maturity in the twentieth century. This was the study of problems in analysis by considering them in terms of operations or transformations acting on an infinite dimensional vector space of functions. The study of such vector spaces and of these operators is called *functional analysis*, a term invented by the French mathematician Hadamard just after the turn of the twentieth century. The very bizarre linguistic usage of *eigenfunction* and *eigenvalue* in English reflects an interesting scientific and national situation. The decisive importance of the concept for the development of the quantum theory of the atom was discovered by the German physicists Werner Heisenberg and Erwin Schrödinger in the mid-twenties of the twentieth century. American physicists who learned their quantum theory from Germany took the usage of *eigenwert* for *characteristic value* and half-translated it into English, producing the polyglot usage which eventually infiltrated back into mathematics.

Set theory and the foundations of mathematics

To conclude our brief summary of the riches of the nineteenth century, let us note the *nonclassical* developments and conflicts that arose in German mathematics in the last two decades of the century. These occurred in two distinct domains: Georg Cantor's development of set theory and of the direct study of infinite sets, and the beginning of the conflict between constructive and nonconstructive mathematics. The two conflicts had only one common element. In both, the proponents of new and nonclassical ideas, Cantor in one case and David Hilbert in the other, faced one primary opponent, Leopold Kronecker.

Cantor is certainly among the most original mathematicians of all time. His contributions to mathematical thought stirred up the most intense controversy in the history of mathematics, or at the very least in the history of mathematics since the Renaissance. This controversy, the so-called *crisis of the foundations of mathematics,* stemmed from the fact that Cantor put forward a concept of doing mathematics, *Cantorian set theory,* which not only took upon itself to deal with the *actual infinite* by direct argument but gloried in the fact.

Cantor's work began in a relatively prosaic way by his continuing a study begun by Riemann concerning uniqueness of trigonometrical series. Riemann had posed the question of determining how far the sum of a series like the Fourier series we wrote above determines the coefficients a_n of that series. Suppose, for example, that we know the sum on a set A contained in the interval [0,1] on which the expansion is supposed to hold (or, more generally, suppose the series only converges at the points of A, and we know the sum there). Does this determine the coefficients, or, more properly speaking, how large must A be in some sense so that it does determine them? Riemann had given initial results, and Cantor obtained better results by studying more carefully the properties of A as a set, and in particular its limit properties. He noted that there was a decisive difference between sets which were countable (i.e., could be put into a one-to-one correspondence with the whole numbers) and those sets which were not countable. In particular, he showed by a celebrated argument, the Cantor diagonal process, that the points of the whole interval [0,1] were not countable. He went on to an astoundingly ambitious program of classifying all sets in terms of one-to-one correspondences, using the term *set* in an extremely imaginative way. Thus there could be sets whose elements were sets, and in one of his most celebrated arguments, Cantor used the definition of the *set of all sets that were not members of themselves.*

Readers of the recent best-seller *Gödel, Escher, Bach* will recognize here the basic footprint of the theme of that work, *self-reflexive argument.* The importance of self-reflexive argument as a philosophical tool to disrupt other people's philosophical complacency had been recognized at the time of the Greeks, where the Skeptical school specialized in creating paradoxes using this form of linguistic practice. So it happened in Cantor's case, and very quickly too. By the middle of the first decade of the twentieth century, there were many paradoxes being exchanged among the experts which illustrated the fact that not only did Cantor's practices lead to a contradiction but so did those of the logician Gottlob Frege, whose efforts to found mathematics on the principles of an idealized logic had little in common with Cantor's passion for the infinities beyond intuitive conception.

Constructivism

Even before the paradoxes had wreaked such havoc with the structure of Cantor's arguments, they had undergone severe attack from Kronecker, who had put forward for the first time the *constructivist* program in mathematics. It can be summarized rather dramatically in Kronecker's famous slogan: *God made the integers; man made all the rest.* In Kronecker's view, the only valid mathematical arguments were those in which the entities and properties studied were constructed step by step from previously known entities and properties. Existential arguments were not sufficient, particularly not those of Cantor, which went beyond anyone's intuition.

Cantor's principal defender after a certain point was David Hilbert, the most eminent German mathematician of the time. In part, Hilbert's defense of Cantor was the continuation of a defence of himself against a similar attack by Kronecker. This had occurred a decade earlier when Hilbert had resolved a problem previously studied by very detailed and difficult computations in the theory of polynomial invariants of transformation groups. He had resolved the question in his *Basis Theorem* by an abstract algebraic argument which was existential and not constructive. It was this feature of Hilbert's work that had attracted Kronecker's sarcastic criticism.

In the ensuing controversies, several schools were formed, one supporting the constructivist position of Kronecker, another backing Hilbert's efforts to defend the practices of classical mathematics, and a third school inspired by Frege that sought to find a foundation for mathematics in logic. Strictly speaking, it is only the last which can be described as dealing with foundations. We shall deal with the development of this controversy in the next section but will close the present discussion by pointing to one fact that in retrospect makes the classical Cantorian position untenable. In some of his most fundamental work on the structure of sets of real numbers, Cantor had posed and tried to resolve a basic problem, the *Continuum Hypothesis.* This is the assertion that for any subset A of the interval $[0,1]$, A is either countable or in one-to-one correspondence to the interval itself. There is some indication that Cantor drove himself into a nervous collapse by his work on whether this is so. The futility of his efforts were disclosed late in the twentieth century when it was shown by Kurt Gödel and Paul Cohen that the Continuum Hypothesis can neither be proved nor disproved from the basic principles of set theory. This is certainly one of the greatest triumphs of the technique of proving impossibility theorems by using models.

Thus the nineteenth century closed with a distinctly uneasy situation in the self-evaluation of the mathematical world. It had seen the rigorization of analysis and the flourishing development of the classical framework of analysis, algebra, and geometry. New mathematical advances were made in various areas, but the controversial impetus of the Cantorian approach produced a massive division of opinion in the mathematical community. Let me assure the reader that despite a recent popular book on the crisis in present-day mathematics, this division over mathematical principles is long out of date and in fact went out of date about fifty years ago. Whatever else contemporary mathematicians are interested in (and we shall give a description of some of these interests in the next section), very few are interested in the foundations of mathematics. Their attitude is best described by the title of a paper by a celebrated philosopher and logician: Mathematics has no foundations and needs none.

Twentieth-century mathematics

The turn of the twentieth century marked a turn in mathematical concerns and perspectives that went far beyond the crisis of foundations. In the decade that followed, new subject matter and new styles of mathematical activity were emphasized in a prominent way that had not been thought of in the preceding decades. We can see this most vividly if we examine the list of problems proposed by Hilbert at the International Congress of Mathematicians in Paris in 1900. The list has become celebrated, and appearance of a problem on the list amounts to its canonization. Yet, if we ask how well that list represents the problems that the leading mathematicians of the ensuing period took as the center of their mathematical interests, the answer is: very little. After all, neither functional analysis nor topology appear on the list in any focused way, and Hilbert himself spent most of the following decade working on functional analysis through his work on the spectral theory of integral equations.

Functional analysis in the twentieth century

We have already remarked briefly on the kind of problems that lead to functional analysis, which is the study of operators acting on infinite dimensional vector spaces. The motivation for its study was as concrete as one could imagine—the need to develop mathematical tools for analyzing the boundary value problems of nineteenth-century mathematical physics, especially for the so-called classical partial differential equations, the Laplace equation, the wave equation, and the equation of heat flow.

The development of physics in the nineteenth century had moved the central axis of physical theory from mechanics to electromagnetic theory, thermodynamics, and statistical mechanics. Electromagnetic theory and its earlier sibling, electrostatics, gave rise to boundary value problems that often could not be resolved by simple explicit formulae. Approximations were needed and some assurance that the approximations were valid.

In the middle of the nineteenth century, Riemann had accentuated the importance of these problems for a broader circle of mathematical ideas by founding his proof of the Riemann mapping theorem—a central result in the theory of analytic functions—upon what he called the *Dirichlet principle:* the assertion of the solvability of a certain minimum problem posed on an infinite dimensional set of functions. It was far from clear, except perhaps by a vague physical analogy, that this problem had a solution in the terms posed by Riemann, and a search for other methods followed for several decades. The first complete solution of the boundary value problem studied by Riemann was given by use of techniques involving integral equations, and equations of this form became an important tool in studying the class of problems of which the Dirichlet problem was a special case. The first explicit vindication of Riemann's variational method was given by Hilbert himself in 1901, and in the same year, Ivar Fredholm published a broad and sensationally successful attack upon the existence theory for solutions of the integral equations that had been studied in earlier decades. Both results used the structure of a certain infinite dimensional space of functions, later called a Hilbert space, which involved in its basic properties not only the vector space structure but a norm based upon an inner product and a characteristic property of metric spaces called completeness.

Topology and the concept of structure

Metric spaces, the first step in the development of general topology, were introduced by M.-R. Fréchet and E. H. Moore in the middle of the decade. The mode of definition involved was characteristically different from the style of the classical analysis of the nineteenth century. Influenced by the ethos of Cantorian set theory, the definitions were couched as a *structure* as we have described it, namely a relation between elements of some abstract set. In this case the relation was not as pure as some might have wished, since it involved the real numbers, a metric being a distance function between the points of the set which satisfied some of the elementary properties of the distance function in Euclidean spaces, namely symmetry and the triangle inequality.

The metric involved in Hilbert spaces was derived from an inner product which generalized the basic elementary properties of the conventional inner product for vectors in two- or three-dimensional Euclidean space. In all these cases, the pattern of definition and argument was strongly reminiscent of Greek geometry as expounded in the pages of Euclid, with one very essential difference. Euclid's geometry was supposed to describe the one unique physical space, while the axioms set down for these newly axiomatized structures held for *all possible* examples of the species you were describing. In principle, too, you could set down any axioms you pleased. In the dictum of Cantor, who had a flair for setting matters in extreme terms: The mathematician has perfect freedom. This could be freedom indeed to be trivially foolish, like one Harvard professor who devoted his entire career to setting alternative axiom systems for the concept of group, or to sink into the quicksands of incomprehensible axiomatics beyond the understanding of others, as E. H. Moore did in his last years.

This concept of mathematical activity was strongly influenced by Hilbert's book, *Foundations of Geometry*, published in Germany in the 1890s, which pictured the axioms of Euclidean geometry as acting on entities whose nature was completely undetermined. Its perspective was the background to the *formalist* attitude toward the foundations of mathematical activity which Hilbert was to espouse in response to the later discussion of foundations. Curiously, it had very little to do with Hilbert's own practice in mathematical research, which was strikingly concrete.

Functional analysis and measure theory

The attempts to axiomatize topology and to clarify the basic definitions used in various kinds of analytic arguments were also clearly influenced by the technical difficulties involved in Riemann's proposed solution of the Dirichlet problem. In particular, the focus on the concept of *compactness,* as introduced by Fréchet, was illuminating for dealing with minimum problems on infinite dimensional spaces, as was the introduction by Hilbert of the concept of weak convergence of a sequence in Hilbert space. Hilbert and his students extended to continuous linear operators in Hilbert space some of the basic machinery applied to matrices in finite dimensional spaces. In particular, they obtained spectral theorems (expansions in eigenfunctions) for symmetric integral operators which extended the corresponding results for symmetric matrices. Fréchet, the Hungarian Frigyes Riesz, and Erhard Schmidt in Germany all developed the theory of Hilbert spaces. Riesz extended parts of the theory to other kinds of functional spaces.

This process was strongly influenced, once it began, by a rather different current of mathematical activity stemming from the work of the French school of analysis, and in particular by Émile Borel, Henri Lebesgue, and René Baire. Building upon earlier work of Borel, Lebesgue built the first successful theory of integration for relatively general functions on the line, a theory which enabled him to find reasonably simple answers to the basic problems of convergence of Fourier series and differentiation of functions. The theory was based upon the concept of a countably additive measure on a family of subsets of the line, involving two other concepts which were clearly influenced by the Cantorian ethos: that of the *countable* as an intermediate category between finite and infinite, and that of a functional defined on a family of *sets.*

The viewpoint of Lebesgue and the techniques created by this school gave rise to a new branch of mathematical research on analytical problems, *real variable analysis,* meaning analysis using the concepts of measure theory. The power of these methods was illustrated by Riesz in his striking results on the structure and duality of the spaces L^p of functions integrable in the Lebesgue sense to the p-th power for real numbers p greater than 1.

Set theory and the crisis of foundations

The axiomatic movement in mathematics reached its peak in the pre-First World War period in the book by Felix Hausdorff entitled *Mengenlehre,* on the theory of sets. Hausdorff gave a general treatment not only of set theory in the sense of Cantor but of general topology as well, introducing what turned out to be the basic definition of a topological space and laying the universally accepted basis for the subsequent development of general topology. This work also presented to a broader mathematical public some of the striking work of Ernst Zermelo on set theory and the axiom of choice.

In the crisis which was set in motion by the discovery of the contradictions that followed from the unlimited application of Cantor's arguments in set theory, Zermelo had set about to frame the principles of set theory as a formal axiomatic system, the system that was to become known after the First World War as the Zermelo-Fraenkel set theory. In studying the general theory of ordered sets, Zermelo established a theorem that, on every set, one could impose an ordering of a very special type, one whereby the set could be *well-ordered,* i.e., for any pair of elements, one of the two preceded the other. The method Zermelo used involved a principle which he called the *Axiom of Choice.* It said that for any family of sets whatever, you can establish a method of choosing one element from each set of the family. For the unaware reader, we must remark that such a choice in the case of extremely large families goes far beyond the domain of ordinary intuition. This principle was developed by Hausdorff in a number of useful alternative forms (one of which became known after one of Hausdorff's students as Zorn's Lemma), and they were extensively used in many domains of mathematical argument. Lebesgue used this principle, for example, to show the existence of a subset of the unit interval which was not measurable.

Intuitionism

The crisis concerning the foundations of mathematics to which we referred in the previous section was an active focus of mathematical argument in the first decade of the century, particularly because of the radical opposition of the views of Hilbert and the Dutch mathematician L. E. J. Brouwer.

Brouwer began as a philosopher but made a great mathematical reputation with his very original work in the topological theory of continuous mappings (he was the principal founder of the branch of topology known later as homotopy theory). His viewpoint in the struggle over foundations was known as *intuitionism* and was rooted in a radicalized version of the constructivism of Kronecker. Brouwer accepted only mathematical arguments based upon step-by-step procedures and explicitly rejected one of the most classical principles of mathematical argument, the *reductio ad absurdum.* This principle of formal logic, also known as the *principle of the excluded middle,* went back at least fifty years before the time of Euclid to Aristotle's work in logic.

To put it in simple terms, the argument asserts that every statement is either true or false. If you wish to prove a statement is true, you may assume it false, and if that assumption leads to a contradiction, then the statement must be true. Hilbert rejected Brouwer's viewpoint on the ground that it would reject not only Cantor's theory of infinite sets but a very large part of classical mathematics going back to the Greeks. It would even lead to the rejection of Brouwer's most famous theorem in topology, the Brouwer fixed-point theorem, which asserts that every continuous mapping of a ball in an n-dimensional Euclidean space into itself must have a fixed point. Brouwer regarded this prospect with equanimity, even going so far as to say in later writings that the result of the theorem was not only unproved but actually false. This was the sort of attitude that led their contemporary Poincaré, who was a sort of ironical sympathizer of Brouwer's, to declare that Brouwer was a great topologist when he forgot his philosophy.

Mathematical logic

The crisis as to foundations also led to a major upsurge in the general mathematical interest in the area of *mathematical logic,* or *symbolic logic.* Its origins go back to Leibniz's program for constructing a universally applicable symbolical system, which he called a *universal characteristic,* and exercizing it by machine. This is a forerunner not only of mathematical logic but of its broad application in the present-day digital electronic computers. Despite this early appearance, and the work in the nineteenth century of Boole, De Morgan, C. S. Peirce, Schröder, Peano, and particularly Frege, the activity in this area had not attracted broad mathematical attention until the controversies over foundations began and such monumental works of erudition as Russell and Whitehead's *Principia Mathematica* rolled off the presses.

The greatest achievement of the history of mathematical logic, and probably of logic in general, was the Incompleteness Theorem of the Viennese mathematical logician Kurt Gödel. In order to counter Brouwer's attacks on the validity of classical mathematics, Hilbert had begun a program of mathematical research by his disciples on the logical foundations of mathematics which sought to counter the Brouwer criticism by justifying *infinite nonconstructive* mathematics by showing its consistency, using constructive arguments. *Consistency* means simply that you will never prove an assertion and its negation. There is no statement which will be proved both true and false.

What Gödel established was that the Hilbert program was impossible, and, indeed, if you could carry it through, you would prove all of mathematics is *inconsistent.* The ideas and techniques he developed for this proof had an overwhelming influence on the later development not only of logic but of its application to general computation.

By relatively simple means, Gödel set up a *universal characteristic,* in terms of which any symbolical system could be represented in terms of whole numbers, and used that representation to generate assertions in that system that could neither be proved nor disproved. Representing a system within itself, the problem of self-reflexive complexity was turned from a tool of harassment into a major tool of mathematical and logical discovery. Almost immediately after Gödel's proof, the English logician A. M. Turing drew out the implications for automata theory in the concept known as the *Turing machine,* which by a principle of automata theory is the universal machine (it can compute anything which can be computed).

The foundations controversy slowly died out as an active concern of mathematicians over two or three decades. It had relatively little effect on mathematical practice, despite the ardent propaganda of Brouwer and the revival of constructivism in recent decades by the American mathematician Errett Bishop. It promises very little for the would-be convert, except the absolute security of a much narrower mathematical universe. This prospect has not attracted a wide following.

The effect of the world wars on mathematics

The First World War provided a major discontinuity in the progress of mathematical research. A considerable part of a major generation of French and German mathematicians was certainly destroyed, and the friendly rivalry of the two major national mathematical schools was turned into an enmity which healed relatively slowly. New major national groups of mathematicians appeared in the United States and Russia to join the older schools in Western Europe. Two major mathematical movements appeared and flourished—the German school of abstract algebra and the newly flourishing development of algebraic topology in both Europe and the United States. Abstract algebra, headed by charismatic figures like Emmy Noether and Emil Artin transformed and extended the broad domain of algebraic activity within an axiomatic framework. Its leading textbook, *Moderne Algebra,* written in German by the Dutch algebraist Bartel van der Waerden, had a tremendous impact on the world's younger mathematicians and undoubtedly set off the effort by the French Bourbaki group to do likewise over an even broader domain.

In the midst of this flourishing activity, the coming to power of the Nazis in Germany drove an astounding percentage of the active German mathematicians out of Germany and effectively destroyed the prestige and activity of the German mathematical school. Most of the emigrés came to the United States, including the leading figures, and the United States became the world's leading center of both abstract algebra and algebraic topology. The trend was accentuated when the outbreak of the Second World War brought some of the leading figures of the Bourbaki group to the United States together with members of leading mathematical schools from the European continent.

The abstract movement and its consequences

The upsurge of the abstract movement in mathematics between the two world wars did not, as has sometimes been remarked, increase the distance between mathematics and the sciences. The development of professional specialization in the intellectual disciplines in general tended to produce separation of interests between mathematics and the development of physics, at least for some German mathematicians like Karl Gustav Jacobi, who issued a personal manifesto declaring his independence of physics. The chief focus of Jacobi's famous statement, however, was no passion for abstraction. It was instead his overwhelming interest in number theory, the chief competitor with physics as a source of intellectual problems for the practitioners of various mathematical fields.

On the other hand, the leading figure in the abstract movement in analysis in Germany in the 1920s and in the United States in the 1930s, was John von Neumann, a brilliant Hungarian mathematician who began his mathematical career in set-theoretical logic at Göttingen. His most important work in abstract functional analysis, the formulation of the abstract theory of Hilbert spaces, the spectral theorem for unbounded Hermitian operators in Hilbert space, and the study of rings of operators in Hilbert space, was all closely related to his strong interest in the development of quantum mechanics. Hilbert space was the native terrain of quantum mechanics. Von Neumann's early book, *The Mathematical Foundations of Quantum Mechanics* (1929), is a broad-scale effort to integrate the problems posed by quantum physics into the development of operator theory.

Similarly, von Neumann's joint book with Oskar Morgenstern, *Theory of Games and Economic Behavior,* which had a strong impact of considerable force upon the postwar development of theoretical economics, is a very principled exercise in the application of the abstract method in a Cantorian framework.

During the thirties and forties, the abstract or axiomatic movement in mathematical research tended to rule the roost without serious challenge. Thus the combinatorial topology of Poincaré, Veblen, Alexander, and Lefschetz became the algebraic topology of the 1930s under the influence of Emmy Noether. The description of the topological properties of manifolds or polyhedra by numbers like Betti numbers and torsion coefficients became homology and cohomology groups instead. The study of Lie groups became the study of topological groups. Operator theory gave way to topological algebra, and even the very concrete analytical work of Norbert Wiener on Tauberian theorems became a branch of the subbranch of topological algebra known as the theory of normed rings.

In functional analysis, the most effective proponent of this movement was the Polish mathematican Stefan Banach, whose book *Theory of Linear Operations* became the Bible of functional analysts. So pervasive was his influence on the folklore of the field that after the Second World War, the theory of normed rings was renamed Banach algebra in the United States (notwithstanding that Banach had never worked on it).

After World War II: the future of mathematics

The Second World War provided another major break in the developing pattern of mathematical research. Postwar development in mathematics as in the other sciences was much more intense and much broader than it had been in any earlier period. The United States became the leading mathematical country without any rivals, with the much smaller French and Russian schools as the only major alternative foci of mathematical activity. The elder members of the Bourbaki group came to power in French mathematics, which as a result moved rapidly and consistently toward a strongly abstract style of activity. In areas like algebraic topology and algebraic geometry, which became so highly algebraized as to lose many of their former connections with their concrete subject matter, this tendency continued without letup. Many other areas of mathematical research, however, moved in somewhat different directions. A mixture of abstract and concrete mathematics began to become a common style in many fields of intense and productive activity. By the beginning of the 1960s it was clear that the Cantorian and Abstract revolutions were over and a strong reflux had begun. The fields of high repute were often fields of a high degree of concreteness relative to the structural criteria of the Bourbaki: Fourier analysis, finite groups, partial differential equations, differential topology, group representations, to name some of the most obvious examples. Fields like analytic functions of several complex variables which had moved sharply in an abstract direction after the Second World War moved sharply and unequivocally back in a more concrete direction. Even algebraic geometry, the apple of the abstract movement's eye, has shifted some of its emphases.

In the past decade the most important new phase of the dominant trends of mathematical activity has been an unequivocal shift toward the involvement of mathematical research in a number of active fields with theoretical problems arising in the sciences. The most active area involves the applications of ideas and techniques from differential geometry and nonlinear partial differential equations in mathematical physics. We can only look to the future to see what new significant forms of mathematical development will arise from this new thrust. We can only speculate as well how mathematics, together with our society as a whole, will respond to the pressures of the Computer Revolution, and how the massive social demands of this kind of mathematical engineering will impinge on the central body of the field.

Mathematics today is a curious mixture of contrasts. It is very old, and it is very young. It is very esoteric for many in our society, but a growing mass of people throughout many sectors of society are learning to perform roles that a few decades ago would have been called the jobs of a mathematician. American society has both a strong mathematical research establishment and the worst system of mass education in mathematics among the developed countries of the world today. We have the best system of university and college education in mathematics of any country in the world for those interested in mathematics, and the lowest degree of interest and achievement on the part of the mass of our students. We shall not be able to live with some of these contradictions under the competitive pressures of the next decades, when the Computer Revolution will make them ever more acute.

The role of mathematics as a component of the social and intellectual process in our world is growing rapidly and without pause. That role cannot be fulfilled without the constantly increasing vitality of mathematics as a research discipline. This in turn cannot be fulfilled without a continuing and ever sharper sense of the importance of mathematics as an ideal of human knowledge.

PART TWO

Reconsiderations of Great Books

Reflections on Galen

Douglas Buchanan

Douglas Buchanan was born at Amherst College in 1922 of parents both of whom were teachers. He received his B.A. from St. John's College in Annapolis, Maryland, in 1947 after an interruption for three years' service with the U.S. Army in the Aleutians. Graduate work at Dartmouth, Yale, and finally the University of Vermont culminated in an M.D. degree in 1953.

After his internship and residency, Dr. Buchanan spent a year as a Fulbright scholar studying tropical diseases in London, England, and later did research in pulmonary disease in Harlan, Kentucky. Then, following ten years of general practice, Buchanan turned to psychoanalysis, which he studied at Massachusetts General and at McLean Hospital outside Boston, where he trained in group psychotherapy.

Dr. Buchanan now has a private psychotherapy practice in Andover, Massachusetts, works as a psychiatrist for the Veteran's Administration, and is on the staff of several Boston area teaching hospitals. He enjoys his hobbies of boat-making, sailing, and "constant, extremely eccentric reading" and describes himself as inordinately proud of his four sons and daughters. He acknowledges the influence in his life of his father, Scott Buchanan, liberal artist and philosopher of the history of science (whose book *So Reason Can Rule* is reviewed elsewhere in this volume), and of Mark Van Doren, who he says taught him that "medicine without poetry is neither Science nor Art."

Introduction

In 1978 *The Great Ideas Today* published the essays on medical matters Leon R. Kass's "Regarding the End of Medicine and the Pursuit of Health" and Franz J. Ingelfinger's "Management Medicine: The Doctor's Job Today." Both writers closed with admonitory finality. Dr. Kass warned that too much emphasis on health and not enough on the soul was doing damage to society, and Dr. Ingelfinger said that "to proceed as at present, with doctor and patient floundering about in what is euphemistically called 'pluralism,' is to perpetuate the basically unsatisfactory nonsystem that for the past decade has produced a fragmented and uncoordinated method of health delivery marked by technical agility and much good will, but also by disorganization, and a distressing lack of equity—and all of this purchased at an exorbitant price."

Both articles were interesting examples to me of defects that many of us in the profession of medicine sense, that we try to express or redress in our practices, but that somehow we also feel discouraged about curing. In the belief that the history of medicine offers parallels to this state of affairs, I have recently returned to my earlier interest in it. Accordingly, I offer here a few introductory paragraphs, a paper on Galen as a physiologist written just as I began thirty-four years ago to study medicine, and a concluding section in which I argue for more study of the history of medicine, after commenting further on Galen and "Galenism."

I was exposed to Galen early in my life when my father, Scott Buchanan, a philosopher of a Socratic persuasion, wrote a book on the need for theory in medicine, called *The Doctrine of Signatures,* which appeared in 1938. We spent a year at Johns Hopkins University School of Medicine while he was researching and writing the book. There we met Owsei and Lilian Temkin of that university's Library of the History of Medicine who together have since written *Galenism, the Rise and Decline of a Medical Philosophy* as well as a lot of articles on Galen, and my father made Galen his paradigm of the liberal artist in medicine in his book.

I became a student of the Great Books Program at St. John's College shortly thereafter and read Galen's *On the Natural Faculties* as well as Hippocrates and Harvey for the first time. Claude Bernard was the subject of my senior paper, and, en route to medical school, I was lucky enough to spend a year at Yale as a physiology graduate student under Dr. John F. Fulton, neurophysiologist, medical historian, and biographer of Harvey Cushing. The latter had been the biographer of Sir William Osler, his former chief at Johns Hopkins Medical School, who had done so much to encourage the study of medical history in this country. I wrote my essay on Galen as part of a festschrift for Dr. Fulton, who liked it and asked me to stay on in the History of Medicine department. Instead I went on to medical school, but I kept in touch with Dr. Fulton at Yale and with Dr. Temkin at Johns Hopkins.

In the thirty years since, practicing first internal medicine and now "psychological medicine" (psychoanalytic psychiatry), I have been impressed by the progression biographically of so many physicians from the anatomic-physiologic-pathologic studies of their youth and middle years to the more philosophic metaphysical concerns of their later ones. A famous case in point is Sigmund Freud, who began experimentally in the laboratory and ended as a world-famous founder of a metaphysical (metapsychological) school of thought, but who always maintained his roots in clinical work. One nourished the other, it seems fair to say, and by so doing enabled Freud to encompass in his thought the care for the soul Dr. Kass is concerned we balance against our concerns for bodily health, and also Dr. Ingelfinger's practical concerns about equity and how we deliver medical services. An example of the latter would be Freud's book, *Question of Lay Analysis.*

I think it is only by the balance of clinical and theoretical work that medicine progresses. The theory must not, however, be only scientific but must broaden to include philosophy. This, I feel, is the lesson that Galen taught us, and it is that concern on my part which has made it seem worthwhile to rework my Galen paper after so many years.

Claude Bernard was very "Galenic" when he stated in *An Introduction to the Study of Experimental Medicine,* "Yet we shall reach really fruitful and luminous generalizations about vital phenomena only in so far as we ourselves experiment and, in hospitals, amphitheatres, or laboratories, stir the fetid or throbbing ground of life. It has somewhere been said that true science is like a flowering and delectable plateau which can be attained only after climbing craggy steeps and scratching one's legs against branches and brushwood. If a comparison were required to express my idea of the science of life, I should say that it is a superb and dazzlingly lighted hall which may be reached only by passing through a long and ghastly kitchen."[1] A suberb experimentalist, Bernard was also a luminous generalizer himself and, in positing the "milieu interieur," a philosopher. Yet sadly today his book is thought of as "antiphilosophic" and as advocating only laboratory experimental work, in particular biochemistry and intracellular physiology. This view of the work, good as far as it goes, leaves out Bernard's true philosophic concerns and, it seems to me, deprives us all of fruitful generalization.

In a real sense we have followed our current version of Bernard far enough and now need to redress the balance. To paraphrase a famous line: what will it avail us if we gain the biochemical-intracellular world but lose our own souls? I think Galen offers us, as has been said, a chance "to unite professional and scientific medicine with a philosophic link." Perhaps we can be concerned with clinical practice, laboratory research, and a philosophy of medicine, based at least partially on medical history, to everyone's advantage.

Galen as physiologist

Galen's life, A.D. 130–200, lasted from the zenith of the Roman Empire to at least the end of its heyday. At the time of his birth the empire encompassed almost all the known world, where "her legions bivouaced by the waters of Babylon and tramped the Yorkshire moors of England." The political independence of Greece had ended and she, with her dependencies, had passed under the Roman power. It was a time, as compared with the immediately preceding time of Ptolemy, the astronomer, of regression. Few contemporaries of Galen ranked with the leading lights of the previous two centuries, such as Pliny and Celsus, Virgil and Lucretius. The second century on the other hand was the period in which the Hebrew text of the Old Testament was finally and completely edited, in which a new surge of Eastern philosophers and theologians tried to reconcile the ideals of Christianity with those of Greek philosophy (and contributed a few martyrs to the history of the Christian faith), and in which the effects of a new renaissance of Greek works in the Roman world, which had begun some fifty years prior to Galen's birth, was being felt. A steady process of Hellenization had gone on in the Roman world, the Greek language had become that of culture as distinct from public affairs, and Greek philosophy had come to be regarded as indispensable to those of learning. Interestingly enough, the Latin language was to some extent neglected as a result, and even the Roman emperors, though often not discriminating patrons of Greek art and customs, as for example in Nero's case, were usually enthusiastic Hellenophiles.

Philosophy itself in this period was principally represented by the emperor Marcus Aurelius, who lived from 121 to 180, and whose outlook on life was Greek in feeling and sympathy.

He was the author of the *Meditations,* a product of Stoic philosophy written in Greek,[2] and he sent the first envoys from Rome to China in 166. Pausanias, the Greek traveler and geographer, was a contemporary, as was Lucius Apuleius, the Platonic sophist of Carthage, who is remembered chiefly for his *Metamorphosis,* now better known as *The Golden Ass.* The whole of ancient science was, of course, in the Greek language and most of the "nature philosophers" were Ionians or Hellenes. The history of science in Rome is therefore the story of the spread of Greek thought.

Galen's father was a distinguished architect of Pergamum in Asia Minor named Nicon, who saw to it that his son was well educated in mathematics, literature, and philosophy. Galen, who was devoted to his father, thought less well of his mother, of whom he later wrote that she was "so irritable in temper that she was forever screaming and quarreling with my father, would at times bite her maids, and was worse than Xanthippe with Socrates." Galen's name means "quiet" or "peaceable" and, although his biographers all avow him to have been a man of "elevated character," many of them feel that his extreme liking for controversy in later years may have resulted from the worst side of his maternal inheritance.

Pergamum was an ancient center of learning containing a library second only to that at Alexandria, a medical school known as an "Asclepiam," and a university in which Galen studied until he was seventeen. When at that age his father was assured his son would succeed in medicine, Galen was placed in the hands of professors and practitioners of that art. He had as teachers the anatomist Satyrus, the Hippocratean Stratonicus, and the empiricist Aeschirion. His eagerness for medical knowledge, coupled with his thorough grounding in mathematics and natural philosophy and his skill in logic and dialectic, led him to observe interesting cases of disease and to enrich his knowledge with medical folklore. Further he studied under Pelops, the muscle anatomist at Smyrna, also at Corinth and Alexandria, and did "autopsies" in Palestine and Asia Minor at the leading medical centers.

After nine years of travel Galen returned to Pergamum. Already at twenty-eight he was assured a reputation by his writings on anatomical and physiological subjects. This reputation helped his appointment as surgeon to the gladiators of a local religious festival, a much sought after position. After four years, desiring to practice in a larger city, he went to Rome where he finally achieved a brilliant reputation both as a practitioner and as a public demonstrator of anatomy; he eventually numbered among his patients even the emperor Marcus Aurelius himself.

In Rome, Galen counted among his friends the great philosophers and savants of the city, many of whom attended his public demonstrations in anatomy and physiology, but his success in all these things, combined with the fame of his writings, incurred the jealous wrath of his fellow practitioners so that, in 168, he was forced to flee the city and return to Pergamum. He had taken no pains to conceal his contempt for the ignorance, charlatanism, and poor practice of his colleagues, many of whom stooped to the lowest means at hand to discredit him. At the same time, he was not himself above exaggeration in his accounts of his therapeutic and diagnostic successes, while polemicizing against his opponents in the school of Asclepiades and Erasistratus, as well as others of the prevalent Vitalistic and Epicurean Atomistic schools of thought. A good example of Galen's invective is his sarcastic attack on the proponents of the opposing view of the action of the nutritive elements in the body. This is from *On the Natural Faculties,* of which it is said that, "if Galen was the crystallization of Greek medicine, then this book is a crystallization of Galen." Galen writes: "Now, speaking generally, there have arisen the following two sects in medicine and philosophy among those who have made any definite pronouncement regarding Nature. I speak, of course, of such of them as know what they are talking about, and who realize the logical sequence of their hypotheses, and stand by them; as for those who cannot understand even this, but who simply talk any nonsense that comes to their tongues, and who do not remain definitely attached either to one sect or the other—such people are not even worth mentioning."

We must recall that sharp criticism and rough verbal treatment of one's opponents were then the fashion and order of the day. But Galen's temper in argument was extremely tart as when he discussed certain of those with whom he disagreed, saying, "Since, then, we have talked sufficient nonsense—not willingly, but because we were forced, as the proverb says, 'to behave madly among madmen'—let us return again to the subject of urinary secretion."

Apparently controversy of this sort, as well as, some say, fear of an approaching epidemic, forced Galen to leave Rome. But his respite from metropolitan life was brief. Within a year, he was summoned back to Rome by imperial mandate. The reason for this was that Aurelius and his co-emperor, Lucius Verus, were about to undertake a campaign against the Germans who were threatening in the North, and Aurelius wanted Galen to accompany him as his personal physician. However, though he returned to Italy, Galen seems not to have been thus patriotically stirred and begged off, to be finally allowed to stay in Rome and care for the young prince, Commodus. During this period, he toured Palestine to collect drugs and stopped at Cyprus to look at the copper mines and products of smelting that had medical value.

From 169 to 180, when Marcus Aurelius died, Galen remained in Rome and gave his undivided attention to his scientific work and his writing. This stay at court was his most productive period. During it he wrote the works (often, it is said, dictating several almost simultaneously) from which was established the great Galenic system that dominated medicine for fourteen hundred years, until the time of Paracelsus and Vesalius. Galen is reported to have died in A.D. 200.

He wrote in all about four hundred works, including some lost in a fire that destroyed the Temple of Peace. He wrote voluminously on medical philosophy and deontology, philosophy and logic, as well as a great body of commentaries on his great guiding mentor, Hippocrates, and he wrote also on such specific aspects of medicine as anatomy, physiology, hygiene, dietetics, pharmacology, and therapeutics. We have remaining eighty-three books which are undoubtedly genuine, nineteen doubtful ones, and fifteen commentaries on the Hippocratic text. Only fragments of his nonmedical books are extant. The surviving corpus comes to something like twelve volumes of a thousand pages each.

Without going into a detailed description of Galen's natural philosophy in this short paper, I shall attempt to state his fundamental concepts and then pass rapidly on to his contributions to physiology.

Galen's guide and ideal, who stands out from his work at all times, was Hippocrates, whom Galen actually speaks of as "the most divine Hippocrates" in *On the Natural Faculties.* On specific matters he is hardly less respectful, as in saying that "if one passes over the Hippocratic view and makes some other pronouncement about the function of the kidneys, one cannot fail to make oneself utterly ridiculous." In another place he says Hippocrates "was the first known to us of all those who have been both physicians and philosophers, inasmuch as he was the first to recognize what Nature effects."

Galen repeatedly reminds us that "Nature does nothing in vain," but the prior question for him is what exactly nature does, thus making him an experimentalist, as we shall describe, in order to set medicine in the direction of becoming an exact science. But the pathfinder for him in this enterprise is Hippocrates, who, he feels, anticipated Aristotle with the four elements; earth, air, fire, and water; as well as with the four humors: blood, phlegm, yellow bile, and black bile. Galen agrees with Aristotle on the other key set of concepts, namely the four qualities: hot, cold, dry, and moist. However, Hippocrates's aegis is always essential to him and to his system.

Galen's own training and bent of mind allowed him to see through and beyond the arbitrary restrictions of the schools of medical thought that preceded and surrounded him. He took the position of rationalism in that he taught that therapeutics should be deducible from knowledge of disease states and of the action of the remedies available. It is true that sometimes his infatuation with the mathematical led him to emulate Euclid's method. For example, in Book III of *On the Natural Faculties,* he says "Thus our argument has clearly shown the necessity for the genesis of such a faculty, and whoever has an appreciation of logical sequence must be firmly persuaded from what we have said that, if it be laid down and proved by previous demonstration that Nature is artistic and solicitous for the animal's welfare, it necessarily follows that she must also possess a faculty of this kind." In general, however, theory and practice went hand in hand with him and modified each other.

Nature, for Galen, was the principle of unity in the living organism which implies that the living thing, *qua* living, is not further divisible and that its parts can only be understood and dealt with in relation to this principle of unity. Thereupon hung most of the fundamental differences of opinion Galen had with the established schools. Most of them held that the organism was merely the sum of its parts, that the individual organs could be individually treated, and that the health of the whole would result. But Galen says, "if there were not an inborn faculty given by Nature to each one of the organs at the very beginning, then animals could not continue to live even for a few days, far less for the number of years which they actually do. For let us suppose they were under no guardianship, lacking in creative ingenuity and forethought; let us suppose they were steered only by material forces, and not by any special faculties (the one attracting what is proper to it, another rejecting what is foreign, and yet another causing alteration and adhesion of the matter destined to nourish it); if we suppose this, I am sure it would be ridiculous for us to discuss natural, or, still more, psychical, activities—or, in fact, life as a whole."

While Galen accepted and propounded teleological principles of this kind, he maintained that the evidence of the senses is the indispensable groundwork of all medical knowledge. Hence the assertion that he tried to unite "professional and scientific medicine with a philosophical link," at the same time attacking oversimplifications of the type the Methodist school propounded, i.e., diseases as distinct isolated entities without interrelationships. Galen was anti-mechanistic, as is clear in the last quotation. His theoretical doctrine of disease was based on the humoral theory of Hippocrates. He did not blindly subscribe to the opinions of Aristotle, that center of the Scholastic storm for two thousand years, but could on occasion take exception to him as is shown in several places in *On the Natural Faculties.* He owes a tremendous debt to Aristotle for terminology throughout, and in the form and style of his arguments.

I think a good bridge on which to cross to a discussion of Galen's physiological work will be via his own statement of the threefold division of the "pneuma," as quoted by F. B. Lund in his book *Greek Medicine.* "The living animal is governed," Galen writes, "as has been pointed out in my essay on the beliefs of Socrates and Plato, by three faculties which differ from one another in their origin, as if each one of them were distributed from a special source to the whole body. Plato calls them 'spirits' (pneumata) and has ascertained the particular character of each one. The first of them is necessary for the nourishment of the animal and is common also to the vegetable world and has as its source the liver, and has, as conduits distributing it to the whole body, the veins. Whether you call it the Appetitive, the Natural, or Nutritive faculty, it makes no difference, or whether you call it a faculty (δυναμισ) or a spirit.

"The second spirit belongs to us not as mere vegetative or living creatures but as animals and is located in the heart, as the source of the innate heat. The conduits for this source are the arteries, and it is called by many names, the Vital faculty, the faculty of Courage, the Vital spirit, or the spirit of Courage.

"The third is located in the head and is the Reasoning spirit, which produces all voluntary motion, as well as sensation, in the whole body. The preservation of these faculties differs in no way from the preservation of life. For it has been demonstrated that when one of them is destroyed, the others are necessarily destroyed together with it."

Galen's physiology is, in the main, an ingenious, special plea for the importance of design in nature. Man shares desires and emotions with the animals, but surpasses them by having conscious thought and voluntary decision. His soul was the Aristotelian one, the final cause of the body, and he added the notion that, because of the close correspondence between mental and physical conditions, a mixture of the elements determined the functions of the soul. In fact the soul for him is rational, passionate, and concupiscent, with corresponding physiological functions and even three different places in the body to inhabit.

It is felt by Galen's biographers that the application of his theories naturally led him to an enthusiastic study of anatomy and his ultimate great skill as a surgeon. Unfortunately his anatomy, applied, as it was later, to man, is in many respects inaccurate. Despite the fact that he took nothing on higher authority, undertook the entire dissection by himself (even removing the skin, an operation formerly done by attendants), and that his technique was obviously much superior to that of his contemporaries, he was forced to work entirely on animals, as the supply of human bodies for dissection was insufficient in even such a center as Alexandria. In all his life, as far as is known, Galen got hold of only two human skeletons: one a body washed out of a grave in a flood, another that of a robber hanged at a crossroad. However, working with animals, especially pigs and apes (he wrote a treatise on the variety most resembling man), he made important contributions to both anatomy and physiology.

He discovered the course of the recurrent laryngeal nerves, recognized loss of voice as the result of injury of these nerves in surgical removals of glands of the neck, and in a famous demonstration in Rome dramatically showed that loss of voice (aphonia)—in a large pig in this case—could be induced by paralyzing all of the intercostal nerves, and then that the voice is regained when the paralyzing ligatures are untied and the function of the intercostal muscles restored. Dr. J. S. Prendergast's monograph "The Background of Galen's Life and Activities" gives the following interesting description:

> This arduous experiment was carried out on a large swine, the scene of the operation being a large, sunny room—'a house full of light'. It was an oft repeated experiment,for he admits to having performed it several times, publically as well as privately, and it formed part of the demonstration which Galen gave in the presence of the most distinguished men in Rome. The experiment is described in detail and we can follow each step of the proceedings with the utmost ease. He points out the difficulties attendant on this operation, for instance the thick muscular investiture which lies along the vertebrae and which makes access to the nerves far from easy. He gives details about the sharpness of the hook to be employed in searching for the nerve, the

kind of blunt hook that was used for exerting traction on the nerve, the curved needle carrying a ligature which was to be inserted under the nerve as near as possible to the spine so as to throw all of the muscles out of action. In these operations he used a thicker kind of ligature which, when moderately constricted, did not damage the nerve—more slender ligatures being obviously unsuitable—and this was tied without, however, forming a "blindknot," one which was rather difficult to untie. The employment of a special kind of noose rendered the demonstration easier and more effective.

When all the intercostal nerves at their emergence from the spine were so secured and, while the unfortunate beast was a shrieking mass of pain and horror, Galen, at a given signal, tightened all the ligatures and the animal, from being the seeming incarnation of clamorous and insistent protest, is suddenly reduced to silence and solemn muteness. The onlookers are amazed at the spectacle, but their wonder becomes greater still when, all the ligatures being simultaneously relaxed, the animal again bursts forth into a yell of howling horror. And so Galen uses the animal as a kind of living musical box, evoking shrill arpeggios and all the compass of sound at will; a pleasant discord of sweet sounds to the ear of one who regarded music not as something designed merely to please and gratify the senses, but as something with a higher purpose, namely, an outlook which is typical of the Greek attitude to knowledge. [*See* note in parentheses in the first paragraph of page 134.]

Galen was familiar with the reciprocal or antagonistic action of sets of muscles, recognized seven out of the twelve "cerebral" (cranial) nerves, distinguished between motor and sensory nerves, and was the first expounder of the myogenic theory of the heartbeat. In line with his systematic investigation of the correlation between structure and function, his great achievement, he was probably the first to produce cerebral lesions in animals to establish a distinction between lesions of the cerebral lobes and those of the brain stem and the cerebellum. He observed that complete section of the spinal cord resulted in complete loss of sensation and movement of all muscles supplied by nerves springing from the cord below the line of section. He demonstrated the effects of hemisection of the cord and, in his extensive studies of respiratory physiology, was quite aware of the different actions of the phrenic and intercostal nerves. He made extensive clinical application of his knowledge of the extent of damage suffered by the upper limb following injuries to the various cervical vertebrae. Dr. Prendergast feels that his greatest contribution to the advancement of scientific thought, "making him of Harvey's rank," was his demonstration that the left ventricle of the heart and the arteries contained blood. This part of the vascular system had, to his time, been felt to be filled with "pneuma," or air, and could only be invaded by the blood system under abnormal conditions.

Sir William Osler is said to have wondered why Galen missed the discovery of the circulation of the blood, but Galen, in fact, had the view that the movement of the blood, which assumed communication between the two ventricles by invisible pores in the septum, consisted in a "to and fro movement" in the arteries and veins, without continuity of the circulation through the anastomoses, which Erasistratus had already pointed out existed for the transfer of arterial "pneuma" to the blood of the veins. The arterial blood, for Galen, conveyed Vital spirits from the heart, the venous blood conveyed Natural spirits from the liver, while Animal spirits descended from the brain via the "hollow nerves" which, unfortunately for the anatomical demonstrator, became solid after death. The right ventricle of the heart existed for the purpose of sending nutrient blood to the lungs, although there is dispute, I have found, as to who actually recognized the "lesser circulation" through the lungs.

There is much that is ingenious about Galen's circulatory physiological picture, much that is inaccurate, but, given his theory and his terms, he managed quite well to explain the appearances. He also correctly described the junction and courses of many embryological blood vessels and even described ducts which afterward had to be rediscovered. Dr. A. J. Brock, translator of *On the Natural Faculties,* says that "Galen's ideas of tissue nutrition via blood are sound and modern." Of course, to us, the striking thing is that the question of the structure of these tissues is somehow never raised. The solids of the body are tendon, muscle, parenchyma, bone, and so forth, and these act because of their nature or because of their "faculty." "Activity is the name I give to the active change or motion, and the cause of this I call a faculty," as Galen says early in *On the Natural Faculties.* Thus no need for microscopes (which, of course, did not exist). For Galen, "faculty" performs or stands for the functions of Aristotle's four causes: material, efficient, formal, and final. All of these are necessary, and an understanding of each contributes to our total understanding of how Galen uses his own term *faculty* to avoid a need to further subdivide matter. Philosophically his system then parallels ours and is, I think, internally consistent.

In *On the Natural Faculties* Galen devotes much space, after a physical-biological-metaphysical section on genesis, growth, and nutrition, to his studies of urinary secretion in the kidneys and their connection to the bladder by the ureters; these he ligated separately and then together to show their true function in refutation of his opponents' theories. He also talks about the function of the spleen, which he says removes black bile from the blood normally, and whose malfunction results in toxemia and jaundice. He illuminates his scientific principles, such as attraction and repulsion, retention and expulsion, with the imaginative use of metaphors such as the bellows, the lodestone, and, in a particularly vivid passage, the stomach as a great cooking cauldron surrounded by viscera "like a lot of burning hearths around a great cauldron—to the right the liver, to the left the spleen, the heart above," all in the service of digestion and assimilation of food.

He compares blood supply with a garden irrigation system as follows: "This you can observe most clearly in connection with garden conduits. For a certain amount of moisture is distributed from these into every part lying close at hand but it cannot reach those lying farther off: therefore one has to arrange the flow of water into all parts of the garden by cutting a number of small channels leading from the large one. The intervening spaces between these small channels are made of such a size as will, presumably, best allow them [the spaces] to satisfy their needs by drawing from the liquid which flows to them from every side. So also is it in the bodies of animals. Numerous conduits distributed through the various limbs bring them pure blood, much like the garden water-supply, and, further, the intervals between these conduits have been wonderfully arranged by Nature from the outset so that the intervening parts should be plentifully provided for when absorbing blood, and that they should never be deluged by a quantity of superfluous fluid running in at unsuitable times." This sounds like modern hydrostatics at first, until one recalls that, for Galen, the need and the purpose of blood supply are determined by "faculty," not modern physics in any sense. Nature is an artist, he repeatedly says.

In fact, the whole book is a marvelously interesting example of scientific principles and experimental data coupled with real insight, imagination, and a deep desire for philosophical unity and logical coherence. We emerge from a reading of *On the Natural Faculties* with respect for Galen, as well as with a feeling that his verbosity overclouds his presentation in places.

Yet we are always sympathetic with his aims, and should be entertained by his wit—even in his most sarcastic polemics. For example, he says "Thus Lycus is speaking neither good Erasistratism, nor good Asclepiadism, far less good Hippocratism. He is, therefore, as the saying is, like a white crow, which cannot mix with the genuine crows owing to its colour, nor with the pigeons owing to its size."

In conclusion, it is possible to comprehend the contradictory picture of this great man in the history of medicine as seen through his biographers and his own writings. They applaud his immense learning, intelligence, facility of expression, and hard work. They feel that his system, though founded as much upon brilliant speculation as upon facts, carried ancient medicine to the highest point which it reached. After him, with a very few exceptions, began a gradual decline during which Galen's works became more firmly entrenched and widely disseminated through compilations made by Byzantine medical scholars, then by assimilation into the Mohammedan world, and eventually through a return to the West, where the teachings of both Galen and Aristotle from the eleventh century onward assumed a position of supreme authority. After 1453, when Constantinople fell to the Turks, the Renaissance and rediscovery of the Greek classics occurred and the Arabic scholastic versions of Galen were confronted with the originals in Greek, making possible, for example, a London publication of *On the Natural Faculties* in Latin by Thomas Linacre, a medical humanist of the period. This period in turn produced two parties, the Arabists and the Greeks, among medical men, and the real beginning of the so-called collapse of Galenic medicine began with the symbolic burning of the Galenic works by Paracelsus in the first half of the sixteenth century, when Galen, so long regarded as the father of medicine, came to be thought of as its fool.

Why it was that Galen's great contribution, namely that of being a guide along the way of experimental research toward a deeper understanding of nature, remained so long ignored, while his dogmatic authority was taken "ex cathedra," remains an irony of history. The question, it seems to me, is not to be idly dismissed, as is done by some of his biographers, but rather considered quite soberly by each reader of Galen who is concerned with what he has to say to us today.

Comment on the preceding

I found considerable light thrown on my final question by Dr. Temkin's 1973 book, previously cited, which considers, as he says, "Galenism as a general intellectual phenomenon restricted to neither medicine nor philosophy, to neither one nation nor one culture," while of course my paper was restricted to the physiology. At the same time, it is hard to separate Galen's philosophy from his medical pursuits, as Dr. Temkin agrees, and so my query as to why his encouragement to investigative work did not survive or outlast the fact that his authority was taken dogmatically and "ex cathedra" is still relevant.

It would have been my earlier view that as Aristotle and Christ have suffered from their dogmatic followers, so also has Galen. As George Sarton put it in *Galen of Pergamon* (1954), "we may perhaps conclude that Galen was in medicine as well as in philosophy an eclectic dogmatist. This may seem a contradiction in terms, but it symbolizes the ambiguity of his attitude. He often expressed doubts in a dogmatic way; he did not indulge in dogmas but unfortunately his own assertions were often accepted as such."

This seemed to me interesting as it illustrates the crucial function of our understanding of the word *dogma.* We use that term variously to mean asserting opinions in an arrogant manner, a body of belief, a system of philosophy based upon reason alone (as opposed to Skepticism), and in science a situation where theories, principles, and laws are embalmed in texts, no longer investigated, and (some would say) thus no longer science. Save in theological circles, we almost invariably use the word *dogma* pejoratively. I suggest that we also use it when we don't understand what's being said, the definitions of words escape us, and the context is forgotten. This obviously results in not following arguments well. I assumed that was what happened to Galen, after his death and well on into the medieval period. And indeed I think it even more true of our reading of Galen now than I did then. We have not the familiarity with Aristotle, his four causes, his *Physics* and *Metaphysics* that much of Galen presupposes. We lack, in short, his context, his view of the world.

Not being modern writers of science, both Aristotle and Galen make assertions, often, I think, to cover doubts. It is a mistake to take this as dogmatism; I think it more a matter of style. I gather both men were positively consumed with curiosity and assumed their readers were too and would investigate. That *they* did is shown in their writings and in the sudden and sometimes startling way their names crop up in widely separated fields, such as "Aristotle's lantern" for the mouth parts of the sea urchin and "the great vein of Galen" in human anatomy still. They even watched play, as Galen says in *On the Natural Faculties,* in which

> children take the bladders of pigs, fill them with air, and then rub them on ashes near the fire, so as to warm, but not to injure them. This is a common game in the district of Ionia, and among not a few other nations. As they rub, they sing songs, to a certain measure, time, and rhythm, and all their words are an exhortation to the bladder to increase in size. When it appears to them fairly well distended, they again blow air into it and expand it further; then they rub it again. This they do several times, until the bladder seems to them to have become large enough. Now, clearly, in these doings of the children, the more the interior cavity of the bladder increases in size, the thinner, necessarily, does its substance become. But, if the children were able to bring nourishment to this thin part, then they would make the bladder big in the same way that Nature does. As it is, however, they cannot do what Nature does, for to imitate this is beyond the power not only of children, but of any one soever; it is a property of Nature alone.

I had also thought that only literal-minded followers of Galen—bothered by doubts, unhappy with any degree of uncertainty, and certainly not curious investigators themselves—would resolve ambiguity into dogma and thus enthrone his pronouncements. I realized that they had, unfortunately, done that and had rigidified "Metaphysics" into a caricature of itself while distorting the scientific truths discovered by Aristotle and Galen to a point where they had to be rediscovered a thousand years or more later. In a simpleminded way myself, I thought they had thus created stereotypes of Aristotle and Galen, which undeservedly still survive when we think of both figures in medicine today.

Dr. Temkin's account of the rise and decline of Galenism is, however, more complicated and really more interesting. I refer you to the whole book for the whole story but would like to cite some particularly interesting insights that Temkin has derived. Within Galenic medicine, let it be recalled, there are four of each of the following: elements (fire, air, earth, and water); qualities (hot, cold, dry, and moist); humors (blood, phlegm, yellow bile, and black bile). Now we find a good example of the mixed and subtle relationship between Aristotle, Hippocrates, and Galen (as they were seen in the Medieval period) occurring in the manner in which blood, phlegm, yellow bile, and black bile came to constitute the four classical temperaments: sanguine, phlegmatic, choleric, and melancholic. Today used as psychologic types, they were then both psychic and somatic. In point of fact, the doctrine of the four humors was not Galenic but Hippocratic. However, the emphasis on these four humors as "the Hippocratic humors," the linking of them with what really were the Aristotelian qualities (hot, cold, dry, moist) and with the tissues of the body was largely Galenic. Temkin feels that "the completed doctrine of the four temperaments is an example of the adoption of Hippocratic notions to medieval systemization, the whole being Galenic in a vague sense." Indeed, the system became remarkably numerological with medicine having two parts, theoretical and practical. Moreover, the theoretical had three divisions: the study of things natural (basic science, in our terms), things nonnatural (hygiene), and things *contra* natural (pathology). And there are seven natural things: elements, temperaments, humors, the parts of the body, faculties, functions, and spirits.

The whole system seems a tower worthy of Dante's vision of the Mount of Purgatory as one contemplates four elements, four qualities, four humors, four principal parts (brain, heart, liver, and testes—together with their parts as well as faculties), four temperaments (which became nine when mixed, with one for "normal"), and so on, numbering, subdividing, and making distinctions. And it is easy to mock all this, though hardly fair to Galen, who did not so structure himself, but who was thus carved and trussed by later simplifiers and popularizers.

Strengths of the Galenic system might be said to include Galen's tendency to generalize, which Temkin feels insulated it from an attack that might have come as early as the third century had the system included more experiments, which could have quickly been superseded. There too, the mere structure of medieval Galenism gave physicians and patients comfortable roles and separated the doctors from the quacks, giving confidence and probably status to both patient and physician (something like a medical guild or modern medical society is brought to mind).

Galenism provided medical categories for relating the individual to health and disease, Dr. Temkin feels. So enduring has it been, he suggests, that "in the West arabized Galenism did not disappear all at once, in the East it did not disappear at all. Even today ancient Greek Medicine in its Arabic modification is still taught and practiced in Islamic countries." I would add to this that Galenism gave medicine a philosophy and an intellectual unity which it sadly lacked in the West until the new scientific medicine really got going around 1870. One wonders what an Islamic comment on our relatively recent recovery of this unity might be? Other commentators seem to agree that Galen's statement of high aims and ideals for his profession was his greatest contribution and his own greatest strength. It certainly made it hard for his detractors and adversaries to dislodge him and his system.

On the other hand, Galen's very devotion to truth opened the way to the challenges and opposition which finally brought his whole system down. This was not sudden nor was there a single cause. Among several causes was the questioning by Paracelsus in the fifteenth century of the moral, religious, and scientific validity of medieval Galenism, which had the effect of splitting East from West and creating two medical camps. Dr. Temkin and other historians make plain the analogy with Luther's effect within the Catholic Church. Western Galenism became something different from the Judeo-Arabic-Christian unity it had been.

Another cause was the acceptance of autopsy, which opened the way for the anatomical revolution of the Renaissance. This was a bigger step than just replacing monkey anatomy with human; it placed direct observation where speculation had been. Social splits within the profession between the new barber surgeons, such as Ambroise Paré, the apothecaries in England, and the traditional Galenists, appeared. Intellectually, Harvey moved from the Galenic position only gradually while, as an experimentalist, as we all know, he made Galen's physiology obsolete by demonstrating the circulation of the blood. This allowed the use of the expression "cardiovascular system," which, interestingly enough, Temkin and others think would have been inappropriate for Galen. He was more "ad hoc," saw problems of respiration, digestion, heart function, pulse (about which he was particularly elaborate and intricate in his books, as I've discovered), nerve conduction, body warmth, and purposeful behavior as questions that needed to be solved as they arose. Again, this reminds me of how differently Galen and his contemporaries looked at the world from the way we do. In Temkin's words, "for the ancient pagan, agnostic or not, air, pneuma, warmth, etc., were associated with traditional images which they do not have for us, who are wont to think in physical terms without religious or animistic associations. The distinction between animate and inaminate nature, so obvious and commonplace to us, was not as clearly drawn in antiquity. Galenic anatomy and physiology must not be seen merely in the context of modern anatomy and physiology, but in the context of ancient medicine, philosophy, religion, and feeling for nature." In such terms there was no need for an idea such as "the cardiovascular system."

Also interesting as yet another factor shaking the Galenic system was the introduction of the clinical thermometer, which, ironically, was introduced to strengthen rather than to weaken that system. For Galen hot and cold were qualities, as we have seen, but were not quantified. "The metamorphosis of objective qualities into subjective qualities was as destructive to Galenic science as doing away with fire, air, water, and earth as chemical elements," Temkin says. We must recall that for Galen hot and cold, dry and moist were meant to have objective existence. For us it is the degrees on the thermometer that are "objective." Thus has modern science come between us and our understanding of ancient science. It has changed the very definitions of words. Temkin points out that this "mechanization of qualities" in post-Galenic medicine was directed more at Aristotle's physics than at Galen, but, though their systems differed, the two men went down together in the face of the scientific revolution's challenge. Aristotle survived on the strength of his position in philosophy, not in medicine, whereas Galen did not, though again his decline was so gradual that it took more than two hundred years—from about 1600 to the early part of the nineteenth century—to complete itself. All sorts of attempts were made to revive Galenism right up to the end, and he has proved to be, as someone said, "a lively ghost."

All the great innovators were most respectful of Galen's influence and reputation. William Harvey refers to him—not ironically, judging by the context—as "the divine Galen" early in *On the Motion of the Heart and Blood in Animals,* and later as "that great man, that father of physicians." Harvey, who uses ligatures in his experiments as we have seen Galen do, says in *On the Circulation of Blood,* "the circulation of the blood does not shake, but much rather confirms the ancient medicine; though it runs counter to the physiology of physicians, and their speculations upon natural subjects, and opposes the anatomical doctrine of the use and action of the heart and lungs, and the rest of the viscera," and obviously wants to placate Galen without appearing argumentative when he says, in the introduction to *On the Generation of Animals,* "And now I seem to hear Galen admonishing us, that we should but agree about the things, and not dispute greatly about the words."[3] Incidentally, the last statement was written after Harvey, having lost his royal patron, King Charles I, had himself survived the English Civil War at Oxford doing the embryology of the chick. He was by then an old man who had long since seen his physiology displace much of Galen's, but he was still respectful of Galen, as the words show.

Andreas Vesalius, the great anatomist and author of *De humani corporis fabrica libri septem,* the *Epitome,* as well as the *Tabulae Sex,* was initially, a century before Harvey, just as respectful of Galen. As a student Vesalius wrote: "As the gods love me, I, who yield to none in my devotion and reverence for Galen, neither can nor should enjoy any greater pleasure than praising him." He was never to oppose himself completely to the Galenic System but rather attempted to reconcile or correct the anatomical descriptions of Galen whenever they were found not to agree with direct observation, dissection at autopsy, or surgery. It is true that he later could say, "I hear that many are hostile to me because I have held in contempt the authority of Galen, the prince of physicians and preceptor of all; because I have not indiscriminately accepted all his opinions; and, in short, because I have demonstrated that some fault is actually discernible in his books. Surely, scant justice to me and to our studies, and, indeed, to our generation!"[4]

It is hard not to read this, with psychological overtones so obviously present, as a statement about the profound ambivalence present when youth replaces or disagrees with age. Yet, though that may be true, I fear such an observation, which smacks more of our psychologically inclined times than the entirely different, more philosophically inclined era in which these admirable men lived and worked. Such a remark seems out of context in every way. It also ignores the courage it must have taken to question authority, speak one's mind openly, and, above all, assert the right to free enquiry and experimentation—all in a time in which, after all, Michael Servetus, another physiologist as well as theologian, was burned at the stake for assuming them. We forget the long struggles and the penalties incurred in making such assumptions of rights in the face of deeply established tradition.

One pays a price for raising doubt about "authority" being right. One can destroy more than should be destroyed, as I think Harvey, in his cautious gentle statements, makes clear he for his part realized. Vesalius too wants to keep the best of Galen.

To return to a point I made earlier, if heresy be considered a legitimate raising of doubt against dogma, one way to resolve the doubt is to snuff out the source—as if that will restore certainty. It all seems to boil down to human beings' dislike of uncertainty and ambiguity, to like firm ground to stand on, even if it's the wrong ground.

Or again, to put the matter simply as I see it, Galen made some anatomical errors and failed to discern some physiological principles, perhaps because, as some have said in the case of the circulation of the blood, he lacked the pump metaphor for the heart. Fifteen hundred years later, in the process of correcting the errors in empirical fact, as we saw Vesalius doing, the trickle of doubt began to undermine the whole Galenic philosophic/medical system, as a dam once built on rock can become silted up and end on sand, with slowly widening leaks. With Harvey's reluctant help, the leaks became a wide breach. The resultant flood became the end of much more than error. It destroyed the comprehension of the system, its admirable aims, its idealism, and its truths.

The pride of the scientific revolution was that it replaced dogma with experiment. I think, rather, that in this it rediscovered much of what Galen had already known and taught.

Toward a philosophy of medicine

I have tried in the preceding to discuss Galen directly, using one of his most general, most wide ranging, and most illustrative books as a source of his ideas. I chose to focus on his physiological ideas, as they interest me particularly. One should thank the translators, the interpreters, and the immense effort made by scholars for giving one this direct access to the works of the great figures in medical history, but it is up to us, I think, to read the authors' words ourselves. Much is lost both by translation and by interpretation, of course. Most of us, not being linguists, must rely on translation, but we can reduce interpretive distortion of the sort one finds in many textbook histories of medicine, which all too often begin by patronizing or even belittling Aristotle and Galen. Aesculapius and Hippocrates, as misty, vague figures, about whom little is really known, fare much better. One gathers that it is more fortunate to be either a god or a clinical prognosticator than to be a philosopher or a physician with philosophic interests, in the eyes of the textbook writers, or, at least, of many such. And, to my way of thinking, there is arrogance and not a little prejudice in thus distoring Aristotle's and Galen's legitimate position in the world of ideas. I think a lot of us misuse such terms as *metaphysics* and *philosophy* rather routinely, probably as a result of the late Medieval Galenic and Aristotelian caricatures, as noted earlier.

Perhaps we have reached the point at which to have a philosopher speak directly about a philosophy of medicine. There is some difficulty for me in doing this, because the example most to the point is my own father, whose *The Doctrine of Signatures,* subtitled "A Defence of Theory in Medicine," to which I have previously alluded, provides the argument I would wish to make. But I urge any reader of this essay to go when he is finished to a library and look up that wise if somewhat difficult book, in which will be found, among many other things, a defense of what seems to me a necessary principle in such a philosophy, which is the idea of the soul as Galen understood it. This is a matter (so to say) which I think Dr. Kass would understand too, notwithstanding that his has been a modern scientific training. I like to think he also would follow *The Doctrine of Signatures* in saying that whatever Galen did not know, he knew what modern medicine refuses to believe, which is that it cannot do without such a conception as that of the soul. Not necessarily the full metaphysical notion, but something not much different either, of which Galen at least was not afraid. And at any rate such a conception, as Buchanan observes, and as I perceive myself, is fundamental in Galenic medicine.

It is true, Buchanan's account tells us, Galen speaks only of the rational form of the body as a soul and relegates the vegetable and animal souls of the Greek tradition to the category of natural faculties. But, Buchanan goes on to say, "whatever the terminological preferences may be, it is clear that Galen is following his determinism to its logical conclusion, which, with the admission that human knowledge is always incomplete, would allow him to say with Scotus Erigena, we know that there is a soul, but we do not know what it is, or with other medievals, that we know what the soul is like, to wit, the form of an organ, but we do not know just what it is in the individual body. It is in this context, with one eye on metaphysics and the other on the future of medicine, that we can say that the soul is the proper subject-matter of the medical sciences, and that all present medical science is, without knowing it, studying the human soul."

Buchanan's own argument takes off from this point. Admitting that the metaphysical notion of the soul is a perilous one for the medical theorist to assume, he asserts that "the metaphysical statement does, nevertheless, provide a regulative principle which guides the analysis and formulation of natural processes, just as the soul itself is said to preside over these processes. Its acceptance by the scientist would mean that he agrees with himself to follow rational procedure where it takes him. . . ." And as if to remind the reader that times have not really changed much since 1938, when *The Doctrine of Signatures* appeared, it goes on to say that "the troublesome material in medicine at present is parted between the specialists, is first called functional, as opposed to organic, and is then investigated as neurogenic or psychogenic by the corresponding specialist. It is impossible for the empirical medical man to deny its existence, but it is equally impossible for him to extend his scientific knowledge or principles to cover it without endangering the more solid basis from which he as a scientist starts. The principles of Galen's physiology apparently do not suffer confusion from such an extension. The recognition of the existence of the soul, in fact, demands the recognition of all that goes on in the body, and offers the notion of the body as artist as an intermediary regulative principle for the assimilation of questionable data."

It is this notion of the body as an artist, following the idea that Nature itself is an artist, that is really the essence of Galenism, I think, and it is a measure of how remote we are from much of the greatest speculative thought in the Western tradition that such a notion seems quaint, if not ridiculous, to us. Yet all other theories—of genetic determination, conditioned reflex, or similarly automatic operation—can only beg the question as accounts of the whole organism and are in fact seldom resorted to for that purpose, since hardly any medical theorist even tries nowadays to explain the whole organism, a subject which has therefore been taken up by nonprofessionals in our society, to the scorn of most of the medical establishment. The heart of the matter is that, in Galen's terms, the body "knows" what it is and how to be what it is, and the task of medicine is thus to grasp this "knowledge" and assist in the face of the myriad things that can and do go wrong. But this is perhaps easier for a psychiatrist to accept than for other sorts of medical practitioners.

At any rate, Galen's work, hard as it may be to reconcile with modern medical perceptions, can serve to show why our determinedly nonphilosophical, marvelously elaborate accumulation of empirical findings leads to the kind of problems that Drs. Kass and Ingelfinger examined in these pages five years ago. In Scott Buchanan's own words, "modern empirical science is frustrated science, and its present dogmatic aversion to metaphysics is but a sign of an internal blindness that threatens the value of basic research and practice. I have emphasized the rational and the teleological aspect of Galen's medical theory, not merely because that is Galen's main emphasis, but because he becomes most crucially important for us when he speaks on these matters. We have learned his curiosity and accuracy in empirical investigations well enough so that we can criticize and correct him there, but we have mistakenly supposed we therefore had the right and duty to ignore him in other matters. I should like to be equally emphatic on the wholeness of his doctrine.

"It is a simple fact, but almost universally ignored in modern thought, that when one loses sight of the end of one's thought and action, the thought and action waver between fanaticism and futility. The good in itself which confers good on all the means that lead to it, if it is destroyed or ignored, destroys or obscures the goods of the means. There are analogous principles in all aspects of life and thought. If one loses the insight which lies at the basis of a science, the truths and certainties of that science are no longer attainable either by labour or thought. The highest activities are said to depend on lower activities, but it is even more true that the lowest become diseased and feeble if the higher activities are stopped or hindered.

"These statements mean that if final causes are not known, the lowest correlations will be meaningless. If the rational sciences are neglected, the empirical sciences will become black arts and their practices will be quackish. If the speculative, imaginative, and useful arts are confused, then the physiological functions will be disordered.

"If medicine is the science of the soul, it is enlightening to recognize that rational science is itself the most important medicine of the soul, a medicine for medicine."

I would myself subscribe to all these remarks written almost half a century ago about the state of medicine as it then seemed to be, and which are equally applicable to the art as it now is. Indeed, the point that Scott Buchanan makes here was made by Daremberg himself, the great nineteenth-century French translator of Galen, who said, with respect to the scientific revolution of the Renaissance, that "this substitution (examination for authority), excellent in itself, but often unintelligent and too precipitous, has condemned the modern generation to reconstruct almost the whole edifice of science." Such a reconstruction was what *The Doctrine of Signatures* was calling for in its day, and the job still remains to be done.

Conclusion

It appears that the study of the history of medicine almost invariably whets one's philosophic concerns. I think it also inspires one, as I think the preceding selection from Scott Buchanan's book demonstrates. It restores the past to the present and puts present problems in perspective and often presents answers. It would be an excellent antidote to overspecialization and would help restore idealism to both medical students and practitioners, if small group seminar discussion based on common reading of some of the great books in the medical tradition was encouraged.

At the same time, I think we have to be very careful lest a return to the medical humanities does not become too superficial and too much "belletristic" in emphasis. Much as I admire Sir William Osler, for example, I can never understand his great admiration, in his essays, for Sir Thomas Browne's little book, *Religio Medici.*[5] There are, surely, wiser and more evocative books to recommend to students and one's fellow physicians. I would propose William Harvey, Claude Bernard, and Valery-Radot's *Life of Pasteur,* after group discussion of the Oath of Hippocrates and its implications.

I hope that it is true, as the prospectus for *The Journal of Medicine and Philosophy* stated in 1976, that "not since Galen's time has the contact between medicine and philosophy been so widespread." There has been a real revival of interest in medical ethics of recent years, as the range and depth of moral dilemmas facing all doctors increase. The problems posed to the profession increase almost exponentially with innovations in technology, on the one hand, and disastrous legal suits, on the other, are threatening. Everything conspires, it often feels, to make it hard to have the time in which to think objectively, for example, about "the public's right to know" and other legitimate issues bearing on the interface between medicine and law. The profession seems to me to be on the defensive more than it need be.

There is no need here to further list problems, with which we are all only too familiar. I do not wish to pretend to know the answers, but I do think there are reasons for hope, some of which have been given already in these reflections on Galen and Galenism. His example points out the importance of reformulating a final cause for the profession, "the big design," what I myself, with considerable temerity, would call the "soul" of the profession, in analogy to the individual's soul.

In short we need purpose and heightened respect for reflective thought. Aimless research, a biology without design or purpose, and an almost doctrinaire invoking of slogans such as "freedom of research" or "pluralistic society" are simply not good enough. "The sleep of Reason begets monsters," as Goya's famous drawing says. It seems to me that the spectre of what happened in physics with nuclear energy should be a clear warning against "just doing it because it can be done." Nature is worthy of more respect.

Obviously it will take a strong effort of the will, careful use of language, and, above all, enough imagination to reintroduce notions like "purpose" or "soul" into medical research and practice. We have such an understandable set of aversive reactions to them, based on their past narrow religious and social connotations, that we forget they are philosophically respectable. (We flinch at their use almost as much as we shudder instinctively when we read of the pain inflicted on animals by Galen's spinal nerve experiment, forgetting that "in vivo" animal experimentation under anesthesia has only been possible for the last century and a half.) We might also remember a sturdier group of men like T. H. Huxley, Bernard, and Pasteur, who openly used the word *truth* in public scientific disputes in the nineteenth century and did not eschew or ignore "nature" or "soul" either, as we do. We are embarrassed by these words but, at our worst, we then proceed to talk about "devotion to truth, dedication, sacrifice," and so forth which "is really cant." More importantly, attention to design, purpose, and soul in biology and medicine will enable us to connect intellectually with ecology, with which concept I think it is obvious that Galen agreed and which he probably helped formulate, judging from his texts, as I have tried to show. In addition to the well-known ecological tenets of harmony between man, animals, plants, and nature, there seem to be a physiological, metaphorical idea of self-regulation, "feedback loops," and homeostasis in the ecological picture of balance in nature. Insofar as we have a philosophy of medicine at present, these ideas are part of it. It is almost as if Galen and Claude Bernard had joined hands, philosophically speaking, over the ages and had pointed the way toward a larger importance for ecology in medicine.

There are signs that this is happening already, especially in the way the public views medicine and asks dialectical questions about the state of the art by questioning the actions of drugs and their side effects, the need for so many operations, why we doctors need so many tests to make diagnoses, our views on diet and on organic foods and vitamins, and now the pros and cons of home delivery of babies. Everything seems to indicate people want more natural and simpler, more direct medical care. We would do well to heed these ecological questions and use them as ideas prompting research. This, I think, is behind much of the talk in Grand Rounds across the country, especially in teaching hospitals, about so-called holistic medicine, which I personally think is less important and fruitful than ecology will prove to be.

Another sign of hope, albeit on the distant horizon so far, is the reintroduction of soul, in its purposeful sense, as Freud in German used it as "der seele," in psychoanalysis. Bruno Bettelheim, in his recent New Yorker article "Freud and the Soul" (March 1, 1982), now a book, makes it clear why mistranslation, as "psyche," into English of this word misled a generation of American and British analysts and psychiatrists into the impersonal connotations sometimes held of the word *psychoanalysis.* Freud, a great humanist and scholar, as well as physician, meant it to convey the whole humanistic tradition of "study of the soul," including of course the emotional overtones. This elucidation applies to "psychosomatics," I would like to point out, which is an increasingly important part of medical theory and practice. Surely, clarity in our use of language and definitions of terms will aid us in expressing the mutual interdependence of body and soul. Thus philosophy will aid the clinician, yet again, but I join my father in suspecting that the benefit will in the end be mutual.

Bibliography

S. M. Buchanan, *The Doctrine of Signatures* (London: K. Paul, Trench, Trubner & Co., 1938).

A. Castiglioni, *A History of Medicine*. 2nd ed., 1947.

R. G. Frank, Jr., *Harvey and the Oxford Physiologists* (Berkeley: University of California Press, 1980).

Galen, *On the Natural Faculties.* Translated by A. J. Brock, M. D. (Cambridge: Harvard University Press, Loeb Classical Library, 1963).

Galen, *On Anatomical Procedures.* Edited and translated by C. Singer (London: Oxford University Press, 1956).

Galen, *On Medical Experience.* Translated by R. Walzer (London: Oxford University Press, 1944). Details on Empirical Medical School in the form of a disputation between Galen's teacher, the Dogmatist Pelops, and the Empiricist Phillipos is an affirmation of the union of Empiricism and Theory that Galen stood for all his life.

F. H. Garrison, *History of Medicine.* 4th ed. (Philadelphia: W. B. Saunders, 1929, reprinted 1963).

F. B. Lund, M. D., *Greek Medicine* (New York: P. B. Hoeber, Inc., Clio Medica, 1936).

R. Major, *Classical Discriptions of Disease* (Springfield, Illinois: C. C. Thomas, 1945).

J. S. Prendergast, "The Background of Galen's Life and Activities," in *Proceedings of the Royal Society of Medicine,* March 5, 1930, pp. 1131-48.

G. Sarton, "The Time of Galen," chap. XVI in Vol. I, *From Homer to Omar Khayyam,* of *Introduction to the History of Science* (Baltimore: Williams & Wilkins Co., 1927).

G. Sarton, *Galen of Pergamon* (Lawrence: University of Kansas Press, 1954).

C. Singer, "Galen as a Modern," in *Proceedings of the Royal Society of Medicine,* XLII (1949): 563–70.

O. Temkin, *Galenism* (Ithaca, New York: Cornell University Press, 1973).

O. Temkin and C. L. Temkin, "Some Extracts from Galen's *Anatomical Procedures*," review in *Bull. Hist. Med.*, vol. 36 (1962), pp. 373-75.

A. Vesalius, *The Illustrations from the Works of Andreas Vesalius*, translated and annotated by J. B. de C. M. Saunders and C. D. O'Malley (Cleveland: World Pub. Co., 1950).

J. Walsh, *Papers on Galen.*

---

[1]See *GIT* 1978, p. 351.

[2]See *GBWW*, Vol. 12.

[3]See *GBWW*, Vol. 28.

[4]Quotations of Vesalius are from J. B. de C. M. Saunders and Charles D. O'Malley, *The Illustrations from the Works of Andreas Vesalius* (Cleveland: World Publishing Co., 1950).

[5]See *GIT* 1973.

Ptolemy, Copernicus, and Kepler

Owen Gingerich

Owen Gingerich is an astrophysicist at the Smithsonian Astrophysical Observatory in Cambridge, Massachusetts, and a professor of astronomy and the history of science at Harvard University. The author of both technical and popular writings on astronomy, he also teaches a science course for nonscientists at Harvard called *The Astronomical Perspective.*

As a researcher he has taken on projects from the recomputation of an ancient Babylonian mathematical table to the interpretation of stellar spectra. His special area of research has been the writings of Kepler and Copernicus, on which he has become a leading authority.

Professor Gingerich has written widely on astronomy and is coauthor of two models for the solar atmosphere, the first an attempt to take into account rocket and satellite observations of the sun. He coedited *A Source Book in Astronomy and Astrophysics, 1900–1975* and is at present working on the 20th-century volume in the *General History of Astronomy.* He has written articles for several journals and encyclopaedias and is well known as the editor of a collection off *Scientific American* articles called "New Frontiers in Astronomy." His article "The Aethereal Sky: Man's Search for a Plenum Universe" appeared in *The Great Ideas Today,* 1979.

A member of several astronomical associations, Professor Gingerich headed the U.S. delegation of the Committee of the International Astronomical Union at the triennial congress in Patras, Greece, in August of 1982. Recently he was elected vice president of the American Philosophical Society.

On the title page of the first edition of Copernicus's *On the Revolutions* appears this text, the equivalent of the modern publisher's dust jacket blurb:

> You have in this newly created and published book, diligent reader, the motions of the fixed stars and planets restored from both the old and new observations, and furthermore, furnished with new and wonderful hypotheses. You also have the most convenient tables from which you can with the greatest ease calculate their positions for any time. Therefore buy, read, and profit!

Fourteen centuries earlier, Claudius Ptolemy's publisher (if indeed there had been "publishers" in the ancient world) could have made an even stronger claim: With his tables you could *for the first time* calculate the positions of the planets for "any time."

To understand the relative contributions of Ptolemy, Copernicus, and Kepler (those authors who appear in Volume 16 of *GBWW*), we must appreciate the fact that each was tackling a fairly esoteric problem—how to find the positions of the heavenly bodies in the sky—and that each had a cosmological framework in which the problem was solved. I say a "fairly esoteric problem" because most people have rather little use for such specific information as to where Mars is to be found at a particular moment, and even less use for a position accurate within two minutes of arc, which was part of Kepler's great achievement.

Nevertheless there are subtle reasons why this quest has been important to mankind. The motions of the planets have a demonstrable, predictable regularity which raised the hope that other aspects of our world might also have underlying regularities, if only the secrets of nature could be teased from the seemingly capricious patterns of weather, catastrophe, or even human personality. In Ptolemy's day (the second century A.D.) there was the lure that the regularity of the stars was reflected in mundane events. Tycho Brahe, the renowned Danish observer and Kepler's sometime mentor, expressed it in the motto, *Suspiciendo despicio*—"By looking upwards, I see below." It was a false scent, to find in the clockwork of the stars the key to personal affairs, yet the knowledge of the planetary rhythms did unlock Newtonian physics and with it the fundamental understanding of the physical universe. The value of accurate planetary positions has come full circle: in their precision came an appreciation of elliptical orbits, then gravitation and planetary perturbations, and now the trajectories of spacecraft exploring the distant new worlds of the solar system—and requiring accuracies undreamed of by Ptolemy or Copernicus or even Kepler.

In the ancient world it was surely the astrological motivation that provided much of the impetus for Ptolemy's treatise and perhaps most of his financial support, just as it supported Kepler in the seventeenth century. But beyond that was the sheer intellectual curiosity that drove all of these men. In some of the manuscripts Ptolemy's treatise begins with a memorable epigram:

> I know that I am mortal by nature, and ephemeral; but when I trace at my pleasure the windings to and fro of the heavenly bodies I no longer touch earth with my feet: I stand in the presence of Zeus himself and take my fill of ambrosia, food of the gods.

Ptolemy's epoch-making book is generally called by its Arabic name, the *Almagest,* meaning literally "The Greatest." Written in Alexandria around A.D. 150, it is indeed the greatest surviving astronomical work from antiquity. What Ptolemy has done is to show for the first time in history (as far as we know) how to convert specific observational data into the numerical parameters for his planetary models, and with the models to construct some ingenious tables from which the solar, lunar, and planetary positions and eclipses can be calculated for any given time. Altogether it is a remarkable achievement, combining in a brilliant synthesis a treatise on theoretical astronomy with a practical handbook for the computation of ephemerides.

Ptolemy accomplished his task within the cosmological framework almost universally accepted in his day, the Earth-centered or geocentric world view. As a consequence of the revolutionary work of Copernicus and Kepler, of Galileo and Newton, the geocentric Ptolemaic system has by now been tossed into the trashcan of discarded theories. Euclid's *Elements,* with its logically ordered series of geometrical proofs, is still honored as a timeless classic, but why should we take time to consider the *Almagest?* Because, more than any other book, it demonstrated that natural phenomena, complex in their appearance, could be described by relatively simple underlying regularities in a mathematical fashion that allowed for specific quantitative predictions.

Ptolemy admits at the outset that it might perhaps be simpler, from a strictly celestial viewpoint, to have the Earth spinning daily on its axis rather than the entire heavens rotating about the Earth. But this, he says, fails to take into account the terrestrial physics: if the Earth moved, "animals and other weights would be left hanging in the air, and the Earth would very quickly fall out of the heavens. Merely to conceive such things makes them appear ridiculous." (*GBWW,* Vol. 16, p. 11). And so, after only a few pages devoted to his cosmological assumptions, Ptolemy marches on to the "practical" matter of a mathematical description of the heavens. Ptolemy's model is Euclid, and even the Greek title of his volume, *Syntaxis* or "Mathematical Treatise," reflects his desire to give a tidy geometrical and numerical account of his subject. As such, it must be considered more as a masterful pedagogical textbook than as an account of discovery.

Ptolemy's attempt to write the astronomical equivalent of Euclid's geometry was all too successful: nobody bothered to copy any competing treatises that might have been available, leaving us with the *Almagest* and rather little else for reconstructing how Ptolemy might have arrived at the main structures of his system. And in retrospect it has become increasingly obvious that in writing his textbook, he has imposed a logical order on the material that is markedly different from the one he actually used to arrive at his conclusions. This in turn has today embroiled Ptolemy in such a heated controversy that one critic has recently called him "the greatest fraud in the history of science."

Despite objections that have been raised against Ptolemy in the past few centuries, it is clear that his work did, in fact, provide the fundamental text for well over a millennium, and it served as the model for Copernicus's *On the Revolutions* in 1543. For better or for worse, Copernicus followed Ptolemy's pattern so well that historians of science learn rather little from Copernicus's book as to why he arrived at the principal features of *his* system, that is, the Sun-centered or heliocentric cosmology. It is not true, as many secondary accounts would have us believe, that the Ptolemaic system was by then falling apart from complex additions that it had accrued, or that it was hopelessly failing to predict the celestial phenomena. By Kepler's standards the tables of both the *Almagest* and *On the Revolutions* were embarrassingly deficient, but the fact of the matter is that in the sixteenth century there was astonishingly little information for choosing between them as far as accuracy was concerned. Copernicus had tried to effect a *cosmological* revolution without really raising the standards of prediction; his was a vision of the mind's eye, not the revolt of an observer with his quadrant or armillary sphere.

In contrast to Ptolemy or Copernicus, Kepler gives us an abundance of autobiographical detail. Thereby we can reconstruct his progress in the reform of astronomy, a prodigious feat in which he raised the accuracy of prediction (take Mars, for instance) from several degrees to within a few minutes of arc, that is to say, from ten times the diameter of the Moon to near the limit of naked-eye astronomy. This magisterial accomplishment was profusely described in his *Astronomia nova* of 1609. Seldom was a scientific treatise better named. The "New Astronomy" broke with two millennia of tradition (a) by introducing elliptical orbits to replace the time-honored combination of uniform circular motions, (b) by showing how to extract intricate details from vast quantities of conflicting observations, and (c) by arguing from physical principles in a way both novel and foreign to astronomical expectations. Kepler's greatest work, the *New Astronomy* is simultaneously a formidably mathematical and exasperatingly obscure book and was therefore with some reason omitted from the *Great Books.* It is easier to get the flavor of Kepler at work from his later *Harmonice mundi* (1619), the "Harmonies of the World," in which he stumbled across his important "harmonic law" and his *Epitome of Copernican Astronomy* (1618–21) in which are given the final and far-better-digested results. Selections from both are found in *GBWW,* Volume 16. Nevertheless, there are several quite accessible portions of the *New Astronomy* that show Kepler forging his new celestial physics, and these have been reproduced (mostly for the first time in English) later in this volume.

In the ensuing sections I shall attempt to lead the reader through the technical positional astronomy as well as the cosmology of these three pioneering astronomers, and for those who want to see how it is *really* done, I shall show how the tables in *GBWW,* Volume 16, can in fact be used to find a planetary position.

Ptolemy's invention

Ptolemy's goal is nothing less than the calculation of planetary positions at any time—past, present, or future. This differed in a major way from the received Babylonian astronomy, which attempted to find the time and place only of specific phenomena, such as the disappearance of a planet in the Sun's rays, its reappearance, or its opposition to the Sun in the sky. To be precise, Ptolemy wanted to calculate the planetary positions with respect to the ecliptic, that is, the Sun's great circle route through the zodiac. (The ecliptic is the line along which lunar eclipses can take place, whence its name.) He wanted to specify the longitude measured eastward along the ecliptic, as well as the latitude, measured in degrees north or south of the ecliptic.

The *Almagest* describes Ptolemy's complete program. On the one hand it uses geometrical mechanisms, based in spirit on Euclid (and Apollonius), and on the other, specific numerical information, coming largely from the Babylonians (and in part transmitted via Hipparchus in the second century B.C.). For the latter, however, Ptolemy had no earlier example to govern his presentation. The origins of his geometrical models are as mysterious and perplexing as the origins of his numerical data. Nevertheless, we can attempt to reconstruct this unwritten background to his treatise.

Ptolemy's *Almagest* is divided into thirteen books, and he does not get to the critical planetary longitude tables until Book XI, nor the planetary latitude tables until the very end, so it is obvious that a considerable foundation must be laid into place before he reaches his goal. Yet it is unlikely that he started as systematically in his researches as his great textbook lays them out.

The problem at hand, already posed by Plato to his students, was finding some explanation for the windings to and fro of the planets. We can take as a prototype the behavior of Mars. This ruddy and not very bright planet moves eastward throughout the zodiacal signs for months on end, but then it slows, comes to a stop against the background stars, brightens, and, now quite conspicuous, moves westward for several weeks before stopping, fading, and finally resuming its direct motion. How could this retrograde motion be accounted for, particularly within the constraint of unending and repetitive circular motions?

In Plato's day his contemporary, Eudoxus, proposed a series of cleverly nested spheres for turning the planets. It was an admirable scheme; in fact, it was far more to be admired than used. Not only did it fail to reproduce the motions except in the most general way, but (because all the spheres were completely concentric to the Earth) there was no way for the planets to approach or recede, and hence no way to account for the changes in brightness.

Five centuries later, by the time of Ptolemy, the works of Euclid and Apollonius were at hand, and also a vast array of specific astronomical data from the Babylonians, who had been making crude but systematic observations since before 700 B.C. For example, the Babylonians knew that in seventy-nine years Mars made almost exactly forty-two complete revolutions through the zodiac, and that it moved 40 percent faster when it was in Capricorn than when it was opposite in the sky in Cancer. Furthermore, the astronomer Hipparchus had made some progress in representing the motion of the Sun and Moon by circles not centered exactly on the Earth. His tables sufficed to get the dates of eclipses. Presumably all these materials were readily available to Ptolemy in the great library at Alexandria.

The challenge facing Ptolemy was to find some geometric model that could reproduce not only the retrograde motion of Mars, but also its faster motion in the half of the sky toward Capricorn. The model needed to take into account the observation that the retrograde loops were about half as long when they were in Capricorn as when they were in Cancer. The task of building a geometric model to predict the detailed positions of Mars had defeated Hipparchus as well as Eudoxus before him, and by A.D. 135 could be considered the outstanding unsolved problem of astronomy.

In seeking a solution to the problem of planetary motion, Ptolemy had available a now-lost work of Apollonius of Perga (c. 200 B.C.). Apollonius had considered the problem of a secondary circle moving on a larger one—an epicycle on a deferent, as it came to be called in the Ptolemaic scheme—and this provided a suggestive clue. A point on the rim of the epicycle traced out a looped path swinging near and far from the center of

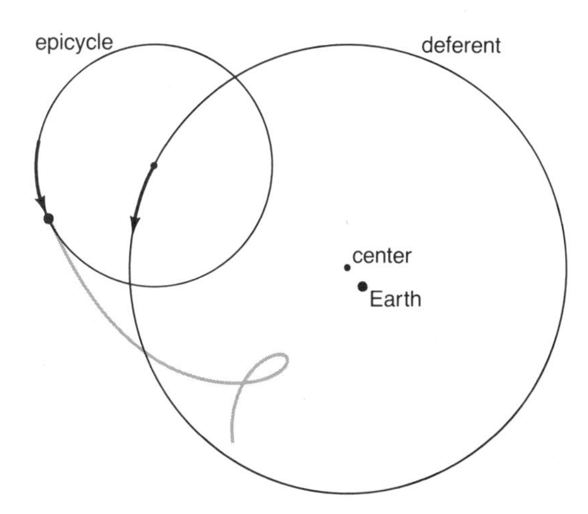

Figure 1. Retrograde motion generated by an epicycle.

the deferent, and moving in reverse (as seen from the center) each time it approached the center (figure 1). The problem was, could the model be made to represent the apparently irregular behavior of Mars while retaining uniform motions for both the deferent and epicycle?

Now the period of Mars to get around the entire sky was known pretty well from the Babylonians, as was the period between retrogressions. Hence Ptolemy could calculate the period of the uniform motion in longitude as well as the uniform motion of what is called the anomaly, in this case referring to the anomalous retrograde motions, to be represented in the model by the epicycle. In fact, Ptolemy tabulates both of these in terms of the motion per unit length of time in the *Almagest,* IX.4 (*GBWW,* Vol. 16, pp. 276–90). Armed with a theorem from Apollonius, he could decide how large the epicycle had to be with respect to the deferent to reproduce the average retrograde loop.

But the observations showed two troublesome details. As mentioned above, Mars appeared to move (after averaging out the effect of the retrogression) 40 percent faster on one side of the orbit compared with the other. Second, the retrograde loops themselves varied in size from one retrogression to another. How could Ptolemy produce the necessary variations in the loops as well as the variations in the speed of the center of the epicycle?

Here the previous work of Hipparchus provided the way. To get a nonuniform motion of the Sun, Hipparchus had placed the solar orbit eccentrically with respect to the Earth. The Sun, in moving along its deferent at uniform speed, actually appeared from the Earth to spend more time in the summer quadrant than in the winter one. The actual motion remained uniform, but the apparent motion matched the observed view from the Earth.

In order to account for the 40 percent faster speed of Mars on one extreme of the orbit compared to the other, the deferent circle could simply be placed eccentric by 20 percent, so that the planet would be 20 percent closer (and faster) than the average in one direction and 20 percent farther (and slower) than the average in the other direction. Alas! While representing the change of speed quite well enough, the computed size of the epicycle came out different at the two extremes; or alternatively, with the epicycle held at a constant size, the sizes of the retrograde loops were absurdly out of line with those observed.

How many solutions Ptolemy may have tried to overcome this dilemma we shall never know. Perhaps the epicycle could be made to expand and contract—not a very nice solution, but perhaps possible. Or another smaller epicycle might ride upon the first. We know, from the work of the Islamic astronomers of the fourteenth century that such a procedure is feasible.

Ptolemy found that he could solve the problem of the size of the retrograde loops simply by making the eccentricity 10 percent instead of 20 percent. This permitted a constant size to the epicycle and correctly varied the loops provided he retained their angular speeds. However, the previous solution to the nonuniform motion of the epicycle center was now spoiled, for the variation in speed about the mean was now ±10 percent, for a total of 20 percent, half the requisite amount, and not the amount he had assumed in his calculation. If only some way could be

Figure 2. Longitude of Mars according to Ptolemy.

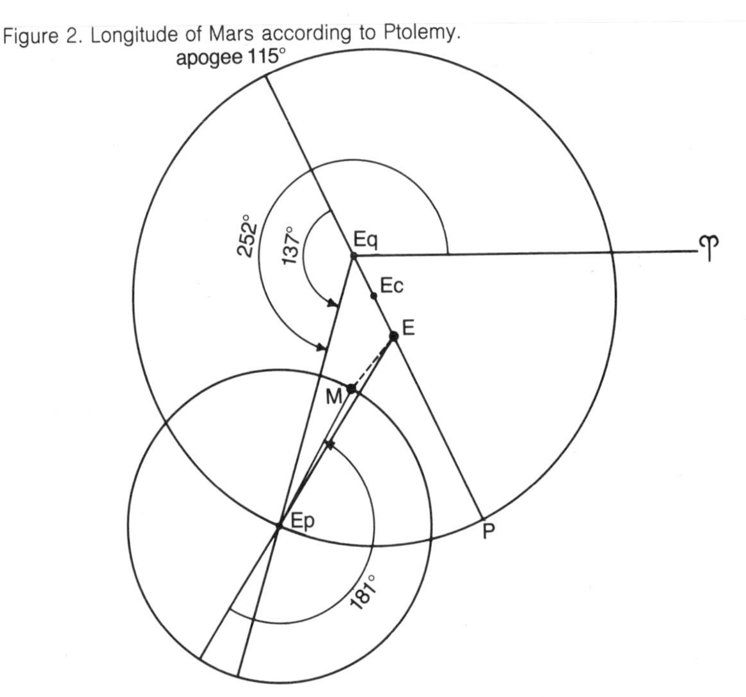

found to vary the actual speed of the epicycle center along the deferent without disturbing the distances, which were yielding the correct sizes! Here is where Ptolemy's solution turned out to be both elegant and unexpectedly accurate.

Ptolemy proposed to insert a seat of uniform angular motion for the epicycle's center at a point equal and opposite from the Earth along the line through the deferent center (figure 2). The arrangement, called an equant, splendidly solved this combination of problems, though it did violate the principle of uniform circular motion, because the motion of the epicycle center along the deferent was now smoothly *non*-uniform. As seen from the equant point, however, there was equal angular motion in equal times; that is, uniformity was preserved from this viewing point although not along the deferent itself.

The foregoing account makes Ptolemy's invention seem all too obvious. Yet we must remember that the observations at his disposal were incomplete and rough. Only for Mars are the effects large enough to show readily. As Kepler was to remark in a similar situation many centuries later, "for us to arrive at the secret knowledge of astronomy, it is absolutely necessary to use the motion of Mars; otherwise it would remain eternally hidden." [See *New Astronomy,* chap. 7, pp. 324–325, in this volume.]

But the *Almagest* is not an account of discovery; rather, it is a textbook, and as such it carefully hides the process of finding the eccentric-epicycle-equant model. In fact, it takes the planets in order, beginning with the awkward, overly complicated mechanism for Mercury, next Venus, whose eccentricity is too small to allow this effect ever to be discovered from the sort of observations Ptolemy had, and finally to the critical case of Mars.

Given the discovery of this model for Mars, Ptolemy must have immediately tried next to work it out in full detail. However, the motion of Mars's epicycle is closely connected with the motion of the Sun. Rather than backtrack to the solar theory, Ptolemy may have simply been content to use the Hipparchan model, which, after all, predicted the eclipses pretty well. To get the precise period of Mars required some knowledge of the solar theory and a long temporal baseline. In the *Almagest* Ptolemy uses a Babylonian observation from 272 B.C. together with those from his own day, around A.D. 135. This is more easily said than done, because the dates for the observations are on disparate calendars. The first is recorded in a Dionysian year with curious zodiacal months, and the others in Egyptian months in years taken with respect to the Emperors Hadrian and Antoninus. Thus, any deep analysis of Ptolemy requires a certain familiarity with chronology, a point that would later cost Copernicus much time before he could safely connect his own age with Ptolemy's.

It was one thing for Ptolemy to establish a successful theory of Mars and another to cast it in a form so that calculations could be made in a routine fashion. He proceeded along the following lines. First, consider the planet moving uniformly around its deferent. One can easily make a table of uniform motions, such as those already cited. What is needed next is to correct these mean motions on account of the eccentric placement of the deferent; this could be simultaneously combined with the effect of the equant. For Mars, these combined corrections can reach a maximum of nearly 11½°. Second, there must be a correction for the effect of the epicycle, the amount of which depends on the degree of rotation of the planet within the epicycle. For Mars, the epicycle can advance or retard the mean motion by something over 41°.

It is here that the real complications begin. If the epicycle is at its farthest point from the Earth, clearly its correction is going to be smaller than if the epicycle were closer. If we wish to tabulate these corrections for every degree, we would need 180 positions for the deferent (symmetry will duplicate the entries for 181° to 360°), and for each of them values for the 180 positions within the epicycle, or a grand double-entry table with 32,400 values! (Actually Ptolemy did not tabulate as closely as every degree.) Ptolemy very cleverly gets around such a double-entry table monster by a multiplicative combination of two single-entry tables, thereby using only 360 values instead of 32,400. His is one of the neatest tricks of practical mathematics from all of antiquity.

Those who do not wish to see in detail how the tables of the *Almagest* work should simply skip past the next section, in which I will show how the Ptolemaic theory can be used to find the longitude of a planet, specifically Mars. The date will be chosen in Ptolemy's system of Egyptian years. For those who wish to find the position of Mars for tomorrow (for example), it will be necessary to cope with Appendix A (*GBWW,* Vol. 16, pp. 466–68), which explains the chronological conversions into the Gregorian calendar. This may not be a fruitful exercise, however, because of the problems with Ptolemy's coordinate system, which I will mention in a subsequent section—problems that become amplified as time marches on.

The longitude of Mars—an example

As an example, we shall calculate the longitude of Mars used by Ptolemy in the *Almagest,* Book X, chapter 8. The longitude is measured eastward throughout the zodiac, beginning at the northbound intersection of the ecliptic and the equator. Ptolemy breaks the ecliptic into twelve 30° segments, each named for a sign of the zodiac. Thus, when he specifies as observation of Mars at "1⅗° within the Archer," we can use the handy table on p. 494 of *GBWW,* Vol. 16, to see that the Archer (Sagittarius) is the ninth zodiacal sign, making the longitude 241°36′. Ptolemy specifies that this observation was made in the second year of Antonine, in the

Egyptian month Epiphi, in the night of 15–16; with the tables on p. 467 of *GBWW*, Vol. 16, we can readily establish that Epiphi is the eleventh Egyptian month (so that 300 days have already elapsed in the year).

The base date or epoch for Ptolemy's tables is midday of the first day of the first month (Thoth 1) of the first year of the reign of King Nabonassar of Babylon. Hence the first task is to discover how much time has elapsed between the epoch and the date of the observation. This is facilitated by a King List provided elsewhere by Ptolemy and conveniently appended in *GBWW*, Vol. 16, p. 466. There it may be seen that

From Nabonassar to the death of Alexander	424 Egyptian years
From the death of Alexander to Antonine 1	460 Egyptian years
From Antonine 1 to Antonine 2	1 Egyptian year
	885 Egyptian years

We now wish to calculate the mean motion for Mars and its epicycle (the "anomaly") over this elapsed time, starting with the positions at the epoch. This is conveniently done by combining the numbers for the various intervals tabulated by Ptolemy in IX.4 (pp. 282–84). Mars moves about half a degree per day, or 191°16′54″ per year. In 810 years (the largest interval Ptolemy tabulates) Mars circumnavigates the sky 430 times with 138° left over, and of course it is only the remainder that is of interest in locating a later position. Note that because Ptolemy begins with Thoth 1 (rather than Thoth 0), it is necessary to take one day less than the day of the month to get the elapsed days; note also that since he specifies the observation as three hours before midnight, nine hours have elapsed since midday. The epoch positions are tabulated at the head of the tables.

	Longitude		Anomaly
At epoch	3°32′		327°13′
810 years	138°15′		24°49′
72 years	92°17′		250°12′
3 years	213°51′		145°26′
300 days	157°13′		138°28′
14 days	7°20′		6°28′
9 hours	0°12′		0°10′
Mean longitude	252°40′	Anomaly	172°46′

These results are obtained after taking out entire cycles of 360°. It is next necessary to establish where the mean longtitude has carried the epicycle center with respect to the apogee (see figure 2) of the planet. The apogee is, according to Ptolemy, fixed with the stars and therefore precessing with them at the rate of 1° per century. For the 885 years since the epoch, the precession amounts to 8°51′, a number that must be added to the specified apogee at epoch:

Apogee at epoch = Crab 16°40′ =	106°40′
Precession	8°51′
Apogee at date of observation	115°31′

We next wish to compute the eccentric anomaly or the "longitude from the eccentric's apogee," as Ptolemy calls it; this is found by differencing the mean longitude and the apogee:

Mean longitude	252°40′
Apogee	115°31′
Eccentric anomaly	137°09′

This value agrees well with the 137°11′ specified in X.8 (p. 339) and will be used in the correction tables in the next step.

For the remaining steps it is worthwhile to consult figure 2 in order to understand why the corrections are added or subtracted. The angles are exaggerated on the diagram for clarity. The Earth is at *E,* the center of the eccentric deferent at *Ec,* the equant at *Eq,* the perigee at *P,* the epicycle center at *Ep,* and the position of Mars at *M.*

The corrections or "prosthaphaereses" are translated as "addition-subtraction" in *GBWW* and are tabulated in XI.11 (p. 388). The first correction, for the equant and eccentric, is found in columns 3 and 4 combined. We enter with 137°09′ in column 1 and interpolate, noting that column 4 is in the negative range and needs to be subtracted from column 3. On the diagram, this correction is angle *EqEpE,* and its effect is to *decrease* the longitude, but to *increase* the angle in the anomaly, which needs to be measured from the line of sight to the Earth *E,* rather than the equant *Eq.* Hence:

Mean longtiude	252°40′	Anomaly	172°46′
$c_3 + c_4 =$	− 8°21′		+ 8°21′
Corrected longitude	244°19′	Corrected anomaly	181°07′

We now enter with the corrected anomaly to find from column 6 the correction for the movement within the epicycle, the angle *EpEM.* Because this observation was deliberately chosen by Ptolemy to be a few days after an opposition and within the retrogression, the value is near the bottom of the table where linear interpolation is not especially accurate but will suffice. Note from the diagram that this correction must decrease the angle and thus be subtracted.

$$
\begin{array}{rr}
 & 244°19' \\
c_6 = & -\ 2°10' \\
\hline
 & 242°09'
\end{array}
$$

The final correction adjusts for the fact that the epicycle is closer than its average position, and therefore an additional amount must be subtracted. This depends both on how much closer the epicycle is and on the position in the epicycle. The former part is given as a proportion with respect to 60 in column 8, whereas the latter part is given in column 5 if the epicycle is farther than the average position, or in column 7 if the epicycle is closer than the average, as in this case. We get the product of these corrections as follows:

$$
\begin{array}{lr}
c_8 \text{ (entering with } 137°09') & 37/60 \\
c_7 \text{ (entering with } 181°07') & \times\ 53' \\
\hline
 & 33'
\end{array}
$$

so that we can make the final correction, obtaining:

$$
\begin{array}{rr}
 & 242°09' \\
c_8 \times c_7 = & -\ 33' \\
\hline
\text{True longitude} & 241°36'
\end{array}
$$

This agrees exactly with the Ptolemy's value in the *Almagest* X.8.

Did Ptolemy cheat?

Disappointingly for the analyst of Ptolemy's achievement, the epicyclic model for the planets appears full grown in the *Almagest.* There are no hints as to what motivated its invention. Ptolemy simply gets on with the business of finding the required numerical parameters. They are

the ratio of the epicycle to the deferent,
the eccentricity of the orbit and equant,
the direction in which the equant-eccentric line lies,
the period of revolution in the deferent,
the period of revolution in the epicycle,
the position in the deferent for a given starting date, and
the position in the epicycle for a given starting date.

Thus Ptolemy requires altogether seven numbers to specify the model for longitude. Two of these parameters, the period of revolution and position in the epicycle, are connected to the solar theory, so that actually only five numbers are needed independently. In order to establish five parameters, it is necessary to have five observations, and for Mars these are given as follows:

				GBWW
Dionysius 13, Aigon 25	[272 BC Jan 18]	Sco	2° 1/4	p. 342
Hadrian 15, Tybi 26–27	[130 AD Dec 15]	Gem	21°	p. 324
Hadrian 19, Pharmouthi 6–7	[135 AD Feb 21]	Leo	28° 5/6	p. 324
Antonine 2, Epiphi 12–13	[139 AD May 29]	Sgr	2°34′	p. 324
Antonine 2, Epiphi 15–16	[139 AD May 30]	Sgr	1° 3/5	p. 339

It is instructive to recompute each of these from Ptolemy's tables; we have done it for one of them in the preceding section, and in carrying out the same procedure for the other four, we obtain an almost perfect match with the stated observations. However, when we use a modern computer to calculate where the planet really was on each of these occasions, we find the following discrepancies:

	Ptolemy	Modern	Difference
272 BC Jan 18	212°15′	212°31′	0°16′
130 AD Dec 15	81°	81°25′	25′
135 AD Feb 21	148°50′	150°15′	1°25′
139 AD May 29	242°34′	242°49′	15′
139 AD May 30	241°36′	241°55′	19′

In other words, although Ptolemy's stated observations are not particularly good and in one case err by more than a degree, they do match his tables in an uncanny way. In fact, this situation prevails throughout the entire *Almagest,* which leads to the suspicion that something is going on that does not meet the eye, something craftily concealed in the writing of the *Almagest.* Here we must remember, above all, that the *Almagest* is not like a modern research paper. It is a well-honed textbook, modeled as much as applicable on Euclid's *Elements.* It was no doubt Ptolemy's intention to present the procedures with sample data so that future astronomers could see how it was done and could introduce their own observations over a longer temporal baseline in order to derive even better parameters. For such a purpose he surely wanted to exhibit mutually consistent observations, the best he could find.

There are several ways that Ptolemy could have obtained such agreeable data. He could have taken five well-chosen observations and fit his parameters to them. Then necessarily the tables would yield back precisely these same five data points. I say "well-chosen" because the final parameters for his models turn out to be remarkably accurate, especially for Mars, and this would hardly be the case if he had picked his five observations more or less at random. Perhaps he used multiple observations and found the average of what seemed to be the most frequent solutions. (It boggles the mind to think how many graduate students he might have had sweating over the calculations!) Given a fairly stable solution based on a series of observations, he could then use his tables to choose which were the best observations. However, I am inclined to think that if he got this far, he may no longer have felt it necessary to find perfect observations, for he could simply have used his theory to judge how much observational error an observation contained, and he could then correct it accordingly. By modern standards, to do this without mentioning it would be considered reprehensible, but in the second century A.D. there were no models and no agreed-upon method for handling redundant data. Remember that any extra data beyond the minimum required were very likely to be self-contradictory on account of the inevitable errors of observation.

For at least a couple of centuries astronomers have been to some degree aware of this problem with Ptolemy's data, but they have generally swept it under the carpet. In recent years it has been rediscovered by the geophysicist R. R. Newton, who has reacted with such alarm that in his *The Crime of Claudius Ptolemy* he has written that it would have been better for astronomy if the *Almagest* had never been written. This judgement is so extreme as to be silly, but nevertheless it has reminded astronomers that the data in the *Almagest* cannot necessarily be taken at face value.

It is generally not, in fact, the task of historians of science to cast moral judgments or to brand a pioneer of the past as a criminal. Rather, it is to study the evolution of ideas, to try to reconstruct *how* and *why* particular ideas were presented in a particular way by a particular person at a particular time. Ptolemy, like astronomers of today, undoubtedly built his edifice on a great array of traditional materials, rejecting, adjusting, or incorporating them as he saw fit, and molding them into a new theoretical framework of geometric planetary models. To examine how these elements can blend together, we now return to the presentation of the *Almagest* itself, to see the difficulties that some of Ptolemy's borrowings have caused him and his successors.

The arrangement of the *Almagest*

The philosophical or cosmological assumptions are tersely stated at the outset of Book I, whereupon Ptolemy turns immediately to the mathematical preliminaries. For the Alexandrian astronomer, this means not only presenting a trignometrical table but explaining in full detail how to compute it. Ptolemy does not use our familiar sines and cosines, but the chord function, which is directly related to them. Following this, he must show how to solve for angles on the celestial sphere, no mean trick considering that spherical trigonometry as we know it had yet to be invented! Although Ptolemy uses the most advanced mathematics of the time, discovered in the preceding generation by Menelaus, the resulting procedures are certainly clumsy. The Menelaus theorem connects six quantities, and to solve for one unknown, the problem must be set up so that the other five are known. Nevertheless, it has been shown that all problems of spherical trigonometry can be solved by this technique.

Given the Menelaus theorem, what problem might require a solution? Ptolemy first picks a simple one: the relation between the equator, which slices the celestial sphere into two polar hemispheres, and the ecliptic, which is the great circle annual path of the Sun, tilted with respect to the equator by an amount called the obliquity of the ecliptic. Ptolemy wishes to relate the angular distance along the ecliptic to the distance of the ecliptic north or south of the equator. He sets up the problem by using the obliquity, the angular distance along the equator as well as its complement, and two other segments known to be right angles; with these five given, the unknown sixth can be calculated and tabulated.

The geometry is impeccable, but the wedding of abstract geometry with particular numerical values immediately poses a conundrum for connoisseurs and critics alike. How can the obliquity be determined? Presumably in a straightforward manner, by measuring the altitude of the Sun at noon when it is highest in the sky in summer, the Sun "standing" (= *sol stice*) at the top of the ecliptic, and then by repeating the measurement at the lowest point, the winter solstice. Ptolemy obligingly gives some details of setting up a calibrated brass circle, or an inscribed stone or wood block whose flat surface is oriented precisely in the north–south–zenith plane. The total angle (twice the obliquity) always lies between 47°40′ and 47°45′, which, he reports, agrees nearly with Eratosthenes (c. 200 B.C.) and Hipparchus (c. 135 B.C.); half of this gives the adopted obliquity of 23°51′20″. The problem is that, to the best of our modern calculations, the obliquity should have been 23°40′50″ in Ptolemy's time.

Apparently Ptolemy has settled on a traditional value, although conceivably he really did try to confirm the obliquity and something subtle went wrong, fooling him into agreement with his predecessors (whose value was just as wrong for them as for Ptolemy). Where could such a value for the obliquity come from? Ptolemy remarks that the double obliquity, 47°42′40″, is almost exactly $^{11}/_{83}$ of the circumference of a circle, and since we know that the Greeks with their elementary mathematics particularly liked ratios of integers, we can guess that in some circuitous way the traditional obliquity stems from that ratio.

In the third book of the *Almagest,* Ptolemy takes on the problem of the length of the year and the seasons. This seemingly simple problem has vexed astronomers of every age, including our own. Roughly speaking, the year is the time required for the Sun to make its circuit through the sky (or the Copernican converse, the time required for the Earth to make its circuit around the Sun). But how do we know when the circuit has been completed? Is it when the Sun has come back to the same position against the starry background? This is not so easy to measure, because of the

Sun's brilliance, which blots out the stars in the daytime. However, during a lunar eclipse we know that the Moon is precisely 180° away from the Sun, so this geometry provides a clever method to pin down the Sun's position among the stars. A year defined this way, with respect to the stars, is called the sidereal year.

Another way to measure a year is to record the Sun's seasonal movement, to document the time that passes between the moment when the Sun crosses the celestial equator northward at the vernal (spring) equinox, and when the phenomenon repeats again the following year. This is called the tropical year, which is about twenty minutes shorter than the sidereal year.

Ptolemy chooses to use the tropical year as his fundamental base, and so he requires observations of the Sun at the equinoxes. Again, Ptolemy describes his observational procedures in some detail; again he claims his results confirm Hipparchus, and again there are problems. Ptolemy reports, for example, that the Sun could be observed as its shadow changed sides on an equatorial ring on 22 March 140 (of course, he specified this in the current Egyptian calendar, which was Pachon (Pactom) 7 of the year Antonine 3; *GBWW,* Vol. 16, p. 82). Now this happens to be exactly the date that would have been predicted by Hipparchus on the basis of the equinox he had observed and with a length of the tropical year of 365¼ days minus $1/300$ of a day. However, the actual date of the equinox in A.D. 140 was March 21, not March 22.

Probably Ptolemy had some trouble making this observation. He actually complains that the old bronze rings in the gymnasium square had settled and sometimes gave spurious results. Furthermore, the phenomenon of atmospheric refraction can also make the observation ambiguous. So far, however, no one has been able to give a completely convincing explanation of how Ptolemy could have misread his instruments to come up with figures that agree so well with the calculated numbers and disagree a day from the actual phenomena.

There is a further hint in the *Almagest* III, however, that his numbers are traditionally based on and ultimately rooted in Babylonian parameters. In addition to finding the length of the year Ptolemy seeks the length of the seasons, because these reveal the nonuniform motion of the Sun and tell him the eccentricity of the Sun's orbit. It is comparatively easy to get the times of the equinoxes because in March the Sun is moving northward quite perceptibly each day, and in September the Sun is going southward quite perceptibly. But, when the Sun rounds the northernmost portion of its path along the ecliptic in June, a week or two can pass with barely any change in the noonday height of the Sun; the same is the case in December when the Sun rounds the southernmost portion of its path. Yet Ptolemy comes up with a pretty good date for the solstice (a day wrong but agreeing with the error in the equinoxes), and hence with a reasonable value for the eccentricity of the Sun's deferent. Interestingly enough, however, the length of summer in the *Almagest* exactly matches the motion of the Sun on the slow arc in the Babylonian solar theory. It is possible that Ptolemy, in borrowing Hipparchus's solar theory, was completely unaware of this. In any event, it seems likely that the rather good value Ptolemy got for the solar eccentricity via Hipparchus stemmed at least indirectly from the Babylonians.

But how could the Babylonians find the length of the seasons so well, since it would have been no easier for them than for Ptolemy to find the time of the solstice by direct observation? The answer seems to lie in the idea that the Babylonian astronomy was thoroughly dependent upon lunar observations, and particularly on a long series of lunar eclipses. Over the past century the astronomical cuneiform tablets have gradually been deciphered, and one of the most surprising things that has emerged is the relatively high accuracy with which parameters can be extracted from very approximate observations. Provided there are enough records over a considerable period of time, even crude measurements furnish quite reliable figures for planetary periods and for their nonuniform motion along the ecliptic.

In particular, the Babylonians discovered that the lunar eclipses repeated in certain patterns, and that the possible eclipse positions were more crowded together in the direction of Sagittarius than in Gemini. This meant that the Sun was moving more slowly when it was in Sagittarius, and conversely. From this observation it was possible to work backward and establish when the seasons began without actually making daytime measurements of the solstices.

There is, indeed, a third kind of year in Babylonian astronomy that is related to the Moon. The Babylonians had set the length of the average lunar synodic month, that is, the time between successive full moons, as

$$29^{d}31'50''8'''20''''$$

or precisely the number adopted by Ptolemy. The Babylonians (and the Greeks as well) knew that there were 235 lunations (full moons) in almost precisely nineteen years, something now called the Metonic cycle. If one assumes this relation is exact and multiplies $^{235}/_{19}$ times the lunar synodic month above, the length of what I shall call the Metonic year is

$$365^{d}14'48''$$

which just happens to be Hipparchus's length of the year, the one quoted approvingly by Ptolemy and adopted by him. Hipparchus had found that this year differs from the sidereal year by about fifteen minutes (of time), leading to a very accurate value of the difference between the two systems of 1° per century. Unfortunately, the year of $365^{d}14'48''$ is about 5½ minutes (of time) longer than the correct tropical year, a difference apparently too small to be noticed by Hipparchus but building up to a full day in the interval between Hipparchus and Ptolemy.

Thus it appears that Ptolemy, by believing that Hipparchus's year was essentially a correct tropical year, and by not observing times of the equinoxes carefully enough, spoiled the numerical foundations of his theory. As we shall see presently, instead of the 1° per century precession given by Ptolemy (which is accurate for the difference between the sidereal and Metonic years but not between the sidereal and tropical years) he should have had 1° per 70 years, an error that was to cause astronomers of the Middle Ages and Renaissance almost endless grief.

After considering the solar motion, Ptolemy turns to the Moon. In Book IV of the *Almagest* he presents the lunar theory received from Hipparchus, which, while quite satisfactory at times of new and full moons (when eclipses can take place), was pretty wretched at the quarters. Ptolemy ameliorates this deficiency in Book V, after detecting a new feature in the lunar motion that has come to be known as evection. This phenomenon, a periodic change in the *range* of the speeds of the Moon, can be interpreted as a regular variation in the eccentricity itself. Ptolemy coped with evection by placing the center of the lunar deferent on its own circle, and as it cranked the deferent nearer and farther from the Earth, the effective eccentricity varied. I suspect that Ptolemy worked unusually hard untangling the lunar motions, for the parameters are astonishingly accurate, better, for example, than those for Jupiter or Saturn.

The task of sorting out the Moon's motion was rendered especially difficult because the Moon, unlike the Sun or other planets, is close enough to the Earth to have a sensible parallax, that is, a change in its position depending on the location of the observer. Hence it is necessary to consider the lunar motion *as seen from the center of the Earth.* When the Moon is directly overhead, so that the observer is on the line between centers of the Earth and Moon, there is no parallactic effect. On the other hand, when the Moon is on the horizon, the effect is the greatest and the apparent position of the Moon is raised by a degree, that is, twice its apparent diameter. Precisely how large this effect is depends not only on the Moon's altitude above the horizon but on its varying distance from the Earth. In trying to sort out the Moon's distance, Ptolemy had a real chicken-and-egg problem: he needed the observations to establish the model, but he needed the model to correct the observations for the distance.

Given the model of the Sun, established in Book III, and of the Moon, completed in Book V, Ptolemy is ready to take on eclipses, which follow in Book VI. Ptolemy's eclipse theory was a pioneering accomplishment, for this was the first time in history that solar eclipses could be calculated for a particular geographical location.

Only after the relatively complicated eclipse procedures are in hand does the Alexandrian astronomer move on to the much simpler topic of stars (Books VII and VIII), and here it becomes quickly apparent why this order is crucial to his presentation. Ptolemy has made the tropical year the essential basis for his astronomy, and from this follows the definition of his coordinate system. Celestial longitude is measured eastward along the ecliptic, so that the Sun and Moon always move to progressively higher numerical values. But where does the numbering begin? By definition, from the intersection of the ecliptic with the equator. Needless to say, this intersection is invisible in the sky and can only be deduced by the motion of the Sun. To transfer the invisible coordinates traced out by the Sun onto the nighttime sky, Ptolemy used lunar positions. Today we could use accurate clocks in conjunction with precise transit instruments to connect the coordinate system from the Sun with the nighttime sky, but for Ptolemy it was essential to have the lunar theory available before discussing the positions of the stars.

Within Ptolemy's textbook everything is, for better or worse, tightly knit; in this case for worse, because his error of a day in the date of the equinox put the Sun behind by about a degree (since the Sun moves 360° in 365 days, and therefore approximately a degree a day). Hence the entire coordinate frame was zeroed about one degree beyond the actual intersection point of the ecliptic and equator. This meant that all the stars listed by Ptolemy had systematically erroneous longitudes, too low by about 1°12′.

Now the errors begin to compound. O unlucky Ptolemy! As I have said, the length of the sidereal year, dependent on the stars, differs from the length of the tropical year, dependent on the time of the equinoxes, by an amount called the precession of the equinoxes. Because Ptolemy's star positions are wrong, when he calculates their differences with respect to the positions in Hipparchus's day (2⅔ centuries earlier), the result is too small, only 2°40′ instead of 3°52′, and Ptolemy ends up with a precession of 1° per century instead of the correct 1° per seventy years. It is no wonder that by the time of Copernicus there were some obvious problems with astronomy, although this was surely not one that cried for a heliocentric solution!

The source of Ptolemy's star catalog has long been a matter of contention. Ptolemy describes his observing procedures, but had an existing catalog been conveniently available, it is likely that he would have made good use of it, just as any subsequent astronomer would have used Ptolemy's as a starting point for his own work. Where Ptolemy has leaned heavily on earlier astronomers such as Hipparchus (in the solar and lunar theories) or Apollonius (in the theorem for retrogressions), he gives them credit, and more generously than most ancient writers who reprocessed material from their predecessors. He credits Hipparchus and Timocharis with certain specific observations, but not with respect to the catalog itself, where he says, "We have not used for each of the stars altogether the same formulations as our predecessors, just as they did not use the same as their predecessors" (*GBWW*, Vol. 16, p. 233). I suppose Ptolemy does not wish to attribute his specific ordering of the stars to them, but he may well have taken most of the positions from a catalog made for the epoch of Hipparchus and simply updated it by adding 2°40′ to each position.

In the final five books of the *Almagest,* Ptolemy addresses the central problem of his work, the modeling of the planets. We have already examined in detail how Ptolemy may have gone about this and how the tables work for the longitude of Mars. It remains to comment on the peculiarly complicated model for the planet Mercury and to mention briefly his latitude theory.

Because Mercury stays comparatively close to the Sun in the sky, it is difficult to get the proper observations to establish its motions. In particular, Ptolemy failed to get observations of the morning elongations from the Sun in the spring and the evening elongations in the fall, something he mentions explicitly. Had Ptolemy stuck with the model he had already achieved for Mars, his results with Mercury would have been ultimately more satisfactory, but this might have forced him to approximate some of his observations. Instead, he took some comparatively poor observations much too seriously and was therefore obliged to invent a second, inner wheel (similar to the scheme for the Moon) in order to reproduce these data. Since Mercury was the second fastest moving object after the Moon, it was placed immediately beyond the Moon's orbit and inside the model for Venus; perhaps Ptolemy thought it might be appropriate for such a transition planet to have a more complicated mechanism something like the Moon's. Like Ptolemy, Copernicus found it impossible to get those key observations of Mercury, and so he simply transferred Ptolemy's model to the heliocentric arrangement. Not until Kepler was the Mercury mechanism made similar to the other planets, resulting in a highly successful prediction of the first observed transit of Mercury across the face of the Sun.

Ptolemy's *Almagest* concludes in Book XII with the theory of planetary stationary points and retrogressions, using (as mentioned earlier) the theorem of Apollonius, and in Book XIII with the theory of latitudes. It is fascinating to note that he uses somewhat different modeling for the latitudes, which reinforces the view that Ptolemy was more interested in the predictive results than in the physical reality of his mechanisms.

Subsequently Ptolemy wrote a more cosmologically oriented work, the *Planetary Hypotheses,* in which he described how the individual mechanisms for the various planets could be assembled into a whole, truly a "Ptolemaic system"; the numbers therein suggest that he was still carrying out improvements to his theory. In the ensuing years, the criticisms of the *Almagest* centered primarily on the philosophical aspects, such as whether Ptolemy correctly preserved the principle of uniform circular motion, and very little on his specific choice of parameters. It is some of these philosophical critiques that we next examine.

Prelude to Copernicus

In the centuries that followed Ptolemy's *Almagest,* astronomy fell into a serious decline. Among the Islamic astronomers were a number who commented intelligently on the *Almagest* and who even criticized it, but no one systematically reworked all the parameters or amended the models to make them more accurate. Part of the reason was a great dearth of suitable observations. From the death of Ptolemy until the birth of Copernicus in 1473 there exist in the West not more than a dozen records with accurate planetary positions.

Nevertheless, it gradually became apparent that Ptolemy's value of the precession was untenable or at least incomplete. Observations revealed that the stars were drifting through the coordinate system more rapidly than 1° per century as specified by Ptolemy. Yet no one had the audacity to challenge the observations recorded by the Alexandrian astronomer, for that would have undermined the entire foundation of astronomy. Instead, an ingenious system of variable precession was introduced in just such a way as to preserve the values between the times of Hipparchus and Ptolemy, but to give a faster rate in the centuries that followed. Called trepidation, the new feature was invented by Islamic astronomers and incorporated into astronomical procedures prior to A.D. 1000.

By the thirteenth century, when the astronomers of King Alfonso X of Spain prepared new and handier tables for finding planetary positions, trepidation had been codified into a standard method. A famous but somewhat dubious anecdote survives from that time: Alfonso is reputed to have told his astronomers, after looking over their work, that if he had been around at creation he could have given the Good Lord some hints. From this has grown a legend that the Alfonsine tables were encumbered with epicycles on epicycles, and that as a consequence the entire Ptolemaic system was crying for reform in order to reduce its incomprehensible complexity. Nothing could be farther from the truth. In the absence of systematic observations during the Middle Ages, there was no basis for making the planetary models more complicated, except for adding the table of trepidation. Furthermore, the clever method of the Ptolemaic tables in coping with the corrections by single-entry tables would have been vitiated by the addition of any independent epicycles.

In the eastern part of the Islamic world, however, astronomers did begin to experiment with new planetary models involving one or more additional epicycles. But, contrary to what we might imagine from a modern viewpoint, such models were not invented to introduce more accuracy into the procedures. Their entire purpose was to satisfy certain philosophical requirements. These little epicycles, or epicyclets, were designed to replace the equant, partly in order to preserve the ancient requirement of *uniform* circular motion, and partly to set up a strictly mechanical model of the planetary system.

In the world view of Aristotle, each planet occupied its own concentric zone of aetherial material, and these spheres were tightly nested together. Ptolemy attempted to preserve certain features of this scheme, and in his *Planetary Hypotheses* he calculated the distances of the planets on the assumption that the epicyclic mechanisms of the successive planets were stacked together as compactly as possible, yet spaced just far enough apart so they would not collide.

By the Middle Ages the Aristotelian aether was envisioned as a hard crystalline substance, smooth and transparent, out of which the planetary spheres were constructed. It was easy to conceive of the epicycle as made of hard crystal, and gliding without friction in a rigid eccentric circular sleeve surrounded by more hard crystal, but it was impossible to construct a mechanical linkage to the equant point without conflicting with other crystalline material. For example, if all the mechanisms were nested one inside another, then the equant point of the large outer assembly for Saturn would fall within the crystal spheres for Mars. Clearly if the Ptolemaic system was to be reconciled with an Aristotelian picture of physical reality, some modification was needed. It was the failure of Ptolemy's model to provide a philosophically acceptable picture that brought his astronomy under increasing criticism throughout the Islamic period, and it was for this reason that astronomers of the thirteenth-century Maragha school (in present-day Iran) explored the epicyclic alternatives to the Ptolemaic equant. (The Maragha astronomers likewise worried about the other two cases in which Ptolemy had used an interior mechanism: for Mercury and for the Moon.) Incidentally, the additional epicyclets adopted by these astronomers did not introduce a further independent motion because they were constrained to duplicate the effects of the equant; hence the appearance of the resulting tables was the same as before.

Precisely how much this philosophical attack on Ptolemy filtered into the Latin West is still difficult to assess, but undoubtedly it helped shape the climate of opinion at the end of the fifteenth century when Copernicus was a student. In addition, the temporary fix provided by the trepidation was coming undone; the trepidation had been set up to provide a variable rate of precession, and by 1500 its effect was diminishing, contrary to the witness of the stars. Some kind of reform was desirable on both accounts, yet neither the criticism of the equant nor the failure of precession theory called for anything as radical as the introduction of an entirely new cosmology. In order to come to grips with that larger issue, we now turn to Copernicus himself.

Copernicus and the heliocentric cosmology

Nicolaus Copernicus was born in Torun, Poland, on February 19, 1473. After his father died, his maternal uncle provided for his education and later arranged for him to become a canon and lawyer at the Cathedral of Frombork (Frauenburg), the northernmost Catholic diocese in Poland. At the historic and flourishing university in Cracow, Copernicus presumably studied the standard medieval curriculum, which included the *Sphere* of Sacrobosco. This beginning textbook gave a very elementary account of spherical astronomy. Probably Copernicus also encountered the second-level text, Peurbach's *Theoricae novae planetarum,* the "New Theories of the Planets," which was a relatively new textbook but not a new theory. While in Cracow, Copernicus took up astronomy with sufficient enthusiasm to buy his own printed copy of the Alfonsine Tables, and his interest continued when he went to Italy for graduate work, even though his official studies were canon (church) law and medicine.

How early Copernicus developed his radically new heliocentric cosmology we do not know for certain. He might have got the first inkling already during his undergraduate days in Cracow, or perhaps in Renaissance Italy, or possibly not until he had returned to northern Poland to work as private secretary and physician to his uncle, who had become bishop. The first indirect hint of his novel ideas comes down to us from 1514 in the inventory of the books of a Cracow scholar, whose library contained a manuscript by "someone who held that the Sun stands still while the Earth moves." Entitled the *Commentariolus* or "Brief Treatise," it represents Copernicus's earliest known foray into astronomy. Closely modeled on Peurbach's *Theoricae,* it criticizes the standard geocentric astronomy and outlines a very different heliocentric arrangement. Without discussing specific observations or presenting tables of planetary motions, the *Commentariolus* includes enough technical details to show key differences from the final version of the Copernican system as given at the end of his life in his major treatise, the *De revolutionibus orbium coelestium,* "On the Revolutions of the Heavenly Spheres."

Copernicus opens the *Commentariolus* with a specific complaint against the equant, a theory that appeared "neither sufficiently perfect nor pleasing to the mind." He then lists seven assumptions, the two most important being

> 3. All the spheres surround the Sun as though it were in the middle of all of them, and therefore the Sun is near the middle of the universe,
>
> and
>
> 7. What appears as the direct and retrograde movements arises not from the planets themselves, but from the Earth. This motion alone therefore suffices to explain many apparent irregularities in the heavens.

These premises form both the basis of, and one of the chief arguments for, the new cosmology; they are important for understanding Copernicus's defense, but they tell little about the genesis of the idea in his mind.

Displeasure with the equant may have turned him toward an examination of the accepted planetary modeling; similarly, the problems with the Ptolemaic coordinate system (that is, precession and trepidation) may also have played a role, since immediately after a short discussion of the solar theory Copernicus turns to a section entitled "That uniform motion should be referred not to the equinoxes but to the fixed stars." Yet neither problem has as its solution a heliocentric cosmology as such.

In the case of Ptolemy, we have only the surviving works themselves as evidence for his thought processes. For Copernicus we do have a few background materials: the much worked-over manuscript of his *On the Revolutions* survives in Cracow, plus some working notes in books now preserved in Sweden where they were taken during the Thirty Years' War. One of the manuscript pages gives some highly suggestive clues as to the route traveled by Copernicus in his examination of the existing planetary models. The argument is subtle, but a modern figure helps us understand the path Copernicus may have taken (figure 3).

In the figure the solid lines represent the Ptolemaic model for Mars. The diagonal arrow represents the direction from the Earth to Mars, which is determined by the motions of the two circles. Of course the primary goal of a planetary model is to give such a direction (i.e., the geo-

Figure 3. The Ptolemaic system (solid lines) and the geo-heliocentric system with its interpenetration of circles for Mars (shaded lines).

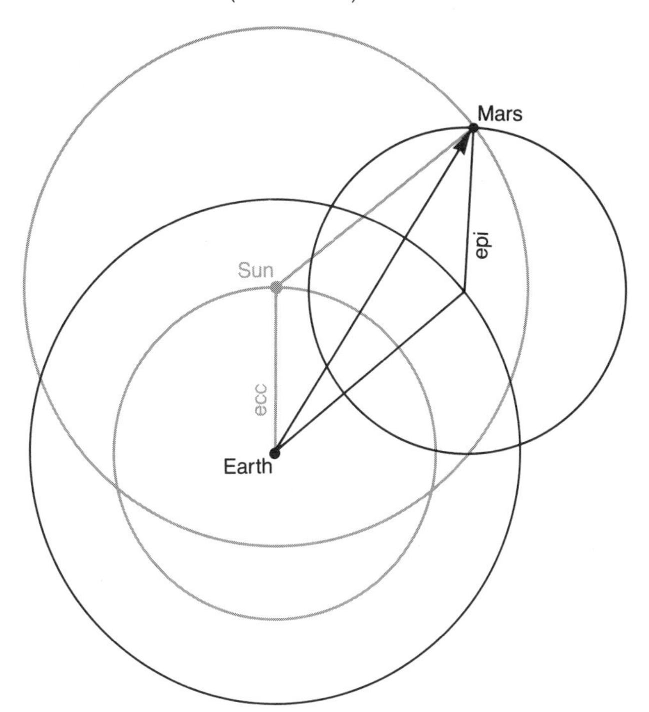

centric longitude), and the procedure can rest on purely fictitious intermediate mechanisms. It is instructive to consider an alternative construction, represented by the shaded lines in the diagram; it can be quickly verified that this variant arrangement will continue to give identical answers for the direction to Mars.

The basic difference in the two schemes is a philosophical one: if the smaller circle is placed in the center, with the larger one riding on it, then the larger circle will cut through the smaller in a way that makes it difficult to think of the circles as rigid crystalline spheres. This interpenetration of the two spheres is a mighty obstacle to anyone taking the idea of solid spheres seriously. We know that Copernicus considered this arrangement, but we suspect that he considered the interpenetration of the spheres such a drawback that he quickly dismissed it as a viable possibility, even though he does not explicitly say so. In the generation after Copernicus, Tycho Brahe made the arrangement the basis of a new cosmology, and he is quite explicit in saying that for a long time he was hung up on precisely this point about the larger circle cutting through the smaller.

The alternative arrangement (the one shown in the shaded lines) has one feature of great interest: when the large and small circles are interchanged, then the direction from the Earth to the center of the larger circle (labeled "ecc") always turns out to be the direction to the Sun! And since the Ptolemaic system gives only relative distances, it is possible to scale the Sun's orbit so that the Sun occupies this point. Now, instead of having two separate mechanisms, one for Mars and another for the Sun, both have been combined into a single system. This is an extremely powerful insight, the crucial beginning of the entire Copernican system. Surely such a detail had been noticed by Ptolemy, and if by some incredible stroke he overlooked it, then it must have been well known by the Middle Ages. Indeed, the Alfonsine Tables take implicit advantage of this possibility in their very organization. But to accept this combination as a physically real picture of the universe meant giving up the whole substance that supported and turned the heavens, the crystalline spheres. This was a formidable leap, one not easily taken.

If Mars and the Sun can be combined, is it possible to combine the Sun with other planets? And if so, would it be possible to increase or diminish the sizes of the circles so as to fit, say, Mars, Jupiter, and the Sun all together? The answer is yes, but it was philosophically very troubling for astronomers accustomed to considering each planet separately.

At this crucial juncture we pause, recognizing that this step must have been psychologically exceedingly difficult, or else it would have been explored much earlier by other astronomers. And we pause to look at the evidence suggesting that Copernicus got to this point and hesitated, appalled at the idea of destroying the crystalline structure of the universe.

The two alternative arrangements in the diagram carry a differing description of the circles. The small solid circle is of course the *epicycle* of the Ptolemaic model. But when it is moved to the interior position, it now delineates the movable *eccentric* center of the larger circle. And remarkably, on a single page in one of Copernicus's books we find a series of numbers labeled "ecc" agreeing exactly with the numbers that Ptolemy sets for the epicycle sizes. There follows a second table, in which each planetary mechanism is scaled so that the Earth-Sun distance (the "ecc") is the same, and all can be superimposed.

At once a common measuring stick appears: each large planetary circle is now scaled and fixed *with respect to the Earth-Sun distance.* "We find that the world has a wonderful commensurability," declares Copernicus in one of his most poetic passages (*GBWW,* Vol. 16, p. 528), referring to this Earth-Sun standard, the "common measure" of the universe.

But nowhere does Copernicus mention this Earth-centered arrangement in which the Sun, with its entourage of planets, marches around the Earth in annual progression. It remained for Tycho Brahe, the Danish observer and cosmographer, to propose it as a serious alternative in 1588. Why does not Copernicus settle for such a scheme, which preserves not only the ancient physics but a literal reading of the Holy Scriptures as well? For Tycho to defend this geo-heliocentric arrangement, he had to take the iconoclastic stand that the crystalline substance of the heavens was a mere fiction invented by the ancients. For Copernicus, who followed his fellow Renaissance humanists in looking back to a golden antique age when knowledge was still pure and unforgotten, such a rejection of ancient wisdom was perhaps too much to consider. And without the spheres, what could keep the planets in their fixed paths? Possibly Copernicus was also an idealist who saw in his mind's eye something still more compelling, something so remarkable and beautiful that he was willing to accept it despite the resulting conflict with traditional physics.

What Copernicus noticed was that the amalgamated arrangement placed Mercury, the swiftest planet, in the smallest orbit; Saturn, the slowest, fell much the farthest from the Sun, and the others were placed in a harmonious progression in between, as shown below:

Planet	*Relative distance*	*Sidereal period in days*
Mercury	0.387	88
Venus	0.723	225
Earth	1.000	365
Mars	1.52	687
Jupiter	5.20	4333
Saturn	9.54	10759

Did it not make sense to assign to the Earth rather than to the Sun the 365-day period, which fit so nicely between the 225 days for Venus and the 687 days for Mars? Besides, to place the Earth in motion around the Sun, rather than vice versa, immediately cleared up the problem of the interpenetration of the spheres!

Copernicus never breathes a hint of that intermediate stepping stone in the path from the geocentric to the heliocentric system. Rather, he proclaims the obvious uniqueness of the Sun: "Who would place this lamp . . . in another or better place than this, from which it can illuminate everything at the same time?" (cf. *GBWW,* Vol. 16, pp. 526–27). He sings of the harmonious arrangement of larger orbs for slower planets: "There is a sure bond of harmony for the movement and size of the orbital spheres that can be found in no other way" (cf. *GBWW,* p. 528). And he proceeds to explain how the different sizes of the retrograde loops for the various planets now have a natural explanation. Copernicus's disciple, Georg Joachim Rheticus, waxes rhapsodic about this point: "For all these phenomena appear to be linked most nobly together, as by a golden chain; and each of the planets, by its position and order and every irregularity of motion, bears witness that the Earth moves."

It is perhaps not surprising that Kepler, who comes after Tycho, argues more forcefully against the geo-heliocentric arrangement. Tycho, in defending this intermediate arrangement that he had adopted, had remarked, "Copernicus nowhere offends the principles of mathematics, but he throws the Earth, a lazy, sluggish body unfit for motion, into a motion faster than the aetherial torches (the stars)." In the introduction to his *New Astronomy,* Kepler argues from a newly-emerging physics:

> Furthermore, it is very likely that the source of the Earth's motion is at the same place as that of the other five planets, namely, in the Sun. For this reason it is therefore very probable that the Earth moves, since there is an apparent, plausible cause for its motions. . . . But let us consider the bodies of both the Sun and the Earth: which would be the better source of motion for the other? Does the Sun, which moves the other planets, move the Earth, or does the Earth move the Sun, itself the mover of the other planets and so many times larger than the Earth? Let us not be forced to concede that the Sun is moved by the Earth, which is absurd. We must concede immobility to the Sun and motion to the Earth. [See *New Astronomy,* p. 314, in this volume.]

Regardless of the path to the new cosmology or the arguments raised in its defense, Copernicus had taken a bold and provocative step, one that required both imagination and courage. He also had the intellectual perception to know that its serious consideration would require more than a simple statement of the new blueprint for the planetary system. Unlike others who may have entertained that same speculation, Copernicus went on to place his ideas into a complete context, that is, a book from which one could actually calculate planetary positions from the heliocentric arrangement.

Copernicus's *On the Revolutions of the Heavenly Spheres*

In the *Commentariolus* Copernicus remarked that "I have decided here, for the sake of brevity, to omit the mathematical demonstrations, which are planned for a larger book." There is no way to know precisely what Copernicus then had in mind, but by the time he had acquired his copy of the *Almagest,* first printed in 1515, he must have realized that for his new theory to rival Ptolemy's, it would have to be set forth in a treatise of comparable structure and magnitude. He labored over his *magnum opus* for almost thirty years, and when he was nearly seventy he was finally persuaded to let it go off to a printer in Germany, even though he was still in the process of making its numbers more self-consistent.

It is possible that Copernicus originally intended to call his larger work by the full title *De revolutionibus orbium coelestium,* "On the Revolutions of the Heavenly Spheres," although there is good evidence that he later changed his mind and preferred to omit *orbium coelestium.* The "heavenly spheres" may have played a key role at first when he opted for a heliocentric system (rather than the geo-heliocentric version Tycho was later to adopt) in order to avoid the interpenetration of the spheres of Mars and the Sun. But evidently his interest in the spheres faded, for his *On the Revolutions* contains neither a description of the crystal spheres nor an indictment of the equant (although he worked systematically to eliminate it by means of a small epicyclet included for each planet).

Now, in defending his new cosmology in his *On the Revolutions,* Copernicus returns to the power of unity, the idea that everything is linked together by the common measure of the Earth-Sun standard:

> Moreover, they [the ancients] have not been able to discover or to infer the chief point of all, i.e., the form of the world and the certain commensurability of its parts. But they are in exactly the same fix as someone taking from different places hands, feet, head, and the other limbs—shaped very beautifully but not with reference to one body and without correspondence to one another—so that such parts made up a monster rather than a man (*GBWW,* Vol. 16, p. 507).

One of the essential differences between *On the Revolutions* and the *Almagest* is the vigorous defense of its cosmology, something that Ptolemy could rather easily dismiss because his readers would have automatically assumed a geocentric framework. Copernicus's arguments rise to a brilliant and glorious polemic in favor of the Sun-centered system by Chapter 10, where, in what is easily the finest passage of the entire book, he proclaims, "In the center of all rests the Sun. . . . as if on a kingly throne, governing the family of stars that wheel around." (cf. *GBWW,* Vol. 16, pp. 526–28). Nevertheless, this opening cosmological section constitutes a mere 4 percent of the treatise, extending through only eleven chapters of the first of its six books. The remaining 96 percent is a technical treatise as formidable as the *Almagest* and in many places parallel to it.

Like the *Almagest, On the Revolutions* includes near the beginning a section on mathematics, complete with a trigonometrical table; but Copernicus can rely on more modern and much handier spherical trigonometry, and instead of chords (despite the table headings) he presents the sine function. In Book II, however, a fundamental distinction occurs: because for Copernicus the "fixed stars" really are fixed and are providing the basic reference frame, he at once provides a star catalog. Unlike Ptolemy, Copernicus makes no claims of having observed the catalog himself; in fact, he states right out that he has for the most part borrowed it from Ptolemy.

Only after discussing the stars does Copernicus turn (in Book III) to the complex threefold motion of the Earth. The Earth not only spins on its axis and revolves about the Sun, its axis slowly changes direction, producing the precession-trepidation phenomenon. Copernicus combines the revolution and the precession somewhat differently than we would today, but the results are the same apart from the fact that we no longer accept an oscillatory trepidation superimposed on the steady precessional motion. More interesting is Copernicus's almost mystical linking of the changes in the eccentricity of the Earth's circular orbit with the direction of that displacement, with the change in obliquity of the ecliptic, and with the period of trepidation. The actual numbers were not well known and were affected as well by the problems of Ptolemy's reference framework. The fact that Copernicus could link all these phenomena together by the single remarkable number of 1717 years is an astonishing display of his intuitive belief in the unity of nature. Such details impressed all the astronomers of the century, whether or not they accepted the heliocentric hypothesis. There was a touch of relativity here: what worked for the Earth's orbit would by reflex also work for the Sun's orbit about a fixed Earth.

In Book IV Copernicus takes up the orbit of the Moon, and here he brings against Ptolemy a perceptive criticism that had already been noticed in the Islamic period. In the *Almagest*'s model, the Moon was sometimes as far as sixty-four Earth-radii and sometimes as close as thirty-four. This should have caused the diameter of the Moon to appear half as large in diameter when it was far compared to when it was close, a variation never observed. "Experience and sense-perception teach us that the parallaxes [i.e., distances] of the Moon are not consonant with those which the ratio of the circles promises," remarks Copernicus (*GBWW*, Vol. 16, p. 678). Although his own model in no substantial way improves the longitude or latitude predictions of Ptolemy, it does greatly ameliorate the problem of the apparent size. In the Copernican model, the Moon varies in size by about ±10 percent, approximately twice the actual change, but a vast improvement over the range in Ptolemy's lunar mechanism.

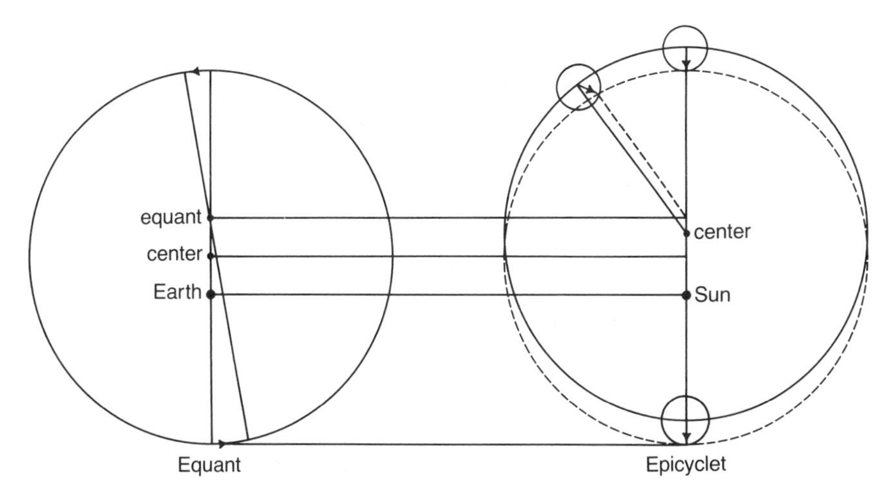

Figure 4. Copernicus's replacement of the equant by a pair of uniform circular motions. The epicycle has a radius of $e/2$ and always moves to form an isosceles trapezoid.

In both the lunar theory and in the planetary longitudes that follow in Book V, Copernicus takes considerable pains to eliminate the detested Ptolemaic equant. The equivalence between the equant and Copernicus's epicyclet is diagrammed in figure 4. If the distance between the Earth and equant in the Ptolemaic arrangement is twice the eccentricity *e,* then in the equivalent Copernican layout the center of the orbit is placed at $\frac{3}{2}\,e$ from the Sun and the radius of the epicyclet is $\frac{1}{2}\,e$. The motion in the epicyclet is uniform, so that a regular trapezoid is generated as shown, with the dashed line always behaving the same way as would the line from the equant. The effective orbit, shown by the dashed curve, is not exactly a circle, but slightly fattened.

In discussing the planetary longitudes in Book V, Copernicus relies on the observations of the *Almagest,* checked by four modern ones of his own. Thus Copernicus, like Ptolemy, gives only the minimum number of observations for finding the parameters. His own observations are not particularly good; in fact, they can be quite dreadful, such as one of Mars that is 2° off the mark! For Mercury, which hovers quite close to the Sun, Copernicus borrowed observations from his near contemporary Bernard Walther. Since these observations were later independently published, we can see that Copernicus gently adjusted them to get them to fit the model.

The advantage of a longer temporal baseline enabled Copernicus to reset the hands of his clockwork, as it were, without changing the mechanism itself. That is, his heliocentric framework with circular orbits and epicyclets simply mapped onto Ptolemy's geocentric framework with its use of the equant, and these changes made essentially no difference with respect to the technical machinery. Indeed, it requires only minor adjustments to use the tables of *On the Revolutions* to predict planetary positions compared to the procedure outlined earlier for the *Almagest.*

Because there were few accurate observations before the time of Tycho Brahe, contemporary astronomers could not, in fact, tell if Copernicus's tables were giving better results than Ptolemy's. Despite this, most of the sixteenth-century astronomers calculating almanacs did convert to the more modern tables. Today we can use electronic computers to calculate where the planets were in the 1500s, and we find that although Copernicus actually improved most positions, the improvement was not enough to get excited about, especially considering how long it had been since the *Almagest* was written. As for the planetary latitudes, discussed in Book VI, Copernicus's work was a disaster. He neither took advantage of the heliocentric geometry to straighten out the *Almagest*'s theory of latitudes, nor did he reobserve the lines of nodes that determine when a planet is north or south of the ecliptic. To be sure, Copernicus here inherited the worst part of the *Almagest,* which was without specific observations, but it was nonetheless an opportunity lost. It would remain for Kepler to use the latitudes in an integrated way with the theory of longitudes, thereby producing a powerful lever for advancing planetary theory.

The reception of Copernican theory

Victorian rationalists, who created such concepts as "martyrs of science" to describe the effects of the religious opposition eventually encountered by the ideas of Copernicus and Galileo, assumed that Copernicus hesitated to publish his book because of an expected adverse reaction from the Catholic Church. But there were at least two other reasons, probably much more likely, that prevented him from trying to disseminate his ideas. On the one hand, he was far from the major international centers of printing that could profitably handle a book as large and technical as *On the Revolutions.* On the other, his manuscript was still full of numerical inconsistencies, and he knew very well that he had not taken complete advantage of the opportunities that the heliocentric viewpoint offered. For example, the theory of Mercury retained curious motions with the period of a year because not all the geocentric elements had been purged from its construction.

Furthermore, Copernicus was far from academic centers, thereby lacking the stimulation of technically trained colleagues with whom he could discuss his work. Then, in 1539, the situation changed: a young professor from the Lutheran University of Wittenberg arrived to learn about the new cosmology. Georg Joachim Rheticus became Copernicus's first and only disciple, and it is owing to his enthusiasm that Copernicus allowed a copy of the manuscript to be taken to Germany for printing. In 1542

Rheticus took the copy to Nuremberg, where the typesetting began. Presently Rheticus received a tempting offer to become professor at Leipzig, so he left the work in the hands of the printer Petreius and his clergyman-proofreader, Andrew Osiander.

The last pages to be printed in the spring of 1543 were the first leaves of the book, and here Osiander conspired with the printer to add an anonymous introduction to safeguard its contents. "These hypotheses need not be true nor even probable," he wrote, "as long as they provide a calculus that fits the observations. . . . Let no one expect truth from astronomy, lest he leave a bigger fool than when he entered" (cf. *GBWW*, Vol. 16, pp. 505–6). When Copernicus, then on his deathbed, saw these pages, he was much agitated. But whether he was well enough to appreciate their contents is not at all clear, and perhaps he was only excited to realize that his life work was at last on the verge of publication.

In any event, this anonymous introduction certainly spared the book the theological criticism it might otherwise have attracted. Throughout the Lutheran university system the book was systematically studied by the advanced students; in the elementary courses Copernicus was held in high regard, but students were carefully shielded from his heliocentric doctrine. The book had been dedicated to Pope Paul III, but because it was published within the Lutheran sphere, relatively few copies of the first edition found their way to England or to Italy and the other Catholic countries. Probably fewer than 500 copies were originally printed, and after the Nuremberg edition went out of print, a second edition was published in 1566 in Basel. This edition was well distributed both in England and the Catholic countries, so by the beginning of the seventeenth century Copernicus's ideas were readily available, even though the heliocentric cosmology was rarely taught openly and then almost always as a hypothesis, just as the anonymous introduction declared.

The outstanding astronomer in the interval between Copernicus and Kepler was Tycho Brahe, the eminent Danish observatory builder. Like the other leading astronomers of the day, he was attentive to Copernicus's innovations, and he found the interlinking of the planets and the Sun particularly appealing. But he had considerable difficulty in accepting it as a physically real system because it contradicted the accepted Aristotelian physics and apparently also the Bible. Unwilling and unable to forge a new physics, he chose instead to modify the cosmology to the geo-heliocentric form. Of course, this shattered the crystalline spheres, a radical step he eventually espoused. That left the heavens with no obvious means of generating their motions, something previously supposed to have been supplied by God at the outside edge of the nested spheres and transmitted inward through the crystal machinery. It is at this point in the story that the young German astronomer Johannes Kepler arrived on the scene, eager to restore some kind of celestial physics.

Kepler

Johannes Kepler was conceived on the 16th of May, 1571, at 4:37 A.M. and born on the 27th of December at 2:30 P.M. Such minutely kept dates remind us that Kepler lived in an age when "astronomer" still meant "astrologer" and when the word *scientist* had not yet been invented. Like many of the world's greatest scientists, including Ptolemy and Copernicus, Kepler had a profound feeling for the harmony of the heavens; although he rejected most of the traditional details of astrology, he believed in a powerful accord between the cosmos and the individual.

There was little in Kepler's youth to indicate that he would become one of the foremost astronomers of all time. A weak and sickly child, but intelligent, he easily won a scholarship to the nearby Tübingen University so that he could study to become a Lutheran clergyman. In recommending him for a scholarship renewal, the University Senate noted that Kepler had "such a superior and magnificent mind that something special may be expected of him."

Yet Kepler himself wrote [*New Astronomy,* chap. 7, p. 324, in this volume] that although he had done well enough in the prescribed mathematical studies, nothing indicated to him a special talent for astronomy. Hence he was surprised and distressed when, midway through his third and last year as a theology student at Tübingen, he was summoned to Graz, far away in southern Austria, to become an astronomy teacher and provincial mathematician. It was there in one of his astronomy lectures that he hit upon what he believed to be the secret key to the construction of the universe.

This key hung upon a crucial thread: at Tübingen, Kepler had become a Copernican. The astronomy teacher at the University, Michael Mästlin, was remarkably knowledgeable about Copernicus's *On the Revolutions.* In his lectures, Mästlin explained how the new Copernican system accounted for the retrogradations in a most natural way, and how the planets were laid out in an elegant harmonic fashion both with respect to their spacing from the Sun and to their periods.

It was undoubtedly the beautiful harmonic regularities so "pleasing to the mind" that appealed strongly to Kepler's sense of the aesthetic and induced him to become such an enthusiastic Copernican. To Kepler the theologian, such regularities revealed the glory of God. When he finally hit upon that secret key to the Universe, he attributed it to Divine Providence. "I believe this," he wrote, "because I have constantly prayed to God that I might succeed if what Copernicus had said was true." Later, in writing to his teacher Mästlin, he said, "For a long time I wanted to become a theologian; for a long time I was restless. Now, however, behold how through my effort God is being celebrated in astronomy."

Because of his preoccupation with the Copernican system, Kepler had begun to ask himself three unusual questions: Why are the planets spaced this way? Why do they move with these regularities? Why are there just six planets? All these questions are very Copernican, the last one particularly so because a traditional geocentrist would have counted both the Sun and the Moon, but not the Earth, thereby listing seven planets.

In illustrating to his class how the great conjunctions of Jupiter and Saturn fall sequentially along the ecliptic, Kepler drew a series of quasi-triangles whose lines began to form an inner circle half as large as the outer ecliptic circle. The proportion between the circles struck Kepler's eye as almost identical with the proportions between the orbits of Saturn and Jupiter. Immediately he began a search for a similar geometrical relation to account for the spacing of Mars and the other planets, but his quest was in vain.

"And then it struck me," he wrote. "Why have plane figures among three-dimensional orbits? Behold, reader, the invention and the whole substance of this little book!" He knew that there were five regular polyhedra, that is, solid figures each with faces all of the same kind of regular polygon. By inscribing and circumscribing these five figures between the six planetary spheres (all nested in the proper order), he found that the positions of the spheres closely approximated the spacings of the planets. Since there are five and only five of these regular or Platonic polyhedra, Kepler thought that he had explained the reason why there were precisely six planets in the solar system.

Kepler published this scheme in 1596 in his *Mysterium cosmographicum*, the "Cosmographic Secret." It was the first new and enthusiastic Copernican treatise in more than fifty years, since *On the Revolutions* itself. Without a Sun-centered universe, the entire rationale of the book would have collapsed.

The young astronomer realized, however, that Copernicus had made the Sun immobile without actually using it as his central reference point; rather, he had used the center of the Earth's orbit. Although the Sun was nearby, it played no physical role. But, Kepler argued, the Sun's centrality is essential to any celestial physics, and the Sun itself must supply the driving force to keep the planets in motion. Not only did he propose this critically significant physical idea, he attempted to describe mathematically how the Sun's driving force diminished with distance. Again, his result was only approximate, but at least the important physical-mathematical step had been taken. This idea, which was to be much further developed in his *New Astronomy*, establishes Kepler as the first scientist to demand physical explanations for celestial phenomena. Although the physical explanation of the *Mysterium cosmographicum* was erroneous, never in history has a book so wrong been so seminal in directing the future course of science.

Kepler sent a copy of his remarkable treatise to the most famous astronomer of the day, Tycho Brahe. Unknown to Kepler, the renowned Danish astronomer was in the process of leaving his homeland. Tycho had boasted that his magnificent Uraniborg Observatory had cost the king of Denmark more than a ton of gold. Now, however, fearing the loss of royal support at home, Tycho had decided to join the court of Rudolph II in Prague.

Kepler describes the sequence of events in his greatest book, the *Astronomia nova* (or *New Astronomy*); the relevant section is among those translated at the end of this volume. Tycho had been impressed by the *Mysterium cosmographicum,* though he was unwilling to accept all its strange arguments; then, Kepler writes, "Tycho Brahe, himself an important part in my destiny, did not cease from then on to urge me to visit him. But since the distance of the two places would have deterred me, I ascribe it to Divine Providence that he came to Bohemia, where I arrived just before the beginning of the year 1600, with the hope of obtaining the correct eccentricities of the planetary orbits. . . . Now at that time Longomontanus had taken up the theory of Mars, which was placed in his hands so that he might study the Martian opposition with the Sun in 9° of Leo [that is, Mars near aphelion]. Had he been occupied with another planet, I would have started with that one. That is why I consider it again an act of Divine Providence that I arrived at the time when he was studying Mars; because for us to arrive at the secret knowledge of astronomy, it is absolutely necessary to use the motion of Mars; otherwise it would remain eternally hidden."

Kepler's *Astronomia nova* was not to be published until nine years later, in 1609. His greatest work, it broke the two-millennium spell of perfect circles and uniform angular motion—it was truly the "New Astronomy." Never had there been a book like it. Both Ptolemy in the *Almagest* and Copernicus in *On the Revolutions* had carefully dismantled the scaffolding by which they had erected their mathematical models. Kepler's book is nearly an order of magnitude more complete and complex than anything that had gone before, but he himself admits that he might have been too prolix.

Kepler had quickly perceived the quality of Brahe's treasure of observations, but he had realized that Tycho lacked an architect for the erection of a new astronomical structure. A devoted Copernican, he nevertheless recognized certain shortcomings in the helio*static* system described in *On the Revolutions,* and he was determined to derive a truly helio*centric* system in which the Sun played a vital physical role in keeping the planets in motion.

In the first three months in Prague, he established two fundamental points: first, the orbital plane of Mars had to be referred to the Sun itself, and not to the center of the Earth's orbit, as Copernicus had assumed; and second, the traditional eccentric circle of the Earth-Sun relation had to be modified to include an equant or its equivalent. Although the other planetary mechanisms had traditionally employed the equant (or the equivalent Copernican epicyclet), the Earth-Sun system did not. Hence, it was of paramount importance to Kepler's physics to prove that the Earth's motion resembled those of the other planets, and this he accomplished by an ingenious triangulation from the Earth's orbit to Mars.

In contrast to Copernicus, Kepler had no objections to using the equant as a mathematical tool, but unlike all previous astronomers, he decided to allow the equant to fall an arbitrary distance beyond the center of the circular orbit. In this way by the spring of 1601 he had been able, with the help of Tycho's accurate observations, to achieve a far better solution for Mars's longitudes than any of his predecessors. By a series of iterations he established a model accurate to 2′; "If you are wearied by this tedious procedure," he implored the readers of the *New Astronomy,* "take pity on me who carried out at least seventy trials."

From the predicted latitudes, however, Kepler realized that his scheme gave erroneous distances; again, unlike previous astronomers, who were satisfied with separate models for longitudes and latitudes, Kepler sought a unified, physically acceptable description. To obtain the correct distances his physical model demanded, he was obliged to reposition his circular orbit with its center midway between the Sun and the equant, but this move destroyed the excellent results he had previously found for the longitudes. The errors now rose to 8′ in the octants of the orbit, and in the *New Astronomy* Kepler goes on to say, "Divine providence granted us such a diligent observer in Tycho Brahe that his observations convicted this Ptolemaic calculation of an error of 8′; it is only right that we should accept God's gift with a grateful mind, because these 8′ have led to a total reform of astronomy."

While Kepler's admiration for Tycho's achievements always remained high, the imperious and high-handed Dane exceedingly frustrated the young German, almost driving him to a nervous breakdown. How well a collaboration between the two very different personalities would have worked in the long run is now impossible to assess, but what actually happened after Kepler had worked with Tycho for only ten months was that his mentor unexpectedly took ill and died. Suddenly Kepler inherited both the use of Tycho's observations and his position as Imperial Mathematician (although at only a third of the salary!). Kepler took time out to complete Tycho's nearly finished book—the *Progymnamata astronomiae instauratae,* "Exercises for the Reform of Astronomy"—and then he returned to his warfare on Mars.

Kepler now revived his earlier speculations on a planetary driving force, something like magnetism, emanating from the Sun. He envisioned a rotating Sun with rotating emanations that continuously pushed the planets in their orbits. His revised model, with the center midway between the Sun and equant, enabled him to formulate what we can call his distance law, that the velocity of a planet is inversely proportional to its distance from the Sun. Finding the angular motion from the distances immediately raised a computational problem of some proportion that could only be solved by tedious numerical summations. Here he had the fortunate inspiration to replace the sums of the lines between the Sun and the planet with the area swept out by the line between the Sun and the planet. This relation is formulated by chapter 40 of his *New Astronomy,* and his abstract of this chapter is given in the selection at the end of this volume. Neither in the abstract, nor in the chapter itself, nor anywhere else in the *New Astronomy,* is this relation, the so-called law of areas, clearly stated. By 1621, however, Kepler finally understood its fundamental nature and clearly stated both the area law and a revised distance law (*GBWW,* Vol. 16, pp. 982–83 and 968–69).

At this point Kepler had an accurate but physically inadmissable scheme for calculating longitudes and an intuitively satisfactory physical principle (the distance law) that worked well for the Earth's orbit, but which left an unacceptable 8′ error when applied to Mars. In order to preserve simultaneously both his accurate longitude prediction and the properly centered circular orbit, Kepler next added a small epicycle to his circle. This was a time-honored procedure, but one that left him distressed by its absurdity. Just as sailors cannot know from the sea alone how much water they have traversed, he argued, so the Mind of the planet will have no control over its motion in an imaginary epicycle except by watching the apparent diameter of the Sun. (This style of argument is outlined in the abstract of chapter 39, found in the selection at the end of this volume.)

Kepler had difficulty in preserving the circular motion when he adopted an epicycle; it is therefore not surprising that he next turned to a closer examination of the shape of Mars's path. Having established the proper position of the Earth's orbit by triangulation of Mars, he was able to turn the procedure around and investigate a few points in the orbit of Mars itself. Although the method did not yield a quantitative result, it clearly showed that Mars's orbit was noncircular. Kepler recognized that observational errors prevented him from getting precise distances to the orbit. Because of this scatter, he had to use, as he picturesquely described it, a method of "votes and ballots."

Armed with these results, Kepler found in the epicycle a convenient means for generating a simple noncircular path. The resulting curve was similar to an ellipse, but was slightly egg-shaped with the fat end containing the Sun. In working with this ovoid curve, Kepler got himself into a very messy computational problem when he tried to apply his area rule to various segments. As an approximation he used an ellipse, but rather different from the one he was finally to adopt. Then, in the course of his calculations, he stumbled upon a pair of numbers that alerted him to the existence of another ellipse, a curve answering some of his requirements almost perfectly. "It was," he wrote, "as if I had awakened from a sleep."

Nevertheless, Kepler was also searching for a *physical* picture of planetary motion, something quasi-magnetic connected with the Sun that would explain not only the varying speed of Mars but also its varying distances. He fervently hoped that the oscillations of a hypothetical magnetic axis of Mars would satisfy his requirements. "I was almost driven to madness in considering and calculating this matter," he wrote in chapter 58 of his *New Astronomy* [*see* p. 333, in this volume]. "I could not find why the planet . . . would rather go on an elliptical orbit as shown by the equations. O ridiculous me! As if the oscillation on the diameter could not be the way to the ellipse! So this notion brought me up short, that the ellipse exists because of the oscillation. With reasoning derived from physical principles agreeing with experience there is no figure left for the orbit except a perfect ellipse."

With justifiable pride he could call his book the *New Astronomy;* its subtitle emphasizes its repeated theme: "Based on Causes, or Celestial Physics, Brought out by a Commentary on the Motion of the Planet Mars." Although his magnetic forces have today fallen by the wayside, his requirement for a celestial physics based on causes has profoundly influenced contemporary science, which takes for granted that physical laws operate everywhere in the universe.

The work was completed by the end of 1605, but publication did not follow immediately, for Tycho's heirs demanded censorship rights over materials based on his observations, and they were displeased that Kepler had chosen a Copernican basis rather than Tycho's fixed-Earth, geoheliocentric arrangement, which of course made little sense in the framework of Kepler's physical ideas. Eventually a compromise was reached, primarily with respect to the dedicatory materials at the beginning of the volume, and the book was at last printed in 1609. Kepler added to the work a long introduction defending his physical principles, and he described how the Copernican system could be reconciled with the Bible. This latter part he had already written in 1596 for inclusion in his *Mysterium cosmographicum,* but the Tübingen University Senate, which had been asked to referee his first publication, had objected to such theological material. Now independent, Kepler had no such restrictions; of all Kepler's writings, this section of the introduction was the most frequently reprinted during the seventeenth century, and was the only part to be translated into English [*see* pp. 318–322, in this volume].

It is difficult to gauge what impact Kepler's new astronomy would have had if he had stopped at this point. His cleansing and reformulation of the heliocentric system had been worked out in theory for only a single planet, Mars, and he had not provided any practical tables for calculating its motions. As Imperial Mathematician to Rudolph II, Kepler had been explicitly charged with the preparation of new planetary tables based on Tycho's observations, an arduous task that he still faced. "Don't sentence me completely to the treadmill of mathematical calculations," Kepler replied to one correspondent. "Leave me time for philosophical speculations, my sole delight."

The Harmonies of the World

Soon after completing his *Mysterium cosmographicum* Kepler had drafted an outline for a work on the harmony of the universe, but his plan had lain dormant while he grappled with the intricacies of Mars. Then, in the fall of 1616, after he had completed the first in a long series of ephemerides based on his work, he began to work intermittently on his *Harmonice mundi,* the *Harmonies of the World.* A major work of 225 pages, it was finally completed in the spring of 1618.

Max Caspar, in his biography *Kepler,* gives an extended and perceptive summary of the *Harmonies,* concluding:

> Certainly for Kepler this book was his mind's favorite child. Those were the thoughts to which he clung during the trials of his life and which brought light to the darkness that surrounded him. . . . With the accuracy of the researcher, who arranges and calculates observations, is united the power of shaping of an artist, who knows about the image, and the ardor of the seeker for God, who struggles with the angel. So his *Harmonice* appears as a great cosmic vision, woven out of science, poetry, philosophy, theology, mysticism. . . .

Kepler developed his theory of harmony in four areas: geometry, music, astrology, and astronomy. It is the latter treatment, in Book V, which commands the primary attention today, and which appears in English translation in *Great Books of the Western World* (Vol. 16, pp. 1009–85).

In the *Mysterium cosmographicum* the young Kepler had been satisfied with the rather approximate planetary spacings predicted by his nested polyhedrons and spheres; now, imbued with a new respect for data, he could no longer dismiss its five percent error. In the astronomical Book V of the *Harmonies,* he came to grips with this central problem: By what secondary principle did God adjust the original archetypical model based on the regular solids? Indeed, Kepler now found a supposed harmonic reason not only for the detailed planetary distances but also for their orbital eccentricities. The ratios of the extremes of the velocities of the planets corresponded to the harmonies of the just intonation. Of course, one planet would not necessarily be at its perihelion when another was at aphelion. Hence, the silent harmonies did not sound simultaneously but only from time to time as the planets wheeled in their generally dissonant courses around the sun. Swept on by the grandeur of his vision, Kepler exclaimed:

> It should no longer seem strange that man, the ape of his Creator, has finally discovered how to sing polyphonically, an art unknown to the ancients. With this symphony of voices man can play through the eternity of time in less than an hour and can taste in some small measure the delight of God the Supreme Artist by calling forth that very sweet pleasure of the music that imitates God (*GBWW,* Vol. 16, p. 1048).

In the course of this investigation, Kepler hit upon the relation now called his third or harmonic law: The ratio that exists between the periodic times of any two planets is precisely the ratio of the $3/2$ power of the mean distances (*GBWW,* Vol. 16, p. 1020). (This is equivalent to saying that the square of the periodic time is proportional to the cube of the mean distance.) Neither here nor in the few later references to it does Kepler bother to show how accurate the relation really is. Using his own data, we can calculate the table he failed to exhibit:

	Period (years)	Mean Distance	Period Squared	Distance Cubed
Mercury	0.242	0.388	0.0584	0.0580
Venus	0.616	0.724	0.3795	0.3795
Earth	1.000	1.000	1.000	1.000
Mars	1.881	1.524	3.540	3.538
Jupiter	11.86	5.200	140.61	140.73
Saturn	29.33	9.510	860.08	867.69

The harmonic law pleased him greatly for it neatly linked the planetary distances with their velocities or periods, thus fortifying the a priori premises of the *Mysterium* and the *Harmonies.* So ecstatic was Kepler that he immediately added these rhapsodic lines to the introduction to Book V:

> Now, since the dawn eight months ago, since the broad daylight three months ago, and since a few days ago, when the full Sun illuminated my wonderful speculations, nothing holds me back. I yield freely to the sacred frenzy; I dare frankly to confess that I have stolen the golden vessels of the Egyptians to build a tabernacle for my God far from the bounds of Egypt. If you pardon me, I shall rejoice; if you reproach me, I shall endure. The die is cast, and I am writing the book—to be read either now or by posterity, it matters not. It can wait a century for a reader, as God himself has waited six thousand years for a witness (cf. *GBWW,* Vol. 16, p. 1010).

Kepler's *Epitome of Copernican Astronomy*

At the same time that Kepler was preparing his planetary ephemerides and his *Harmonies of the World,* he also embarked upon his longest and perhaps most influential book, an introductory textbook for Copernican astronomy in general and Keplerian astronomy in particular. Cast in the catechetical form of questions and answers typical of sixteenth-century textbooks, the *Epitome* treated all of heliocentric astronomy in a systematic way, including the three relations now called Kepler's laws. Its seven books were issued in installments; the first three appeared in 1617 and the final three in 1621.

Although Book IV, on theoretical astronomy, came last conceptually, it was published in sequence in 1620. Subtitled "Celestial Physics, that is, Every Size, Motion, and Proportion in the Heavens Explained by a Cause Either Natural or Archetypal," it is the most remarkable section of the *Epitome.* To a large extent it epitomizes both the *Harmonies* and Kepler's new lunar theory, completed just before this part was sent to press.

Book IV opens with one of his favorite analogies, one that had already appeared in the *Mysterium cosmographicum* and which stresses the theological basis of his Copernicanism: the three regions of the universe were archetypal symbols of the Trinity—the center, a symbol of the Father; the outermost sphere, of the Son; and the intervening space, of the Holy Spirit. Immediately thereafter Kepler plunges into a consideration of final causes, seeking reasons for the apparent size of the Sun, the length of day, and the relative sizes and distances of the planets. From first principles he attempts to deduce the distance to the Sun by assuming that the Earth's volume is to the Sun's as the radius of the Earth is to its distance from the Sun. His result is twenty times greater than that assumed by Ptolemy and Copernicus, but he shows from a perceptive analysis of the observations that such a size is not excluded. Subsequently he argues that the sphere of fixed stars must be 2,000 times larger than the orbit of Saturn, thereby advocating a size of the universe vastly greater than that considered by the ancients or even by Copernicus.

Kepler's third or harmonic law, which he had discovered in 1619 and announced virtually without comment in the *Harmonies,* receives an interesting and extensive treatment in the second part of Book IV. His explanation of the $P = r^{3/2}$ law (where P is the period of revolution of a planet and r is the mean distance from the Sun) is based on the relation

$$\text{Period} = \frac{\text{Path Length} \times \text{Matter}}{\text{Magnetic strength} \times \text{Volume}}.$$

Clearly, the longer the path, the longer the period; the greater the magnetic emanation reaching the planet from the Sun (which furnished the driving force), the shorter the period. The matter in the planet itself provides a resistance to continued motion: the more matter, the more inertia, and the more time required. Finally, with a larger volume of material, the magnetic emanation or "motor virtue" can be soaked up more readily and the period proportionately shortened. According to Kepler's distance rule, the density of each planet depends upon its distance from the Sun, a requirement quite appropriate to his ideas of harmony. To a limited extent he defends this arrangement from telescopic observations, but he generally falls back on vague archetypal principles.

In the third part of Book IV Kepler continues his discussion of the physical causes of planetary motions, and in particular the irregularities of speed and shape of orbit. "But the celestial movements are not the work of mind," he states, and by implication he accepts that their motions, either elliptical or circular, are compelled by material necessity after having been so arranged by the Creator. In his *New Astronomy* Kepler had been much more equivocal on this point, and certainly in his *Mysterium cosmographicum* he had endorsed the idea of animate souls as moving intelligences for the planets. Now, in the *Epitome,* he seeks an explanatory foundation based strictly on the solar magnetic emanations and their interactions with the magnetic poles of the Moon and planets. In this framework he introduces the magnetic influence of the Sun, likening it to the laws of the lever and balance, and then he uses the oscillations or "librations" of the magnetic poles to explain physically the elliptical orbits.

With the way prepared by the discussion of the magnetic forces and the elliptical orbit, Kepler turns to the most complex case of all, the lunar theory. Although he understood the complications of lunar motion well enough to offer reasonable predictions for the Moon's positions, for the most part, his efforts yielded an ad hoc scheme that failed to provide any foundation for further advances.

Book V of the *Epitome* (which together with Book IV appears in Volume 16 of the *Great Books of the Western World*) treats certain practical geometrical problems arising from elliptical orbits, and here Kepler considers the ellipse in considerably more detail. It is in this section that he correctly formulates his "distance law" in a form equivalent to the modern law of conservation of angular momentum (*GBWW,* Vol. 16, pp. 968–69), and here he also candidly apologizes for the fuzzy statement of the law of areas in his *New Astronomy,* saying, "I confess that the thing is given rather obscurely there, and most of the trouble comes from the fact that there the distances are not considered as triangles, but as numbers and lines" (*ibid.,* p. 983). Also introduced in this book is what is now called Kepler's equation, used in the practical application of the law of areas to an elliptical orbit.

Kepler's *Epitome* can be considered the theoretical handbook to his *Rudolphine Tables,* finally published in 1627; this monumental work furnished working tables based on his reforms of the Copernican system. Kepler's planetary positions were generally about thirty times better than any of his predecessors', and in 1631 (the year following Kepler's death) they provided the grounds for a dramatically successful observation, for the first time, of a transit of the planet Mercury across the face of the Sun. In 1632 a further impetus to the Copernican system came through the brilliant polemic of Galileo's *Dialogue Concerning Two Great World Systems.*

Precisely how influential Kepler's *Epitome* was is difficult to assess. His reputation was considerably enhanced by the publication of his *Rudolphine Tables,* and the Copernican idea was rapidly gaining in acceptability. Thus, by 1635, there was sufficient demand for the *Epitome* to warrant reprinting it, and for many years it remained one of the few accessible sources for the details of the revised Copernican system.

Evaluation

With Ptolemy and Copernicus, Kepler shared a profound sense of order and harmony. In Kepler's mind this was linked with his theological appreciation of God the Creator. Nowhere is this more movingly expressed than in the prayer near the end of his *Harmonies:*

> I give thanks to Thee, O Lord Creator. . . . Behold! now, I have completed the work of my profession, having employed as much power of mind as Thou didst give to me; to the men who are going to read those demonstrations I have made manifest the glory of Thy works, as much of its infinity as the narrows of my intellect could apprehend. . . . If I have been allured into rashness by the wonderful beauty of Thy works, or if I have loved my own glory among men, while I am advancing in the work destined for Thy glory, be gentle and merciful and pardon me; and finally deign graciously to effect that these demonstrations give way to Thy glory and the salvation of souls and nowhere be an obstacle to that (*GBWW,* Vol. 16, p. 1080).

Repeatedly, Kepler stated that geometry and quantity are coeternal with God and that mankind shares in them because man is created in the image of God. From these principles flowed his ideas on the cosmic link between man's soul and the geometrical configurations of the planets; they also motivated his indefatigable search for the mathematical harmonies of the universe.

Contrasting with Kepler's mathematical mysticism, yet growing out of it through the remarkable quality of his genius, was his insistence on physical causes. In Kepler's view the physical universe was not only a world of discoverable mathematical harmonies but also a world of phenomena explainable by mechanical principles. The result of his work was the mechanization and the cleansing of the Copernican system, setting it into motion like clockwork and sweeping away the vestiges of Ptolemaic astronomy.

It remained for Isaac Newton to banish the last traces of Aristotelian physics and to place the heliocentric system on a consistent physical foundation. Although Newton indirectly owed much to Kepler's insistence on physical causes, he rejected the type of physical arguments so dear to Kepler's mind, and with it, he tried to withhold credit for Kepler's achievement. As a result, Kepler is nowhere mentioned in Book I of Newton's *Principia* (*GBWW,* Vol. 34). Nevertheless, Newton's contemporaries felt differently, and thus his work was introduced to the Royal Society as "a mathematical demonstration of the Copernican hypothesis as proposed by Kepler." Perhaps the fairest evaluation of Kepler has come from Edmond Halley in his review of the *Principia:* Newton's first eleven propositions, he wrote, were "found to agree with the *Phenomena* of the Celestial Motions, as discovered by the great Sagacity and Diligence of *Kepler.*"

PART THREE

Editorial Essay

The Idea of Civil Police

I. Introduction

Aristotle, in the fourth century B.C., observed that bad men obey the law not out of respect for the justice of its commands but only because they fear the punishment their disobedience may incur.

Thomas Aquinas, in the thirteenth century, commented on the difference between a private person giving another individual advice and a government laying down laws for the people to obey. "If his advice be not taken," he wrote, "it has no coercive power, such as the law should have," in order for its commands to be efficacious.

Four centuries later, John Locke declared that "where the laws cannot be executed, it is all one as if there were no laws." This implied, it would seem, some agency of law enforcement for the execution of the laws.

If we read these remarks, covering the whole span of Western history from antiquity to the end of the seventeenth century, in the light of our own experience in today's world, we might be led to suppose that there has always existed in political communities like our own something like the police force with which we are acquainted in the cities in which we live.

If, throughout this time, political philosophers so clearly insisted on the need for law enforcement, how could it be that they did not have in mind some agency of law enforcement—a police force somewhat like our own?

Not so, surprising as it may seem! If we were to make the supposition that would so naturally occur to us on reading the passages cited above, we would be greatly mistaken. The historical facts are quite otherwise than we would have supposed.

Discovering this led the Institute for Philosophical Research ten years ago to undertake a study of the idea of police power and law enforcement, both in the writings of political philosophers and in the history of political institutions.

The first indication of the need for this undertaking came from implications in Plutarch and in Gibbon that there were no police to speak of—no governmental institution designed to enforce the law and preserve the peace—until very recent times. A police force, such as we know one today, did not come into existence anywhere in the Western world until the establishment of the Metropolitan Police in London in 1829. The establishment of a roughly comparable institution occurred two or more decades later in our American cities—in New York, Boston, and Philadelphia.

So complete was the absence of any such institution in Rome, for example, that both of the Gracchi—successive consuls who endeavored to redistribute a measure of the city's wealth and who thereby incurred the wrath of powerful interests—were assassinated in circumstances that make clear the absence of police protection. They were set upon by their enemies while going about the public business and murdered before the populace.

Much the same lack of police protection is evident in accounts of ancient Athens, in the Renaissance republics, and in England of, say, the seventeenth and eighteenth centuries, though we do hear much of sheriffs, bailiffs, and constables such as Shakespeare parodied.

In addition, beyond brief passages like the ones already cited, we found little or no discussion of police as a necessary institution in the literature of political philosophy. This lack was observed all the way from the writings of antiquity by Plato and Aristotle through those by John of Salisbury, Aquinas, and Marsilius in the Middle Ages, down to Bodin, Hobbes, Locke, Rousseau, Kant, Hegel, and Mill in modern times.

We could not help being impressed by the apparent novelty of police as an institution, both in theory and in practice. Were the appearances illusory or could we take them as evidence of what really was the case? Had the literature of the subject and its history been adequately examined?

As to the first, there was not much more that could be done. It is impossible to prove a negative in such cases. The absence of discussion of the principle of police in any selection of writers on political philosophy, however large, does not prove a similar absence in the work of someone else whose work has not been read. All that can be claimed is that, so far as could be determined, political philosophy has almost completely overlooked this fundamental element of government. It has conceived civil society as existing without any police power designed to enforce the law or to maintain the peace, with little or no indication of the need for such an institution.

More could be learned, of course, about the history of the subject beyond what the classic literature provided. There was an extensive literature devoted to the police in many countries, some of it extending far back in time. This was explored in depth and has since been further examined with results that will be set forth later on. Nevertheless, it may be said at once that, while much interesting material was found, little of it—indeed substantially nothing—modified the conclusion reached tentatively on the basis of reading in more general histories. With minor exceptions, institutions to enforce the law and keep the peace did not exist in civil society before the first half of the nineteenth century, though after that they became general and were everywhere taken for granted.

In order to avoid misunderstanding, it must be acknowledged that in all these reflections and researches, it was only with "civil" police, "civil" or constitutional government, and "civil" society that the Institute study was concerned. Had it been otherwise, had the inquiry been into government generally, considered simply as ruling power, the result would have been very different, both as to political philosophy and also as to history.

It may be pointed out here that both political philosophers and historians have sometimes overlooked a distinction of fundamental importance in these matters. This is particularly so with regard to accounts of the police in various countries of the world from earliest times on, where the presence of such an institution has been detected and traced unbroken down to our own age, with no perception that what is described is for the most part not civil police at all (in our sense of that term) but something quite different, though it is often called by the same name.

The distinction that the words *civil* or *constitutional* introduce as adjectives qualifying the word *government* and the word *society* is one between two kinds of government and two kinds of society that are so different as to be radically opposed.

Civil or constitutional government, creating civil society, is government authorized by the consent of the governed to wield the powers conferred on it, and limited to the powers that are thus authorized. It is radically distinct from what may be called despotic government, the power of which is not constituted or authorized, and which is simply force, however dignified or however circumspectly used.

So much is this the case that Locke makes what might at first appear to be the extreme statement that an absolute monarchy is not civil government at all and does not create a civil society. There are passages in Rousseau and Aristotle that imply the same thing. Only with the advent of constitutional government does the state, the truly political community, come into existence for Aristotle. Only with the social contract does civil society come into existence for Rousseau. What then comes into existence is a republic.

Just as Aquinas says that a tyrannical or unjust law is a law in name only (an expression of force devoid of authority and justice), so it seems equally necessary to say that a despotically governed state is a state—or a civil society—in name only; for it, too, is a manifestation of pure force—of might without right, devoid of authority and justice.

By the same token, the adjective *civil* attached to the word *police* introduces a fundamental distinction between two kinds of police or governmental force. It differentiates that which has constituted authority from that which does not. It divides that which is limited by just laws and natural rights from that which is not.

Because this is so, the police of a government that is not constitutional must be regarded as a police in name only, having in fact unlimited and

"From about the beginning of the fifth century B.C., the Areopagus functioned as the governing body [in Athens], *administering justice, inflicting punishments, and exacting fines."*

unauthorized powers over the populace, which it controls without legal restraints. Indeed, so far as it is a "police" at all, it is usually a paramilitary force, a secret rather than a civil police. The citizenry it controls is without recourse against it. It really stands not as a police force does to a citizenry, but rather as an army to an occupied country.

With these distinctions in mind, it makes sense to say that most of the governments under which men have lived in the course of history have not been civil at all, but only the rule of force in one form or another. Civil government has existed only at those relatively rare moments and particular places where human beings have been able to consent to and authorize, in one way or another, the power by which they are governed and so to limit it.

This happened briefly in ancient Athens, in the Roman republic, in certain of the medieval cities, and since the nineteenth century in the majority of the countries that comprise the Western world.

Similarly, it makes sense to say that most of the coercive force that has been exercised in human societies has not been civil police force at all, but merely the operating arm of largely despotic governments. Civil police, properly speaking, have existed only in those times and at those places where true civil governments have undertaken to create them, limiting their power over citizens to that of enforcing the law and keeping the peace.

It is true that civil governments have existed, at least briefly, before modern times in the places we have mentioned. They have been understood in principle by political philosophers since Aristotle. Notwithstanding, it is also true that civil police, save in the most rudimentary sense and without any clear rule or structure, can hardly be said to have existed anywhere before the nineteenth century. That institution was not recognized until then as essential to the task of civil government. Therein lies our story.

II. Authorized and unauthorized government

The two kinds of government we have distinguished are based on correspondingly different conceptions of the relation between law and justice.

In one conception, law is prior to the principles of justice. Man-made law in any community determines what is just or unjust there. Accordingly, might—the power of a *de facto* government—makes right. "Whatever pleases the prince has the force of law," writes the Roman jurist, Ulpian, who thereby described the form of government we call despotism, one in which justice, as Thrasymachus long ago observed in the *Republic,* is simply the interest of the stronger.

In the other conception, the principles of justice—everywhere the same—are prior to the law. Accordingly, it is possible to say that man-made laws are just or unjust.

From this basic distinction follows the distinction between the two kinds of government already referred to—despotic and civil or constitutional government. One rules by the consent of the governed, the other without it. The consent of the governed may be explicit, as in a written constitution that establishes a government authorized to *make* laws. It may be implicit in an unwritten constitution such as that of Great Britain. It may otherwise be expressed in what Rousseau called the social contract—an agreement among the constituents of government that is anterior to the enactment of any laws.

The distinction between these two kinds of government is *not* that the one exercises force and the other does not. All governments must somehow exercise force, the difference being that in the one case it is authorized force, in the other, not.

Where the force is not authorized, the need for it arises from a defect in the laws themselves, to which the governed have not given their consent. When consent has been given and force is authorized, the need for it arises from a defect not in the laws but in those who are governed.

This is what Aquinas means when he says that of the various kinds of law that exist—divine, natural, moral, and man-made or human—all but the last function without need of coercion, having the penalty for their disobedience within them. Only the last requires the exercise of coercive force. Human law, according to Aquinas, is "nothing other than an ordinance of reason for the common good, made by him who has care of the community, and promulgated." But that is not enough to exact obedience from any save the perfectly virtuous. All others—which is, doubtless, on one occasion or another, all without exception—require at least the threat of coercive force.

The importance of this point for any discussion of the civil police is very great. The necessity of this institution is not entailed by a defect in man-made laws, but by a defect in the human beings whose conduct the laws direct. If men were angels, laws having the support of coercive force would not be necessary. But men are not angels.

The notion of consent is not inconsistent with that of coercive force. Where government is duly authorized—i.e., constituted—it is the governed who ultimately have the authority and power that they vest in a government to which they have given full consent. Coercive force, as Aquinas says, "is vested in the people as a whole or some public person who is their vice-regent or representative, to whom it properly belongs to inflict penalties." As we have seen, Locke also says that "where the laws cannot be executed, it is all one as if there were no laws; and a government without laws is a mystery in politics." A government that does not exercise coercive force is equally a mystery in politics. The only question is: How should it be exercised?

Authorized coercive force imposes no infringement on freedom or liberty but only on license—lawless conduct. Liberty, but not license, occupies all the ground that a virtuous person can wish to occupy, which is to say, the right to do only what does not violate either the rights of others or the common good. That is all an authorized government, operating with the consent of the governed, can reasonably be expected to insure. Nothing is lost with prevention of license except what no reasonable government can be required to preserve, nor what any virtuous person wishes to possess.

Virtuous citizens of a constitutional or civil government never *need* coercion, or even the threat of it, in order to obey the laws. Their obedience follows necessarily from their virtue. It is only persons who are not virtuous—or, more realistically, all citizens to the extent that they lack virtue—who need to be coerced into doing what they ought to do, or prevented from doing the opposite.

Because the virtue of citizens or their lack of it is relevant to their need for coercion, the laws of a legitimate or authorized government are regarded as having in themselves a didactic function. Plato observes this when he has the Athenian Stranger say that laws are only in part framed for those "whose spirit cannot be subdued, or softened, or hindered from plunging into evil." They are also framed partly "for the sake of good men, in order to instruct them how they may live on good terms with one another."

Similarly, Aristotle remarks in the *Ethics* that one of the objects of law is to "give youth a right training in virtue." Good citizenship in his view is a function of good habits, to which he adds that "while people hate men who oppose their impulses, even if they oppose them rightly, the law in its ordaining of what is good is not burdensome." Aquinas likewise says that "the purpose of human law is to lead men to virtue."

No doubt this moral improvement comes about to some extent also in the deliberation and choice by which the laws of an authorized government are made and accepted—what we have come to call the political process. To put it another way, the virtue that laws foster in the citizenry is not merely personal, still less private, but is also common and politic. It derives from the need to formulate and understand the common good.

This may be characterized as the continuous operation of consent in such a governed society, where the process extends even to the kind of obedience the laws receive. Such consent is neither given nor asked for by a despotic government, in which the laws *may* serve the common good but are not designed for that purpose.

It is nonetheless *obedience* that authorized laws require. They still remain *commands.* The difference lies in the consent that such laws receive. This consent operates under authorized government because it has operated earlier, first, in constituting the government that makes the laws, and second in limiting the power of the rulers, or representatives, who have been given the authority to make laws.

It is incorrect to suggest that the laws of an authorized government are not commmands at all, but are only tenders of some sort, or questions, which citizens are free to reject if they please. It is also wrong to suggest that the consent of citizens has fulfilled itself merely by their act of constituting a government in the first place, and that thereafter they are subject to the laws in the same way as are the nonconsenting subjects of an unauthorized government.

Citizens are not subjugated by civil law in the same way as are the subjects of despotic law. Nor can they be, if consent is not a fiction, or at best a formality. To be genuine, consent must be manifested in every political act, and especially in every act of obedience, including those acts to which the coercive force of government applies. The presence of consent is indicated clearly by the apparent absence of it on occasions that may take one of two forms.

One form is that of civil dissent. This occurs when citizens find themselves opposed to laws and regulations they regard as unjust and wish to have altered or removed. Expressions of dissent may be made in assem-blies called for the purpose, by individual utterances, by political action of various kinds, and by voting. All such expressions are law-abiding, however, and involve no disobedience or withdrawal of consent. To call them expressions of consent is merely to acknowledge that consent necessarily involves the right of dissent—even more than the right, the duty.

The second form is the one we call civil disobedience. This may express itself in the refusal to obey a law the citizens find unjust, or, more commonly, in disobedience to a law that is not in itself objectionable, where the disobedience serves the symbolic purpose of calling attention to a law or policy that is unjust.

The civil rights protests of twenty years ago in the United States took both these courses at different times: the first at Montgomery, Alabama, and elsewhere, when segregation laws were defied; the second at Selma and other places where ordinances limiting or forbidding acts of protest were disobeyed. When such disobedience is accompanied by acceptance of the penalty imposed for disobeying the offending law—or its surrogate, symbolically defied—the coercive power of the state is not denied or defied. Then the disobedience is still within the boundaries of consent.

In ideal terms, both civil dissent and civil disobedience fall within the boundaries of consent. Only when the situation is not ideal—either because the injustice of the law is so immediate or so extreme in the opinion of those who oppose it as to require efforts to prevent its execution, or because those who disobey the law are themselves intemperate (which is to say, lacking in civic virtue)—must the coercive force of government really assert itself. Only then is civil peace or civil law threatened. Unfortunately, it is precisely at such times, when the fabric of consent has been stretched thin, that it is likely to be broken by an unrestrained response from the police themselves, made fearful or enraged.

The protests against the Vietnam war provide us with a case in point. Some of those protests were brought on by the protesters' concern that measures for the prosecution of the war would cause irreversible and unacceptable destruction if carried out, making moot the question of their justice. There were also many provocations by those who protested, who were as scornful of civility as they seemed incapable of it. Whichever motive was dominant on these occasions (a notorious example being the Democratic National Convention at Chicago in 1968), the police response lacked all restraint. It was indistinguishable from that of tyranny intent upon subjection.

Activities of that sort occupy what may be characterized as a gray area within the body politic—one that lies between consent in all its various forms and outright rebellion involving complete withdrawal of consent. The features of this latter condition occurred in the protests against the Vietnam war.

To a portion of the citizens the object against which they were protesting was not merely an unjust law. If the question were merely one of injustice, it could have been met by the normal operation of the political process. Failing that, it could have been accepted, however regretfully, as the decision of the majority. To the extremist protesters, the object they opposed was profoundly and irremediably unjust, to a degree that the political process could not be quick enough to redress, and that rendered the absence of redress intolerable.

There can also be disaffection in at least a portion of the citizenry which makes it incapable of the normal political process, either from ignorance, arrogance, or excitement. Some or all of these qualities were evident during the 1960s among the students in the universities, whatever the merits of their cause.

The signs were those of a populace not previously active politically, which had been brought to the point of protest by the strength of its feelings. These signs are endemic, it seems fair to say, among interest groups nowadays, representative of what is called "single-issue" politics, in which anger or fanaticism often seeks not to use but to paralyze the political process in order to achieve its purpose.

There is also an excessive use of coercive force, the relevance of which is not that it can be provoked but that the enforcers do not know how to remain a civil agency. They opt instead for a paramilitary status that appears stronger and therefore safer. But the strength they seek is inappropriate for civil government. So, too, the safety they desire is only the fear inspired by the man who is armed to the teeth.

It seems to be a fundamental temptation of police to make this kind of mistake, to wish to transform themselves into an instrument of naked force. It may even be the temptation of civil government in a constitutional republic to want to rid itself of its restraints and seek unchallenged power. The mistake, so far as the police are concerned, is hard to avoid when other pathologies of the sort here described are manifest among the citizenry, and when the question is not merely one of control but of survival.

Granting that coercive force is consistent with government by consent, such pathologies raise the question whether its active exercise is not always a sign of civil distemper.

The answer is yes, insofar as the need for force is occasioned by a defect in human beings, whose lack of civic virtue requires it. As long as this lack is confined to criminality and unruly behavior—neither of which involves any withdrawal of consent—the show of force, in the actions of police, would seem to indicate no more than the inevitable imperfections to which even just and prosperous societies are in some degree subject.

It is only when criminality and unruly behavior are excessive, only when social conditions approach the gray area just described, that the grasp of the law, if not the law itself, seems flawed. The defect may then be said to be in the operation of the body politic, not in the character of its members.

Antiwar demonstrators clash with police during the 1968 Democratic National Convention in Chicago. *"The police response lacked all restraint. It was indistinguishable from that of tyranny intent upon subjection."*

With considerations of this sort in mind, political philosophers have maintained that the laws of a civil or constitutional government do not function as they should until they have been taken into the hearts and minds of the citizens. That is why Lycurgus, we are told by Plutarch, having given laws to the Spartans, then absented himself from the city for ten years so that the citizens would learn to obey the rules before they could be challenged.

Plato, Aristotle, Aquinas, and others have argued that the laws should be changed infrequently because they believed that the mere passage and promulgation of a law was only the beginning of its life. It had to become ingrained through practice before it could really function.

"The law has no power to command obedience except that of habit," Aristotle writes. This is not to say that power, or police, cannot command obedience, but that the law by itself cannot, save as it becomes, through virtuous habit, a kind of second nature.

The function of a civil police force may seem mostly a negative one, manifesting itself when there is some failure of civic virtue in the populace. This is consistent with constitutional government so long as the failure does not involve a withdrawal of consent. Yet such a manifestation may well seem at best a kind of danger sign within society, ominous according to the frequency and severity of its occurrence. Even if it does not seem so, is there not some other role for the police to play, something corresponding to the positive function of government conceived as inducing acceptance of the laws through an habitual obedience?

The notion may seem fanciful, ideal, even academic. Nevertheless, there is reason to insist that such a corresponding function inheres in the nature of the civil police, and, moreover, that in fact it was precisely this conception that made possible the formation of the first great civil police institution in the Western world, the Metropolitan Police established in London in 1829. With that, we now move from these speculative considerations to the history of the subject.

III. Historical evolution of the police

If we confine our attention to those times and places where we know that government has been constituted by the people, who thereby become its constituents as well as its citizens, we find the historical evidence is very slight, at least before the nineteenth century.

Among the ancient Greek cities, Athens is the first example that comes to mind. We know that there, from about the beginning of the fifth century B.C., the Areopagus functioned as the governing body, administering justice, inflicting punishments, and exacting fines. Zimmern, in *The Greek Commonwealth,* says that the city had a kind of constabulary, as did most of the other Greek states, but it was neither effective nor respected in its duties. Its members were mostly amateurs or Scythian archers—barbarian slaves imported from the region of the Black Sea—and "the laughing stock of free-born citizens." Such a police was apparently not expected to do anything about the dirty, narrow, ill-lighted, and ill-paved streets lacking all sanitation. On the other hand, Zimmern reminds us, Greek cities did without most of what nowadays we think of as essential services. No regular schoolteachers, postmen, not even any tax-collectors, properly speaking, existed at all.

There was, however, a body called *The Eleven* that was somewhat like a police commission, as we might call it, having charge of prisons and the punishment of criminals. Perhaps the better analogy would be with a modern sheriff's office. How much it had to do is unclear. Most punishments in criminal cases consisted of deprivations of civil rights—disenfranchisement, loss of the right to speak in the assembly, to be a senator, to bring a public suit, to enter the marketplace, to sail the Hellespont, and so forth. At one time or another many persons were subjected to one or more of these restrictions. Those caught in disobedience were liable to summary arrest and prosecution by any citizen, which made fertile ground for sycophants and personal enemies to work in.

Apart from this, there was little law enforcement. Athens relied mainly on a system of self-redress. In private cases the law would sanction punishment by the victim of a crime against the perpetrator of it. Thus Vinogradoff, in his *Outlines of Historical Jurisprudence,* tells us that in the city "a thief could be taken, bound, and led off to prison by the injured party." But this was the institution of private redress, not of public law enforcement.

The other obvious example from the ancient world is the Roman republic, where the absence of any effective body to keep the peace and enforce the laws was one of the inspirations of this study. There, too, self-redress had obtained since the time of the kings, when there was not yet even a judicial system. As late as the Christian era, punishment by self-redress was allowed in private affairs, though not in public ones. Heads of households still had absolute authority in domestic matters and could exile or execute their servants and dependents.

Extreme penalties required the sanction of a family council, a semi-public court that was never interfered with. It remained within the law to slaughter an entire household of slaves and servants for the murder by one of them of the master, a practice that dated from primitive times. But acts of this kind were rare, Plutarch tells us, and a matter of public concern when they occurred.

Such powers of life and death did not extend beyond a man's threshold. Between one man and another, as in cases of debt, those who were brought to trial and had judgment entered against them could be seized by the person to whom the debt was due and forced to work it off.

In the public sphere, law and order seem to have been maintained, at least in the time of the Roman republic, by the *aediles,* who were magistrates ranking between the tribunes and the praetors. They had public works, fires, public decency, and other civic concerns under their charge, as well as weights and measures in the markets and the supervision of certain public games, which they organized. Like other magistrates, as well as the high priests and other important public officials, they were served by *lictors,* salaried retainers, appointed annually, whose function, besides carrying the *fasces,* was to clear the way for the magistrates in crowds, see that they were received with respect, stand by them at the tribunal, guard their houses, summon offenders before them, and scourge such persons as they ordered punished.

In the later years of the Roman republic, certain *triumvirs* were added—inferior magistrates whose duties included the guarding of prisoners condemned to execution, the carrying out of the sentence, and the supervision of criminal justice generally. The triumvirs were given the duty of keeping prisoners in preventive detention and producing them for criminal trials. When sitting as a court, they heard ordinary police-court charges such as vagrancy, nocturnal disturbances, and so forth. Otherwise, they functioned as chiefs of police who had the patrolling of the city and the preservation of order within their charge. Of the force that was presumably at their command to carry out such duties, we hear little, not even whether it was formally instituted.

Still later, Augustus established the first real organized police force in Rome under the authority of the prefect of the city, whose office dated back to republic times, when it was the custom to appoint such a person in the absence of the two consuls, and whose responsibility, in the words of Tacitus, was "to overawe the slaves and that part of the population which, unless it fears a strong hand, is disorderly and reckless."

Under Augustus, this functionary was civil not military, and is sometimes cited as a forerunner of a modern superintendent or chief of police, with whom, indeed, it shared many similarities. But the coercion this position represented was not civil coercion as we have defined it. On the contrary, all aspects of Augustan rule were extensions of the imperial power. The prefect of the city was not in any sense a constituted official.

The free societies of Athens and Rome in their republican days remain the only ones we know anything about in ancient times where coercive force—to the slight extent that it existed—had a character consistent with republican principles. The same cannot be said of barbarian and medieval Europe, where histories of police try to point out interesting attempts at law enforcement, some prophetic of modern forms and practices. Whether they served to keep order, to enforce judicial decrees, or to maintain the security of the State, they were in every case the emanations of a ruling power that was essentially despotic.

With the Renaissance, we have the rebirth of free institutions—in the Italian republics, for example. But there is little indication that they had any apparatus for the maintenance of public order or law enforcement. Machiavelli's *History of Florence* makes no mention of such a thing in that city. On the contrary, the signs are that it was totally absent, as on the occasion in the fifteenth century of the attempt by a certain Rinaldo degli Albizzi to restore the nobility.

This undertaking failed for lack of sufficient support, but while the threat existed, there was no machinery to oppose it. At the height of the crisis, according to Machiavelli, "the Signoria, knowing Rinaldo and his party had taken arms, [and] finding themselves abandoned, caused the palace to be shut up." In an earlier period, when some especially unjust ruler of the city had become intolerable, he was likely to have been hauled into the streets by the populace, or at least the armed partisans of one or another disaffected family, and butchered. This was less common later on. Nevertheless, in times of tension there was always danger of assassination, even during the great days of the Medicis. Prudent men wore armor under their clothes in public places. One can hardly suppose in those days that among the fierce rivalries of the houses of the city any effective police force would have been accepted, nor is there any indication that it ever was.

Apart from the Italian republics—apart also, perhaps, from the Swiss cantons—the place of greatest interest for our inquiry is England. There in the nineteenth century the establishment of the Metropolitan Police of London brought into being the first effective force of its kind that civil or constitutional government had ever achieved on any considerable scale and for anything except brief intervals.

That this should have happened may seem astonishing. England had never until that time been a well policed country, especially not London, certainly not in the sense that France, and particularly Paris, had been well policed, with some exceptions, since the seventeenth century. Indeed, the secret police of Paris (hardly a civil police force) was the only successful institution of its kind since that of Rome under Augustus. It was everywhere recognized as such.

In England, it was otherwise. While the history of peacekeeping and law enforcement—in the sense of apprehending lawbreakers—goes back to Anglo-Saxon times, the traditional English machinery for these tasks, comprising chiefly justices of the peace in the counties and constables within the towns, had the reputation of being ineffective to the point of ridicule. We learn this unforgettably from Shakespeare, who gives us not only Dogberry but Justice Shallow. Yet, both the constabulary office and that of the justice of the peace had worthy origins in English law, and both functioned well enough, though in limited ways, up to the beginning of the modern age, when changes in English society gradually made them obsolete.

By the eighteenth century, alternatives had begun to appear. Thus, in London, from the time when Sir John Fielding, brother of the novelist, was magistrate in Bow Street, a system of enforcement based on what were known as runners, because they were dispatched to perform the business of the court, had been formed in a manner that indicated some recognition of the uses of a police such as the city eventually created.

Nevertheless, it was not so much a gradual recognition of the need for a civil police in the emerging civil society of England as the critical failure of existing law enforcement resources at the end of the eighteenth century and the beginning of the nineteenth that led up to the establishment of that institution. The facts given us by an English historian of the subject,

Charles Reith, and others, suggest that the signal lessons were those provided by a series of popular disturbances, beginning with the Gordon riots of 1780, that threatened the whole fabric of English society and were beyond the existing means of authority to control.

In these disturbances—these times of rage and riot brought on for the most part by Parliamentary enactments against which no orderly means of protest existed—the pattern was always the same. Called into the streets by rabble-rousers in the pay of disaffected interests for the Gordon riots, or by their own anger and despair in the Luddite and Corn Law agitations of a later day, the mostly poorer segments of the population of London would gather in front of public buildings and the houses of the great or march in demonstration through the city, often at night with torches.

Sometimes the chief objects of their wrath—judges, say, or ministers—would flee to the country while others remained to watch helplessly the vandalism that occurred. At other times, when the threat to order and defiance of the law seemed general, or when some person of power decided on violent reaction, soldiers were called and sent in to threaten or fire upon the crowds with results which were, at least in some cases, the opposite of those intended. Thus, in the Gordon riots, when the Guards rode down the mob with flashing sabers, the effect was incendiary, notwithstanding that at least one person died, bringing out more rioters than had been present to begin with and sending them on a rampage that, as Dickens said in *Barnaby Rudge,* bathed the whole city in fiery light.

It was recognized from the outset, at least by certain persons, that such outbreaks, assuming they could not be prevented, required some means of control other than by the fragmented, weak, and corrupt magistrate-dominated constabulary system then at the command of the borough alderman, which was far too weak for the purpose, or by the military forces, which were far too strong.

It was perceived that what was needed was the same thing we would now recognize as a civil police. So clearly was this understood, in fact, that after some delay, while the government of Lord North ran out its time in fruitless struggles to regain the American colonies, a bill was introduced in 1785 under the leadership of William Pitt that would have established just such a police. But it was withdrawn in the face of opposition by the aldermen, who saw in it a threat to their local powers, on the excuse that it would create a body like that of the secret police of Paris, who were believed by most Englishmen to be heavily involved in espionage and tyranny, and who were at any rate the arm of a despotic government.

Such were the vagaries of politics and history that, despite subsequent riots hardly less serious than those of Gordon's time and much discussion of the problems of crime and disorder, it was almost forty years before another ministry under Sir Robert Peel was able to formulate another bill to the same end. It was passed several years later.

The issues raised by the discussion of the subject during those years, in which Samuel Romilly and Jeremy Bentham played important parts, were, first, whether a civil police was desirable at all; and, second, supposing it were desirable, whether it could be instituted on terms strong enough to maintain control while at the same time restrained enough to preserve liberty.

It was the conviction, among those who were opposed to any civil police at all, or at least to any great reliance upon such a force, that the remedy for widespread crime and persistent disorder lay in reform of the criminal laws. This was Romilly's position, and it was derived in part from the classic work on the subject by Cesare Beccaria, *On Crimes and Punishments* (see *GIT* 1974, pp. 352–407). Beccaria had argued for a rational correspondence between crimes and punishments as distinct from the arbitrary and savage system of penalties common in the eighteenth century. Particularly did that seem a necessary reform in England, where it was legal to hang a child for the theft of a handkerchief worth a shilling.

Those who approved of such severity did so on the ground that it was ultimately merciful, that "terror alone" would dissuade those otherwise inclined to crime from committing it. Those who argued for rational punishments, and especially for a reduction in the number of capital offenses, maintained that, since juries would not subject persons to capital punishment for petty crimes, they in effect escaped justice entirely. The way to control them was by a humanly acceptable system of penalties that juries would not hesitate to impose.

What is relevant in all this is the assumption, persisting into the nineteenth century, that law as such, or at least the judicial branch of government standing for trial and punishment, could sustain itself without the intervention of coercive force—that, in effect, it constituted such a force in itself, beyond which nothing was either necessary or desirable.

There is an echo in this of the political philosophers who, since Plato, have insisted that laws can be maintained through civic virtue and habitual obedience. But the vision of a citizenry deeply ingrained with good civic habits is a far cry from the subjection through terror of a population otherwise disposed to vandalism and criminality. The criminal law reformers sought merely to make the governance of law more effective by making it more proportional, as between crime and punishment.

At the same time, a police reform movement had begun in England. It need not have run counter to the criminal law reformers, but it did. This was because the existing police structure, consisting of alderman-magistrates, constables ("Charlies"), watchmen, and runners who did court business for fees, was so weak and so corrupt as to seem unworthy of increased powers. Such powers the criminal law reformers were reluctant to give.

Their opposition was quite different from that of those who genuinely feared a strong police establishment, believing, in the words of one historian of the subject, that even "the mildest form of police supervision" would necessitate the use of domiciliary visits, universal espionage, and official interference with the concerns of daily life." These two anxieties combined to prevent any real progress toward reform for two generations, during which industrialization was creating an increasingly large and desperate population in London. It was also a time when the French Revolution offered men everywhere an example of what defiance and disorder could accomplish.

To make a long story short, the measure that Peel introduced in 1822, which led ultimately to establishment of the Metropolitan Police in 1829, indicated two purposes that reassured or disarmed at least the more principled among its opponents.

These were, first, that the intention was primarily to prevent crime, as distinct from its punishment. The proposed Act would, therefore, not involve the apprehension of criminals and all the devices of detection and surveillance that struck fear into the hearts of Englishmen. Second, the object was to protect the individual citizen from lawlessness rather than from the State.

While the last of these aims had been at least implicitly the concern of watchmen and constables elsewhere at earlier times, the first was without substantial precedent anywhere. Both were alien to the only two examples of centralized and efficient police forces that history provided, which were those of Imperial Rome and of Paris, neither of which were truly civil police.

Certain features of the constabulary to be created were intended to overcome the same fears and objections. The constables were given uniforms, not so that they might be taken for soldiers, but that they might be visible in their blue frock coats. They were also armed with truncheons, but these were hidden. They were trained, salaried, and employed full-time, to be the more effective in their duties, but also so that they might be regarded with the respect that is usually accorded to professionals.

For the same reason, they were selected for education, bearing, manners, and even height superior to that found in most of the inhabitants of the neighborhoods they patrolled. They were schooled to be knowledgeable about trouble spots in the metropolis, on which they kept special watch, and where they could assemble quickly. Even then they were instructed to use violence only as a last resort. Above all they were told to avoid rudeness, the use of hostile language, and unnecessary arrests on the ground that "the more respectful and civil the police are upon all occasions of duty, the more they will be respected and supported by the public in the proper execution of their duty."

All this was to the end, as Reith observes, not that "the weight of the law" might "prevent the prospective criminal's choice being free," but

"The Gordon riots of 1780. . . threatened the whole fabric of English society and were beyond the existing means of authority to control."

according to a vision of "law-observance and order . . . induced successfully by defined behavior on the part of administrators and servants of the law," who would thereby reduce the need and the desire of people in the streets to act so as to require the law's weight to be used.

IV. One model of civil coercion

It is easy to see many of these details of the Metropolitan Police Act as mere particulars of the time, the place, and the people who created them, having no larger importance than that in the development of the idea of civil police. The concerns of the English in the early years of the nineteenth century with regard to a police system, and the terms by which they were eventually persuaded to accept such an institution, were doubtless in many respects peculiar to themselves.

It was especially fortuitous that the first superintendent of the Metropolitan Police, Charles Rowan, was a veteran of Wellington's army who did not believe in Wellington's idea of discipline as blind obedience maintained by merciless force. He held instead that the power of a military command was best maintained by good example. He translated that idea into the deportment of the London constable and his superiors, not only in their chain of command but with respect to the populace over which they were given control.

Equally important, perhaps, was that this and other aspects of the Metropolitan Police were from the start matters not only of municipal but national concern. The police were placed under the authority of the home secretary, a member of the Cabinet. Whatever they did or did not do, and whatever was said about them, was a matter of Parliamentary business.

England was a country in which Romilly could take up the business of criminal law reform in earnest before the House of Commons within twenty-four hours after he had been set upon with criminal intent while sitting on a bench in a London park. Their location gave the London police a kind of visibility and importance that those of New York, say, or Boston did not have. They were largely unnoticed in the history of their times.

Still, when every allowance is made for these factors, a kind of insight, a sort of wisdom, seems to have been at work, however fitfully, in the creation of the Metropolitan Police. This undertaking raised most of the important issues that coercive force in a civil context generates. It also provided solutions that in important respects still serve as models for any discussion of the subject.

Of these issues, apart from the question of efficiency, which inevitably is technical, the primary one was, and still is, whether coercive force can be held accountable for its operations. The second is whether these can be carried on in such a way as not to stifle the process of consent without which no society is free. If these two questions are combined into one, it is, in effect, whether a truly civil police can exist at all.

The English solution to the first problem was to place the police force under control of a Cabinet officer answerable to Parliament. This was perhaps peculiar to English institutions. It was nonetheless a measure admirably conceived as combining a command at once powerful yet not beyond review.

The real genius of the conception was, however, in its manner of dealing with the question of consent. This, as Charles Reith noted, was to make the constable a kind of example who ideally would never have to use the powers he was given. In philosophical terms it was a way of making him the embodiment of the law, its personification. He would serve by his conduct to inspire the kind of obedience that for so long has been recognized as an expansion of civic virtue.

It may be argued that this was, in fact, the only way (whatever variation in detail there might be) a truly civil police can exist. What the Metropolitan Police Act achieved was the reconciliation of coercion with consent, and not until this had been done could the problem of a civil police force be solved. Not until then was it seen that the only acceptable relationship between coercion and consent in a free society is essentially a didactic one with the law as teacher visible in a police presence inculcative of obedient habits.

If this is the right moral to be drawn from the English precedent, it survives despite the sober fact that a sizable part of the population of London in the early 1830s was hardly capable of consent at all, being impoverished and illiterate. When the English middle class congratulated itself on at last being able to sleep safely in its beds, it did so without much interest in those who had nowhere to rest. Nor must the point be given up in the light of subsequent history, which has transformed the London constable into a figure far less able or willing to rely on moral persuasion than he used to be.

When coercive force operates through fear only, it is indistinguishable from what it would be under a despotic government, though it is still restrained by law, which would not be the case under a despotic government. This merely proves the connection between consent and coercion. When the one withers, the other dies.

Consent is parodied by the hoodlums of our day who assert their rights when what they seek is license. Civil coercion is perverted by police who demand what they call respect when what they mean is dread. The parody and the perversion are each what the other deserves. Still the principle remains: where a civil police can exist, it is only on the terms we have described. No others are consistent with free citizens living under authorized government.

Such at any rate was the conclusion reached by the Institute study of the subject a decade ago. It is here summarized in its essentials in the belief that it remains correct.

The one modification that may be necessary is one that recent history suggests. What, at the beginning of the last decade, appeared a sudden and temporary decline of consent in free societies everywhere seems to have become a fixed if not permanent state of affairs, at least among that part of the citizenry in such societies with which the police have most to do.

We may not soon again enjoy the possibility of a return to the social behavior that prevailed in at least some parts of the world for the better part of the past two centuries, when coercion had little overt part to play save as demonstrated by routine criminality and ordinary public disorders. If we do not have that possibility, neither will there be any chance of a truly civil police. We must expect instead coercive enforcement that in many respects is paramilitary and that has more faith in manipulation and technology than in an open presence and civil exchange. These were characteristic police traits in free societies throughout the world for what may have been only an historical moment.

V. Bibliography

Among the writings in political philosophy that were consulted for this study, the following are of special interest or importance: Plato, *The Republic, Laws;* Aristotle, *Ethics* and *Politics;* the *Policratus* of John of Salisbury; Aquinas's *Treatise on Law;* Marsilius's *Defender of the Peace;* Jean Bodin's *Six Books of a Commonweal;* Hobbes, *Leviathan;* Locke, *Second Essay on Civil Government;* Rousseau, *The Social Contract;* Kant, *Science of Right;* Hegel, *Philosophy of Right;* Mill, *On Liberty* and *Considerations on Representative Government;* Hans Kelsen, *What is Justice?*

Works of an analytical character on the subject of police that were consulted include George Berkley, *The Democratic Policeman* (1974); Michael Banton, *The Police in the Community* (1964); D. J. Bordue, ed., *The Police: Six Sociological Essays* (1967); Jerome Skolnick, *Justice Without Trial: Law Enforcement in Democratic Society,* 2nd ed. (1975); J. Q. Wilson, *Varieties of Police Behavior* (1968); Claud R. Sowle, ed., *Police Power and Individual Freedom* (1972); Geoffrey Marshall, *Police and Government; The Status and Accountability of the English Constable* (1965); Brian Chapman, *Police State* (1970); August Vollmer, *The Police and Modern Society* (1936).

General surveys, partly historical, of the police are not very common, and of those that exist some are rather old. Still useful, however, are John Coatman, *Police* (1959); Bruce Smith, *Police Systems in the United States* (1940, 1960); David G. Williams, *Keeping the Peace: The Police and Public Order* (1967); and James P. Hall, *The History and Philosophy of Law Enforcement* (1975).

Comprehensive studies of police in the ancient world do not exist, apparently, but the subject is treated in Alfred Zimmern, *The Greek Commonwealth,* J. B. Bury, *History of the Later Roman Empire* (especially at the time of Justinian); Leon Home, *Roman Political Institutions* (1929); and in *The Cambridge Ancient History* (1934), especially in the chapter on "The Augustan Empire." Among the studies of Florence other than that by Machiavelli, of interest are Ferdinand Schevill's *History of Florence* (1961), a standard work, and G. A. Brucker's more recent *The Civil World of Early Renaissance Florence* (1977).

Venice, among other Italian republics, may be studied in the standard histories and in *Rich and Poor in Renaissance Venice* (1971), by B. S. Pullan, which deals with social conditions. But none of these works has much to say about police. The literature on the police of England, and especially that of London, is extensive. Of particular usefulness and importance are Patrick Colquhoun, *The Police of the Metropolis* (1806); F. W. Maitland, *Justice and Police* (1885); Charles Reith, *A New Study of Police History* (1956); T. A. Critchley, *A History of the Police in England and Wales, 900–1966* (1967); and W. L. M. Lee, *A History of Police in England* (1901). In addition, works can be found that treat the subject of police in various American cities, among them Houston, New York, and Philadelphia.

PART FOUR

Special Features

Dante the Thinker: Poetry and Philosophy

Otto Bird

Born and raised in Ann Arbor, Michigan, Otto Bird attended the university there, graduating in 1935 with honors in English, to which he added a masters degree in comparative literature the following year. He took his doctorate in philosophy and literature at the University of Toronto in 1939.

From 1947 to 1950 he served as associate editor of the *Syntopicon,* for *Great Books of the Western World,* working with Mortimer Adler. In the latter year he joined the faculty at the University of Notre Dame, where he was director of the General Program of Liberal Studies until 1963. He was executive editor of *The Great Ideas Today* from 1964 to 1970, when he was appointed university professor of arts and letters at Notre Dame, from which he retired in 1977.

He has written four books, *The Canzoné d'Amore of Guido Cavalcanti with the Commentary of Dino del Garbo* (1942), *Syllogistic Logic and Its Extensions* (1964), *The Idea of Justice* (1967), and *Cultures in Conflict* (1976), besides articles on the history and theory of the liberal arts. In addition he was a major contributor to the *Propaedia,* or Outline of Knowledge, of the current (fifteenth) edition of the *Encyclopaedia Britannica.*

Mr. Bird now spends much of the year in Shoals, Indiana, where he has built a house and grows grapes for making wine. He continues to be active in editorial projects of Encyclopaedia Britannica, Inc., and remains consulting editor of *The Great Ideas Today.* His discussion of Pascal's *Pensées* appeared in last year's volume.

In one of those swings that occur so frequently in critical opinion, recent work on the poetry of Dante is now stressing and praising the very features that only a generation or so ago were belittled and denigrated. Dante the thinker is now being brought to the fore, his philosophy hailed as an important ingredient of his poetry. In particular, two books from the University of Cambridge have undertaken the task of showing that the poetry is even a function of the philosophy. Thus Patrick Boyde, in the first of a projected three-volume work, entitled *Dante: Philomythes and Philosopher,* insists that Dante is not only "first and foremost a poet of the intellectual life," but also that "most of the distinguishing features of his mature poetry derive from his study of philosophy." So too Robin Kirkpatrick's *Dante's Paradiso and the Limitations of Modern Criticism* is especially concerned to show that critics who downplay Dante's intellectual interests fail to grasp and to appreciate the full beauty of Dante's achievements.

The critical opinion now being opposed is best represented by the Italian philosopher Benedetto Croce and the American-English poet and critic T. S. Eliot. According to Croce, poetry is so essentially a work of the non-conceptual lyric imagination that intellectual thought is an obstacle to its expression. Hence he argued that the intellectual structure and content of the *Divine Comedy* must be sharply separated from its poetic value, and he even went so far as to recommend that the former could be neglected without any loss to the appreciation of the poetry. Eliot seemed to go even further. Croce at least allowed that there was thought in the *Comedy,* whereas Eliot denied that Dante "did any thinking on his own" and claimed that "for a poet to be also a philosopher he would have to be virtually two men." Admittedly there is hyperbole here, for Eliot did not deny that Dante expounded an explicit philosophy. Nevertheless, he strongly maintained that Dante as a poet was not making philosophical statements and that the philosophy as such contributes little if anything to the value of the poetry.

Between these two opposed positions regarding the relation between poetry and philosophy—represented by Boyde and Kirkpatrick on the one side and Croce and Eliot on the other—there are at issue a number of important topics well worth serious consideration. Granted that Dante is somehow a philosophical poet, or a poetic philosopher, what does it mean to make such an assertion? What is his conception of philosophy, and is he, as Eliot claimed, not an original philosophical thinker? How does his philosophy enter into his poetry, and how does his poetry affect the philosophy and the expression of it? To understand Dante's poetry, is it necessary to know what Dante himself thought to be true? Is he attempting to make true statements about the nature of things, and, if so, does he succeed? If he did believe thai he was stating truths, and expected his reader to accept them as such, what is the situation of the reader who does not share his beliefs? Is belief in their truth of no relation to and no part of the reading and understanding of the poetry as poetry? On these questions and their implications Boyde and Kirkpatrick have much to say and suggest that is both interesting and illuminating.

Dante the philosopher

That Dante had a deep and genuine interest in philosophy we know quite apart from the evidence of the *Comedy.* The *Convivio* (or *Banquet*) is an unfinished prose work that he wrote after he had told the story of his love for Beatrice celebrated in the poems of the *Vita Nuova,* his first book. The *Convivio* tells how he had sought consolation after the death of Beatrice by turning to the study of philosophy. Following the example of Boethius in *The Consolation of Philosophy* [see *GIT* 1982], he claims that he addressed philosophy in the guise of a woman and declared his love for her in a series of poems. Readers in his own day, and many since, have questioned whether there was not in fact a lady of flesh and blood who was the real object of his love. It was to correct such false suspicions, Dante claimed, that he was inspired to write the *Convivio.* It consists of a series of prose commentaries on the poems that show how philosophy was celebrated in them under an allegorical mode. These commentaries not only tell how he came to the study and love of philosophy but also propose to offer an introduction to its study for public leaders whose concerns leave little leisure for such undertakings. Hence, for understanding Dante's interest in philosophy it is irrelevant to consider whether or not there was a living lady who was the inspiration of the poems.

Philosophy, as Dante conceived it, must not be restricted to one branch of knowledge distinct from other arts and sciences. The *Convivio* begins by citing the claim made at the opening of Aristotle's *Metaphysics* that all men by nature desire to know. From this Dante at once concludes that man's distinctive happiness consists in satisfying the desire to know taken in its fullest amplitude. Philosophy for Dante therefore comprehends not only all that is now included under the natural and social sciences but also the arts, and especially the liberal arts that are propaedeutic to all the others—the linguistic arts of grammar, rhetoric, and logic, and the mathematical arts of arithmetic, geometry, music, and astronomy. It also includes, in addition to rational philosophy—as divided into natural philosophy, ethics, and metaphysics—supernatural theology based on principles that exceed the grasp of reason and derive from faith in divine revelation. As commonly accepted today, philosophy is identified with the study of both things and knowledge in their most general principles. Dante would not deny such a characterization, but he would not limit it to that. For him philosophy is general not only in its principles but also in its scope as comprehending all the kinds of knowledge, which are all "members of wisdom."

However, philosophy is not only a knowledge, it is also a love, and the *Convivio* dwells at some length on the etymology of its name as love or friendship (*philos*) of wisdom or knowledge (*sophia*). Whence Dante observes that "in a certain sense everyone may be called a philosopher in virtue of the natural love which begets in everyone the longing to know." But this observation is immediately qualified by the claim that in the proper sense he alone deserves the name who possesses good will and zeal in the truest and best friendship of wisdom. Then, using the distinctions Aristotle had made among the kinds of love, Dante declares that the love which is philosophy must be for the sake neither of the profit nor of the pleasure that can be derived from wisdom, but solely for the worth of wisdom in itself. Such a love entails that the lover "feels this friendship in virtue of right appetite and right reason." The philosopher in the proper sense of the name must be good as having right desires ordered rightly to real goods and wise as having his reason set upon knowledge of the truth.

Dante's interest in philosophy and his growing love for it led him to frequent "the schools of the religious orders and the disputations of the philosophers." In Florence, the Franciscans had such a school at the church of Santa Croce, the Dominicans one at Santa Maria Novella. The *Convivio* shows by its numerous references and quotations how well versed Dante became in the writings of Aristotle and the scholastic commentaries upon them. However, although still a neophyte, he was not at all a slavish copier, as is shown by his departure from traditional teachings. His originality is especially apparent in the hierarchical classification of the sciences that the *Convivio* provides.

For the allegorical interpretation of one of his poems Dante needed to compare the various sciences with the different heavens. The Ptolemaic system of astronomy used by the scholastics distinguished ten heavens rising in an ascending order of dignity and beauty above the earth. But the traditional order of the sciences Dante wanted to accommodate consists of the seven liberal arts, the three parts of philosophy—natural philosophy, moral philosophy or ethics, and metaphysics—all of them capped by theology, the "queen of the sciences." Since Dante had eleven sciences and only ten heavens, he had to assign two sciences to one heaven. In doing so, he established a hierarchy of the sciences that departed radically from the traditional teaching. His classification can be tabulated as follows:

1. Grammar	Moon
2. Dialectic	Mercury
3. Rhetoric	Venus
4. Arithmetic	Sun
5. Music	Mars
6. Geometry	Jupiter
7. Astronomy	Saturn
8. Natural Philosophy	Starry Heaven
9. Metaphysics	Starry Heaven
10. Moral Philosophy	Primum Mobile
11. Theology	Empyrean

Since it is the hierarchical classification that is our concern—i.e., the ranking of higher and lower—the various arguments Dante musters to accomplish the correlation need not detain us. It suffices to know that the Empyrean represents the highest as the purely spiritual abode of God and the blessed. Hence, as theology is correlated with the Empyrean, it constitutes the highest knowledge, a claim in which Dante did not depart from his teachers. Nor did he in putting grammar in the lowest place, however indispensable knowing one's letters is to further knowledge. In placing rhetoric above dialectic, or logic, he sided with the poets (since poetry was considered part of rhetoric) rather than the philosophers who assigned dialectic, or logic, the higher place. But that was not his most remarkable innovation. Dante's greatest departure from the tradition of his teachers lay in placing moral philosophy, or ethics, above metaphysics, for this makes moral philosophy the highest natural, or rational, knowledge. In so doing, Dante in effect asserted his independence from Aristotle and his scholastic followers, for whom metaphysics constitutes the highest and architectonic science, as is asserted in Aristotle's book bearing that title. As noted by the eminent historian of medieval thought, Étienne Gilson, Dante in asserting the primacy of moral philosophy over metaphysics "maintained a position entirely extraordinary in the middle ages."

This position has further repercussions, especially on the way Dante views the relation between theology and philosophy and, of more practical importance, the relation between church and state, and how man can best achieve happiness—all topics to which there will be occasion to return. Taken together, Dante's position on these matters and the arguments advanced for its support suffice to establish him as an original philosopher. In fact, Gilson concluded from his study of Dante's works that Dante holds a unique place in the history of medieval philosophy in that his position with regard to philosophy, and especially in political theory, "cannot be reduced to any other."

That Dante maintained the primacy of moral philosophy in rational knowledge is not without relevance to his as well as our own understanding of the *Divine Comedy*. In the letter written to his patron Can Grande della Scala, presenting the *Paradiso,* Dante expressly claimed that his *Comedy* is a work in moral philosophy. For "the end of the whole and of the part," he wrote, "is to remove those living in this life from the state of misery and lead them to the state of felicity. But the branch of philosophy which regulates the work in its whole and in its parts is morals or ethics, because the whole was undertaken not for speculation but for practical results. For albeit in some parts or passages it is handled in the way of speculation, this is not for the sake of speculation, but for the sake of practical results." Hence, granting the authenticity of this letter (about which there is some dispute), we must acknowledge that Dante himself considered his poem a work in philosophy, and moreover the highest branch of philosophy.

The earliest readers of his poem agreed with Dante's own verdict. For, as Boyde notes, they hailed him as "a supreme philosopher, although a layman," "a man of piercing intellect and tenacious memory, and most assiduous in his studies," "a theologian to whom no doctrine was unknown," "a poetic philosopher by profession." This last attribution came from Marsilio Ficino, who was himself a philosopher, and is especially significant in that it emphasizes that Dante is first a philosopher rather than a philosophical poet.

Boyde's own work is planned on a grand scale. Its aim is to provide the whole matrix of terms and ideas from which Dante drew the scientific, philosophical, and theological materials of his poem. His procedure varies in that he sometimes begins with an exposition of the ideas and goes on to show how they are used to form an episode in the *Comedy,* whereas at other times he reverses this, beginning with a particular episode and indicating how the intellectual background can explain and illuminate it.

The first published volume, subtitled *Man in the Cosmos,* surveys the view of the natural world that Dante had at his command from the natural philosophy and cosmology of his day. For the most part this material is taken from the works of Aristotle and the scholastic commentaries upon them, especially those of St. Thomas Aquinas. The second and third volumes are still to come. The second, to be subtitled *Man in Society,* will deal with Dante's moral and political philosophy, illustrated again largely from Aristotle, especially the *Nicomachean Ethics.* The third and final volume, *Man and God,* will take its materials mainly from the Bible and the theologians. When completed, the three-volume work will provide a comprehensive account of Dante's entire world-view, explained and illustrated from the basic documents that Dante could have drawn upon.

Up to now, however, our attention has been directed to only one part of the overall title, Dante the philosopher. Turning now to the other part, we must consider:

Dante is pictured amid three settings that helped to shape his poetic philosophy: at left is a scene from the *Inferno;* center, Dante's concept of the universe; at right, the city of Florence.

Dante *philomythes*

Boyde derives the title for his work from St. Thomas's commentary on the *Metaphysics* at the place where Aristotle was attempting a reconciliation between philosophy and myth by noting that "the lover of myth is in some sense a lover of true knowledge, because a myth is composed of wonders." This statement led Thomas to remark that "the lover of true knowledge (*philosophus*) is in some sense a lover of myth (*philomythes*)." Boyde further expands that into "a lover of the old stories and legends, or, as we might say today, a lover of fiction."

For Dante, as for Thomas and Aristotle before him, it is the wonderful or marvelous that provides the link joining the philosopher and the philomythes, to whom it is of common concern. In the case of the philosopher, or lover of knowledge, wonder, arising from ignorance as to why things should be so, awakens the desire to find out, and thus leads to the search for knowledge. Hence, according to Aristotle, philosophy first arose from wonder, and may so arise still.

One could scarcely ask for an occasion productive of greater wonder or of more marvels than a journey through the lands of the living dead, from the lowest hell to the highest heaven. Dante himself declared, in the letter to Can Grande, that the matter with which his poem is concerned is the marvelous (*admirabilis*), and he described the marvelousness or wondrousness of the *Paradiso* in particular as consisting in "such lofty and sublime things as the conditions of the celestial kingdom." Dante the writer of the story or *mythos* is thus a philomythes. But so too is Dante the pilgrim-character within the story. He is portrayed, not only as moving among marvels, but also as exciting wonder in the spirits he encounters, who are frequently presented as being astounded that a living body should be found walking awake among the spirits of the dead. Dante-pilgrim likewise is shocked as he proceeds into surprise and wonder, which lead him to question and seek and find enlightenment and the satisfying of his desire to know. As Boyde points out, Dante the protagonist is a "*philosopher in fieri*," i.e., one who is becoming a philosopher, whereas Dante the author is a "philosopher *in actu*." But both Dantes are also philomythes—Dante-protagonist as a wonderer and Dante-author as story- or myth-teller.

Philosophy-into-poetry

One may well agree that Dante—both Dantes, in fact—are lovers, and yet still one would want to know how the two kinds of love are related: how the philosophy affects the poetry and the poetry the philosophy. Is it any more than that philosophy, in the very broad sense used here, supplies material for the poetry? Or is there a more intimate relation, some sense in which there is a way or kind of poetic philosophizing?

To make the question more precise, it would be well at the start to restrict the sense in which we shall talk of poetry. The only one with which we will be concerned—the one that will supply the test—is the story-aspect, i.e., poetry as "myth" in the sense that Aristotle gives it in the *Poetics* when he declares that the *mythos,* usually translated as "plot," is the soul of poetry. Such a stringent limitation, it must be admitted, leaves out a great amount of what counts as poetry; in fact, some might claim that it leaves out all of it.

And of what it leaves out, Dante is usually master. For he tells his story in verse of rhyme and rhythm and imagery, in language of such purity and variety as to make his poem one of the most musical and beautiful in all of world literature. No translation can approach the limpid translucency of such lines as those (*Par.* 30.39–42) that describe the highest heaven as

> ciel, ch'è pura luce:
> luce intellettual piena d'amore,
> amor di vero ben pien di letizia,
> letizia che trascende ogni dolzore.

> the Heaven which is pure light:
> light intellectual full of love,
> love of true good full of joy,
> joy which transcends every sweetness.

There is doctrine here, and it would not be difficult to explicate the relation between light, intellect, love, joy, and delight from the teachings of his masters. Yet there is also such verbal beauty that great delight is to be had merely from repeating the Italian over and over again. It is significant that Dante characterized the philosophical mind as one which "not only contemplates the truth, but also contemplates its own contemplation and the beauty thereof, turning upon itself and enamouring itself of itself by reason of the beauty of its direct contemplation." Words can be an expression of doctrine, but they may also be an expression of such beauty that they can be contemplated for themselves. One might well find it useful and illuminating to pursue this line of thought as adumbrating a theory of philosophical poetry or of poetic philosophy as a way of thought and expression that achieves a closer union than otherwise between beauty and truth.

For the moment, however, we will seek an easier reading by investigating the relation between story and thought; and for this purpose a literal prose translation can be almost as serviceable as the original, providing it remains faithful to the story. To start with, we will consider a fairly complex episode in the *Paradiso* which embodies some of Dante's most original contributions to philosophy. It is also an episode that has received extensive analysis by both Kirkpatrick and Gilson, inasmuch as it concerns directly Dante's own conception of philosophy. For, just as the sun provides in its illumination an image of wisdom, so those blessed spirits whom Dante-pilgrim meets as he journeys through the heaven of the Sun represent the thinkers whom Dante-author considered to be wise, i.e., lovers of wisdom. Hence the story episode provides a way of expressing Dante's conception of the work of philosophy.

The heaven of the Sun

In the episode of the Sun, which occupies Cantos 10–14 of the *Paradiso,* Dante meets the spirits of men who in this life pursued many different kinds of learning. Representing lovers of wisdom, i.e., philosophers, they indicate immediately what a very broad view Dante had of philosophy; this is manifest from merely listing the names of the spirits he meets there. Taken in the order of their appearance and identifying them first by name and then by their profession, we have:

1. Thomas Aquinas	theologian, philosopher
2. Albert the Great	theologian, philosopher, scientist
3. Gratian	lawyer
4. Peter Lombard	theologian
5. Solomon	king
6. Dionysius the Areopagite	mystical theologian
7. Paulus Orosius	historian
8. Boethius	philosopher, theologian
9. Isidor of Seville	encyclopaedist
10. Bede the Venerable	historian, theologian
11. Richard of St. Victor	mystical theologian
12. Siger of Brabant	philosopher
13. Bonaventure	theologian
14. Illuminato	Franciscan friar
15. Augustine	Franciscan friar
16. Hugh of St. Victor	theologian
17. Peter the Eater	historian
18. Peter of Spain	logician
19. Nathan	Old Testament prophet
20. Chrysostom	theologian, preacher
21. Anselm of Canterbury	theologian
22. Donatus	grammarian
23. Rhabanus	encyclopaedist
24. Joachim of Calabria	prophet

Among this group—certainly heterogeneous, at least to modern eyes—it is significant that two at most of the twenty-four would now be considered to be primarily philosophers, that is, Boethius and Siger. And as we shall see later, to Dante's contempories it might well have seemed scandalous to find Siger there at all, and especially to be introduced by Thomas Aquinas.

However, it is more to our immediate purpose to note that Dante here is in effect doing philosophy poetically. He is literally "demonstrating," i.e., showing and pointing out what he understands by philosophical knowledge in telling a story. His pilgrim protagonist is on the way to the heaven of the Sun, where he meets Thomas and Bonaventure, who, in turn, identify the other dwellers of that heavenly realm, thereby naming the wise, those who deserve to be called philosophers as lovers of wisdom. Dante-author has thus provided an "ostensive definition" by pointing out instances that illustrate the use of the term *philosopher.*

Much else is also being said merely by means of the story taken at this overt level. The fact that the meeting occurs in heaven means, of course, that the dwellers there are already blessed, which is to say that they are saints. Dante is thus canonizing them, though many of them were not yet canonized, or ever would be, by the church. Thomas, for example, was not declared a saint until 1323, two years after the death of Dante. By placing in heaven these men who were known primarily as thinkers, Dante is also claiming that knowledge and learning, taken as broadly as it is from these representatives, provide a way of getting to paradise; or, if this is claiming too much, the claim at least is that knowledge is no insuperable obstacle to saintliness.

Of the twenty-four spirits in the heaven of the Sun, only three speak directly to Dante: Thomas, Bonaventure, and Solomon. This fact in itself is significant since, as the spokesmen of the wise, they serve as their representatives and thus are the most representative of wisdom at its highest. The first two are both speculative theologians, and by placing them foremost Dante makes the claim that theology is the highest form of knowledge, thereby making "poetically" the same point that he had made in the *Convivio* "philosophically."

But why should there be two theologians, Bonaventure as well as Thomas? Although the work of both is speculative and highly "scholastic," it differs in one respect that is significant in thinking about heaven. According to Bonaventure, it is love that is the primary ingredient in the paradisal experience, whereas according to Thomas, it is not love but knowledge. Dante holds with Aquinas on this point, as we shall see later on. Here, however, by including both in the heaven of philosophy, he is showing that both love and knowledge are necessary and present in heaven so that the question of which is primary is somehow secondary.

Why then among these various lovers of knowledge should Solomon be the only one other than Thomas and Bonaventure to be given speech? Well, for one thing he represents, as the wisest king, the highest knowledge in the practical order of political action, whereas the other two stand for theoretical or speculative wisdom. But that is only part of it. To understand the full import of Solomon's presence, it is first necessary to consider further details of the story itself.

The three and a half cantos of the Sun episode contain four discourses, two of them by Thomas, spoken on different occasions. Of the four, the two longest are those in which Thomas praises St. Francis, the founder of the religious order to which Bonaventure belongs, and Bonaventure sings the praise of St. Dominic, founder of the order of which Thomas was a member. It is emphasized, however, that to praise one is to speak of both, for both worked to one and the same end (*Par.* 11.41–42). Yet a distinction is drawn between the temper and inspiration of the two founders. Francis is described as being "all seraphic in ardor," which is as much as to say that he was afire with divine charity, since the seraphim for Dante were symbolical of love as the highest of the angelic hierarchy. Dominic is said to have been "through wisdom on earth a splendor of cherubic light," and hence eminent for knowledge, since the cherubim, second in the hierarchy, symbolized knowledge.

By so praising their founders in the heaven of the wise, Dante, in effect, was stressing that the Franciscans and Dominicans should be the main teaching orders to guide the church, as they were in his day. In fact, Thomas and Bonaventure were for one period colleagues together at the University of Paris, then the principal center of theology in the western world.

That the praise of each order should be placed in the mouth of a member of the opposite one is also to imply that the two orders should be collaborators in a common work, not rivals and competitors as they often were. The criticism implicit here becomes outspoken in their discourses, and especially in that of Thomas.

His speech contains two statements that puzzle Dante and raise questions to which Thomas later returns to give an answer. The first of these occurs at the beginning of his remarks, where Thomas declares that he belongs "to the lambs of the holy flock which Dominic leads along the way where they fatten well if they do not stray" (*Par.* 10.94–96). It is this latter clause that Dante finds perplexing, and to answer his doubt Thomas declares that Dominic's "flock has become so greedy of strange food that it cannot but be scattered over diverse meadows; and the farther his sheep, remote and vagabond, go from him, the more empty of milk do they return to the fold" (*Par.* 11.124–29). In other words, the Dominican teachers have abandoned the way of their master and sought learning that cannot yield the truth that it should. Or, in short, they have left the path of true philosophy. This is clear from Dante's castigation of the learning of his day at the beginning of Canto 11, which parallels his contention in the *Convivio* that no one is a true philosopher "who is a friend of wisdom for profit, as are lawyers, physicians, and almost all the members of the religious orders." Thomas thus condemns his own order for abandoning the purely spiritual vocation to which its founder had called it. And it is especially appropriate that Thomas in praising Francis stresses repeatedly his love of poverty.

Bonaventure makes the same point in his praise of Dominic. He characterizes the founder of the Dominicans as "the amorous lover of the Christian faith" (*Par.* 12.55–56), but then declares that he was truly "the messenger and familiar of Christ, for the first love that was manifest in him was for the first counsel which Christ gave" (*Par.* 12.74–75). But the first counsel, according to *Matthew* 19:21, is that of poverty. Bonaventure, like Thomas, then attacks his own order for having departed from its founder's teachings by seeking worldly goods. The criticism directed against the two orders is also against the church itself inasmuch as the providential task assigned to them was to recall the church to its spiritual mission and keep it from wandering after material and temporal goods.

Dante was neither the first nor the last to condemn the worldliness of the church and its leaders. If that were all he were doing here, there would be nothing original about it. However, the basis on which he rests his criticism shows great originality. The evidence for that appears first in the reasons that are given for including Solomon in the heaven of the wise and, second, by the mere fact of including Siger of Brabant and Joachim of Calabria among the twenty-four examples.

Solomon appears to Dante among the first twelve lights and is described by Thomas in the following words: "The fifth light, which is most beautiful among us, breathes from such love that all the world there below is greedy to know tidings of it: within it is the lofty mind wherein wisdom so profound was put, that, if the truth be true, to see so much no second has arisen" (*Par.* 10.109–14). The "truth" referred to is the biblical account of Solomon's dream in which the Lord offered Solomon a gift and he asked for wisdom and was granted it with the promise that it would be such "as none before you has had and none will have after you" (*1 Kings* 3:12).

Dante is perplexed by the claim that Solomon has had no second, and Thomas provides the needed clarification, thus resolving the second doubt that Dante had had from his discourse. After explaining that the influence of divine power was so immediate in the creation of Adam and of Mary that "human nature never was, nor will be, what it was in those two persons," Thomas directs Dante's attention to the special feature of Solomon's request, so as to note and "clearly see that he was a king, who asked for wisdom, in order that he might be a worthy king." Solomon is praised for requesting the knowledge appropriate to his function: not for the knowledge of the scientist, "to know the number of the motors here on high"; nor that of the logician, "if *necesse* with a contingent ever made *necesse*"; nor that of the mathematician, "if in the semicircle a triangle can be made so that it should not have one right angle"; but for that particular knowledge that a king requires, namely, "a kingly prudence," to enable him to judge and rule rightly (*Par.* 13.88–108).

Dante thus distinguishes among functions the knowledge appropriate to each and praises Solomon just as he had Francis and Dominic for knowing their function and not departing from it into ways foreign to their special calling. Dante's doubt is resolved by showing that it is *among kings* that no second has arisen to equal Solomon in kingly wisdom.

The art of distinction

Thomas answered Dante's question by drawing a distinction among kinds of knowledge or wisdom. He concludes his discourse by warning Dante of the crucial importance in right thinking of the ability to *distinguish* (*Par.* 13.112–42). This advice is especially appropriate to the historical Aquinas, since his own works abound in the making of distinctions, and the same is no less characteristic of Dante the writer.

Thomas declares that his advice concerns the art of fishing for the truth and warns that there are two faults or errors to avoid. The first is that of hasty judgment, against which he recommends that "this ever be as lead to thy feet, to make thee move slowly as a weary man, both to the *yea* and to the *nay* which thou seest not." In other words, the advice is to be careful, to avoid making a hasty affirmation or denial in matters where the truth is not evident. "For he is very low down among the fools who affirms or denies without distinction." Over-hasty judgment carries the added danger that it commits the person who makes it, whereupon self-love then perpetuates him in it: "oftentimes the hasty opinion bends in false direction, and then self-love binds the intelligence."

As examples of thinkers who so erred, Thomas cites two philosophers, a mathematician, and two theologians. The philosophers cited are Parmenides and Melissus, whose arguments for the unity of all being are refuted by Aristotle in the first chapters of his *Physics*; the mathematician is Bryson, whose proof for squaring the circle is attacked as fallacious by Aristotle in his logical works. The theologians are two who denied the Trinity of divine persons: Sabellius, who claimed that the three are only different names for the same person, and Arius, who denied that Jesus Christ was divine as well as human. Both of these are heretics whose persistence in error manifested their bent self-love.

The second error to be avoided if one is to think rightly is overconfidence in one's judgments, especially in those concerning the future. The instances that are given of such overconfidence are forecasting the harvest, where one may err by underestimating it, as one who on observing the briar stiff and cold all winter long fails to expect the rose; or by overestimating it, as one who, after seeing that a ship has run a straight course, is confident of a safe landing, only to see the ship crash and sink in the very harbor.

Last and most important, one should avoid overconfidence in judging from appearances what God's judgment of persons may be: "Let not dame Bertha or master Martin, seeing one rob, and another make offering, believe to see them within the Divine counsel"—one as condemned, the other as saved: "for the one may rise and the other may fall" (*Par.* 13.112–42).

As readers we would do well to ponder this advice, with its emphasis upon the art of distinction, and to see how it applies to the understanding of the Sun episode. There are at least three important respects in which it is particularly applicable: first, with regard to the discourses themselves; then, with regard to the effect that Dante-author has achieved; and finally, with the interpretation that we as readers should make of this whole episode.

With regard to the first, the praises of Francis, of Dominic, and of Solo-

mon all center upon the claim that all three were expert in distinguishing their special functions and abiding by them, whereas their followers are accused of having in the one case abandoned the purely spiritual vocation of the two religious leaders, or, in the case of kings and rulers, to have failed to distinguish as Solomon did the special and proper task and function of a ruler.

With regard to the effect that Dante-writer has achieved, as well as our understanding of it, we must avoid being over-hasty in assenting to his "*yea* and *nay,*" or overconfident in our own judgment of the divine judgment upon certain thinkers, and especially upon that of Siger and Joachim, whose position in the circle of the wise we are now prepared to consider.

Siger and Joachim

That special attention is to be directed to these two figures is clear from the position they are given in the heaven of the Sun. Siger is the last of the wise to be named by Thomas and stands immediately to his left, while Joachim stands in the same relation to Bonaventure. Yet the closeness they are given to their spokesmen here in heaven is the very opposite of that which they had when they were alive on Earth. For Thomas strongly attacked the teachings of Siger, as did Bonaventure those of Joachim and, far from being saints, they were held by some as no better than heretics. Thus Dante-author, by the position he has allotted them, has placed two thought to be heretics next to two widely reputed to be saints, and has

In the heaven of the Sun, only three spirits speak directly to Dante: Bonaventure (opposite page, left), Thomas Aquinas (opposite page, right) and Solomon (above). *"As the spokesmen of the wise, they. . . are the most representative of wisdom at its highest."*

thus made friends in heaven of those who were enemies on Earth. It might be argued that such is the prerogative and bliss of heaven that even former enemies are there perfectly reconciled. But a little further consideration of the teachings of Siger and Joachim soon shows that Dante is implying much more than this and making poetically a philosophical point of his own.

Much of the history of Siger of Brabant is obscure, but from the little that is known it appears he was teaching philosophy at the University of Paris in the early 1270s, at the time that Thomas was also teaching there. At that period Thomas wrote a small work *On the Unicity of the Intellect against the Parisian Averroists,* an early manuscript of which identifies it as having been written "against master Siger of Brabant and many other regents in philosophy at Paris."

The philosophical problem at issue is an involved and difficult one, but it arose from the claim advanced by the Arab philosopher Averroes, then the leading commentator upon the works of Aristotle, and defended by his Latin followers, that there is but one intellect for all men. This proposition has many consequences, among others that there is no personal immortality directly contrary to Christian teaching. But the point of particular interest to Dante was not its bearing upon immortality but the fact that, in holding it, Siger was defending the distinction and independence of philosophy from theology.

That Siger did maintain such a position would seem clear from the quotation that Thomas cited, presumably from a work of Siger, in which he declared: "By reason I conclude that of necessity the intellect is one in number; however, by faith I firmly hold the opposite." But Thomas would have none of such a distinction as this, for it would imply that since the faith holds the opposite to a necessary truth, it must be "false and impossible," and such a proposition, he wrote, "the ears of the faithful cannot bear to hear." Then, in conclusion, in one of his very rare expressions of emotion, Thomas declared that if anyone wanted to attack his arguments, which were based "not on the teachings of faith, but on the reasons and words of the philosophers," he should come forth and "speak not in corners, nor before boys, who do not know how to judge about such difficult matters, but let him write against this treatise, if he dare."

Thomas's little book did not stop the spread of this doctrine, and Siger and others continued to assert the independence of philosophy by asserting the truth of propositions they held could be proven in philosophy even though they were contrary to the teaching of the church. The ecclesiastical authorities reacted by issuing condemnations. Siger was cited to answer charges of heresy, which he avoided by leaving Paris and the university as well as disappearing from history. One hearsay report holds that he died sometime between 1281 and 1284, stabbed to death by a demented servant.

With this information about the historical Siger, let us now see what

Dante has Thomas say about him when he appears in the heaven of the Sun: "This one . . . is the light of a spirit to whom, in his grave thoughts, it seemed that death came slow," which is to say that he considered problems so deep and perplexing that he looked anxiously to learn the truth about them in heaven after his earthly death. "It is the eternal light of Siger, who, reading in the Street of Straw, syllogized invidious truths." The Street of Straw, the Rue du Fouarre (now called Rue Dante) is in the Latin Quarter on the left bank of the Seine, in Paris, where the faculty of philosophy met and taught. There Siger demonstrated truths that were invidious in that they excited envy in others and so caused him to be hated.

From this speech as well as the position that he occupies next to Thomas it seems clear that Dante is offering a vindication if not a defense of Siger. But why should he want to do so? What is there in Siger's teaching that would have attracted him? Given the main tenor of the doctrine proclaimed and imaged in the heaven of the Sun, Dante would seem to be asserting that Siger merits praise for—like the others already mentioned—being expert in making distinctions and keeping separate that which should be kept so. But in Siger's case, what seems worthy is the distinction between philosophy and theology, an "envious truth" that led to his earthly downfall in Paris.

The reader has been warned, as we have seen, against making hasty and overconfident judgments, especially with regard to a person's standing in the "divine counsel." Hence it would be prudent of the reader not to condemn either Siger or Dante-author for putting in heaven one who had been charged with heresy. Nor should an ironic appropriateness be overlooked in making Thomas Aquinas the spokesman for Siger on such a ground. For Thomas himself also maintained the distinction between philosophy and theology and, in the eyes of some contemporary theologians, appeared to be almost as bad as Siger was. However, for Thomas the distinction in this instance did not mean separation and independence, as it did for both Dante and Siger.

In Dante's thought there are many separations or divisions that parallel the one between philosophy and theology: divisions between reason and faith, between earthly and heavenly happiness, between the mortal and immortal in man, body and soul, church and state. All of these separations are strongly marked in the *Divine Comedy* itself, but to track them down would take us too far afield and away from our main purpose, which is not the philosophy of Dante, but rather how he philosophizes poetically. However, a succinct statement of these separations can be found in the magisterial conclusion of Dante's treatise on world government, with which Boyde concludes the first volume of his work, translating:

> Man is unique amongst all beings in linking corruptible things with those that are incorruptible; hence the philosophers rightly liken him to

> the line of the horizon which is the meeting-place of two hemispheres. For if man is considered according to his essential constituents, that is, his soul and his body, he is corruptible in respect of one, the body, but incorruptible in respect of the other, the soul. . . . And since every nature is ordered toward some ultimate goal, it follows that man's ultimate goal is two-fold; because since man is the only being sharing in both corruptibility and incorruptibility he is the only being who is ordered towards two ultimate goals. . . . The first is happiness in this life, which consists in the exercise of his own powers and is typified by the earthly paradise; the second is the happiness of eternal life, which consists in the enjoyment of the divine countenance, which man cannot attain to of his own power but only by the aid of divine illumination, and which is typified by the heavenly paradise. . . . We attain to the first by means of philosophical teaching, being faithful to it by exercising our moral and intellectual virtues. We arrive at the second by means of spiritual teaching, which transcends human reason, in so far as we exercise the theological virtues of faith, hope, and charity.

The one has the state for its authority under the rule of the emperor, the other the church under that of the pope. Things go wrong when the separation is neglected or abandoned and one teaching usurps the function of the other, as Dante stresses time and again during the course of the *Comedy* in the criticism directed against the leaders of both state and church.

Having considered at such length why Siger, in Dante's view, should have been given a place in heaven, we need only a little additional information to appreciate the significance of Joachim. He was a Calabrian abbot of the late twelfth century who called for a complete separation of the spiritual from the temporal order. In this demand he was followed by a group within the Franciscan order that advocated an extremely rigorist interpretation of the Franciscan rule of life. Bonaventure, as master general of the Franciscans, opposed this position and attacked the writings of Joachim as those of a false prophet. The position of Joachim at the side of Bonaventure in the *Comedy* thus parallels that of Siger next to Thomas and for a similar reason: he urged a separation, that of the spiritual from the temporal. And again there is an ironic appropriateness, since Bonaventure, as contrasted with Thomas, tended to derogate the claims of nature and of reason in favor of those of grace and of faith.

The philosophical implications of the Sun episode are still far from exhausted. We have done no more than mention the remaining nineteen members of that heaven, and much could be learned from considering who they are and why Dante should have selected them to represent ideals of the intellectual life. Yet interesting and rewarding as such a study might be, it would be out of place in such an essay as this. For our purposes it is more useful, as well as more "poetic," to inquire into the overt imagery used to celebrate the ideal of philosophy.

The imagery of the heavens

The astronomy of the time provided Dante, as already noted, with ten heavens arranged hierarchically, one above the other. Lowest and closest to Earth is the Moon, highest and farthest removed, the Empyrean, which is not a place at all, being purely spiritual. The Sun occupies the fourth place in the hierarchy. Below it are the three heavens that were said by the astronomers to fall within the projection of Earth's shadow on the heavens. This shadow is taken by Dante as indicating the presence of some fault in the character of the spirits who appear in the first three heavens: in the Moon, the inconstant in vows who were defective in will; in Mercury, the overly ambitious for fame; in Venus, lovers excessive in misdirected love. The Sun, then, as the first heaven beyond the reach of Earth's shadow, and the heavens above it, together represent stages of perfection: in the Sun, that of the wise; in Mars, the warriors; in Jupiter, the just rulers; in Saturn, the contemplatives. There is then another break indicated by a golden ladder that ascends to the secrets of God, extending above Saturn through the heaven of the Fixed Stars and the Primum Mobile to the highest Empyrean.

By identifying the heaven of the wise with the Sun, Dante has thus ranked the life of the learned on a lower grade of perfection from that of the military, the rulers, or the contemplatives. What, one well may ask, is the significance of this ranking? Why and how should the intellectual life be somehow less than that of the others? The image is obviously saying something about the nature of philosophy and the life of learning.

The answer is to be found in the principle that Dante used to organize the structure of paradise. First, it must be understood that the true place of all the blessed, of the lowest as well as the highest, is in the Empyrean in the mind of God. All are equally happy in enjoying to the full of their capacity the vision of God. This much is explained to Dante as soon as he reaches the first heaven, that of the Moon: "Of the Seraphim he who is most in God, Moses, Samuel, and whichever John thou wilt take, I say even Mary, have not their seats in another heaven than those spirits who just now appeared to thee (i.e., in the Moon), nor have they more or fewer years for their existence" (*Par.* 4.28–33). If Dante encounters spirits at different levels in the heavens, the ranking is done for his and the reader's sake. For while all enjoy the beatific vision, they "have sweet life diversely, through feeling more or less the eternal breath." And since man's intellect is such as to depend upon sense to obtain understanding, the spirits of the blessed appear to Dante in the various heavens to manifest the diversity of their experience of paradise: "These showed themselves here, not because this sphere is allotted to them, but to afford sign of the celestial grade which is least exalted" (*Par.* 4.34–42).

Granted, then, that the heaven is not a place to be literally identified with any of the planets or stars, how does meeting the blessed in different heavens indicate the grade or degree of their bliss? What is the principle of gradation? It is to be found in the interpretation the theologians gave to the Gospel statement: "In my Father's house are many mansions" (*John* 14:2). As explained by St. Thomas, "the plurality of mansions corresponds to the differences of happiness on the part of the blessed." The degrees of happiness are distinguished on the one hand by "the difference of disposition," according to which, one is capable of receiving more of the divine vision than another, though each receives all that he is capable of; and, on the other hand, by "the merit by which they have obtained that happiness," i.e., not just according to natural ability alone, but by "the natural ability together with the endeavor to obtain grace" (*Summa Theologica,* Supp. 3.3, 2–3; *GBWW,* Vol. 20, pp. 1039b–40c).

It is then by ability, together with merit, that the degrees of perfection are to be measured. But why by such a measure should the life of learning rank lower than the others? It is easy to understand why the contemplative monastics should be placed above the other ways of life in the heaven of Saturn. A standard treatise among Dante's theologians was devoted to the comparison of the contemplative and the active life, and Thomas could find no less than eight reasons in Aristotle and several in the Bible for awarding first place to the contemplative among the ways of life open to us in this life. (*Sum. Theol.* 2–2.182.1; *GBWW,* Vol. 20, pp. 620–21). Yet the question remains why the life of learning should rank below both that of the military and of the rulers, especially since the life of teaching combines the contemplative with the active life.

Since merit provides one of the ranking principles, the reason must lie in the fact that there is greater merit in reaching heaven as a ruler or a warrior than as an intellectual. And so Aquinas declared in his treatise on the ruler, where he wrote that "a preeminent degree of virtue is required to rule justly, i.e., without respect to personal advantages. Therefore a just ruler merits a far higher reward than others." A ruler then, and presumably the same holds true for a soldier, has greater temptations to face than an intellectual does; theirs is a harder and more difficult life in which to keep to the way of perfection. All things being equal, it should be easier for a man of learning to find and to keep to that way. Of course, even if such is the case it by no means follows that any more will reach heaven. Dante meets as many of the learned in hell as he does in paradise.

The Sun then is a fitting image for the heaven of the learned: Learning is a leading way of perfection, so above the less exalted ways to heaven, yet it is also an easier and so a less meritorious way and hence a lower heaven that that of the military, the rulers, and the contemplative mystics. One image is an especially appropriate one inasmuch as the sun provides our greatest source of illumination, just as learning furnishes illumination to the mind and lights our paths before us. For this reason, too, the spirits of the learned and wise present themselves to Dante as lights that dance and sing in joyous festivity, since learning at its height is also an activity of great joy.

It still seems somewhat paradoxical that the intellectual life should hold only a middle rank when the paradisal experience itself is presented primarily and preeminently as one of intellectual joy in the satisfaction of an ever keener desire for truth. This is the very theme in all the heavens, and Dante sounds it again and again lest his reader should miss it. It is struck in the very first canto when Dante on rising into the heavens is so overcome with wonder that it kindles in him a desire to know "never before felt with such keenness" (*Par.* 1.82sq). Knowledge through causes is the Aristotelian definition of science, i.e., of certain knowledge, and heaven manifests itself as an ever more intense search for certain knowledge and consequently a greater joy in its accomplishment. Since there is no end to the desire for knowledge, and it is thus infinite, this desire can find no rest until it reaches the infinite God and the beatific vision. For this reason the whole of the *Comedy* is structured as much on the state of the intellect as on man's relation to God. Hell contains those who have lost the good of the intellect (*il ben de l'intelletto—Inf.* 3.18); Purgatory those who are on the way to regaining it through reform of their moral life; and Paradise those who have regained and perfected it. Heaven is also filled with love, joy, beauty, and festivity. But Dante emphasizes that the first ingredient and the base of all other bliss is the intellectual apprehension of truth. Thus Dante declares in the very first canto that he "clearly see(s) that our intellect is never satisfied unless the Truth illume it, beyond which nothing true extends. In that it reposes, as a wild beast in his lair, so soon as it has reached it: and it can reach it" (*Par.* 4.124–28). Then, when he reaches the Primum Mobile and sees the angelic loves, Beatrice tells him that he should "know that all have delight in proportion as their vision penetrates into the Truth in which every understanding (*intelletto*) is at rest. Hence may be seen how beatitude (*l'esser beato*) is founded on the act which sees, not on that which loves, which follows after" (*Par.* 28.106–11).

If the intellectual search and its achievement constitute the very essence of heaven, it should occasion no surprise that discourse occupies so much of the *Paradiso.* Discourse provides a major image itself, since it is in and through discourse that the good of the intellect is obtained. Beatrice discourses often and sometimes at length, not only to Dante's intellectual satisfaction, but also to the increase of his love for her as well as to the increase of her beauty, shining especially through eyes and smiles. Love finds expression through eyes and smiles as well as speech. But for Dante they also function in an allegorical mode. In commenting upon an early canzone of his in the *Convivio,* he wrote that "he who would behold salvation heedfully let him look upon this lady's eyes," in which he also found an image for philosophy: "The eyes of this lady are her demonstrations, the which, when turned upon the eyes of the intellect, enamour that soul which is free in its conditions." Beatrice then is also an image of philosophy itself, so that Dante is never without a philosopher in his journey through the heavens. Hence Dante-pilgrim has not left philosophy behind on passing beyond the heaven of the Sun.

That the intellectual search for truth cannot rest short of the vision of God nevertheless explains why the contemplative monks should occupy a higher heaven than the learned. And this is really the point. As St. Thomas asserted in claiming primacy for the contemplative life, it is more meritorious in that it "pertains directly and immediately to the love of God," since it is the truth that is God "above all which the contemplative life seeks" (*Sum. Theol.* 2–2.182.2; *GBWW,* Vol. 20, p. 622b). That life is the highest way of perfection in this world because it brings one closer to God. So Thomas can cite eight reasons from Aristotle for its primacy, as noted above, but he can do so only by accommodating those reasons to his Christian doctrine. By contemplation, Aristotle understood the reflection of the intellectual philosopher, not the vision of the monkish ascetic, as Thomas and Dante did.

If heaven consists primarily in an intellectual seeing, a vision, it is not surprising that Dante employs images of light as one of the principal ways of representing the experience of paradise. As a writer, he faced a much more difficult task in composing the *Paradiso* than he did in either of the other two canticles. In both the *Inferno* and the *Purgatorio* he had for his subject the human experience of sin and evil and of efforts at moral reform and purgation, and any of his readers can have firsthand knowledge of at least some of that matter. But in the *Paradiso,* Dante set out to represent the experience of such bliss, joy, and happiness as few if any of his readers would ever have; to describe it, he had to raise his reader beyond the Earth to heaven and up to the very sight of God, to the beatific vision. Accordingly, he images heaven (in the lines already quoted) as shining, dazzling, overwhelming with light:

> pura luce:
> luce intellettual piena d'amore,
> amor di vero ben pien di letizia,
> letizia che trascende ogni dolzore.

Poetry, truth, and belief

Paradise is pictured as a search for truth in which Dante the seeker succeeds in achieving his goal. That character, who is also the narrator of the story, frequently emphasizes his own truthfulness and his care to make his words express the truth: "so that the speech may not be diverse from the fact" (*Inf.* 31.12); that his "conceptions be well expressed" (*Par.* 24.60); and that "having seen the truth . . . you may confirm (it) in others"

Woodcut from a 14th century manuscript shows Beatrice and Dante in the *Paradiso.* *"Dante employs images of light as one of the principal ways of representing the experience of paradise. . . . such bliss, joy and happiness as few if any of his readers would ever have."*

(*Par.* 25.43–45). But these are the words of Dante-philomythes, the teller of the story who makes the narrator part of the story of his search for truth. How about Dante-philosopher? Is he also telling the truth about things as they are?

At this point it becomes important to distinguish between the various Dantes: There is Dante the character and protagonist presented in the words of the poet-narrator of the story. There is Dante the writer and thinker who composed the words that tell the story. There is also Dante the man, the historical figure who lived and wrote his story in early fourteenth-century Italy. On some questions it is crucially important to distinguish clearly between these various Dantes if one is to avoid very serious confusion. It is always risky, to say the least, to identify the first-person narrator with the historical man himself. Even the writer with the best intentions to tell the truth about himself as a man may be mistaken. It is no rare occurrence to be mistaken or deceived about oneself. Narrators are not always reliable.

Yet there is a strong presupposition in favor of believing that Dante the writer was intensely determined to tell the truth. Once he took the original step of making historical figures, in many cases his own contemporaries, the characters of his story, he at once subjected his writing to a test of truth that is verifiable or falsifiable. Not that this is so because in every case he places such figures in hell, purgatory, or paradise; for about the truth of such judgments as these we have no way of knowing, short of the beatific vision itself. But besides such judgments as these, the story contains many historical references to the features, characteristics, and actions of the persons represented, and of the times and places in which they occurred. And such representations could be checked for their veracity, and can still.

There is also no doubt that Dante the writer made every effort to be accurate and exact in his presentation of the natural world. Indeed, he is famous for the accuracy of his descriptions of nature. But, as Boyde has well documented, Dante also made every effort to express clearly and exactly the best knowledge available to him of the physical structure of the world, of its elements and their combinations, of its climatology, geography, astronomy, even of its embryology. It is for this reason that Boyde takes as true of Dante the words from the English poet W. H. Auden that he cites as epigraph to his book:

> . . . it's as well at times
> To be reminded that nothing is lovely,
> Not even in poetry, which is not the case.

Marianne Moore was another poet who shared the same concern and expressed it in words that are even more applicable to Dante. Poets, who wrote, must be "literalists of the imagination" who can present for inspection "imaginary gardens with real toads in them." Dante's imaginary world not only contains real people; it is described in terms that Dante and the most learned men of his time held to be true, from the lowest elements to the highest heaven.

Even critics who maintain that there is a sharp divide between poetry and philosophy are still willing to admit that a poet means what he says and that it would be worse than disconcerting to discover that a poet believed as a man the very opposite of what was expressed in his poetry. Even Eliot acknowledged that were we to learn that Dante was the author of the materialistic, even atheistic, *De rerum natura* ascribed to Lucretius, as well as of the *Divine Comedy,* "our capacity for enjoying either poem would be mutilated."

But to admit that the poet means what he says and is telling the truth, at least as he sees it, does not get rid of the problem of poetry and belief. It

Ingres pictures the fateful moment for "Francesca di Rimini et Paolo." *"It was the reading of a romance that brought Francesca and Paolo to the pass that led them to the hell of the lustful."*

merely shifts the question of belief from poet to reader. For it can still be asked whether the reader has to share those beliefs to appreciate fully the poetry. If he accepts that the poet believes what he says, must he, the reader, also believe it to be true?

One way to meet the question is to dissolve it and reject it by claiming that in reading poetry there is no question of either belief or disbelief in the sense of judging what it says to be true or false. Thus Eliot declared that "poetic assent" must be distinguished from both philosophical and scientific belief in that, unlike these two, poetry involves a suspension of both belief and disbelief; so that it is no more necessary to believe in Dante's physics or theology than in the literal reality of the journey that he describes. As readers, we must enter imaginatively into the world that he has constructed and for that purpose we must do all that we can to understand its physics as well as its theology. The physics and theology as well as the astronomy and geography of that world may well be false in not being in accord with the way things actually are and as we now know them to be. Yet that this is so need not, and should not, prevent a good reader from understanding and appreciating the poem as poetry.

Yet even for Eliot a poetic reading is not a morally irresponsible one. He praises Dante for introducing into hell fictional as well as historical characters and cites the case of Ulysses (*Inf.* 26.52–63) as showing how one can be "damned or blessed in the creatures of his imagination," no less than through his actions. Dante himself would certainly agree that reading can lead to either hell or heaven. It was the reading of a romance that brought Francesca and Paolo to the pass that led them to the hell of the lustful:

> "We were reading one day, for delight, of Lancelot, how love constrained him. We were alone and without any suspicion. . . . When we read of the longed-for smile being kissed by such a love, this one, who never shall be divided from me, kissed my mouth all trembling"
> —*Inf.* 5.127–36

So Francesca tells Dante in the first infernal circle. But reading can lead to blessedness as well as condemnation, as Dante learns when he meets among the prodigal in Purgatory the soul of Statius, the Roman poet, who then accompanies him to the terrestrial paradise. For in the conversation that Statius has with Virgil about his life and writing and how he became a Christian, he confesses that he owes both his art and his faith to his reading of Virgil: "Through thee I became a poet, through thee a Christian" (*Purg.* 22.73).

Eliot as well as Dante are thus affirming, each in his own way, that the reading of poetry can affect radically the character of persons and make them either better or worse. Such an assertion certainly seems to be one that is either true or false. If so, does "poetic assent" to it absolve the reader entirely from making any judgment whatsoever regarding its truth or falsity? Perhaps besides distinguishing various kinds of belief, we need also to distinguish different kinds of truth. The Statius episode just referred to provides plentiful evidence of the need. For within a few lines it contains statements that clearly stand in different relations to the truth.

First, Statius tells Dante that he lived during the time of the Emperor Titus and came from Toulouse (*Purg.* 21.82–89): Two historical statements of which the first is true, the second false. Statius lived c. 45–96, while Titus ruled from 39 to 81, but he was born not in Toulouse but in Naples. Statius then declares that he owes to Virgil both his poetic art and his Christian faith. Again, the first statement is verifiable whereas the second is neither verifiable nor falsifiable. His epic poem, the *Thebaid,* obviously reveals the influence of Virgil's own epic verse, but that he ever became a Christian there is no historical evidence either for or against. In answer to a question that Virgil puts to him, he explains that he has to remain so long in Purgatory, no less than 500 years, in order to purge himself of the damage that prodigality and lukewarmness in his faith had done to his character. Then in answer to an inquiry of Dante's, how bodiless spirits can suffer bodily symptoms, Statius delivers a long discourse indicating how man is both bodily and spiritual, formed by both nature and God, and so both temporal and eternal (*Purg.* 25.32–108).

From even so bald a summary, it is evident that anything approaching an adequate explication would require many more pages than are available here. Boyde, for example, needs ten pages to explain the theory of embryonic development that Statius expounds. But for our purposes all that is needed is the evidence that poetry, at least that of Dante, involves statements that stand in different relations to the truth, and of that there is plenty.

First, there are clearly statements, i.e., assertions, about historical fact the truth of which can be tested by historical criteria. For "poetic assent" it would not seem to make any great difference that one of those made above is true and the other false, although the reader would not be wrong, perhaps, in wishing that the poet had got his facts straight. For understanding the story, it is essential to know that Statius is a poet, but this much is readily gathered from the words that Dante puts into the mouth of Statius. The reader is told something that is verifiably true about the dependence of Statius's own poetry upon that of Virgil, which is also to claim that poets learn from one another and even from those who are centuries apart in time; and if this were not in accord with the way poets work, it would be a hindrance rather than a help in understanding the story. But that reading Virgil helped to make Statius a Christian, a statement for which there is no historical evidence—what is the reader to make of this? Only that Dante-writer thought there was reason for attributing something of Christian value to the person and poetry of Statius, just as he made a much greater claim in this regard for Virgil, making him in fact the guide for Dante-traveler through hell and purgatory up to the very gates of paradise; and, further, that there is an important continuity, at least in western civilization, between Christian and pagan. These are all truths in the historical order, but in value rather than in fact.

Still further removed from the literal level as an integral part of the story is the account of the purgation of Statius. Yet even this is not entirely divorced from the question of truth: The story, abstracting from both the fictional journey and the theological doctrine involved, is saying at least that prodigality and lukewarmness constitute defects of character that prevent its full development and that need to be overcome if that is to be achieved.

Finally, the discourse on human reproduction is the most complex of all in its relation to truth. Boyde shows in considerable detail that the account is based on the teaching of Aristotle as expounded by his Christian commentators as well as on the medical writings of Galen and Avicenna and their commentators. It contains assertions in the scientific, the philosophical, and the theological orders. The explanation of embryonic development that is given is fanciful, which is to say false in the light of modern biological discoveries. But the point that is made regarding the radical difference of man from other animals and of the intervention of God in his generation is philosophical and theological, neither of which orders is as such falsifiable by science, and both of which are still held to be true by some philosophers and theologians. The uniqueness of man is seen when Statius explains how from an animal the embryo becomes a human being in becoming *fante,* i.e., a speaking being (from *fari*—Latin "to speak"), since Dante holds that it is by his use of language that man displays his radical difference from other animals (*Purg.* 25.61). The other sign of uniqueness is his capacity for self-awareness: "One single soul which lives and feels and circles on itself" (*Purg.* 25.75). Both speech and self-awareness are traits of man upon which philosophers still ground the claim of man's uniqueness in the animal creation. Statius, however, advances further and makes a theological point: These distinctive traits depend upon the possession of an incorporeal power that cannot derive from corporeal nature and that therefore must come directly from God himself, who "breathes into it (the embryo) a new spirit replete with virtue" (*Purg.* 25.71–72). That the human soul is directly created by God is a theological statement and hence distinct in kind from the previous scientific and philosophical statements.

But to return to the story, we can still ask why Dante should have placed such a complex doctrinal account in the mouth of Statius, who in his historic person certainly possessed no such knowledge. Again, the image is that of a poet discoursing, and indeed much of the conversation in which Dante, Virgil, and Statius engage concerns poets and poetry. Hence for Statius to be given such a learned discourse—scientific, philosophical, and theological—implies among other things that poets are teachers, that they are capable of teaching the truth, and truths of different kinds as appropriate to different disciplines. Through statement as well as image and story, Dante is even proclaiming that poets not only can teach truth but that they have in fact done so, and that in his own case, he was actually doing so as he wrote. Having come so far, it is difficult to see how poetic assent does not also demand the reader's belief.

The reader's burden

Granted that at some point the reader must believe with the writer that what he says is true, where is that point to be located? Not even the poet demands that the reader assent to everything he says as being literally true. There is obviously a sense in which a "poetic assent" exists apart from belief. It would be a serious misreading to take the story literally as a historic account of a living man's journey through the realms of the dead, even though Dante as a "literalist of the imagination" does everything he can to make it as realistic as possible. So, too, readers who share neither Dante's faith nor his philosophy can read his poem with pleasure just as Dante the Christian obviously read the pagan poets with delight. Yet it is no less obvious that he read them also for knowledge, and his use of that knowledge illuminates how assent can move toward belief.

Virgil escorts Dante through the Inferno in Delacroix's "Barque de Dante."
"*In both the* Inferno *and the* Purgatorio, [Dante] *had for his subject the human experience of sin and evil.*"

Consider the passage in the first canto of the *Paradiso* in which Dante describes the change that occurred in him as he gazed upon Beatrice while she looked at the heavens:

> Looking at her I inwardly became such as Glaucus became on tasting of the grass which made him consort in the sea of the other gods. Transhumanizing cannot be signified in words; therefore let the example suffice him for whom grace reserves the experience.
> —*Par.* 1.67–72

Dante derived the comparison from a story in the *Metamorphoses* of Ovid (13.906–63; see *GIT* 1966): Glaucus was a fisherman who was surprised one day while counting his catch on a remote shore to see that the fish, although half-dead, on eating of the grass, revived and at once regained the sea. Glaucus, marveling, ate of the grass and, like the fish, also sought the sea, where he was transformed into a marine god. Dante did not have to believe that the story was literally true to recognize in it an image of the experience he wanted to describe. Like Glaucus he was undergoing a sea-change and entering upon a new element that carried him beyond human experience. But for his experience, unlike that of Glaucus, he lays claim for truth that can be verified by anyone who receives the divine grace that alone makes it possible—an experience that transcends the power of words to express, but for which the image of Glaucus provides an example, an illustration.

Now why may not the reader of this passage in the *Paradiso* who does not share Dante's faith be in the same position as Dante was in reading Ovid's words about Glaucus and see in it an image and example of a radically transforming experience such as he might have? He will not be excused thereby from reading as a believer would, since he would not understand Dante's words if he did not see that Dante based the possibility of "transhumanizing" upon divine grace. So, too, although the reader may lack Dante's extremely lively sense of the presence of the dead, he will not be understanding the poem unless he too believes that it is possible to learn from the dead, as, of course, the reader himself is doing as he reads the text of a poet long since dead.

Dante as a reader was familiar with the age-old practice of Christians reading the Old Testament by "spiritualizing" it. As Dante explains in his letter to Can Grande, the biblical account of Israel's departure from Egypt can also be interpreted as signifying the redemption of man by Christ, the conversion of the soul from the state of sin to that of grace, and the departure of the holy soul from Earth to heaven. He invited his readers to interpret his own *Comedy* in the same way. But if so, there is nothing to hinder the reader from also "secularizing" it and reading it as providing an image of man's search for truth and perfect happiness, but in a way other than that proposed in his poem. And that reading will be true if the poem is truly an image, a likeness, of that experience and thus in accord with it.

Kant once observed that, in meaning, there is no difference between the idea of ten dollars and ten dollars actually in the pocket. Of course, in efficacy and power there is a world of difference, since the ten dollars can actually be used to buy real goods. There is a similar difference between Dante's poem as an image of a possible experience and as a statement of how to get to heaven. For if it is true in the latter sense, it can actually lead the reader *to* heaven, providing that he believes as Dante teaches.

Documentation

The Divine Comedy is cited according to the translation of Charles Eliot Norton in *GBWW,* Vol. 21, and the Italian text according to the edition of Charles S. Singleton, *The Divine Comedy,* Princeton University Press, 1970–75, 6 vols., including text, translation, and commentary.

The Convivio, translated by P. H. Wicksteed in The Temple Classics, London, J. M. Dent and Sons, 1912.

The Letters, translated by P. H. Wicksteed in *Latin Works of Dante Alighieri,* The Temple Classics, London, J. M. Dent and Sons, 1934.

* * * * *

Patrick Boyde, *Dante: Philomythes and Philosopher,* Vol. 1: *Man in the Cosmos,* Cambridge University Press, 1981.

T. S. Eliot, "Dante," in *GGB,* Vol. 5, pp. 371-403.

E. Gilson, *Dante et la philosophie,* Paris, 1939.

R. Kirkpatrick, *Dante's Paradiso and the Limitations of Modern Criticism,* Cambridge University Press, 1978.

P. Toynbee, *A Dictionary of Proper Names and Notable Matters in the Works of Dante,* revised by C. S. Singleton, Oxford, 1968.

The Child as Reader

Clifton Fadiman was born in New York City in 1904 and was graduated from Columbia University in 1925. He was book editor for *The New Yorker* for ten years and has served as editor or consultant for many other publications. A member of the Board of Editors of Encyclopaedia Britannica, he has edited several of Britannica's publications for children, among them the *Young Children's Encyclopedia.* To the Britannica itself he contributed the article entitled "Children's Literature."

A well-known author and lecturer, Mr. Fadiman has always taken a special interest in children and their literature. Among his books for children are *The Story of Young King Arthur, The Voyages of Ulysses,* and *Wally the Wordworm.* His *World Anthology of Children's Literature* will be published in 1984. Mr. Fadiman has also served as consultant for several television and motion picture projects, including *The Borrowers* (1973).

He is married to Annalee Whitmore Fadiman, a former war correspondent and coauthor of *Thunder Out of China.* He has three children. Wine is a hobby of Mr. Fadiman's, on which he has written books, as is what he calls "the avoidance of exercise."

There is, of course, no such thing as "the child as reader." Children come in wholes. "There is no isolated reading," writes Alexander Beinlich, "but a human being who speaks and listens all day long and also reads." Nevertheless, children seek in books certain new experiences and confirmations of old experiences that are peculiar to them. With no thought of splitting off the reading child from the rest of him, let us consider whatever it is that, when he opens a book, distances him from the grown-up.

C. S. Lewis warns us that children are not a species, certainly not a literary species. "Juvenile taste is simply human taste, going on from age to age, silly with a universal silliness or wise with a universal wisdom, regardless of modes, movements, and literary revolutions." Fair enough: some children like trash, others William Mayne; and on the whole their taste is less a matter of fashion than is the adults'. But they read different books—not merely simpler ones—in a different way for different reasons.

I suspect, for one thing, that proportionally there are more six-to-sixteen book readers than there are post-sixteen book readers. Dr. Richard Bamberger estimates that about 20 to 30 percent of children are book readers. Doubtless his eye is fixed on Western or perhaps Central Europe, but I should think the figure might generally obtain. Does one out of three or five post-adolescents read books habitually? I doubt it. The simple fact, then, that childhood and early youth are preeminently the reading age would in itself set off young readers from the rest of us. Agreed, among children there are many more nonreaders than readers. Indeed an observer, Tudor Jenks, noted that "children who still 'love reading' are old-fashioned." But what is interesting about the remark is that it was made in 1901, more than three-quarters of a century ago. Reading has always been a minority sport.

When do they start to read? More to the point, when *can* they start to read? We really do not know. Piaget's "reading readiness" theory and findings strike a responsive chord within any culture that, like our own, is wary of the intellect. But these findings have been questioned by other researchers, especially John Downing and D. V. Thackray in England. Some experimenters have found that children—"normal" children, I hasten to add—can be taught to read, as well as typewrite, at three. I myself, an egregiously normal child, with parents not highly literate in English, was reading books at four. The issue is controversial, but my impression is that the "reading readiness" theory has delayed for many children the pleasure that lies in books.

Let us assume, however, that Jane or John has been taught to read and is ready for "real" books. What will she or he pick off the library shelves? Can we say anything sensible about the literary taste of the young?

It is often said that the "best" children's books are not popular with children. It is a statement equally difficult to prove or disprove. In *Chosen for Children,* an account of the books awarded the Carnegie Medal from 1936 to 1965, the editors commented: "It would however be as unlikely that such books, which make demands on the imagination and concentration of their readers, should enjoy the widest popularity as that the novels of Virginia Woolf and E. M. Forster, or even those of Graham Greene, should be the most popular of adult books." True. Why expect children to be any more discriminating than their seniors?

Logically we should have no such expectation. But in fact we demand that they develop better taste than our own. We go to great pains to urge the best upon them, to discourage the reading of comics, to endorse the classics. This zeal may be rooted as much in our disillusionment with ourselves as with our ambition for our children. No matter. The net effect is probably good. What harm can there be in giving our daughters and sons the best possible opportunity for developing whatever powers of discrimination they may have? The question sharpens when we consider that the average American child, from age seven to age fourteen, reads a total of five hundred books *maximum*. That's about seventy per year, read during the period when his reading tastes are often decisively formed. How much trash, out of a maximum of seventy books per year, can the child afford to read?

On the other hand, there is Talleyrand's "Not too much zeal!" The critic Enzo Petrini writes: "The habit should not consist of ordinary reading, but rather of creative, stimulating, discriminative reading." Well and good, as pure ideal. But there may be times in the child's life when he *needs* trash, as indeed we all do. There is a certain repellent immaculateness about the person who has never read anything but the best. The point is that, because the child is plastic, he can be gently and gradually led away from the trash he occasionally needs. Furthermore, even trash has for him a value denied to adults: it is, until he becomes used to it, novel—for in his early years everything is novel. Here is one adult reader, remembering:

> I didn't know what I liked. I just knew what there was a lot of. . . . The pleasures of reading itself—who doesn't remember?—were like those of a Christmas cake, a sweet devouring. . . . Selection was no object. . . . There was one thing I wanted from those books, and that was for me to have ten to read at one blow.

Signor Petrini would surely shake his head at such uncritical, undiscriminating reading. Yet the woman who wrote these sentences turned out to be one of the finest of our short-story writers, Eudora Welty.

A sweet devouring. . . . Yet the child is no omnivore. He selects, choosing sometimes what he "should" have, more generally what he needs. And he rejects. He reads within limits, limits set by his unarticulated vision of the moral universe. In her study, "General Criteria for Selection and Use of Materials," Yolanda Federici refers to those authors and publishers who around the turn of the century began to produce books that children really liked:

> These emancipators realized that children were interested in anything and everything but that their understanding, and, therefore, their enjoyment, had limitations according to their chronological age. They realized that children understood death—at least, as well as some adults—but not suicide; unhappiness but not despair; disappointment but not hopelessness; frustration but not bitterness; cruelty but not viciousness; love but not passion; justification but not rationalization.

Children probably are interested in more things than are their elders. The capacity for boredom is the proud distinction of maturity. But everything? No. Otherwise the statement is perceptive.

Disappointment but not hopelessness. Of all the myths, the one truest to the world of childhood is that of Pandora. It was not meant to emblem childhood, but humanity. Yet hope is the peculiar inalienable possession of the child. He lives by it. As we age, hope grays into mere curiosity; all of us live in the expectation of tomorrow. But for the child, hope is more than curiosity, more even than the translation into emotional terms of the biological struggle for survival. It is, except in unusual circumstances, unconnected with the fear of death. It is a shadow-companion present in every experience, including unhappy ones.

Because hope is intricately woven into the child's unconscious, the unhappy ending poses an esthetic problem in his literature, though not in the adult's. Unamuno's tragic sense of life is an acquirement, time's dark gift. It is not for children; and if life so arranges itself as to impose upon the child a tragic sense of life, he suffers a kind of deformation, a crippling, a forced rather than a natural growth. "When hope is gone, childhood is gone," says Jean Karl.

In his classic *From Two to Five,* the great Russian writer for children, Korney Chukovsky, tells a charming anecdote bearing on this point.

> An eight-year-old Octobrist once said:
>
> "Ania, I went to see 'Chapayev' ten times and still he was drowned at the end of the movie. Maybe if I go with my dad . . . ?" He liked to think that the death of Chapayev had been some kind of mistake in the motion picture and this morbid cinematic error would somehow be

> corrected by his father, thus ensuring that the hero, Chapayev, would not die; for this reason the tragic ending in the film about a loved hero seemed to him to be against nature and some kind of unbearable mistake. The literary characters who become dear to the child must succeed in their enterprises, and one must not, no matter what, allow them to die, since it is with them that the child identifies.

While this desire for happiness is doubtless fundamental, it is nonetheless true that sadness, even death, seems also to give the child a certain melancholy pleasure. Without the account of the death of Beth, *Little Women* would have been a less popular book. Everything, however, lies in the handling. Alcott's handling is gentle and consolatory, whereas the deathbed scenes of the Sarah Trimmer school are grisly and scary. Naturally the reception of tragedy or sadness is dependent on the age of the young reader.

The motion picture executive Dore Schary once called the United States "a happy-ending country." If true, we are not yet, as a people, grown up. But the republic of small children *is* a happy-ending country.

On the other hand, we must be wary of Wordsworthian sentimentality. The passion for the happy ending does not imply that the child desires merely a reflection of his own life. Indeed, as Aristotle tells us, perhaps happiness (defined as the consequence of making the correct moral choices) is a condition denied to the child. Yeats recalls his great-uncle William Middleton once remarking, "We should not make light of the troubles of children. They are worse than ours, because we can see the end of our trouble and they can never see any end."

Love but not passion. One school of modern writers for children denies this. Sexual love is now a standard ingredient in stories read by ten-year-olds, as infant damnation was one hundred and fifty years ago. I think the child is confused now, as she was then. Because the media deluge her with images of physical passion, she (it's more usually she) feels guilty unless she is "involved." But she is not equipped for involvement. The consequence is the assumption of an aggressive sophistication that conceals fear and lack of understanding. In precisely the same way the media press upon the child images of objects (cars, refrigerators) that grown-ups are ordered to buy. The child cannot buy the refrigerator but feels it is the right thing to do. So he internalizes its possession as a kind of status symbol. The normal consequence of this process is neurosis.

From three to at least twelve (but I have observed it in boys and girls of eighteen) the child's moral universe reflects tension between two poles: the desire for freedom, the desire for security. To rest within the warm nest and to transcend it—indeed, to remain a child and to grow out of childhood. As a whole, children's literature reflects this tension, the balance inclining now one way, now the other. Children like "series" books, for example, because a series offers familiarity, a word derived from family. A series is comfortable. And when a great book is written that clas-

"When a great book is written that classically combines the lure of freedom with the snugness of security, children flock to it, never to abandon it. Such a book is Robinson Crusoe."

sically combines the lure of freedom with the snugness of security, children flock to it, never to abandon it. Such a book is *Robinson Crusoe.*

The child's moral universe, as Ms. Federici says, simply excludes certain things. For example, it is closed, I think, to mysticism: juvenile mystics are rare. But, of course, the young reader is wide open if not to mysticism, then to the mysterious. That is why his literature is so rich in stories involving worlds outside our time. Isabelle Jan speaks of the "stopped clock" as a frequent symbol in children's books. *Tom's Midnight Garden* and Nesbit's *House of Arden* (one could name a hundred others) are, as it were, enclosed in child-time. In *The Harried Leisure Class,* Staffan B. Linder suggests that the more affluent the economy the scarcer the time. Children, until forced into it, live—or would like to live—outside the economic system. But they are dragged into a culture of time-scarcity. In their books they escape from the culture, into more flexible and generous time-systems. Like the inhabitants of poor countries, they do not understand punctuality, part of the work ethic that produces affluent societies.

With respect to what children shut out of their cosmos, critics are not always agreed. For example, Anatole France is convinced that "children have most of the time, an extreme dislike for reading books that were written for them. . . . They find the writer who binds them in the contemplation of their own childhood a terrible bore." Compare Mme. Lucie Delarue Mardrus: "I am absolutely convinced . . . that children love only books written specially for them. . . ." Anatole France's dictum may be true for the precocious, for the child who, like himself, is fated to literature. But commonsense observation tells us that while children eagerly take over a certain proportion of adult literature (*Robinson Crusoe* is the key example), they even more eagerly accept books, good and poor, "written especially for them." This does not invalidate the fact that the *very* best books are written not so much for "the market" as for the child hidden in the writer.

There is disagreement also about books in which adults hardly figure or figure not at all. The French critic Marc Soriano (*Guide de la littérature enfantine,* Paris, 1959) writes: "To present the child with a world composed exclusively of children is to nourish fictions that are hardly reassuring and which in the end dispose him to revery and maladjustment." If this is true, it makes hay of Arthur Ransome and others, including Nesbit, many of whose books are virtually adultless. But if we are to attack the children's book on the ground that it presents a false view of reality, why should we not turn the argument against any number of adult novels which are totally without children? For all his liberalism, I think Soriano writes like a Frenchman who still believes the main purpose of childhood is adulthood and for whom "revery" is a bar to growth. Let us keep in mind what the Opies point out in *Childhood Games in Street and Playground,* "Our vision of childhood continues to be based on the adult-child relationship . . . we largely ignore the child-to-child complex. . . ." Though members of a larger society, children are also members of a smaller one, their own. Nesbit and Ransome are often criticised for excluding adults (in effect) from their books. But they might also be credited with a recognition of the exclusive child atmosphere in which the preadolescent largely lives. Gang stories and school stories, now perhaps past their peak in popularity, recognize this. So do animal stories in which the animals are children in disguise. Finally the whole question is complicated by the identification process. *Jane Eyre* is a book about grown-ups. But, for the fifteen-year-old girl who projects herself into Jane it both is and isn't a book about grown-ups. This does not hold, however, for *Madame Bovary,* though the novels have much in common. Why? Is it because Jane's sexual career (for that is what the story is really about) satisfies the fantasies of the preadolescent or adolescent, whereas poor Madame Bovary cannot even satisfy her *own* fantasies?

There is one kind of book, now flooding the market, that I feel children, if they had their druthers, would instinctively reject, but which the publishers force upon them. I refer to the scaled-down adult book. There is a one-to-one correspondence theory, held usually, but not exclusively, by nonfiction writers, which asserts that for every adult interest there is a corresponding juvenile interest. Is this true? There may be an adult audience for a book about the Amalgamated Clothing Workers of America—a most meritorious organization indeed—but I see no reason whatsoever to expect any normal child to read with interest or pleasure a book entitled *Sidney Hillman: Great American.* It may be high-minded to use the juvenile novel or biography to turn the child into an internationalist or race tolerance buff. But I would suggest that he first be allowed to turn into a boy or girl. The Good Little Citizen seems to me no improvement over Pious Little Rollo. Let the little reader breathe his own air. Being a child is in itself a full-time profession.

I recall reading about an author who, in a high-minded endeavor to create a juvenile equivalent of *Hamlet,* dreamed up a story about the Prince's three offspring (Ophelia helped here) who, with the aid of their tutor Horatio, defeated the villainous Fortinbras. Upon finishing this stirring tale an eleven-year-old commented, "I think it very misleading to put Hamlet and Ophelia into such a story."

What the child will welcome or exclude turns partly on the nature, but more essentially on the depth, of his experience. We habitually say that the child differs from the adult in that he has less experience. When we say this, we are thinking in quantitative terms. It is true that he who lives longer has had more things happen to him. But the word *more* is not the only operative word.

The child has certain qualitative experiences which are of tremendous importance to him at the time, but which fade away as he becomes an adult. What a child feels when he and his family move, or what he feels during his first day in school, or what he feels when he makes a new friend—all these experiences are quite as significant to him as might be the first experience of love or paternity or failure or triumph in business when he is older.

The state of innocence of which Blake speaks is also a form of experience. That is why a good book for children is not predicated merely on the notion that the child has had far less quantitative experience than the adult. It is based on a sense of the richness or uniqueness of whatever experience the child has had or is able to anticipate or desire.

Keeping in mind the bounds of the child's moral universe and the special nature of his experience, we try to discover what he seeks, what he admires, in imaginative literature. There is no single answer. Perhaps we will never know; perhaps the young reader himself does not know. The results of investigations into the problem seem to vary somewhat in acceptance with the culture out of which the investigation proceeds.

For instance, in the March 1973 *Bookbird* the Marxist Jaroslav Tichy maintains that it is their *heroes* who are responsible for the persisting popularity of such classics as *Don Quixote, Tyl Eulenspiegel, Gulliver, Baron Munchausen's Travels, Robinson Crusoe, The Three Musketeers, Alice, Pinocchio, Treasure Island.* (As a Marxist he is obliged, of course, to place in the same category certain Soviet productions—Ostrovsky's *How the Steel Was Hardened,* Fadeyovova's *Young Guard:* books whose very titles guarantee their vulnerability to time.) For Tichy, "the Robinsonian attitude" is the thing, "the passionate desire to turn one's idea into reality." For him, this impulse is important because it can be harnessed to the requirements of the state. It outweighs by far the hunger for fantasy, humor, and suspense. Such motivations are not quite so harnessable and indeed might very well turn out refractory to the state's requirements. From the totalitarian viewpoint humor and fantasy, as properties of literature, are suspiciously delinquent.

While the classics Tichy cites do maintain their popularity (less so in the United States), it is more probable that their heroes are admired for two simpler reasons. First, their adventures are just plain interesting (aside from any desire on the hero's part to "turn [his] idea into reality"). Second, these heroes, including Alice, are all outlaws. This is the normal role of the child, or of his unconscious, until he is conditioned to adjustment to society. Robin Hood is loved, not because his actions foreshadow a proletarian revolt against the lords, but because it must have been fun to live like that in the greenwood and constantly to outwit the Nottingham Sheriff, surrogate for the reader's parents and teachers.

Tichy's contention that in their books children admire a heroic attitude toward life (ignoring the instrumental use he makes of the contention) is to some extent borne out by the results on some research into the reading tastes of eight- to fifteen-year-old Hungarian children, who also live behind the Iron Curtain. Bravery, heroism, and daring are the most admired qualities, reports Dr. Bela Toth, in "The Meaning of the Hero and Heroic Traits for the Literary Experiences of the Young Child." (He seems to have worked with boys only.) Uprightness, kindness, love of country falter far behind. After heroes and muscular strength come "spiritual traits"—intelligence, cunning. Dr. Toth is surprised (many child-study researchers have a low-surprisability threshold) to find that, "though the main activity of the children . . . is learning," hardly any of the 654 boys questioned admired "eagerness to learn" in their literary heroes. (The same would be true here, of course.)

Whatever the young reader is looking for, it is fairly clear that a radical change occurs with the approach of adolescence. The preadolescent reader, as Walter Scherf believes, probably has a desire "to play out his own confict, to re-experience station after station of his own childhood dream." And this holds true, as Dr. Scherf says, whether we are talking of folktales or their modern equivalents. But adolescence means this dream-play gives way to more purposive reading. Boys and girls read so that they may, in Alexander Beinlich's phrase, "understand why they live and for what end."

It is difficult for grown-ups to understand how children read when they are really engrossed in a book. A haze of sentimentality, nostalgic and self-appreciative, blurs our perception. Here is Agnes Repplier, writing in 1888: "Somewhere about the house, curled up, may be, in a nursery window, or hidden in a freezing attic, a child is poring over *The Three Musketeers,* lost to any consciousness of his surroundings, incapable of analyzing his emotions, breathless with mingled fear and exultation over his heroes' varying fortunes, and drinking in a host of vivid impressions that are absolutely ineffaceable from his mind."

Was this true even a century ago for any other than the "sensitive," gently bred child? And how true is it today when the juvenile reading public and the variety of reading matter are both vastly extended? Is the general decline of attention, apparent in adults, equally marked in children?

Ignore the millions of children who might have been readers had they not been seduced, raped, by the electronic media. Ignore also the millions who, for whatever reasons, have not been taught to read properly. Millions of real readers remain, devouring books on all levels of taste.

How do they read? How far off is the dewy-eyed Victorian Miss Repplier? We admit at once that today's children are more skeptical, closer to images of adult reality, closer to adult reality itself, and pressured by their environment to depreciate the claims of the imagination. Nonetheless, because they need books in a different way, I believe they read in a manner not open to grown-ups. For most of us the reading of fiction is an add-on, undertaken for entertainment, to keep-in-the-know, to develop ourselves culturally. Children read (those who do) because they have to. Their reading is not adjunctive but a centrally important activity, like play. Indeed, it has been described by Nicholas Tucker as a type of internalized play. But the play is serious. "The man writing on motherhood is merely an educationalist; the child playing with a doll is a mother," remarks G. K. Chesterton.

Especially in the early years, reading is undertaken in close cooperation with the child's unconscious, whereas the grown-up reader prizes the "detachment" which permits him to judge or evaluate the book. Bruno Bettelheim points this out clearly: "Literacy, man's great achievement, began as sheer magic, and was not created to serve utilitarian purposes. But modern education stresses only utility and 'getting ahead,' thus robbing learning to read of the greatest incentive which could support it. . . . I suggest that learning, particularly learning to read, must make a powerful appeal to our unconscious. . . ."

John Steinbeck tells us how his character Tom "got into a book, tunneled like a mole among its thoughts, and came up with the book all over his face and hands." "She always has her nose in a book." This is equally metaphor and description of fact. The child really does get inside the book whereas grown-ups extract the characters from the book and situate them in the larger reality of which they are more aware than is the child. The two modes of reading differ. The dilemma of the adult critic of children's literature is that he has forgotten how to stick his nose in the book. One must somehow grow, specially devised for the purpose, an additional nose.

The English drama critic James Agate, writing in *The Later Ego,* quotes a sentence from a friend's letter: "Have you ever seen a child reading *Alice*? Intense *interest,* but not a smile, it being of course his or her world." The picture is true only, of course, of those children who like *Alice;* many don't. But the observation is important: a smile would be a tiny signal of detachment, of a distance between the book and the Reader. Instead there is serious absorption, union with the book. They are interested in Reading. It is this same absence of split between themselves and their immediate environment that makes invariably graceful the gestures of children—as Joshua Reynolds, an authority on the subject, once noted.

The child reading his book and the adult reading literature differ in still another way. The adult reading, let us say, *War and Peace,* is constantly, though unconsciously, matching his own experience of human life against Tolstoy's. His reading activity is rooted in comparison. The child, on the other hand, has a much thinner experience. Hence his reading activity is rooted, not in comparison, but in discovery and exploration. For this reason he may get as much enjoyment out of trash as out of what we call worthwhile books. For a time the trash is just as novel, just as stimulating to his curiosity, as *The Wind in the Willows.* If his environment is adverse, he may remain at this level all his life; comics are read as much by grown-ups as by children. But if his environment is normally stimulating, he will gradually discover that the trash offers diminishing returns in the

"For many children . . . Alice [in Wonderland] *is merely puzzling. For others. . . it remains what it is—probably the most deeply searching fantasy ever written about the unconscious life of the child."*

way of novelty and surprise, whereas certain other books offer richer returns.

But we must keep constantly in mind that most children often seek things in books not sought by the critic or by the exceptionally sensitive child. What such children like is not necessarily "good." It may merely be what they *need* at a certain time, and that is not quite the same thing. A child who at a certain period is looking for swift action or self-identification, and not for emotional enhancement or the pleasure derived from well-composed English, may pass up the so-called classics in favor of Nancy Drew or Batman. This is not necessarily bad. It is a mistake, for example, to remove the Oz books from the library shelves merely because the style is mediocre. Even though it is.

There is still a third way in which the child and the adult differ in their reading experience. It is hard for us to understand that reading, for a child, at least up to about twelve or thirteen, is done in two languages simultaneously. We grown-ups read in one language, for the most part: that is, we more or less understand at once what the words intend to convey; and if we do not understand, the noncomprehension will be cleared up by further reading. Or we automatically judge the partially uncomprehended passage to be unimportant as compared with the larger part that we do comprehend.

For the child it is different. What he does not at once comprehend may be a large proportion of the text; what he does comprehend, he may comprehend only dimly. He is at once reading a familiar language and *learning a new one,* new words, phrases, sounds, behind which lie new feelings. The extra effort, if the book is a good one, or even if it is not, is not attended by pain, but by a vague, shapeless pleasure—like the pleasure he feels in daydreaming or in exploring a strange vacant lot or an unfamiliar cellar or attic. The uncomprehended or dimly comprehended may suffuse an aura of attractive mystery. The unclear may be quite educational.

A simple example: There is an excellent nineteenth-century boy's book, *The Story of a Bad Boy* by Thomas Bailey Aldrich. Chapter Two is headed: "In Which I Entertain Peculiar Views." I can still remember the puzzled interest with which, when I was nine, I read these six words. The phrasing, "in which I entertain peculiar views," is adult phrasing—quite properly, for the narrator is telling, from the perspective of maturity, the story of his boyhood. To me, a small boy, it hinted at some puzzle which was to be resolved. It used two words—*peculiar* and *entertain*—in a way new to me. It was untried territory. And therefore it somehow promised delight. Part of my mind understood the six words—that is, I did not need the dictionary to define them for me. But another part of my mind did not quite understand, yet with pleasure accepted them. This is what I mean by saying the child often reads in two languages at once and experiences thereby a certain richness or *thickness* of experience denied to the completely literate. The younger he is (the nearer to his original analphabetism) the richer, the thicker, the experience.

At four, I read my first complete book. *The Overall Boys* was a rousing tale of the adventures, recounted in monosyllables, of two devoted brothers, aged five and seven, on a farm. In a sense every book that followed has been an anticlimax. One's first book, kiss, home run, is always the best. Early reading is in large part discovery; grown-up reading in large part recognition. For the child his beginning books are all, like *Alice Through the Looking-Glass,* entries to other worlds. *Other* is the operative word on which all fantasy is based—but to the very young child it operates also even when he reads here-and-now books.

For children, at a certain age, words can be things, things that generate emotion—and the emotion is not necessarily linked to the precise meaning of the word. In his brilliant study of Dickens, G. K. Chesterton quotes an autobiographical passage from the novelist which mentions the coffee shops he frequented during the wretched days of his London childhood. Dickens writes: "I recall one in St. Martin's Lane, of which I only recollect that it stood near the church, and that in the door there was an oval glass plate with 'COFFEE ROOM' painted on it, addressed towards the street. If I ever find myself in a very different kind of coffee-room now, but where there is such an inscription on glass, and read it backwards on the wrong side, MOOR EEFFOC (as I often used to do then in a dismal reverie), a shock goes through my blood." In a way all children's reading is the reading of that sign. Everything is MOOR EEFFOC-ish.

Some worthwhile children's books

Unless supplemented by examples, the foregoing reflections may not be very useful to parents who would like their children to read. They want recommendations. It would be easy enough to append a list of one hundred children's books that experts (and children) generally agree are superior. Many such lists are available. But I prefer here to discuss briefly a mere score or so—books that in one way or another connect with the preceding pages. Some of your favorites (and some of mine) are not represented. Each book mentioned, however, offers telling and varied evidence of the single, simple truth that justifies all first-rate reading: the largest part of our whole universe of space and time can never be apprehended by direct, first-hand experience. Hence the nonreader, and especially the child nonreader, no matter how well adjusted or successful, remains mentally and emotionally handicapped. Long ago Plato implied this when he declared that the perfect society would emerge only when philosophers (who are readers) were kings and kings philosophers.

Of the titles listed below, the last three are books of verse. The rest are arranged in loose order. We pass from the completely impossible to the

readily acceptable, from what we conventionally call fantasy to what we conventionally call reality. The truth of the imagination is common to both groups. A Mother Goose rhyme may hold far more basic human nature than the latest teenage novel about abortion. All these books may be read by the intelligent adult with a pleasure quite free of condescension. More to the point, they should help the child reader—if he likes them at all—to become a good grown-up reader. They may even help him or her to become a good adult, a commodity in short supply.

A final word: plenty of books—and good ones—are available for the average or slow child. As for those noted below, the more intelligent the child the more he or she will delight in them: if this be elitism, it is in honor of the books.

Maurice Sendak: *Where the Wild Things Are* (Harper & Row)

The picture book, as distinguished from the illustrated book, is a distinct literary genre, like the epic or the novel. Small children *read* picture books; they do not merely look at the pictures. That explains why they notice and react to details that escape you and me. Sendak is the greatest living master of the picture book, which at his best he reinforces with an economical narrative text of considerable subtlety.

When *Wild Things* burst upon us twenty years ago the children—though not all adults—decided at once that it was a great book. (Only grown-ups need the crutches called literary critics.) A small boy named Max, sent to bed supperless (he's been mischievous), finds himself entering a country Where the Wild Things Are. They are quite dreadful creatures, but of course Max tames them and becomes their king. Then he finds he needs something else. He "wanted to be where someone loved him best of all." He travels back home to his own room where his hot supper awaits him.

That's all. But into the scary pictures and simple text is crammed a considerable part of the unconscious of small children. Sendak knows that his little readers are themselves "wild things." His monsters are the objective correlative, as it were, of the night side of a child's life. Contemplating them seems to help the small reader, to use Aristotle's familiar formula, to purge himself, through the medium of art, of his own terrors. Or, as Sendak puts it, "to turn a vulnerability into a fantasy where children can control their environment." Little Max finds freedom in his mastery over the grotesque products of his imagination; he finds security in the warm bedroom of his real home and the love that awaits him there. There are a few readers who might be frightened by this book, but the more general experience is one of joyous terror mixed with laughter.

Russell Hoban: *The Mouse and His Child* (Harper & Row)

Published in 1967, this was hailed at once as a work of high quality in England. It fell fairly flat here. But it will resurface and endure. For a children's book it's quite long—200 solid pages. Length, however, never fazes the real reader; he can't lose himself in a sparse forest, and losing himself is one of the experiences he seeks. It contains echoes of Lewis Carroll and *The Wind in the Willows,* but no matter: fine writers always echo great ones, as indeed they should. I think it one of the few original children's books produced during the last two decades.

It's about clockwork toys and animals. There's only one human character—a tramp who at the outset winds up the clockwork mouse-father and the clockwork son to whom he is indissolubly connected. He winds them up on page 25, says to them, "Be tramps" and then not another word out of him until the last line when he says only, "Be happy," and vanishes like Charlie Chaplin—or Mr. Russell Hoban. Between these laconic parentheses lies a whole scaled-down world: villainous Manny Rat who rules a garbage dump; Frog, both charlatan and philanthropist; C. Serpentina, a philosophical playwright along Beckett-Sartre lines; two crows who run a repertory company called The Caws of Art; and various agreeable creatures, including a clockwork elephant, a seal, a parrot, a muskrat, and many others.

What the mouse and his child want, as we all do, is to be self-winding, to feel like free beings. Like us, in the end they achieve part but perhaps not all of their aim. Like many children's books (as with fine adult novels the archetypes are few but reliable), this one stresses with extraordinary subtlety the child's two conflicting passions: to feel secure, to feel independent.

Beneath this enduring theme lies another, denied to grown-up novelists: the profound relationship between a child and his toys. Somewhere Mr. Hoban writes: "Most adult books are about clockwork dolls who copulate. *The Mouse and His Child* happens to be about clockwork mice that walk, and therefore it is a child's book." In a letter to me Mr. Hoban remarks on the mysterious appeal clockwork toys (think of the present and rather dubious video game mania) have for children, as they have for him. "As metaphors," he writes, "I consider them profound." And his book, on the child's level, is profound. There's plenty of violent action, robberies, small wars—but also a good deal of what we can only call metaphysics, or perhaps intellectual action. And, as a tender exploration of the relationship between fathers and sons, I find it considerably more satisfactory than Turgenev's novel bearing that title.

Marcel Aymé: *The Wonderful Farm* and *The Magic Pictures* (Harper & Row)

England and the United States have produced the finest literature for children, with Scandinavia and Germany as runners-up. For some reason France does not take easily to the form. Perhaps the French still think in Aristotelian terms: if the child's final cause is adulthood, then nourish him on grown-up books as soon as possible. There are, however, several noble exceptions in French children's literature. We think, for example, of Jean de Brunhoff and his Babar series. And there is Marcel Aymé.

One French critic has called Aymé the writer "most akin to Perrault and Grimm who has so far appeared in our midst." Others compare him to the great classic fabulist La Fontaine.

He has written seventeen stories about two little girls and the animals with whom they live on a Franche-Comté farm. The best are collected in the two volumes above mentioned, containing charming black-and-white illustrations by Maurice Sendak. "Age level" is of course a silly phrase; a fine children's book can be read at any age. But Aymé will probably appeal most to seven-to-tens.

We make a good deal of fuss these days about the new school of South American novelists and their "magic realism." Magic realism is old stuff to the writers of children's books. In Aymé the real and the merely imaginable blend perfectly. A tone of French *bon sens* is maintained, as in La Fontaine, along with fantasy. Animals talk, all sorts of metamorphoses occur, a little white hen turns into an elephant—but a kind of rustic, down-to-earth realism pervades every small miracle.

The humor and wit are peculiarly suited to children. For example, the father, addressing Delphine and Marinette, reminds them: "Remember you're no longer children. Together you're almost twenty years old." The child reader, figuring this out, is delighted to find that he can actually use the arithmetic he has learned in school. In one story the little girls invite all the animals to come into the house so that they may play Noah's Ark. The cow is particularly interested in what is visible behind the glass doors of the cupboard. "She could scarcely take her eyes off a cheese and a bowl of milk, and she murmured several times: 'I see . . . *Now* I understand!' "

Aymé stands squarely in the tradition of the animal fable but adds to it a Gallic charm and sly wit all his own.

Mary Norton: *The Borrowers*; *The Borrowers Afield*; *The Borrowers Afloat*; *The Borrowers Aloft*; *The Borrowers Avenged* (Harcourt Brace Jovanovich)

In every household, no matter how well-run, small things somehow mysteriously disappear—that thimble, needle, piece of cheese, matchbox, pencil. How did they vanish? No one knows.

Mary Norton knows. The Borrowers take them. A full-grown Borrower is perhaps six inches tall. Borrowers dwell in odd places in the attic or basement, behind walls, in unused closets, sometimes out of doors. They live on us. As Arrietty says, "Human beans are *for* Borrowers—like bread's for butter!"

Once the reader accepts this agreeable premise, all fantasy disappears. So does all coyness and cuteness. The Borrowers series is a realistic study of a complete miniature world. The Clock family (the entrance to their apartment is behind the grandfather clock) lead large and full lives. It's true that they make a living out of us—but we do the same thing, with perhaps more questionable consequences. They have their own class and family structure, contend with enemies (rats, for example), learn, suffer, are frightened—Pod, the father, tells Arrietty, "If there's snow, we're done."

Their minds are subtly different from ours, because their world (like that of small children) is in part a function of ours. The intersection of the two worlds is handled in nonmechanical terms. Swift used his Lilliputians to make statements about the human race, the diminished scale being a mere device. Swift was no novelist, Mary Norton is a very fine one. The Borrowers are neither mannikins nor reduced humans. They are, as close observers know children to be, a race apart.

The child finds no difficulty in accepting them. Neither will any intelligent grown-up, for the nutshell universe of the Borrowers is far more complex, more beautifully described and indeed more moving than the standard-scale universe of most serious adult novels.

Philippa Pearce: *Tom's Midnight Garden* (Lippincott)

Clocks and watches were invented for the convenience of adults. Children (and primitives) have to be taught our simple, linear notion that Time is something defined by the circular motion of a sweep-hand and also that it is something to be "saved." The child's sense of Time is richer, more flexible, more creatively confused. That may in part account for his reluctance to appreciate the high virtues of punctuality and scheduling. Imagination stands in his way.

Time travel, time warping, multiple time—such concepts have long been a staple of children's literature. Indeed all science fiction involving time distortion may be a kind of children's literature. All science fiction may be.

Among those stories based on the flexibility of time *Tom's Midnight Garden* (1958) remains a classic. It involves a young English lad, Tom Long, who's shipped off (his brother Peter is quarantined with the measles) to stay for awhile with his aunt and uncle in their apartment not far from Ely. In the house is a peculiar grandfather clock, one of the story's many symbols that are just sufficiently insistent (but no more) to stretch the young reader's imagination. Back of the house is a ratty little backyard area into which Tom one night wanders. But the backyard, when he later visits it, has changed into an old-fashioned garden and in it he meets Hatty, an equally old-fashioned girl. She belongs to another time, perhaps seventy-five years prior to the time of the story.

The garden, of course, is Eden or—more broadly considered—the imaginative life of children. The book, like Wordsworth's *Ode,* is about growing up, about the tension between the inevitably precarious security of childhood and the necessary adaptation to the "real world." Tom "wanted two different sets of things so badly: he wanted his mother and father and Peter and home—he really did want them, badly; and, on the other hand, he wanted the garden."

Whether thought of as a non-scary ghost story, a suited-to-children disquisition on the nature of Time, a dramatic representation of the dream life of the young, or as science fiction presented in terms of perfect realism—*Tom's Midnight Garden* works beautifully.

Lewis Carroll: *Alice's Adventures in Wonderland* and *Through the Looking-Glass* (Bantam)

There's not much to be said about the most famous children's story ever written, though hundreds of very serious people have written very seriously about it. One or two points might be made. Many books for grown-ups become children's books: *The Yearling,* for example, among hundreds of others. But *Alice,* as the acute critic Martin Gardner has pointed out, seems to be reversing the trend. H. L. Mencken once wrote that he couldn't read it "until he was a grown man, and far gone in sin." Though it has been translated into scores of languages, it cannot really be said to be a universal classic. The French scholar Isabelle Jan thinks it "a profoundly national book. Among non-English-speaking children its mysteriousness arouses uneasiness without arousing curiosity; its humor seems plain lunacy."

Furthermore, among English-speaking children today it is probably, for many, one of those books they read because they are forced to. *Alice* deals not only with dreams and psychic derangements (which *are* part of the child consciousness) but with language, specifically the English language. Our present school system and, more especially, the successfully competitive system of television tend to blunt and coarsen the child's sense of language. For many children, therefore, *Alice* is merely puzzling. For others, the saving remnant, it remains what it is—probably the most deeply searching fantasy ever written about the unconscious life of the child.

Dr. Seuss (Most titles published by Random House)

We owned twenty Seusses. Then the children grew up overnight and we stopped adding to the collection. I suppose there must now be about forty or fifty titles in print, some of them (the Beginner Books) for very small children. They are all good; you may choose almost blindly. Our favorite is *On Beyond Zebra,* which deals with the many necessary letters after Z. *And To Think That I Saw It on Mulberry Street* is as fresh and funny as it was when first published in 1937. Other classics: *The 500 Hats of Bartholomew Cubbins, Horton Hatches the Egg, If I Ran the Zoo, How the Grinch Stole Christmas.*

It is easy to say that the good doctor writes jingles and draws technicolor cartoons. Easy—and wrong. These jingles are written with Flaubertian care. The loony stories are so constructed as to *compel* the turn of the page. The vocabulary, while simple, is never flat and always cunningly chosen so as to lead the child into the oddities and delights of our language.

As for the pictures, it is true that they are not "art" in the conventional sense. Says Dr. Seuss: "I cannot draw things as they are. . . . I stumbled onto a style made of mistakes." But these "mistakes" have given us a whole cosmos of odd creatures—Sneetches, Mop-Noodled Finches, Nerkles, Ooblecks, and Drum-Tummied Snums.

Dr. Seuss has perfected the art of making quite thoughtful statements about human nature while apparently relying entirely upon graphic and verbal nonsense. There has never been anything like him in the field of children's literature and there never will be, for the quality of his vision is entirely his own.

Beatrix Potter: *The Tailor of Gloucester; Peter Rabbit;* et alia (Frederick Warne and Co.)

The Lord must not have loved very good writer-artists for very small children, for He has made so few of them. By common consent, Beatrix Potter is the best.

If you poke about in the cemetery of Gloucester, England, you may come upon the tombstone of one Pritchard, identifying him as "The Tailor of Gloucester." There really was such a person and he really did fashion a splendid waistcoat for the mayor. Miss Potter, substituting some warmhearted mice for his two devoted assistants, in 1901 wrote the story we now know, accompanying it with twelve of her most exquisite watercolors. It can be read in either the original longer version (which I prefer) or in a briefer one, published as one of the delightful tiny Beatrix Potter books that are known all over the world. Of these latter, the first one, *The Tale of Peter Rabbit,* is the most famous.

The Tailor was Miss Potter's own favorite; Rumer Godden once called it "perhaps the most subtle children's book ever written." It has that rarest of virtues, being a tale crafted by a cunning artist that sounds precisely like the finest work of, as we say, the "folk" imagination.

Can Literature, with a decided capital L, be composed for those who can barely read? The evidence for the affirmative is sparse: Miss Potter's twenty-odd miniature narratives (of which her delicate, pastel-toned watercolors form an integral part) comprise the bulk of it. The purity of the prose ("I read the Bible to chasten my style.") accounts for some of her appeal. Her feathery humor, too: you will recall Mrs. Rabbit explaining to Peter, "Your father had an accident there; he was put in a pie by Mrs. McGregor." Still, the magic is inexplicable.

Publishers' blurbs are usually suspect. But the sentence found on the front flap of each of her books is true as can be: "Her many picture stories should be among the first books owned by children." Very small ones—and also by the grown-ups Dr. Seuss calls "obsolete children."

E. B. White: *Charlotte's Web* (Harper & Row)

Good writers of adult books who also write well for children are few in number. Among them E. B. White stands out. He does so, I think, because the E. B. White who created the superb essays is the same E. B. White who created the children's books. He does not don another hat, change gears, write down (or up or sideways), or even use a notably simpler vocabulary. Indeed he hardly seems to be aware of an audience of children existing somewhere out yonder. He writes because he is interested in a mouse-boy or a trumpeter swan or a spider. If the story that emerges should turn out to be peculiarly suited to children—well and good. What counts is that it should be suited to E. B. White.

Charlotte's Web (1952) is a funny, serious book about a spider, a pig, a rat, and an eight-year-old girl named Fawn. The plot turns on the need to save Wilbur the pig from becoming bacon. To this end Fawn and Templeton the rat and Charlotte the spider all turn their energies, though their motives differ. So much for the plot.

No good book is about its plot. This one is about quite fundamental things: love and friendship (Charlotte, wisest and most literate of spiders, understands these things), generation, maturing, death. Also such fundamental matters as the natural life around farms, the fact that organisms—even Charlotte—feed quite horribly on each other, the fact that humanity likes to be deceived.

Apropos of writing for children Mr. White once remarked, "I am not averse to departing from reality, but I am against departure from the truth." True, *Charlotte's Web* is about animals who talk to each other. One of them (her professional name is Charlotte Aranea Cavatica) weaves into her web such messages as *Some Pig* and *Terrific.* But the book never departs from the truth.

Kenneth Grahame: *The Wind in the Willows* (Scribners)

Like *Alice, The Wind in the Willows* is not currently fashionable among children, or adults either. It was inspired by a rural England now obsolescent. At its worst the style is period and "literary." Its references, of course, date: in Mr. Toad's day the motorcar was a marvelous romantic object rather than a polluter and killer. As a work of art it is flawed. Its lyrical digressions do not quite work for us, the joinings of the animal and human worlds are awkwardly carpentered. Finally—in 1908 the argus-eyed *Times* of London perceived this at once—"as a contribution to natural history it is negligible."

Nonetheless, for those select young readers wise enough not to care about "relevance" it still holds its enchantment. The peaceful, human-scaled countryside of Edwardian England may seem alien to young readers whose imaginations have been paralyzed by the curare of television. But there are others still able to respond to the undying appeal of wood and river and riverbank, to swaggering Toad, warmhearted Rat, home-loving Mole, and no-nonsense Badger. These characters live a triple life, for they are at once animals, adults, and children, and it is this complexity that gives the book some of its depth.

Like many of the finest stories for children, it balances the themes of freedom and security, thus offering a kind of dress rehearsal of what will later also be the basic concern of maturity. It works with simple materials that can never quite lose their appeal for children: the joys of rambling, of "messing about in boats" counterpointing the grateful delights of snug-

THE WIND IN THE WILLOWS

Kenneth Grahame

pictures by

John Burningham

ness, the hearth, the home. Sentiment alternates with humor, adventure relieves those quieter passages into which Grahame has filtered his pervasive love of the English countryside and the small animals that are its almost invisible life.

Louise Fitzhugh: *Harriet the Spy* (Harper & Row)

First published in 1964, this book precipitated an uproar. It was revolutionary for its day. Eleven-year-old Harriet's parents are smart, upper-middle-class New Yorkers, no better than they should be. Harriet is attended by Ole Golly, a non-whimsical Americanized version of Mary Poppins, given to quoting Wordsworth, Emerson, and Dostoevsky. Harriet's schoolmates reflect the pressures of broken homes, social-climbing parents, and other deplorable phenomena of New York familial life. The lower-class types are presented without patronage or sentimentality; Ole Golly's mother, for example, is mentally retarded. There are references to traditionally taboo subjects, such as throwing up and the uses of bathrooms. There's even—a novelty in 1964—a child's psychiatrist.

And there's Harriet. This peeping Thomasina, a budding novelist, spies on everybody; classmates, parents, neighbors. What she learns is more instructive than edifying, and all of it goes into the notebook that eventually lands her in trouble. No heroine is Harriet; often mean, always sharply critical, intense, precocious, complex—in fact, subversive. One dismayed professional critic was certain children would not take to the book because they "do not enjoy cynicism."

She was mistaken. *Harriet the Spy* enjoyed great success and has held its own for twenty years. The reasons are multiple.

First, though it pioneered the new school of realism in children's fiction, it has no thesis. Its aim is to draw character, to show modern New York kids as they are, and not as adults would like them to be. Second, it's very funny, because Harriet's mind and mode of expression are quirky, offbeat, completely surprising. Third, while it's *not* "cynical," it does show children as sometimes selfish, uncharitable, affected; and they are all these things not because they are evil but because, being relatively weak and vulnerable, still unable to communicate clearly, still uncertain of their identities, they must in self-protection try on mask after mask. And not all masks are pretty.

The realistic school that has in the last twenty years changed the face of children's literature (mainly in our country) has produced almost nothing of literary value. *Harriet the Spy* is an exception. In its small, simple way it is not unworthy of comparison with Henry James's *What Maisie Knew*. James and Miss Fitzhugh work with similar materials, and Miss Fitzhugh does pretty well with hers.

E. L. Konigsburg: *From the Mixed-up Files of Mrs. Basil E. Frankweiler* (Atheneum)

This intriguingly titled affair came out three years after *Harriet the Spy* and belongs roughly to the same genre. It too caused quite a furor by reason of its humor and originality. There was even a film version starring Ingrid Bergman.

Its theme is traditional: running away from home. The handling is completely unconventional. Claudia Kincaid, almost twelve, persuades her brother Jamie, nine, to run away from their comfortable suburban home in Greenwich, Connecticut. It's a nice home and these are nice children. It's just that Claudia feels she is unappreciated. Her idea, carried out with superb organizing skill, is for them to take a train to New York and spend a week in the Metropolitan Museum of Art. This they do, living very well on Jamie's forty-three dollars and twenty-three cents (he's the chancellor of the exchequer). They even manage to sleep in the bed in which Amy Robsart, so they say, was murdered.

The book might be called a kind of mini-*Robinson Crusoe,* a study—urban, modern, and funny—of adaptation and survival. There's a plot involving a statue reputed to be by Michelangelo, but what really counts is the two children, gravely mastering and controlling a situation seemingly ridiculous. As it is a rich old lady, Mrs. Frankweiler, who tells their story, a certain distancing effect is created, making the comedy accessible, though in different ways, to both young and grown-up readers.

Like *Harriet,* this is one of the few novels of the realistic school that will stay around for awhile. If children's literature can be said to have the quality of sophistication, this has it.

Laura Ingalls Wilder: The *Little House* series (Harper & Row)

The series comprises eight volumes. Particularly recommended are the first two (*Little House in the Big Woods, Little House on the Prairie*) and *The Long Winter*. Mrs. Wilder's mildly fictionalized account of her and her family's life on the then frontier more than a century ago has become a classic. Possibly ten million copies of the entire series have been sold. They are great library favorites: as one librarian put it, "These books don't get damaged or lost. They are simply read to death."

The westward migration is, of course, one of the three or four truly character-forming experiences in our history. Here it is rendered in domestic terms, from the viewpoint of a child and, as she matures, a young woman. While the tone is generally "wholesome" and "American," there is little sentimentality. The profound influence of racism and narrow puritanism is accurately reflected.

Laura Ingalls Wilder

LITTLE HOUSE ON THE PRAIRIE

PICTURES BY GARTH WILLIAMS

Children continually want to know how their ancestors—or indeed anybody's ancestors—lived. Mrs. Wilder's stories satisfy them. In her recollective genius lies her central appeal. One eleven-year-old Danish girl reader said, "Laura experienced things while they were still brand new."

Robert Westall: *The Machine Gunners* (Greenwillow)

In my view this English story is the finest book for youngsters to come out of World War II. In a wood near the town of Garmouth (it's really the author's native Tynemouth) a teenager discovers a shot-down Heinkel. The dead pilot is clutching an intact machine gun. Chas and five of his friends liberate it, set up a den as an emplacement, and prepare to defend the town against the presumed German invaders. But their enemy is the whole adult world, though of this they are barely conscious.

A few false touches creep in, but in general *The Machine Gunners,* played against a sharply depicted background of real air raids, wartime living, and universal fear, rings true. It won the Carnegie Medal in 1976 and deserved it.

Meindert DeJong: *Journey from Peppermint Street* (Harper & Row)

Mr. DeJong was born in Friesland, part of The Netherlands, and with his family came to our country when he was eight. Many of his score or so of books are drawn from recollections of his childhood, as is this one. In view of his somewhat unusual background, it's interesting to note that in 1962 he was the first American to win the Hans Christian Andersen Award, the nearest thing in its field to the Nobel Prize.

If childhood is mainly feelings, not understandings, *Journey from Peppermint Street* is, as I think, as true a book as any in the literature. It is a child's size Odyssey. Nine-year-old Siebren leaves his native Weirom (we are in the early 1900s), accompanied by his grandfather, to visit his aunt who lives inland in a converted monastery. On the way they have (though action is not Mr. DeJong's forte) many adventures, including the crossing of a perilous marsh by night, an episode almost as effective as the cave chapter in *Tom Sawyer.*

Siebren's important encounters, however, are not with physical dangers, but with fear, cruelty, kindness, love, and especially wonder. The inner and the outer journeys are perfectly orchestrated. The author is not so much close to Siebren as inside him—a remarkable feat of empathy. The sombre grandfather and the sensitive boy are played off against each other so that each enlarges the other's world.

This is a leisurely book, for Siebren needs time to observe and register everything he encounters along the Frisian roadways and dikelands. For the right child it will be a revelation; for the TV-conditioned it may seem remote. I think it a beautiful book.

Iona and Peter Opie (eds.): *The Oxford Nursery Rhyme Book* (Oxford); *Come Hither: A Collection of Rhymes and Poems for the Young of All Ages,* made by Walter de la Mare (Alfred A. Knopf); David McCord: *One at a Time* (Little, Brown & Co.)

To enjoy verse is quite normal for children. Or was—for technology, as it systematically deprives children of their childhood, makes them impervious to the oldest and highest form of literature. I do not know what can be done about this, unless commercial television is banned and a new race of teachers and parents created. While awaiting that consummation, I suggest, among hundreds that might be recommended, three volumes of verse. Two are anthologies, the third is a one-man show.

The Opies include 800 rhymes. Of their superb collection I once wrote, "If your child does not like this book, don't get rid of the book; get rid of the child." A drastic injunction, but it breathes the right spirit. An English-speaking child brought up minus Mother Goose will suffer all his or her life from an insufficiency disease. In an 1833 edition Ma'am Goose, talking to two small children, scorns the notion of a "new" Mother Goose. As well, she says, "write a new Billy Shakespeare. . . . We two great poets were born together, and we shall go out of the world together." Straight talk, that.

Nursery rhymes are often attacked as irrelevant to our day. But it is "Star Wars" and similar noxious techno-fare that are irrelevant. Nursery rhymes concern realities, handling them with enduring insight and humor. They deal, to be alphabetical, with such matters as: apple pies, cakes, cats, courting, donkeys, eating, farming, fighting, geese, guns, horses, knaves, laziness, mice, millers, owls, pedlars, petticoats, pigs, priests, puddings, shoes, tarts, thieves, and washing. An education, if not for the whole man, at least for the whole three-year-old.

For the older child willing to give poetry a chance there are many fine anthologies. De la Mare's is one of the most comprehensive, if a little old-fashioned. In addition to 483 poems, arranged by subject, it contains 324 pages of notes and ruminations, at once strange and scholarly. These are only for future Keatses and T. S. Eliots.

One at a Time, by David McCord, collects seven volumes by the most skillful living writer of verse for children. His acrobatic word-foolery will enchant all youngsters sensitive to the miracle of our great English tongue. Beyond this, in poem after poem, he touches, mingling grace and insight, on the interior life, hidden from most adult eyes, of children.

PART FIVE

Reviews of Recent Books

Braudel's *Mediterranean*

Charles Van Doren was born and raised in New York City. In 1947, after service in the Air Force, he was graduated from St. John's College, Annapolis, Maryland, and two years later he took a master's degree in mathematics from Columbia University, where he also received his doctorate in English literature in 1959, and where he taught literature from 1955 to 1959.

In 1965 he joined the Institute for Philosophical Research in Chicago as assistant director under Mortimer Adler. From 1973 until last year he was also vice-president, editorial, of Encyclopaedia Britannica, Inc. Now retired, he remains a member of Britannica's board of editors.

He is the author of *Lincoln's Commando* (1957), *The Idea of Progress* (1967), and several children's books. In addition, he was editor, with Clifton Fadiman, of *The American Treasury* (1955); was executive editor of the twenty-volume *Annals of America* (1967), of which he wrote most of the two-volume *Conspectus;* was one of the general editors of *Makers of America* (ten vols., 1971); edited, with Mortimer Adler, the *Great Treasury of Western Thought* (1977); and was supervisory editor of four volumes of documents on various aspects of American history edited by Wayne Moquin between 1971 and 1976.

Since his retirement, Mr. Van Doren has been busy as a writer and consultant. He and his wife Geraldine spend a portion of each year in their small house in Italy. His article "Machine Thinking and Thinking Machines" appeared in last year's edition of *The Great Ideas Today.*

There is a sense in which this enormous, great book by Fernand Braudel* does not actually begin until page 901. For it is not until then, after 900 wonderful pages of "introduction," as one might say, or "background" or "setting of the scene," that the "history of its subject," as we ordinarily understand the word *history,* can be said to begin—the history, that is, of the events, and of the men and women who caused and engaged in and were affected by them, that occurred in a certain part of the world ("the Mediterranean") during a certain period of time ("the Age of Philip II"). Indeed, when the first edition of the work was originally published in French, in 1949, after twenty years of almost unremitting labor, a friend of Braudel's wrote him that he could have written it the other way round: "beginning with events, then moving on from that spectacular and often misleading pageant to the structural features underlying it, and finally to the bedrock of history." (p. 903.) In that case, of course, the *last* 900 pages would have become a kind of vastly extended appendix, a series of notes, and we would not have read them and would have missed one of the richest experiences we have ever had, and we would not have known—perhaps no one except the experts would have known—that Fernand Braudel is one of the great historians.

In any case we see immediately that Braudel was right to do as he did, see it as soon as we look back at the words we have used to describe the book's subject matter. "The Mediterranean"—what is "the Mediterranean"? What is "the Mediterranean World"? Is it that wild and beautiful inland sea alone, or is it not also, certainly, the land that surrounds it and the peoples who live there and use the sea to communicate with one another, to make their living, to wage war on their enemies, both near and far? But if so, how far away from the Mediterranean Sea does the Mediterranean world extend? The "geographer's Mediterranean," as Braudel calls it, is clear enough: climatically speaking (and "climate is history"), the Mediterranean extends from the Straits of Gibraltar to the Straits of the Bosporus, and from the northernmost line (in Africa) of compact palm groves to the northernmost line (in Europe) of olive groves. On that

***The Mediterranean and the Mediterranean World in the Age of Philip II.* Tr. from the French by Siân Reynolds; 2nd edition, 2 volumes, 1375 pages (New York: Harper & Row, 1972, 1973).

basis, we can easily draw a map that responds to our question, and we shall not need 900 pages to answer it.

But is it really correct to say that Gibraltar is the western limit of the Mediterranean world, Istanbul the eastern one? Or that Florence is a Mediterranean city because olive trees grow in the valley around it, and that Milan is not because the olive does not thrive in most of the Milanese? Large, compact palm groves are found along the very shore of the Mediterranean from Tripoli to Alexandria; does that mean the Mediterranean littoral from the Gulf of Tunis to the Nile is not part of the Mediterranean world (because it is south of the line of compact palm groves)? And what of the wagons that lumbered over the Alpine passes, both summer and winter, into Germany and Austria and France, laden with silk and pepper and silver; or the ships that left Venice and Ragusa (Dubrovnik) and Naples and Genoa and Marseilles and Barcelona and Valencia and Lisbon (the last already outside the Pillars of Hercules but a Mediterranean city for all that) and sailed south along the coast of Africa, around the Cape of Good Hope and into the Indian Ocean, or north along the coast of Europe to Dover and Calais and Antwerp? Were these cities, too, part of the Mediterranean world? At the very least, would they have been what they were without the enormous and never-ceasing influence of that world, for good and for ill? And what of the treasure ships that brought Spain's silver all the way from America to feed the voracious imperial appetite? Was the Atlantic, or part of it at least, also "in" that world? Finally, are we justified in closing the eastern door of the Mediterranean at Constantinople when to do so is to cut into two (unequal) parts that other great quasi- (at least quasi-) Mediterranean empire, besides the Spanish one, the Turks under Süleyman the Magnificent and his successors, whose galleys under the famed Barbarossa and *his* successors tormented Mediterranean shipping for three-quarters of a century? In short, the Mediterranean world—we see that we must conclude; Fernand Braudel makes us see that we must conclude—is larger even than the inland sea and all its bordering lands and peoples. It stretches out to touch and affect a very much larger world.

At the same time Braudel forces us to agree that we should draw the line *somewhere,* though in no inflexible and unchanging manner, around that throbbing Mediterranean heart. It takes some pages to make all this clear—352 pages, to be exact, which comprise Part One of *The Mediterranean,* "The Role of the Environment," where "environment" is to be understood in the widest sense as the overall background of the piece or, in Braudel's wonderful phrase, "the bedrock of history."

But we have addressed only one of the questions that naturally arise when we consider the title of this book. If we know now, in some sense (and nothing that I can say in these few pages is to be thought of as a satisfactory summary or substitute for the joy of reading these first 352 pages), what "the Mediterranean World" means, we have still not defined "the Age of Philip II." When does this begin? On the day in 1556 when the young Philip becomes King of Spain? But at that time his father, the Emperor Charles V, is still alive and still very much the master of Spain (despite his having given its crown to his oldest son as a birthday present), as he is of the Netherlands and of (most of) Italy and of the rest of his far-flung Hapsburg dominions.

Does this Age begin, then, on the day in 1558 when Charles V dies? But the world that Philip II inherits on that day, and especially all the problems of that world, have not come into existence on that day; they have been forming for many a year, for as long as a century, and Philip II is no more able than any mortal man to reverse the past; he must needs accept for what it is the world his father has made for him (along with many other men and women, to be sure) and do the best he can with it.

Similarly, does the Age of Philip II end on September 13, 1598, the day on which Philip, after heroic suffering during which he remains lucid and even cheerful (he confesses and cleanses his soul for three whole days at the very end), dies at the Escorial? Again, the world that survives him is not so very different for years after his death—perhaps for fifty years. Strange as it sounds, therefore, we come to understand—Fernand Braudel brings us to understand—that "the Age of Philip II" is almost a 200-year period (from about 1450 to about 1650) or, at the very least, a 150-year period (from about 1480 to about 1630), during which certain "Collective Destinies and General Trends" (the title of Part Two, which runs from page 353 to page 900) occur and must be understood if we are to make any sense at all of the events of the forty-eight years from 1550 to 1598 that are the subject of the third and last part of the book—the "history," as we are accustomed to call it, of the reign of Philip II of Spain.

It is important to realize that Braudel was reluctant, as he himself admits, to publish this third part, "describing events in the Mediterranean during the fifty years of our study: it has strong affinities with frankly traditional historiography. . . ." Still, he continues,

> it must be included, for there is more to history than the study of persistent structures and the slow progress of evolution. These permanent realities—the conservative societies, the economic systems trapped by the impossible, the enduring civilizations, all the legitimate ways of approaching history in depth we have surveyed in the preceding chapters, undoubtedly, to my mind, provide the essentials of man's past, or what we today in the twentieth century consider to be the essentials. But they cannot provide the total picture.
>
> What is more, this method of reconstructing the past would have been most disappointing to Philip II's contemporaries. As spectators and actors on the sixteenth-century stage, in the Mediterranean and elsewhere, they felt, rightly or wrongly, that they were participating in a

> mighty drama which they regarded above all as one personal to them. Possibly, probably even, they were under an illusion. But this illusion, this feeling of being an eye-witness of a universal spectacle, helped to give meaning to their lives. (p. 901.)

The problem, Braudel maintains, is that "events are the ephemera of history; they pass across its stage like fireflies, hardly glimpsed before they settle back into darkness and as often as not into oblivion." (p. 901.) The kind of history that is based on events tends to recognize—almost is required to recognize—"only 'important' events, building its hypotheses only on foundations which are solid or assumed to be so. The importance in question is obviously a matter of opinion." (p. 902.) In the sixteenth century, as Braudel rightly says, the choice would have been made from "the chain of political events in the wide sense, wars, diplomatic treaties, decisions and domestic upheavals." (ibid.) Nowadays, as he also rightly says, we tend to see as even more important a "chain of economic events and their short-term conjunctures." (ibid.)

> For us, there will always be two chains—not one. So even in the realms of traditional history, it would be difficult for us to tread exactly in Ranke's footsteps. In turn we should beware of assuming that these two chains preclude the existence of any others, or of falling into the trap of naïvely assuming that one can explain the other, when even now we can guess at further possible chains composed of data from social or cultural history and even from collective psychology.
>
> In any case, by admitting that economic and political realities can be classified more easily, in the short or very short term, than other social manifestations, we imply the existence of some global order going beyond them and the need to continue the search for structure and category behind the event. (ibid.)

Fernand Braudel: man and historian

Who is this man Braudel, who has been called "perhaps the most influential living historian"? He is French; he is eighty-one years old. He has been married to the same woman for fifty years. He qualified as a history teacher at twenty-one and went first to Algiers and then to Paris and Sao Paulo to teach history, to high school students, then in college. The greatest influence on his own thought has been *Annales d'histoire économique et sociale,* founded by Lucien Febvre and Marc Bloch in 1929. Febvre and Bloch were impatient with the academic history of their time and its emphasis on the lives of great men. History had to remake itself, they insisted, had to incorporate within itself, as auxiliaries, all the sciences of man: geography, economics, psychology, sociology. Braudel had decided on the subject of his doctoral thesis: a study of the policies of Philip II in the latter half of the sixteenth century. He had begun his research, but not in published texts; he was determined to rely only on original sources. To this end he traveled all over the Mediterranean during his school vacations, poring over old tomes and dusty documents in Paris, Madrid, Venice, Dubrovnik, Istanbul and making copies of them. In effect he invented scholarly microfilming: "I was no doubt the first user of true microfilms," he wrote later, "which I developed myself and later read, through long days and nights, with a simple magic lantern." He learned to photograph as many as two or three thousand pages a day; all told he photographed, developed, and read hundreds of thousands of pages. (The bibliography of *The Mediterranean* fills seventy close-set pages.)

The first issues of *Annales* were an inspiration to this hardworking young scholar; here were men who not only thought as he did but also confirmed and enlarged his concept of history. He became Febvre's disciple and later his friend. At the same time his conception of his dissertation both broadened and deepened. It would be, he determined, a work worthy of *Annales,* incorporating within itself all that was known by all the human sciences about the Mediterranean world of the sixteenth century. He worked feverishly; he became thirty, then thirty-five; he was probably the best-known ABD (all-but-dissertation) in France. Finally, in 1939, he was ready to start writing. His vast files of notes around him (the published version of *The Mediterranean* has some 8,000 notes), he set to work. That same year Germany invaded Poland.

The history of his own time had supervened. Braudel was called up, as an army lieutenant, for service on the Maginot Line guarding France's eastern front. The winter of 1939–40 was a time of frustration for him, as it was for all Frenchmen; the Germans did not attack, there was nothing anyone could do but anxiously wait. The war began in earnest in the spring, and by June 1940 France had surrendered and Fernand Braudel was a prisoner of war. He spent two years in a prison camp at Mainz, fretting about history and his own book, then was transferred to a camp for rebellious prisoners at Lübeck. He was chosen as leader of the French POWs, which entailed serious responsibilities, but he nevertheless found himself with time to spare. He determined to make use of it.

He had been, as he later admitted, a mediocre student at the Sorbonne during those years after World War I, but he had had an excellent—even a phenomenal—memory, and this had enabled him to graduate "without difficulty." Now, in Lübeck, during the long prison days and nights, he set himself to remember all that had been in those vast files of notes. He filled school copybook after copybook with lucid prose. By the time of his release in 1945 he had completed his dissertation, which he defended in 1947—after inserting thousands of page-number references and citations. The book was published in 1949. It was immediately acclaimed as a "majestic monument of twentieth-century historiography." Braudel was forty-five when he finally received his doctorate.

As early as 1937 he had become, on the recommendation of Lucien Febvre, a director of studies at the Ecole Pratique des Hautes Etudes in Paris. Now, in 1947, there was no question of his occupying a teaching post other than at the very center of French historical scholarship. He returned to the Ecole Pratique des Hautes Etudes as director of the Centre de Recherches Historiques of the famous sixth section (economic and social sciences); he became president of this highly influential section in 1956. Febvre had called him as well to *Annales,* of which he became editorial director in 1956 (the year of Febvre's death). Braudel gave up the position to younger colleagues in 1968 and resigned his professorship of modern history at the Collège de France in 1972. Since then he has been administrator of the Maison des Sciences de l'Homme in Paris, where he has lived for nearly forty years.

The Mediterranean was a great work, but there were ways in which Braudel knew it could be better, and he began an extensive revision soon after 1949 in preparation for a second edition that appeared in two volumes in 1966. This publication was met by nearly unanimous praise. Most of the world's leading historians reviewed the book and pronounced their approval and support not only of the work but also of the kind of history it represented and exemplified.

Fernand Braudel, scholar of scholars, was not content. *The Mediterranean* had been only a first step; there was a larger world that demanded to be considered. He set to work to do for the entire globe, and not just over a period of 50 (or 150 or 200) years but over four centuries, from 1400 (the end of the Middle Ages) to 1800 (the beginning of the Modern Period), what he had done for the Mediterranean in the sixteenth century. *Civilisation matérielle et capitalisme, XVe–XVIIIe siècle* appeared first in 1967 and then in an extensively revised three-volume edition in 1979. The new work is now being translated into English by Siân Reynolds; the first volume of the translation, *The Structures of Everyday Life: Civilization and Capitalism, 15th–18th Century,* has already appeared, and the others are following in due course.

The theme of the new work is indicated by a subtitle: "The Limits of the Possible." (In French the entire title is "Les Structures du quotidien: Le Possible et l'impossible.") This indeed is the subject, as we now perceive, that has fascinated, not to say obsessed, Fernand Braudel throughout his life. The present first volume contains eight chapters dealing, successively, with Population (how many people, really, did the world contain in 1400? in 1800?), Daily Bread (the three great staples—wheat, rice, and maize), Food and Drink (luxury for some; for the masses, the fact of there never being enough of anything), Clothes, Houses, Fashion (the conflict, here as elsewhere, between rich and poor), Technology (sources of energy and the development of metallurgy), The Spread of Technology (borrowings, revolutions, and delays), Towns and Cities (as outposts of modernity, urbanization taken as the sign of modern man).

This book, richly illustrated—"the great gallery of pictures," Peter Laslett wrote, "are a masterpiece in themselves"—has been condemned by some reviewers who feel that even a Braudel is not equal to the task of writing an *Annales* history of the whole world over a period of 400 years. There are errors in the book, it has been pointed out, there are "occasional dubious and portentous generalizations, [and] a cloudy overall structure." Nevertheless, the critic who wrote thus also praised Braudel's vivid style and concluded that "again and again he strengthens the conviction that this is the way history will go, and must go." At any rate, and despite its undoubted errors, *The Structures of Everyday Life* is an absolutely marvelous "read"; it is, quite literally, an enormous work of historical scholarship that it is also impossible to put down.

The history of civilizations

If Braudel's *Mediterranean* and his later *Structures of Everyday Life* are the richest gift to us of the *Annales* school of historians—an assertion that Braudel himself would certainly deny, for he is naturally a humble man and would prefer to say that it was Lucien Febvre who was the most influential historian of our age—then we can at least redress the balance somewhat by recalling another singular achievement of this school (not so successful or well known as *The Mediterranean,* but important nevertheless) in which Febvre played the leading role and Braudel only a minor one. This was the *Encyclopédie française,* a work that I have elsewhere declared to be one of the half-dozen most interesting encyclopedias to be published in the twentieth century.

The *Encyclopédie* was begun in the early 1930s, under the direction of Febvre and Anatole de Monzie, then French minister of culture; the issuance of individual volumes was interrupted by the war. It was never a great commercial success, as it was an encyclopedia published not in alphabetical but in topical sequence, and this has seldom attracted a public that does not really want to be enlightened by an encyclopedia but prefers to have its questions answered in the narrowest rather than the broadest terms. Nevertheless, *Encyclopédie française* attracted the attention and employed the talents of almost everybody who was anybody (intellectually speaking) in the Fourth Republic, and Fernand Braudel was naturally drawn to it as well, and not only because his mentor Febvre was its general editor.

All of the separate volumes of *Encyclopédie française* are fascinating, not least the one titled *La civilisation quotidienne,* which throws light on a French and indeed a Western way of life of only half a century ago that seems to us almost a museum piece today. But the volume to which Braudel made his own distinctive contribution was Volume 20, *Le Monde en devenir (Histoire, évolution, prospective),* for which he wrote a chapter entitled "The History of Civilizations: The Past Explains the Present." These lucid and provocative forty pages are reprinted in a slim volume, *On History,* a collection of scattered pieces by Fernand Braudel with various subjects (he has not written many of the sort of "articles" or "essays" that could be included in such a volume). We owe a debt to the translator of the collection, Sarah Matthews, for giving us some valuable insights into the thought of Braudel, otherwise unavailable in English.*

"The question under discussion in the present chapter," writes Braudel for *Encyclopédie française,* "is a fairly unusual one: can the history of civilization . . . help us to understand the present time and thus, necessarily, the future—for today can hardly be understood except in relation to tomorrow?" (*On History,* p. 176.) Considering this question, Braudel first reviews the contributions and pretensions of several important books, among them Guizot's two *Histories of Civilization,* the one in Europe, the other in France; Burckhardt's *Civilization of the Renaissance in Italy;* Spengler's *Decline of the West;* Toynbee's *A Study of History;* and Alfred Weber's *History of Cultures.* Gracefully, and with due praise for the merits of each of these books, Braudel finally discards them all, and for much the same reasons: they are all oversimplifications. His remarks about Toynbee suggest his approach to all these mistaken attempts (as he views them):

> Arnold Toynbee's way of thinking . . . is very like that of a scientist looking for a world system, a system whose clear order and exclusive relationships must be imposed authoritatively, for better or worse, onto the teeming mass of reality. (*On History,* p. 193.)

But this will not work, according to Braudel, the exceptions are too numerous, one can only go so far in simply ignoring phenomena that fail to fit one's theory, the world is just not like that. Nevertheless, something must be done "to justify history to itself"; how then *would* one go about composing a proper and defensible "Study of History" at the present day?

First, says Braudel, make certain sacrifices and renounce certain traditional ways of speaking. "Thus let us no longer speak of a civilization as a being, as an organism, as a figure, as a body, even a historical body. Let us no longer say that it is born, develops, and dies, which comes to the same thing as lending it a simple, linear, human destiny." (*On History,* p. 200.)

Second, define "civilization." This is easier said then done, but we can make an attempt. Admit to begin with that a civilization is a space, a "cultural area," a "locus."

**On History,* by Fernand Braudel, tr. by Sarah Matthews (Chicago: University of Chicago Press, 1980).

> Within the locus, which may be more or less extensive but is never too confined, you must picture a great variety of "goods," of cultural characteristics, ranging from the form of its houses, the material of which they are built, their roofing, to skills like feathering arrows, to a dialect or a group of dialects, to tastes in cooking, to a particular technology, a structure of beliefs, a way of making love, and even to the compass, paper, the printing press. It is the regular grouping, the frequency with which particular characteristics occur, which constitute the first signs of cultural coherence. If to this spatial coherence can be added some sort of temporal permanence, then I would call civilization or culture the "totality" of the range of attributes. It is this "totality" which is the "form" of the civilization thus recognized.
> (*On History,* p. 202.)

Then, realize that these cultural goods, "the microelements of civilizations," are constantly in flux. Civilizations never stop exporting or borrowing them in turn.

Finally, recognize too that "not every exchange proceeds straightforwardly." There are, also, refusals to borrow—"whether a way of thinking, of believing, or living, or just simply a tool." Of course, every refusal, says Braudel, is of capital importance. "It is thus, and, in those situations, that each civilization makes its decisive choice through which it asserts and reveals itself." (*On History,* p. 203.)

These rules of construction are to be seen at work both in *The Mediterranean* and in *The Structures of Everyday Life,* which do not, however, proceed to the conclusions arrived at in this chapter of *Encyclopédie française.* Here, Braudel faces the present—reluctantly, as he says every historian is wont to do—and looks boldly into the future. A new age, which began "not yesterday" but sometime around 1750, is upon us, he says, and is impelling us, at a rate faster than we want to go, toward a unity that we embrace at the same time that we fear it. Not that there was no unity in the past. "During the Middle Ages, and even into the sixteenth century," he writes, "the poverty of technology, of tools, of machinery, the rarity of domestic animals brought all activity back to man himself, to his strength and his labor. Man everywhere was the same rare, fragile creature, with a life that was nasty, brutish, and short." (*On History,* p. 213.) All activities, all civilizations were thus "deployed" within a very narrow range of possibilities ("the limits of the possible" again).

Nor, on the other hand, are there lacking diversity and cultural refusals today. Airports may all look alike, everywhere in the world, but even the looks on the porters' faces are different, and the cities the airports serve, though alike in some respects, are very different in others. And one has only to move a few miles outside of the great cities of today to discover the resistant and nearly ineradicable root ways of thinking and acting and building and eating and, as Braudel says, making love that differentiate Mexico from Spain, say, or France from Italy, or China from Japan, to say nothing of Bangkok from Chicago or Riyadh from Stockholm. What historians "are perhaps more familiar with than any other observers of the social," says Braudel, "is the fundamental diversity of the world." (ibid.) And indeed we heave a sigh and repeat the old cry: "Vive la différence!"

At the same time, we share an earthly destiny, we human beings of the twentieth century. Do we, then, have need of a "new, third word, besides *culture* and *civilization,*" asks Braudel, "both of which have come to appear invalid?" Might this new word, and the needed new idea, be *humanism*—a kind of modern humanism that the world has not seen before?

> Humanism is a way of hoping, of wishing men to be brothers one with another, and of wishing that civilizations, each on its own account and all together, should save themselves and save us. It means accepting and hoping that the doors of the present should be wide open on to the future, beyond all the failures, declines, and catastrophes predicted by strange prophets. . . . The present cannot be the boundary, which all centuries, heavy with eternal tragedy, see before them as an obstacle, but which the hope of man, ever since man has been, has succeeded in overcoming. (*On History,* p. 217.)

The Mediterranean: the physical place

Let us return to Braudel's *Mediterranean,* in order to be able to say something more about the kind of book it is and, if possible, why it succeeds so well in what it tries to do. This cannot be effected, as I have said, in a summary. Ideally, the whole work must be read in order to understand fully any part of it. But it may be possible to sample it—the samples chosen with affection, but also almost arbitrarily—in order to convey the flavor of the whole. For the whole book has a unique flavor, or essence, that lies at the heart of its meaning and its importance.

We may start, therefore—and why should we not, since Braudel himself does?—with the environment of the Mediterranean in those far-off years of the "extended sixteenth century" (1450–1650 or 1480–1630). "Mountains come first," says Braudel; they form the almost permanent shallow basin in which lies the ever-changing inland sea. But "what exactly is a mountain?" Braudel asks, and we become at once acquainted with his relentless, questioning spirit (this is only the sixth page of text). To define mountains by an arbitrary line of altitude—say, 500 meters—will never work, declares Braudel; better to define them as "the poorest region of the Mediterranean, its proletarian reserve," or as a "refuge from soldiers and pirates, as all the documents bear witness, as far back as the Bible. Sometimes the refuge becomes permanent." (p. 31.) Finally, it is possible, says Braudel, "in general terms, to talk of the dilution of the mountain population, and even more, of a partial and incomplete form of civilization, the result of inadequate human occupation." (p. 33.) "In the mountains," furthermore, "civilization is never very stable." (p. 35.) Nevertheless, life is free and in its way rich because of its variety. Finally, mountains have ever been the source of men, who come down out of the heights whenever they are forced to by hunger or cold or loneliness to share in the wealth and relative comfort of the plain.

In the Mediterranean world these plains are not, however, very wealthy or comfortable in absolute terms. There are no "Great Plains"; there is no area that is comparable at all to the rich expanse of western France or the prairies of the American midwest, where the topsoil is (or was) 100 feet deep and the artesian wells shoot (or shot) 60 feet in the air whenever a hole was dug through the tough prairie sod. The Mediterranean plains were all—without exception—subject to destructive flooding and, where the water collected in shallow ponds and swamps, to malaria. The Tuscan Maremma, the Val di Chiana, the great valley of the Po, the country around Aigues-Mortes, even the country to the east and west of Algiers, were—and to some extent still are—persistent malarial sites, where men went out to work, in fields that they knew held mortal danger, from their cities and villages perched on the hillsides, safe there (as they hoped) from human and other marauders including (as we know now) the Anopheles mosquito. "Acqua, ora vita, ora morta," they repeated: "water, that now gives life, and now gives death." The solution, of course, was to be found in scientific engineering, in the draining of the marshes and the maintenance of the drainage canals and ditches. But the necessary knowledge was not yet available and besides in the sixteenth century there were not enough men to do the work. Only in rare cases—around Milan, or in the Venetian *terra firma*—was there any kind of success, and even there the irrigation systems were the first things attacked and destroyed by the troops of an invader. And there was always an invader, if not this year then next year or the next.

If the land was inhospitable and hard to work, the sea was not more friendly. The waters of the Mediterranean are not rich in life, despite the acclaim for *frutta di mare* on Mediterranean tables. Nor are the waters calm. Mediterranean weather, for the most part—despite our nearly universal image of blue skies and sea, white marble columns gleaming in the sun, and perfumed nights, soft and made for love—is *brutto* ("ugly"), as the Italians say, or as they also say, *cattivo* ("naughty"), which is not much better. Starting in October (sometimes even in September), the stationary high over the Azores moves southward and the way is left open for the great winter lows that snake through the Straits at Gilbraltar and spread over the entire Mediterranean area, producing storms at sea and on land the dark, somber winter days that are often accompanied by drenching rain. Around the first of April the Atlantic anticyclone moves northward again, and the Atlantic weather is blocked out of the Mediterranean, leaving the area to be affected by the eternal Sahara high pressure system, which produces the long, hot, parching days of summer around the shores of the inland sea, whose waters stagnate in the sun when they are not whipped into fury by the relentless desert winds. These patterns are summed up in a Spanish proverb: "Nine months of winter and three months of hell," which requires no comment—except to say that bad as the weather often is, the area has its compensations!

The Mediterranean: man and his activities

The combination of physical hardship and scarce resources has produced, says Braudel, a distinctive Mediterranean attitude toward life that, he adds, is still evident today. The Mediterranean man and (perhaps preeminently) the Mediterranean woman is everywhere a most parsimonious individual. French adventurers, as early as the fifteenth century, noted the sparsity of comestibles on Italian tables—even the noblest—and later cisalpine visitors echoed their surprise. The Mediterranean is a place whose peoples are very aware of the necessity of saving, and where waste—except for the rich, who glory in it—is severely condemned and occurs rarely. Even today, a single man with a small cart that he pushes up the steep hilly streets by hand is able to collect all the "garbage" of an entire *borgo* of an ancient Tuscan hill town; and newcomers to the area, fresh from the expansive atmosphere of America, very soon adopt the native custom and discover that it is not necessary to produce more than a tiny (by American standards) sackful of trash to be picked up each morning. Neighbors remind one if the lights have been left on or the thermostat is set too high, and the man at the gas pump spills not a drop as he carefully removes the nozzle from the tank. It is not a bad way to live, in fact, even if the necessity that lies behind it (or lay behind it for many centuries) is a bleak and somber one.

> A double constraint has always been at the heart of Mediterranean history: poverty and uncertainty of the morrow. This is perhaps the cause of the carefulness, frugality, and industry of the people, the motives that have been behind certain, almost instinctive, forms of imperialism, which are sometimes nothing more than the search for daily bread. To compensate for its weaknesses, the Mediterranean has had to act, to look further afield and take tribute from distant lands, associating itself with their economies: in so doing it has considerably enriched its own history. (pp. 245–46.)

This is not, however, to deny—rather, it is to emphasize—the age-old hospitality of Mediterranean peoples: Greeks, Italians, Spaniards, if no others. Indeed, such generosity, which often is almost overwhelming, is all the more appreciated when one knows how really poor most people are.

Despite the difficulties, of course, life went on and even flourished during the extended sixteenth century. There was constant trade and commerce, more in summer than in winter, but in winter too. The majority of commerce traveled by sea, but there was never a lack of wagon trains struggling over the Alps: in Asia and Africa, transport was effected by caravans of camels that linked the Mediterranean "on one side to the Far East, and on the other to the *Bled es Soudan* and Black Africa. . . . The caravans served merchants, and therefore towns and active economies, in a world context; they were a luxury, an adventure, a complicated operation." (p. 181.) Braudel describes a caravan of pilgrims headed for Mecca:

> It formed at 'Birca,' three leagues from Cairo, twenty days after Ramadan, and consisted of up to 40,000 mules and camels and 50,000 people, the merchants anxious to protect their goods walking at the head, sometimes selling along the wayside the silk, coral, tin, grain, or rice that they would for the most part exchange at Mecca, and the pilgrims, free of possessions, looking only after their own persons, coming behind. This procession of rich and poor had its military commander, the 'captain' of the caravan, and some guides; at night, the latter would carry dry-wood torches to light the way, for they preferred to journey between two o'clock in the morning and sunrise, to avoid the heat of the day. An escort was provided against Arab raids on the Red Sea coast: 200 spahis and 400 soldiers, plus field artillery, some six pieces drawn by twelve camels, which served to terrify the Bedouin and make a noise at the triumphal entry into Mecca. (p. 181.)

Still, the sea was "the great highway," and it was plied by ships of every size, description, and nationality. Some were enormous, "like a great house of five stories rising out of the middle of the sea," as a Swiss medical student wrote of a Genoese vessel in the harbor of Marseilles in 1597. "I estimated that its capacity must be at least fifteen thousand quintals [about 750 modern tons]. It had eight or ten sails on two masts of prodigious height, one of which I climbed by means of rope ladders. From that height I could see far and wide including the Chateau d'If, which has a windmill similar to those in the town." (pp. 297–98.)

Of course most ships were smaller, although always busy about their business, and crewed by a variety of men of all nations. Usually, they kept fairly close to shore, counting it a solid day's work to sail from one headland to the next, putting into port at night to avoid every sort of peril—which they did not always avoid, because the sudden, unpredictable Mediterranean storms were deadly for small ships moored over their light anchors on a lee shore. But these dangers were as nothing compared to those of the open sea, where storms often destroyed whole fleets of ships, capsizing vessels and sending their passengers and crew to the bottom, to be buried with all their hopes.

If the sea did not get you, pirates very well might. Although sixteenth-century pirates were probably more merciful than muggers and house-breakers today (if only because you could be held for ransom or sold into slavery and were therefore more valuable alive than dead), they were also subject to the same necessities and would always drown you if they saw this as a reasonable guarantee of their own safety (in a dangerously overloaded ship, for instance).

And if you escaped both the sea and the privateers, there were still hunger and thirst and disease, which often decimated crews on long voyages. In July 1602 a great ship from the Indies came to shore a few miles from Lisbon, with "two million in gold on board" but with a surviving crew of only 30—out of perhaps 600 or 700 that had begun the voyage, which turned out after all to be in vain, for the exhausted vessel was seized by English privateers under the very eyes of watchers in the town. In September 1614 a ship arrived off Lisbon with a million on board and 16 left out of a crew of 300. "The extreme case is that of the return of a Manila galleon to Acapulco, on the Pacific, without a single living soul on board, but still carrying all her treasure; the ghost ship sailed into port on her own." (p. 378.) What a wonderful image for mythmakers, then and now!

Life was hard indeed, but hardest of all, of course, for the poor. Braudel shows how a "long-term secular trend" of increasing population, inflation (more than 300 percent in a century and a half), and expanding wealth marked the period he is studying. But the buying power of the "urban proletariat" and the peasants of the Mediterranean area did not much increase, if in fact it did not decrease, during these years.

How poor were the poor? An income below 20 (Venetian) ducats a year, says Braudel, "was a subsistence wage"; between 20 and 40 ducats "small"; and between 40 and 150 "reasonable" (the terms coming down from a contemporary document). (p. 458.) But how much was a Venetian ducat? At Venice the boys who kept watch at the Zecca (mint) were paid less than 20 ducats a year in 1554. The petty official who "divided the gold and silver" (the *partido*) received 60 ducats a year; an accountant received 180. A workman in the Arsenal, doing work essential to the security of the state, received a ducat or a ducat and a half a week—between 50 and 75 per year; a skilled caulker might make 100 or more a year. This was for hard labor, sunup to sundown, six days a week. A father of a family could manage to live on 60 to 75 ducats a year, apparently, though hardly in affluence.

But the difference between rich and poor was enormous. Landowners and merchants might live on 5,000 to 10,000 ducats a year and great lords might have 40,000 or more a year to spend. With such an income, a rich man could be served by as many poor folk as he pleased. Very large numbers of servants were common in great houses. This could be the case in less grand circumstances, too. The young Count Olivares—scion, it is true, of one of the greatest families of Spain—while he was a student at Salamanca, "had a tutor, twenty-one servants, and a mule to carry his books from his lodgings to the university." (p. 459.) Of course a number of these servants were bodyguards; the young lord would have been a marked man and probably could not have walked safely unattended down any street in Spain in the sixteenth century.

No one was richer than the king of Spain, whose galleons brought many millions of ducats of American gold and silver to his coffers each year, to be minted into the famous doubloons and pieces of eight and other coins. At the same time his expenses were enormous—usually greater than his income—and this had the result of enriching other men besides himself. The vast riches that Spain received from America during the sixteenth century, most notably from the mines of Potosí, high in the Andes, where thousands of Indians were worked to death at altitudes above 15,000 feet above sea level, stuck to relatively few Spanish fingers but instead flowed out from Madrid almost faster than they flowed in, to pay for the Empire's far-flung enterprises, mostly wars—in the Netherlands, against Spain's rebellious provinces there; in the Mediterranean, against the Turkish fleet and the Barbary pirates; and in assorted other places as well. But how did one go about transferring half a million ducats, say, from Madrid to Antwerp—especially when one possessed silver and one's army insisted on payment in gold? The story of how Philip II managed to make such transfers, throughout the half-century of his reign, is just one of many fascinating tales told by Braudel in this book.

Certain facts have to be kept in mind. First, the Atlantic route was not safe; English or Dutch ships were too likely to intercept ships carrying bullion. Second, although the overland route through France could be used, a large guard (that could not always be trusted) was needed, and gold and silver are heavy and, especially in the case of silver, very bulky to carry in the large amounts needed. Finally, and most important, the king of Spain (like most governments after him) usually needed to spend his money before he had received it from America (the galleons were often late and sometimes they did not come at all; but the troops would not wait). The only solution was bills of exchange, whereby a merchant in one part could draw on monies owed him in another. But to handle such transactions required a central banking system, and there was only one such in the world—the system set up by the so-called *hombres de negocios,* a group of Genoese bankers who were, as Braudel says, "centuries ahead" of all the rest of Europe in their understanding of money.

The system worked like this. The king would inform the *hombres de negocios* that he would need 1,000,000 ducats, say, in gold, in Antwerp on such and such a date, and that he was willing to issue a certain sum in government bonds (*asientos*) to the benefit of the bankers who, he presumed, would arrange for the transfer. The Genoese then would sell the bonds, mostly to Spanish buyers, at a discount sufficient to make everyone comfortable, then begin to draw on their network of debits and credits throughout Christendom. The end result would be that, by a long series of exchanges, they would discover enough debtors in the Netherlands who would be willing to discharge their debts for purchases from the South by paying over the aggregate sum of 1,000,000 ducats in gold to the Spanish paymaster in Antwerp.

This system worked so well that it seemed simple to the king and his advisers. But it was costly. Thus the idea occurred to them of avoiding the fees to the *hombres de negocios*—sometimes as much as 30 to 50 percent—by taking over the system themselves, with the assistance of their old financial partners, the German banking house of the Fuggers. The first of several such attempts was made in 1575, and the description of it fills two of the finest pages in Braudel's book. A decree was handed down on September 15, 1575, declaring all *asientos* granted since 1560 invalid, and establishing payment terms for the loans from the Genoese bankers that resulted, for them, in heavy losses. Naturally they rebelled, immediately blocking the delivery of gold to Flanders. They may even have lent temporary support to the Protestant rebels in the Netherlands. But a rebellion broke out in Genoa as well, at the end of the year, convulsing the city and bringing it close to civil war. In addition, there was not a monetary exchange in all of Europe that could continue normal operations in the circumstances.

Let us allow Braudel to tell the rest of the story.

> Total victory for the Genoese bankers did not come until two years later with what was for them the compromise agreement, the *medio general* signed with the king of Spain on 5th December, 1577, abrogating the draconian measures of 1575. It was a victory owed entirely to the incompetence and inexperience of the Castilian merchants and of all those, including the Fuggers, 'unconditional servants' of the Habsburgs, who sought to intervene. The capital they advanced was insufficient, it was recalled too soon and yet it moved too slowly. Moreover, the Genoese embargo on bills of exchange and gold was effective. They held all the best cards, leaving their would-be competitors little room for manoeuvre. Whether it was sent through Florence, Lisbon, Lyons, or even Paris and the French roads, their rivals' money did not travel quickly enough. As a result, the unpaid Spanish troops mutinied and, after a series of disturbances, captured and violently sacked the city of Antwerp in November, 1576. These dramatic events—in which it would be as naïve to assume that the Genoese had no hand as it would be to assume that Spain had nothing to do with the December uprising in Genoa—forced the king into a reconciliation. Until then he had shown 'poco voluntà di mitigare il rigore del decreto,' as a Genoese correspondent put it. But how could he any longer pursue the unbending policy he secretly favoured? In March, 1577, serious talks began. Agreement was reached only on 5th December, 1577, when the *hombres de negocios* immediately made available to the Spanish king five

> million 'golden crowns in gold,' payable at Genoa, Milan, and if necessary Naples or Sicily. . . . Through Genoa the Mediterranean long held the key to the control of world wealth. (pp. 506–7.)

We may add that these dramatic events, which are intelligible to us today, were absolutely mysterious to most men in the sixteenth century, including the king of Spain and his expert financial advisers. "Wise and honest men had always assumed," comments Braudel, "that money followed trade in commodities; by 'real exchange' they meant what resulted from such straightforward dealing, but that money should lead an existence apart from commodities was difficult for them to accept; or that . . . everything could apparently be settled by juggling with a set of figures." (p. 509.) The Genoese were thus the first capitalists to understand that money itself is the greatest of commodities; they invented the buying and selling of money that the Dutch bankers in the next century carried to even more exalted heights; but neither the Genoese nor the Dutch learned what we know now: The way to sell money at a really high profit is to sell commodities "on the installment plan," in other words, as the saying goes, "to bait the hook with merchandise."

The Mediterranean: social facts

The "bedrock of history"—its infrastructure, as it were—consists of the conditions and circumstances we have been treating here. But there are other matters as well that must be addressed before we can turn our attention, in the last 350 pages of the book, to the "history" of the Age of Philip II. There are certain "conjunctures," as Fernand Braudel calls them, not always-enduring facts like mountains and seas and weather, but instead extremely long-term ones like empires and societies and civilizations and war, the subjects of the last four chapters of Part Two of *The Mediterranean.*

Here indeed we must proceed more rapidly than the material deserves. We are to understand, Braudel tells us, that the sixteenth century marked a great turning point in the history of the Mediterranean world, when the age of city-states came to an end and that of empires began. "Everywhere the city-state, precarious and narrow-based, stood revealed inadequate to perform the political and financial tasks now facing it." (p. 657.) We who know the history, during the fifteenth and sixteenth centuries, of the Tuscan city-states are well aware of this; but the fragility of the city-state was also "strikingly demonstrated by the capture of Constantinople in 1453, the fall of Barcelona in 1472 and the collapse of Granada in 1492."

> It was becoming clear that only the rival of the city-state, the territorial state, rich in land and manpower, would in future be able to meet the

> expense of modern warfare. . . . And its advance was long to be irreversible. Examples of the new pattern emerging at the end of the fifteenth century are Aragon under John II; Louis XI's expansion beyond the Pyrenees; Turkey under Muhammad II, the conqueror of Constantinople; later France under Charles VIII with his Italian ambitions and Spain in the age of the Catholic Kings. Without exception, these states all had their beginnings far inland, many miles from the Mediterranean coast, usually in poor regions where there were fewer cities to pose obstacles. In Italy by contrast, the wealth and very density of the cities maintained weaknesses and divisions as modern structures emerged only with difficulty from the grip of the past, particularly when that past had been a glorious one and much of its brilliance remained. (pp. 657–58.)

The trend once established, larger and larger units were created, the largest of all being the Spanish and Turkish empires. "In the East the Ottomans; in the West the Hapsburgs." (p. 669.) The history of the later sixteenth century is largely to be understood in terms of the continuing animosity between these two, which was inevitable unless one of them was to give way and cede dominion to the other over the entire Mediterranean world—but that was not to be a second time, as it had been under the Romans fifteen centuries before.

The wealth and power of these new political amalgamations was almost inconceivable to most men and women in that world; so was the vast difference between the high and the low, the rich and the poor—a distance that seemed to increase throughout the century. As a result, or perhaps as a cause, Braudel says, "human life was not valued highly in the sixteenth century." This in fact is one of the period's most distinctive characteristics. A thousand examples could be given; we shall simply quote "the remarks attributed to Charles V on the occasion of the siege of Metz, by Ambroise Paré, physician to the besieged."

> 'The Emperor asked what manner of people were dying, whether they were gentlemen and men of note; he was told that they were all poor soldiers. Then he said it was no harm if they died, comparing them to caterpillars, insects and grubs which eat buds and other fruits of the earth and that if they were men of property they would not be in his camp for six *livres* a month.' (pp. 751–52.)

Such an attitude would certainly lead to, and permit, the endemic cruelty that helped to give the century its tone.

States and empires did not become dominant everywhere; their power was often sharply limited. "Even in the time of Cromwell," Braudel reminds us, "once the traveler left the main road he found himself in an ancient England of forest and heath, the haunt of vagabonds." (p. 385.) Just so did it remain true, in the age of empires, that they were "mere pinpoints and narrow strips on the map. . . . Of the [Mediterranean] region as a whole, we can say what Lucien Romier said of France under Catherine de Medici: everything becomes clear 'when restored to its natural setting, a vast, semi-feudal kingdom.' Everywhere the creation of the state, a social revolution (though barely begun) as well as a political one, had to contend with these 'owners of fiefs, lords over village, field and road, custodians of the immense rural population.' " (p. 705.) Everywhere, too, the old nobility, great and small, resisted the changes that nevertheless overwhelmed them in the end. Was this not a case of one civilization trying, and failing, to resist another?

Landlords and peasants, if not separate civilizations (in Braudel's terms), are at least separate societies, as are the bourgeoisie, who were also resistant to the new order of things. The Florence of Lorenzo the Magnificent—which is to say, of the late fifteenth century—coincided, Braudel points out, with "the heyday of an opulent and cultivated higher bourgeoisie. . . . The Florentine Renaissance represents the achievement of a bourgeois order." (p. 728.) The severe depression of the 1520s both advanced the movement toward imperial amalgamation and broke the power of the bourgeoisie. When the smoke had cleared the Renaissance was over—and (it is one of Braudel's most breathtaking pronouncements) the Baroque had begun.

> The Renaissance was the child of the Italian cities. The Baroque drew its strength both from the huge spiritual force of the Holy Roman Empire and from the huge temporal force of the Spanish Empire. (p. 827.)

The world was vastly different now. "With the Baroque a new light began to shine; since 1527 and 1530 and the tragic end of the great cities of the Renaissance, Florence and Rome, the tone had changed: new and more lurid colours now bathed the landscapes of western Europe." (ibid.) This is soaring prose; but it is good art criticism, too.

Concerning two other "civilizations" Braudel has perhaps too little to say, because what he does say is of such interest. One of these is the Islamic civilization that dominated the eastern end of the Mediterranean world and produced, in its second flowering, the Turkish Empire. The other is the civilization of the Jews, "one civilization against the rest." Braudel might well write a book about the history of the Jews, that far-from-fossil civilization, as he declares, once again twisting Toynbee's nose. He does write revealingly in these few pages about the Jewish contribution to the origin and development of capitalism. "Capitalism, to be successful," he says,

> presupposes a network, the organization of mutual confidence and cooperation throughout the world. The Revocation of the Edict of Nantes (1685) did not automatically lead to the success of Protestant banking, which had been inaugurated in the sixteenth century, but it ushered in a period of great prosperity for it, the Protestants possessing in France, Geneva, the Netherlands and England a network of

> intelligence and collaboration. The same had been true for centuries of the Jewish merchants. They formed the leading commercial network in the world, for they had representatives everywhere: in backward or under-developed regions where they were artisans, shopkeepers and pawnbrokers and in key cities where they participated in economic growth and booming trade. (p. 817.)

Finally, in these chapters of preparation, Braudel turns to war, or rather, as he says, "the forms of war," for there were very many in those days, as there are in ours. First, formal war, which in the Mediterranean meant (at least after 1550) naval squadrons and fortified frontiers. Declaring that "war is not simply the antithesis of civilization" and admitting that "polemology, if indeed it is a science at all, is still in its infancy," Braudel goes on to arrive at striking conclusions, such as that the end of war in the Mediterranean around the end of the sixteenth century—within a few years after the famous Battle of Lepanto—was in a sense the end of the Mediterranean itself as an historical unit.

> *Bellum omnium pater,* the old adage was familiar to the men of the sixteenth century. War, the begetter of all things, the creature of all things, the river with a thousand sources, the sea without a shore: begetter of all things except peace, so ardently longed for, so rarely attained. . . . In the Mediterranean, official hostilities were over after Lepanto. Major war had now moved north and west to the Atlantic coasts—and was to stay there for centuries to come, where its true place was, where the heart of the world now beat. This shift, better than any argument, indicates and underlines the withdrawal of the Mediterranean from the centre of the stage. (p. 891.)

The nostalgia in these sentences is not for war; Braudel knew war, and hated it. It is for the Mediterranean and its waning destiny. Thus he can add: "When in 1618, the first shots of the Thirty Years' War rang out, and nations went to battle once more, it was far from Mediterranean shores: the inland sea was no longer the troubled centre of the world." (ibid.)

The Mediterranean: history and the meaning of history

So we come to the end of the best part of this wonderful book. From now on it is true, as Braudel says, that "Leopold von Ranke, if he were alive today, would find much that was familiar, both in subject matter and treatment, in the following pages." (p. 901.) The last 350 pages of Braudel's *Mediterranean* are fine in their way. They are especially valuable for a reader who has tended to view this crucial period from a northern perspective—from the point of view of Paris or London. Rightly, Braudel tells a story whose centers are first Madrid and Istanbul, and then, when Istanbul turns its back on the Mediterranean toward the end of the century, Madrid alone. (Braudel's first teaching position was in Algiers, where, he said, it was revealing to "see the Mediterranean upside down.")

There is nothing that is surprisingly, shockingly new. This is, of course, to take nothing from Braudel; he has warned us that it would be so; and at the same time the lack of novelty is partly because he has guided us so well through the infrastructure of this world that its *événements* now seem almost familiar, like the "headlines" of our own time. The story, at any rate, must and does come to an end, on September 13, 1598, the day that Philip II died—or within a few years thereafter—or perhaps fifty years, but who is to say exactly? Books are finite, if history itself is not.

At the very end Fernand Braudel does not resist the temptation—and we are glad he does not—to explain to us once more what he has been about. The work, he says, is "an attempt to write a new kind of history, *total history,* written in three different registers, on three different levels, perhaps best described as three different conceptions of time, the writer's aim being to bring together in all their multiplicity the different measures of time past, to acquaint the reader with their coexistence, their conflicts and contradictions, and the richness of experience they hold. My favourite vision of history is as a song for many voices. . . ." (p. 1238.) The first of these registers, however, what Braudel calls, in the wonderful French phrase that sounds what it means, the *longue durée,* is the most important; "in historical research as I see it, rightly or wrongly, the long run always wins in the end."

Braudel is as he himself says "a 'structuralist,' little tempted by the event, or even by the short-term conjecture which is after all merely a grouping of events in the same area. But the historian's 'structuralism' has nothing to do," he concludes,

> with the approach which under the same name is at present causing some confusion in the other human sciences. It does not tend towards the mathematical abstraction of relations expressed as functions, but instead towards the very sources of life in its most concrete, everyday, indestructible and anonymously human expression. (p. 1244.)

So the book ends, and we close its last page. But we cannot so easily close our minds on its author. He has gone along with us on this long journey, we have become more and more aware, like a patient teacher explaining his lecture to us, telling us *how* history should be written at the same time that he is writing a history. The living presence of Fernand Braudel within the pages of his *Mediterranean* is one of its most distinctive qualities. Braudel speaks in his own voice on hundreds of pages, tells of his discovery of this, his struggles to understand that, his disagreement with so and so about the other. One example may help to suggest the temper of the man.

He has been discoursing on the history of grain shipments in the Mediterranean, which obviously were affected by periods of scarcity and plenty. The question that concerns him most is when—at what approximate date—the Mediterranean became unable to feed itself, ceased to be self-sufficient and began the absolute dependence on outside (northern and eastern) sources of grain that marked the later seventeenth century, and that obtains today. When he was writing the first edition of the book, Braudel says, he had every reason to believe that this date was somewhere around 1590. A document described by a German scholar who had read it in the Vienna Archives showed that from about 1590 on, Sicily was a net importer, not exporter, of grain. But if Sicily was an importer of grain, then, from everything else that Braudel knew about the grain trade of the entire Mediterranean, the Mediterranean itself must have been an importer of grain—which meant to him that its great age had come to an end.

But in the interim between editions, Braudel tells us, he continued to worry about his conclusion, which seemed to be contradicted by much other evidence. And he realized that he himself had not actually seen and read the document from the Vienna Archives but had relied on a secondhand report of its contents. He managed, with great difficulty, to obtain a photocopy—yet one more to add to his files. "On receiving the photocopy I was shocked," he writes,

> to discover that the interpretation of this list of figures was based on an almost unbelievable series of misunderstandings: the word *introyte,* which means income, revenue, in this case customs duties, had been taken to refer to incoming goods, while *grani* (which in this context indicates a subdivision of the monetary unit the *taro*) was translated by cereals; as a result, wheat was deduced to be entering Sicily, when in fact the document quite clearly refers to *exports* of *silk,* raw and blanched, as can be seen from the first lines. (p. 603.)

The problem was solved. There were fluctuations, of course, depressions, periods of great prosperity. But on balance, "Sicily throughout the seventeenth century remained the island of wheat." (p. 604.) And her production meant, when all was said and done, that the Mediterranean as a whole continued to feed itself until at least the middle of the seventeenth century.

It is a great historian who, when old, still is capable of making such an effort for the truth. And it is a great man who confesses the mistake that drove him to undertake it.

Scott Buchanan's *So Reason Can Rule*

Ramsey Clark was born in Dallas, Texas, in 1927. He received his B.A. degree from the University of Texas in 1949 and in 1950 was graduated from the University of Chicago with both an M.A. in history and a law degree. He practiced law in Dallas until 1961, when he was named assistant attorney general by President Kennedy. He went on to serve as deputy attorney general (1965) and attorney general (1967–69). From 1969 through the present he has been practicing law in New York and in Washington, D.C.

Mr. Clark has written several articles on crime, civil liberties, education, and other topics for various magazines and journals (including a 1972 *GIT* article entitled "Police That Serve Society"). He is also coauthor of the widely discussed *Crime in America; The Role of the Supreme Court* (1970).

In his years in the attorney general's office, Mr. Clark worked on several landmark cases. He argued for the U.S. in the Supreme Court in the first federal open housing trial, and he authorized both the first northern school desegregation case and the prosecution of Chicago Police for brutality after the 1968 Democratic Convention riots. In his private practice he served as lawyer for the president of the Kent State student government following the shootings at Kent State University and helped secure the largest native land claim in history for the Alaskan Federation of Natives.

The book with which we have to deal here is a collection of essays, *So Reason Can Rule,* by Scott Buchanan. Most of them were written while Buchanan was a fellow of the Center for the Study of Democratic Institutions at Santa Barbara in the 1960s, though two or three of the pieces are earlier than that.

Collected by his friends, the papers are dialogues with thinkers through the centuries, searching together in quest of truth. As if at one table, relaxed and in the best of persuasive health, Socrates, Hobbes, Smith, Kant, Montesquieu, Marx, and scores of other colleagues help Buchanan reason his case. Ten of the thirteen papers were presented at or prepared for the Center, where their resonance with its spirit enriched us all.

To read the book is to encounter a most improbable man: a twentieth-century thinking man, a learning man, a reasoning man. He is disciplined, principled, rational. Buchanan believed observation and reason, constantly honed by conversation, could identify the great ideas of our human experience and apply them to contemporary problems.

While he loved ideas for themselves, savored them, he also believed that they could help a lost people find their way. What the people were seeking, or should seek, in his view was one idea in particular—justice. And not the bookish justice of the scholars. Buchanan did not return to the past for the comfort of well-worn observations. Rather he brought the valuable insights and inspirations of the past to the human concerns of the present to help us reason toward a better tomorrow.

His faith in reason is stunning. Drawing on Plato and Aristotle to help us understand our contemporary crises, he observes:

> It is one of the melancholy facts of history that the Greek city-state did not recover from its fatal corruption by the Peloponnesian War; that the great intellectual effort to meet the crisis, initiated by Plato and completed by Aristotle, was too late.

If only there had been more time, he seems to say, we all might have enjoyed an enduring golden age of Greece!

Without yielding an inch of his commitment to reason, Buchanan retained a measure of humor, essential to a philosopher's sanity. Thus, arguing that the city can provide a political basis for contemporary life, he observes that "politics originated in the city, the polis," and cites Lewis Mumford to show that "the city happened from the implosion of several ancient organizations of human beings: the market, the temple and the palace." To this he adds:

> The Greek city-state was almost a miraculous result; Athena was born from the brow of Zeus. Plato and Aristotle, and the citizens of that city-state, almost equally miraculously, were able to give a rational account of the politicization, the civilization, that the Athenians and others suffered or accomplished.

Then, contemplating the American city, he sees that:

> The physical city, once a high composite work of art, is now the outward and visible sign of an inward political and spiritual disgrace.

But, after discussing why the city is nowadays not what it ought to be, he wryly concludes:

> I shall make no further attempt to clarify this problem; if I did, it would most likely refute the main thesis of this paper.

His notion of reason is not a simplistic "Think." It requires a lifelong, universal learning tested by rigorous dialogue, held up to nature for comparison, measured by actuality. It seeks the assistance of past wisdom, the best minds, the broadest experience, the great ideas. It must contain the three qualities for which Lucifer, we are told by Anatole France, was banished from heaven: "liberty, curiosity, and doubt." It is advanced by "intellectual intuition" that is not mystical but arises from a fact sparking on a mass of tested observation.

Buchanan does not think reason can fully comprehend the idea of the world which "liberal artists" ought to pursue. It is simply the best means we have to try to understand, to know the truth, to live virtuously and seek justice.

He is an idealist, an optimist; he insists that "all men by nature will that justice be done." Yet in the first and last of these essays he reminds us of F. H. Bradley's warning, "this is the best of all possible worlds, but everything in it is a positive evil." Hence he quietly contends: "If human society is more than biological and more than economic, there must be more of reason in it than the persuasion of the jungle and of the marketplace provides."

Analyzing the chaos science and technology have made of the world and man's mind, Buchanan writes: "Either we reinstate Aristotelian science and show how it can assimilate and improve modern science, or we assume that it is dated and outmoded, abandon it, and trust our legal and moral future to the inherent regenerative powers of reason and observation." Then he calmly observes: "The latter alternative puts us back with the original problem of the Greeks."

So what does a man of reason do in an age of incoherence? Buchanan says that he reasons his way to the limits of his light, urging others to do the same, standing on the shoulders of the giants who help illuminate our journey. Like the last movement of Beethoven's C-sharp minor Quartet, he is "an indomitable (reasoner-) fiddler, whirling with us toward the abyss."

Wallace Stevens seems to have known a Scott Buchanan before he wrote "Asides on the Oboe," though Buchanan never believed there was "time to think enough."

> The prologues are over. It is a question, now,
> Of final belief. So, say that final belief
> Must be in a fiction. It is time to choose . . .
>
> If you say on the hautboy man is not enough,
> Can never stand as god, is ever wrong
> In the end, however naked, tall, there is still
> The impossible possible philosophers' man
> The man who has had the time to think enough,
> The central man, the human globe, responsive
> As a mirror with a voice, the man of glass,
> Who in a million diamonds sums us up.

A life of observation, classical education, dialogue and thought persuaded Buchanan that law, politics, constitutional principles, and constitutional institutions ought to be central to man's life. He cares deeply about law, yet the care is thoughtful, rational, recalling Harry Kalven's definition of law as "disciplined passion."

Law has as its purpose "chiefly justice, but also freedom, peace and order." It is the teacher. In Buchanan's view, it is a question to be answered. What do we the people stand for? What are our values? To what do we consent? Law seen as a question penetrates to the heart of human freedom. Law is the means by which we persuade ourselves what is right.

Such a lofty concept of law will astound most of its practitioners mired in litigious contentions and seeking fat fees. Caught in its proliferation and competent in only special fields, lawyers rarely have a philosophy of law. But Buchanan is speaking of the idea of law, of law as it ought to be. He presents law as humanity's major alternative to violence, its best chance for understanding.

In one of the papers presented for discussion with the staff of the Center for the Study of Democratic Institutions, *What Every Man Should Know: Law,* he writes:

> The classical definitions of law say that law is the rule of reason for the common good. It is somewhat of a mystery how apparently infinitely complicated persuasions result in rules of law.
>
> . . . The law must be looked at in almost a contemplative mode, as one would look at a piece of pure mathematics or a hypothesis in

> science, to see if it is consistent with itself or with other laws, if it has general comprehension and incisiveness, perhaps to see if it is faithful to its intention and just and workable in a wide range of circumstances. . . . If such considerations are successful, the law itself appears to be independent of the pressures and persuasion from which it has arisen and it takes on a life of its own. . . . The law can be such an object of contemplation for the common man, as many religious cults have found it. Law at this summit of dialectic is luminous and majestic.

Law is the system through which consensus is created, discovered, and expanded. Due process of law, Buchanan declares, is due process of education. This is a proposition that will leave most lawyers and libertarians in a fog. But if we bear with him, his idea holds. To be law, to be effective, the rules must be known, respected, and accepted by the people.

He tells us in the paper that gives the book its title, *So Reason Can Rule,* that any proposition,

> if it is to become a law, . . . must transcend the welter of facts and pressures of persuasion and become a rule of reason that will persuade free human beings to cultivate new behaviors, actions, habits, and even new institutions as means to the common good. Too often legislative reason tries to meet these criteria by simply adding a penalty to the primitive legal hypothesis. There is some semblance of validity in this appeal to force, since behavior and habits can be formed by coercion, and it is said that a political community has a monopoly of power to accomplish that. But for any human community, it is a cruel regression to the lower levels of civilization, and it is merely an illusion to suppose that coercion is the basis of law and order.
>
> . . . As a good teacher must respect the intelligence of his pupils, so the law must appeal to the sense of justice of the community. A law exists in the reasonableness it brings to the people, and it is to this that they consent. . . . The final verification of the law is given only in the settled habits that it induces in the citizens. Ultimately, this is the meaning of the consent of the governed; all the other preliminary experessions of consent—polls, caucuses, party platforms, citizens' ballots, and votes in legislative chambers—are only the external conditions for the generation of the internal substance of legality in the habits of the community.
>
> . . . It is said in the legends concerning Solon and Lycurgus that when they had drawn up a code of laws for their respective polities they got an agreement from the people that the laws should not be changed for ten years, and during that interval they absented themselves from their communities so that the requisite habits could be generated in the people. . . .
>
> . . . In the political thought of the ancients, these legends were honored by Plato, Aristotle, and Thucydides in their rule that laws should not be changed rapidly. This is often taken to mean that these thinkers were simply conservative; they feared the open society. But

> their true meaning is that the real existence of the law is not in enactments or books but in the hearts of the citizens.

The measure of law and government under the law—their worth, their virtue, their viability and durability—is therefore found in the understanding and commitment of the people to them. How is this commitment created, how does law find its hold on the hearts of the people? This requires a vast popular effort to make central the Res Publica, to devote a lifetime to its understanding through education and observation, to believe the common good can be discovered through law. Or as Buchanan concludes in his longest essay, *The Public Thing* (*Res Publica*): "The future of justice and freedom depends upon our ability to find the assurance that we can do what we ought to will in public law—in short, to put our confidence in political liberty."

Once there is this popular concern for the public thing, the task becomes one of persuasion, which Buchanan calls ". . . the all pervasive life of the body politic." Hardly naive about the many forms of persuasion, from the "persuader" of the holdup man to the pure reason of Immanuel Kant, Buchanan knows the role of force in its many forms. He sees the idea of persuasion as the sum of effective political power in a community. Reason is for him the essential element in persuasion because it identifies the common good.

Law seeks formulations, ranging from basic principles such as those contained in the First Amendment to the practical procedures in *Robert's Rules of Order,* in order to maintain and increase the ratio of reason to force in the body politic. "Contrary to much current theory, truly effective and dependable power is increased as reason prevails," Buchanan assures us. Force can be relied on only to "deal with the gap between habit and reason. If the law turns out to depend on its effectiveness just on force alone it is not law."

Buchanan does not thrust such epigrammatic conclusions full blown upon us. The bulk of this volume is devoted to detailed dialectic about key elements of law, politics, and constitutional government. We find Buchanan's devotion to common law and the U.S. Constitution as great as it is to Plato's *Republic.* He converses as often with Locke, Montesqieu, Mill, Alexander Hamilton, Tocqueville, John C. Calhoun, and Woodrow Wilson as he does with ancient minds. Calling on their diverse observations, he achieves some remarkable insights.

Buchanan loves the common law, the accumulation of case law in English and American jurisprudence. On a first reading, the average lawyer might see nothing he recognizes in the descriptions presented here of that law. But upon consideration he will see that the substance of it has been revealed.

Most lawyers, whose minds have been sharpened by narrowing, do not know that the common law, for all its high development and pervasive usage, is related to procedures found in eastern, mideastern, African, and western cultures. Courts known in Ancient Egypt, early Rome, and Islam all used such private processes. The trappings and terminology might differ. The function was the same.

Buchanan loves common law because it is a process of reasoning based on the solid angularity of fact. Persons recognized for wisdom and reason are chosen to resolve disputes. Those having such disputes consent to the process and agree to abide by the resolution. Private grievances involving property, contracts, and personal wrongs are settled by reason.

Principles are applied that find wide acceptance and become precedents for more general application. The subject matter is private, among individuals, families, or groups. Thus, "law is made and found as we think about what we do: . . . it is the community's way of getting a true understanding of itself." Yet there are limits to such insight.

Throughout the colonial period, indeed as we approached the Civil War, common law served well, Buchanan suggests, because its private character was distinct from public law and government in the United States. From Independence to the Civil War, America was "teacher of jurisprudence and political science to the world." But as our economy became more complex, our society more pluralistic, common law expanded into spheres properly public.

Relying upon common law—the law concerned with private rights—to resolve public issues which affect the common good where this was made a matter of private control and special interest, law and government lost the capacity to serve the general welfare.

The present need, Buchanan finds, is to "clarify the confusion in which our institutions are caught, and to see if the public realm, purged of the spirit and habits of private law, might not be able to develop its now-smothered potentialities."

Buchanan thrusts this idea into the midst of the great question confronting American law, government, and courts today. Can we break out of the hold which a number of private interests have on public attention and opinion, on legislative calendars, and on administrative proceedings, and court dockets, so that law and government can address public concerns in understandable ways?

While Gulliver is bound by thousands of special little ties, he cannot serve the public interest. The very hope that the people might address law and politics as their principal purpose is frustrated. Pursuit of this idea could liberate law for the general welfare, something all the present efforts at legislation, codification, law reform, better administration, and increased personnel cannot offer.

It is clear that, much as he loves the common law, Buchanan also loves the U.S. Constitution. His reverence for this enables him to write pages on its Preamble, to suggest volumes. Its several phrases are seen as ". . . variations of the traditional conditions for the existence of a political community." They indicate the purposes of government: justice, freedom, peace, and order.

Buchanan concedes:

> The Preamble may not be the best possible statement of American goals, but its brevity and comprehension stand as a challenge and a warning to those who are ambitious to improve it. . . .
>
> . . . It may be recalled that some years ago there was an attempt to conduct a great debate about our national goals. It is noteworthy that none of the contributions to that discussion reached any novel purposes that transcend the statement of the Preamble; most of them fell far below.

Buchanan notes that the clause ". . . in Order to form a more perfect Union . . ." was of special concern when the Constitution was drafted. He himself sees it as an enduring challenge for our government:

> The revival of politics depends to a great extent on finding both the theoretical and the practical meaning of the purpose expressed in the clause "in Order to form a more perfect Union." . . . Finding the units of government and legitimizing their respective functions is the main business of government. And this is begun and continues by the making and remaking of the Constitution.
>
> . . . So the perfection of union is a permanent dedication of the Constitution to the process of political progress as history poses new questions for political solution. This suggests the evolutionary order over which the Constitution presides.

Constitutional scholars are likely to be confounded when, after detailed examination of constitutional issues like representation, federation, separation of powers, the legislative, executive, and judicial parts, the First Amendment, and other provisions, Buchanan says: "I am chiefly interested in seeing the Constitution in its function as generating, guiding, and refining persuasion." But he means exactly that.

> By now it must be clear that I have been outlining a utopia, a cloud-cuckooland, made out of the conjugation of a Greek verb, *to persuade.* I believe it is the vision that our Founding Fathers saw when they wrote the Constitution. It was an ideal to be fulfilled as far as human beings were able with the help of law.

Buchanan's idea of the purposes of constitutional provisions harmonizes with his idea of law. Often his is not the prevailing view. The First Amendment places more value on individual privacy, the right to be let alone, and personal freedoms of speech and conscience than on individual responsibility. Buchanan is concerned with the public duty to engage in robust, open, uninhibited dialogue about the Public Thing. In "the great conversation that is the substance of our political life, . . . the citizen has the duty in a democracy to exercise his freedom of speech in playing his part in self government," he says.

The purpose of separation of powers, one of many "checks and balances" in the Constitution, is not to diffuse power, to prevent its usurpation because we fear human nature. "Under our law," Buchanan insists, "the Constitution divides itself so that reason can rule."

* * * * * *

Nowhere among his ruminations does Buchanan's mind grip more powerfully, persuasively, and practically than when he analyzes the impact of economic phenomena on law, politics, and the hope for moral, rational man. His understanding of the industrial and postindustrial revolutions, of science, technology, and the modern corporation is profound.

Thinking man in the eighteenth century, he suggests, saw clearly, understood his own world, and conceived coherent ideas. He was not faced with the chaotic actuality of the nineteenth and twentieth centuries. Now, the diffusion of power, authority, knowledge, responsibility, and comprehension in a massive, urban, technologically advanced society has debilitated law, government, and education. No longer can education teach virtue, nor can law provide a rule of reason for the common good, nor government pursue agreed upon ends. We cannot identify our common purpose. We can no longer even state the central American proposition, because this generation has not made up its mind.

The Constitution protected property and the integrity of contracts, Buchanan notes, but the Founders did not foresee the future role of the corporation and the way it would dilute the function of constitutional government. They lived, it is true, in a time teeming with corporations and knew their history from Rome and earlier civilizations. They knew the corporation in the Church, the universities, the Royal Charters that preceded colonial government, and in finance, trade, and commerce. But the authors of the Constitution saw no further than did their contemporary, Adam Smith, who thought the business corporation had no significant future. Some probably agreed with Thomas Hobbes that corporations were "worms in the body politic" and "chips off the block of sovereignty."

In fact, however, the corporation assumed a major role in our society. It usurped the potential of law and caused a schism between government and economics that must be healed if we are to address basic problems of our time.

Corporate policy on wages, working conditions, benefits, promotions, transfers, plant closings became more important to some communities than any law. Loyalties and dependencies were transferred from government to corporations. Government itself served private corporate interests, not the public good.

Even education on which law and politics depend has yielded to economic interest. As individual skills and functions narrow, education has become more specialized, emphasizing means of livelihood, making social movement more difficult. In law school we teach private law for economic gain. We are not teaching, studying, or practicing the idea of public law. By Buchanan's view of what law ought to be "we are legal illiterates and incompetents."

It is true we have learned other things, by experience, in the course of our national existence. Among them, Buchanan says,

> Without doubt, the industrial discipline, including those phases of it that we call technological, financial, and commercial, has been the most popular, the most fundamental, and the most effectual of our informal educational enterprises. We began in the colonies as farmers and craftsmen, and Thomas Jefferson still saw us as such, but the combination of the manual arts and skills with the machines and the mechanical arts began almost immediately. Yankee ingenuity and frontier resourcefulness welcomed machinery and organization. The instinct of workmanship was open to mechanical development and was free to take on organized efficiency as a virtue that magnified rather than restricted its capacities. Here, more than in the older countries, the new discipline struck deep into the mentality of the people.

By now, however, an all enveloping web of business corporations, municipal, state, and federal agencies has been created, beyond the comprehension of most citizens, who are entrapped by it. Hence the task is now to see that ". . . all these artificial social organisms in which we live and move and have our being are before us for a gigantic attempt to understand them, if the Republic in its full function is to survive." The process has only begun, Buchanan says.

> We are withdrawing and detaching ourselves from many of our institutions, but we are not yet retreating to the wider community the Romans discovered. Rather, we are developing a passion for indiscriminate togetherness and trying to find the one subcommunity into which we can put our hearts and souls. . . .
>
> . . . We become identified with aspects of ourselves, masks that we put on and take off as our roles change from day to day, sometimes from moment to moment. Inside we are hollow men, zero members of "the lonely crowd," shadowy participants in the American way of life.

We must ask ourselves, these essays contend,

> . . . whether the political nature of the corporation has been recognized and whether it would not be good for our whole political life if the recognition were formalized in the body of corporation law. These questions are hidden in the phrase *private or invisible governments.* The answers . . . have been in the negative for more than a generation.

But the questions will not go away. They ask, what

> kind of human beings . . . are being formed by the corporations they belong to [and] . . . how do the political habits formed by members of corporations fit with the habits that republican forms of government have developed in their citizens heretofore?

Buchanan suggests that corporations engaged in inherently public activity be required to meet constitutional standards. Do they provide republican forms of government? Do they violate the Bill of Rights? Law must address these questions. Federal charters for corporations may be required to assure these protections. Law must see that corporations do their public duty. "Agencies like the Federal Trade Commission might even be expanded and given permanent powers to revise corporation law."

Closely related to the problem of the business corporation is the sweeping impact of science and technology. Economic interest has obliterated the line between science and technology much as it has the lines between public and private law and between government and the private corporation. Industry sees no difference between science and technology. C. P. Snow is cited for the proposition that "scientists and technologists have become soldiers."

Economic theory has not been used to serve the general welfare or even the wealth of nations. It has been privately hired to justify and build the industrial system. The economist serves the manager to "make industry hum and grow." Now, "the dynamic mechanism of technology sets the conditions and supplies the reasons that the market does not know, but to which it has to respond." In brief, technology has become a system of exploitation of natural and human resources.

Calling on Plato, Aristotle, Newton, Descartes, Kant, Whitehead, Ellul, and others to help with his reasoning, Buchanan offers this conclusion about the industrial era:

> Viewed in retrospect, this period has been marked by the unregulated exploitation of nature, both human and nonhuman. . . . Even the workers themselves at first found a new utility for their powers and consented to the conspiracy of exploitation. Later, when they realized that they were being not only used but also used up, they gradually withdrew consent. But by this time the factory and the business system were recognized as the master organizations of men for the exploitation of natural resources. As natural resources became the new name for the lower orders of the kingdom of nature, so "goods" became the name for the products of the factory as they poured into the market. The only limit on the spread of exploitation of this kind was the demand of the market and the ingenuity of the producers. Both of these were objects of scientific and managerial attention, the science of economics for demand and supply, the natural sciences for the methods of natural investigation.

> Both kinds of science became mechanistic, ready to serve any purpose, and public, ready to serve any agent of exploitation. The accompanying styles of thought were matter-of-fact and utilitarian. Law and morals followed the fashions at decent distances.
>
> . . . The absorption of men, machines, and materials by technology blots out the intrinsic goods, the ends-in-themselves, of the kingdom of nature, and substitutes for them the quite incommensurable and wayward series of means.
>
> . . . Abstracted and combined with others, and the ensemble studied for itself, it seemed to take on a macabre life of its own, the Newtonian mechanical universe. . . . This means that the technical phenomenon as a whole is a vast system of exploitation without a purpose.

If we are to regain ascendancy over technology, Buchanan suggests, we must

> . . . trace the human role that the system involves and detect where we have surrendered our judgments and our wills. If we can find these points of default, we may be able to recover our truly scientific understandings, our objective knowledge of our ends and the ends of nature, and our individual and common wills. This might give us back our reverence and love of nature, beyond our shrewd ingenuities in exploiting it.

Underlying his concern with technology is Buchanan's belief in natural law. This is what we must consult, he argues, if we are to gain control of our techniques. For technology does not make moral judgments; only man does, and he must apply those judgments through law that is in harmony with the world as it is. Buchanan does not regard this as impossible. It is "quite clear," he writes,

> that natural law, whatever its transcendental derivations, is fully available to natural human reason. It is not, as often said, a matter of faith, religious commitment, or mysticism. It is a matter of knowledge if one chooses to use his natural intellectual powers in the modes of theoretical and practical reason. In fact, the seeds of natural law are embedded in every human reason, and some of its most genuine expressions come from the untutored and unsophisticated mind. If we could find some way of eliminating conventional and sophistical corruptions, we could say that the knowledge of natural law is moral common sense. . . .

* * * * * *

We must wonder, reading these essays, whether law, largely helpless, is able to persuade, to reason its way to the right questions. Buchanan acknowledges that we have "failed miserably" in fulfilling the vision of the Founding Fathers, but he hopes that "we still persist in the vision." If we do, it is in spite of recent setbacks to the hope of democratic institutions and to our faith in free government in such events as the bombing of Beirut, the massacres at Sabra and Shatila. Then, too, Reaganomics seeks to cement the schism between government and economics that Buchanan believed fatal. The FTC is more likely to be abolished than empowered to monitor the public side of corporate law and federal charters for multinational corporations are less probable now than ever.

Nonetheless, Buchanan will show us to ourselves as we ought to be, not only as we are. "A crisis in human law is the occasion for discovery in jurisprudence," he writes. It is the argument of these essays that this discovery must ultimately be based on speculative wisdom such as we derive from natural law. In Buchanan's words,

> A part, the essential part, of natural law doctrine is speculative in both senses of that troubled word. It must be theoretical in its insistence on dealing with the facts for what they can yield in the way of knowledge, and it must dare to go beyond facts, to explore and exhaust what the always meager data indicate in the way of abstract knowledge. This is to say that we must recognize, trust, and follow reason, wherever it leads.

That is what, patiently and soberly, Buchanan himself manages to do in these essays appropriately called *So Reason Can Rule.* They tell us, in sum, that each human being is responsible for evil anywhere in the universe, that governments are formed to discharge their responsibility to justice, that law is the way we identify justice, that rational, natural man can reason and will his way to justice, that this is his purpose, that however greedy, lustful, power craving, hungry, or violent, we still love justice. It is the measure of Buchanan's own persuasive powers that, hearing as we do from him these unlikely propositions, we come to believe that, after all, they may be so.

NOTE TO THE READER

Some of the articles in this year's issue of *The Great Ideas Today* will take readers directly to the *Great Books.* Such is the case with Professor Stanley's essay on evolution, which evokes *The Origin of Species* (*GBWW,* Vol. 49); with Dr. Buchanan's account of Galen, whose *On the Natural Faculties* is in *GBWW,* Vol. 10; and of course with Professor Gingerich's discussion of Ptolemy, Copernicus, and Kepler, all of whom appear in *GBWW,* Vol. 16.

The *Syntopicon* will nevertheless prove useful in following the ideas and arguments of this year's contributions to particular passages and other *Great Books* whose relevance may not have been perceived by some readers. See with respect to Professor Stanley's article Chapter 24, EVOLUTION, especially the readings under Topics 4*b* and 4*c,* which deal with the fixity and mutability of species and the origin of new forms of life; also those under Topic 5*a,* which are concerned with natural selection, the extinction of intermediate varieties, and the difficulties of evolutionary theory; also the passages at 6*b,* which deal with the geographical distribution of the forms of life in relation to the genealogy of species.

In connection with Professor Browder's article on mathematics, the relevant chapter of the *Syntopicon* is, of course, number 52, all of which is to the point except possibly the readings that deal with the mathematical structure of nature (Topic 5*b*). The place to start is probably the passages at Topic 1*a,* which are concerned with the distinction between mathematics and other sciences. These can be followed by consulting the readings at Topic 3 having to do with method and mathematical models, and those at Topic 4, which deal with techniques and operations.

With respect to Galen, see Chapter 55, MEDICINE, in particular the passages cited under Topic 2 dealing with medicine as an art; those at Topic 3*a* and *b,* which are concerned with relevant aspects of medical practice; those at Topic 4, where the concept of health is discussed; and those under 5*d*(1) and (2) that have to do with the humoral hypothesis and the psychogenesis of bodily disorders.

Concerning Ptolemy, Copernicus, and Kepler, see Chapter 5, ASTRONOMY, beginning with the readings at 2*b* and *c* having to do with method, in particular the geocentric and heliocentric hypotheses and the role of mathematics in astronomy. See also passages at 3*b* dealing with gravitation and action-at-a-distance; Topic 5, where are listed readings that treat of astronomy, cosmology, and the theory of the universe as reflecting astronomical conceptions (as distinct from the mythic or the fantastic, for example); also Topic 8*c*(2) and (3) where the forms and laws of celestial motion are considered (as circles, ellipses, and the laws of celestial mechanics); also 9*c* and *d,* which list passages having to do with the earth and other planets among particular heavenly bodies; and finally the readings at Topic 13, which are concerned with the history of astronomy—all these to the end that the pervasive interest of the authors of the *Great Books* in astronomy may be perceived, as well as the particular development of the subject in the works that Professor Gingerich expounds.

As for Mr. Bird's discussion of Dante, Chapter 66, PHILOSOPHY, is relevant, in particular the readings at 1*a* and *d* dealing with the relation between philosophy and theology or religion on the one hand, and between philosophy and poetry on the other (relevant also are the readings at 6*c* having to do with the need to add faith to reason in the search for truth). See also Chapter 69, POETRY, especially the readings at Topic 5 which treat of poetry in relation to knowledge. And at least one Topic is relevant to Mr. Fadiman's discussion of children's literature, namely 4*b* in Chapter 58, MIND, where readings are listed dealing with the mentality of children.

In connection with Nietzsche's *The Birth of Tragedy,* see two essays that have appeared in earlier issues of *The Great Ideas Today,* viz. M. I. Finley, "New Developments in Classical Studies" (1971), and Seth Benardete, "On Greek Tragedy" (1980).

Finally, those who own *Gateway to the Great Books* may wish to consult the portion of Darwin's *Autobiography* which will be found in Volume 8 and the selections by Euler, Laplace, and Poincaré among those that appear in Volume 9, the entire contents of which is devoted to the subject of mathematics. As to astronomy, see Kees Boeke, *Cosmic View,* and the selections by and concerning Galileo in Volume 8. With respect to the article on children's literature, it may be noted that *Robinson Crusoe* is in Volume 2, along with a selection from Kipling ("Mowgli's Brothers"). And of interest also in this same connection is the selection from the *Autobiography of John Stuart Mill,* which appears in Volume 6.

PART SIX

Additions to the Great Books Library

Astronomia Nova

Johannes Kepler

Editor's Introduction

Of the great astronomers, or at least students of the solar system, whose works appear in Volume 16 of the *Great Books of the Western World* (discussed by Owen Gingerich elsewhere in these pages), Kepler is the closest to us in spirit, as he is the nearest in time. Not that the others are without interest—even Ptolemy, of whose life we know substantially nothing, but whose serenity, whose high Platonic vision, remain both moving and impressive to reflect upon. The excitement of Copernicus at his perception of the Sun's true position can be discerned too. But Kepler is something else. His endlessly inquiring intelligence, his struggles with personal difficulties, above all the passion with which in his researches he kept his mind upon the idea of a universe really—that is, bodily—arranged according to the most beautiful mathematical order, render him both human and heroic to contemplate, and this is true also of the writings he left, at least some of which seem still to have about them the force and freshness of the insights that inspired them.

Had it not been for his brains, we would likely have heard nothing of him, for his father was a ne'er-do-well mercenary soldier, his mother an innkeeper's daughter. Happily, however, the dukes of Württemberg in what is now Germany, where in 1571 he was born, believed in scholarships for the bright children of their poorer subjects, and accordingly Kepler was given an education culminating in studies at the University of Tübingen. There he had the further good fortune to study astronomy under Michael Mästlin, a professor of the subject who believed that Copernicus's account of the heavens was not only good mathematics but actually true. Thus Kepler early accepted the idea that the Earth really does revolve around the Sun—a conviction that underlay all his life's work.

Despite this schooling, he would have become a Lutheran minister, as he fully intended, had it not been that upon the completion of his studies in 1594, a professorship in mathematics became available at Graz, for which he was recommended, and which, somewhat against his inclination, he took up. At Graz in 1595 he noted as a "discovery" that "God in creating the universe and regulating the order of the cosmos had in view the five regular bodies of geometry known since the days of Pythagoras and Plato." This striking perception he subsequently set forth in his first published work on astronomy, his *Cosmographic Mystery* (1596), a work that brought him to the attention of the two greatest figures of the day in astronomy, Galileo and Tycho Brahe, whose correspondent he became.

In 1600 Kepler was offered a post as assistant to Brahe at the observatory near Prague, and the next year, upon Brahe's sudden death, he succeeded him in the post of imperial mathematician to the court of the Holy Roman Empire. He thus came into possession of Brahe's planetary observations, the finest and largest collection of its kind that existed. This material proved invaluable in the theoretical work that eventually culminated in his formulation of the elliptical orbit of the planets and the law of equal areas (as distinct from equal arcs), which brought the theory of such motion into harmony with observation while at the same time preserving the principle of uniformity. These are the two insights which, along with his earlier recognition of the geometry of the five regular solids, are the discoveries by which he will be forever known.

The laws of planetary motion were set down by Kepler in his *Astronomia Nova,* or *New Astronomy* (1609), a difficult and often obscure work in which the researches that led to his astronomical discoveries are described. It has never yet been published in its entirety in an English translation, and only parts of it are included here. They include the introduction, where Kepler summarizes his approach to celestial physics and his new discoveries, and in which he refutes or sidesteps the Aristotelian and biblical objections that seem to lie in his way. Here also are chapter 7, in which he suggests that Divine Providence led him to the problem of Mars; chapter 34, which describes his views on the magnet-like forces that control the solar system; chapters 39 and 40, which begin to deal with the relation between speed and distance, and the way the area within the orbit can be substituted for the sums of many distances; chapter 58, in which he almost but not quite hits upon the elliptical orbit of Mars and teases the reader with his own blind alley; and finally, chapter 59, which is very difficult to follow, but in which the law of the ellipse and the law of the areas are both expounded, though not as clearly as we might like: the dramatic character of Kepler's discoveries is hardly evident in these pages, which seem rather to struggle toward the profound advances in the human knowledge they contain.

The translations of chapters 34 and 58 have been made by William Donahue, that of the other material by Owen Gingerich. Both scholars had the benefit of a preliminary translation by Ann Wegner.

Astronomia Nova

Introduction to the Work

It is very difficult these days to write mathematical books, especially astronomical ones. For unless you use real precision in the propositions, explanations, demonstrations, and conclusions, the book will not be mathematical; but if you do use this the reading becomes very trying, particularly in Latin, as it lacks the articles and graceful expression that written Greek has. This is why there are at present very few suitable readers; the rest generally reject such works. How many mathematicians are there who have taken the trouble to read through the *Conics* of Apollonius of Perga? And yet, that sort of material is far easier to express in figures and lines than astronomy is.

Even I, who am considered a mathematician, exhaust the powers of my mind in rereading my work and trying to remember from the figures the sense of the demonstrations that I myself originally introduced into the figures and text. But if I mitigate the obscurity by inserting explanations, then I commit the opposite error of making the mathematics verbose. And prolixity in expression carries its own obscurity no less than terse brevity does; the latter eludes the mind's eye while the former distracts it; the one lacks light while the other overwhelms by its abundance; the latter does not arouse the sight, whereas the former clearly dazzles it.

For this reason I resolved, by means of a rather clear introduction to my work, to aid the reader's comprehension as much as I can.

In fact, I have wanted my introduction to be two-fold. First, I present a synoptic table [not included here] of all the chapters of the book. I think this will be useful since the material is unfamiliar to many readers. The different terms and the various constructions in it bear a great resemblance to one another and are similar both in general and in specific details, so that juxtaposing all the terms and constructions, and including them in a single display, makes them mutually explanatory. For example: I discuss the natural causes, which led the ancients, in their ignorance, to set up an equant circle or a point. This I discuss in two places, namely, in the third and fourth sections. The reader involved in reading this third section might think I was already treating the problem of the first inequality, which belongs to the motions of the individual planets. But this condition is not discussed until the fourth part. In the third part, as the synopsis indicates, I am dealing with the equant that, under the name of the second inequality, commonly varies the motions of all the planets and is primary in the theory of the Sun itself. The synoptic table will therefore serve to distinguish the subject matter.

Nevertheless, this synopsis is certainly not of equal benefit to everyone. There will be some to whom this table (which I offer as the thread to guide readers through the labyrinth of my work) will seem more complex than the Gordian Knot. For their sake, therefore, many things that are now dispersed here and there throughout the work and are not so easily noticed in passing ought to be stashed in heaps here in the front. Furthermore, especially for the sake of those who make a profession of physics and who are angry with me, and even more with Copernicus and remote antiquity, for our violation of the fundamentals of science by the Earth's motion, for their sake, I say, I will faithfully disclose the arrangement of the main chapters that deal with this problem, and I will place before their eyes all the principles of the demonstrations on which I base my conclusions, so inimical to them.

When they will have seen this faithfully presented, they will have the free choice of either reading through the work and understanding with a great deal of effort these demonstrations, or treating me as a professional mathematician and believing in the sound geometrical method; they, for their part, will turn to the principles of the demonstrations that I have thus collected before their eyes, and will examine them, convinced that unless they are refuted, the demonstration built on them will not topple. I will also do what is customary for physicists by mixing the necessary with the probable so as to draw from the mixture a plausible conclusion. Since in this work I have mixed celestial physics with astronomy, no one ought to be surprised that I have employed a certain amount of conjecture. For this is the nature of physics, of medicine, and of all natural sciences, which employ other axioms besides the most certain evidence of the eyes.

The reader should understand that there are two schools of astronomers—the one distinguished by Ptolemy as leader and with the allegiance of many of the ancients; the other attributed to more recent times although it may be even older. Of these, the former treats the individual planets separately and assigns the causes of their individual motions to their own spheres; the latter school compares the planets with each other, notes what is common to their motions, and deduces from this a common cause. The latter school is subdivided again. Copernicus, along with Aristarchus of antiquity, believed that the planets seem to stop and move backwards because of the motion of our home, the Earth, with which I agree. But Tycho Brahe assigns this cause to the Sun in whose vicinity the eccentric circles of all five planets have a connection, or some sort of node (surely not physical, but still quantitative), and it is as if this node revolves along with the solar body about the immobile Earth.

These three theories concerning the universe [*mundus*] have certain other individual peculiarities by which these schools are distinguished, but with a little thought each of these peculiarities can easily be emended and altered so that even the three principal theories (so far as astronomy or celestial appearances are concerned) become in effect precisely equivalent and produce equal results.

My primary intention in this work is to correct the astronomical theory (especially relating to the motion of Mars) in all three versions so that what we compute from our tables will correspond to celestial appearances—an operation which, up to now, could not be performed with enough certainty. In fact, in August of 1608, the planet Mars was a little less than 4° beyond the position which the Prutenic Tables predicted. In August and September of 1593 this error amounted to a little less than 5°, although the error is now completely suppressed in my new calculation.

In the meantime, in presenting this and cheerfully following my course, I shall also review Aristotle's metaphysics, or rather his celestial physics, and I shall inquire into the natural causes of motions. From such a consideration, very clear arguments will arise to the effect that only Copernicus's opinion about the universe (with a few changes) is true and the other two are demonstrably false, and so on. Indeed, all the theories are so involved and so intertwined with each other that in order to correct the basis of astronomical calculations, I have tried many

CAP. LIX.

Arcum ellipſeos, cujus moras metitur area AKN, debere terminari in LK, ut ſit AM.

Hactenus enim verſamur in hac fictione, ſi quis tantum abundaret ocio, ut aream ellipſeos vellet computare, futurum eſſe, ut area ellipſeos AMN uſus, loco diſtantiarum ipſius AM totidem, quot ſunt in AK arcus æquales, non ſit a ſcopo aberraturus. Hæc ſit nobis inſtar propoſitionis majoris hactenus demonſtratæ.

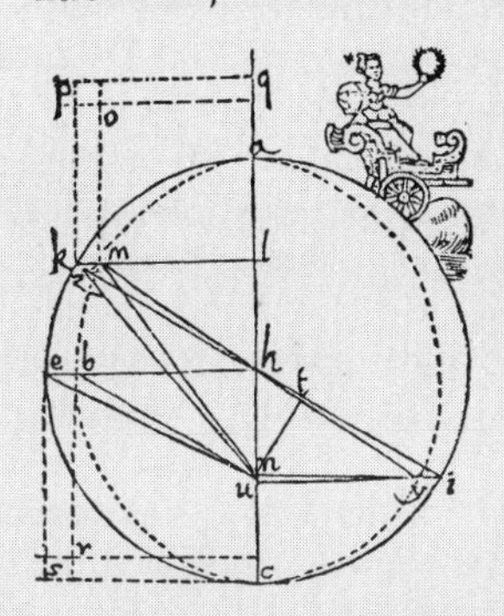

Minorem jam ſubjungam ex protheoremate hujus capitis III. in quo oſtenſum eſt, uti area AKC *ſe habet ad aream* AMC, *ſic etiam eſſe aream* AKN *ad aream* AMN. *Concluditur igitur, cum æquemultiplicium proportio ſit eadem, ipſam etiam aream circuli* AKN *metiri ſummam diſtantiarum diametralium (ut* KT, TI*) ſeu ellipticarum, ipſius* AM*, totidem, quot inſunt partes in* AK. *Vnde patet, recte partibus ellipſeos circa* A.C. *confertiores tribui diſtantias, totidem nempe, quot conſtituuntur in ea ſectiones, per perpendiculares* KL, *ab æqualibus arcubus ipſius* AK *venientes.*

Ne quis de veritate rei dubitet, diffiſus ſubtilitati & perplexitati argumentationis, res ipſa prius innotuit per experientiam in hunc modum. Conſtitui ad ſingulos gradus anomaliæ eccentri, pro diſtantiis ab N, lineas KT, TI diametrales. Singulas etiam ordine ad ſummam priorum adjeci. Collectis omnibus ſumma fuit, 36000000, ut par eſt. Comparatis igitur ſingulis ſummis cum totali, ut (in regula proportionum) ſumma 36000000 ſic eſſet ad gradus 360 (nomen artificiale temporis totius reſtitutorii) ut ſummæ ſingulæ ad ſuas ſignificatas moras: præciſiſſime prodiit idem, in ſecundis etiam ſcrupulis, quod prodibat, ſi dimidiam eccentricitatem in ſinum anomaliæ eccentri multiplicaſſem, & cum area circuli, quæ valeret itidem 360 gradus (nomen artificiale temporis reſtitutorii) comparaſſem.

Deinde, cum eſſem in ea opinione, juſtam diſtantiam NM, applicandam eſſe lineæ KH, ut eſſet ZN, itaque anomaliam coæquatam ZNA inquiſiviſſem, attribuens eam anomaliæ mediæ AKN: manifeſte diſſenſerunt æquationes a mea hypotheſi vicaria capitis XVI. eratque circa 45, coæquatæ exceſſus a vero, per experientiam obſervationum invento, minutorum $5\frac{1}{2}$ defectus; circa gr. 135. circiter 4 minutorum. At AM ſic applicatâ, ut in KC terminaretur, tunc MNA coæquata applicata mediæ anomaliæ AKN, exquiſitiſſime cum vicaria, hoc eſt, cum obſervationibus conſenſit. Cum igitur conſtaret de reipſa, poſtea impulſus ſum ad inquirendam, ex principiis ſemel ſuſceptis, ipſam etiam cauſam rei, quam hoc capite, quam potuit fieri artificioſiſſime & cla-

Ornate diagrams characterized the 1609 edition of *Astronomia Nova* from which the page above was reproduced.

tentative methods, built partly from ways well trodden by the ancients and partly in imitation of them or on their example; no method would succeed except that which enters from the actual physical causes of the motions, which I establish in this work.

The first step in tracking down the physical causes of the motions was for me to demonstrate that the point common to the eccentrics is located not at some point *near* the Sun but at the *very center* of the solar body, contrary to what Copernicus and Brahe believed.

If this correction of mine is introduced into the Ptolemaic theory, it would lead to an investigation of the motion not of the center of the epicycle (about which the epicyclic motion is uniform), but of some other point which in proportion to the diameter is just as far from that center as the center of the solar orb is (for Ptolemy) distant from the Earth, and is either on that line or one parallel to it.

The Braheans could have raised the objection against me that I was too rash an innovator; they themselves, in holding fast to the accepted opinion of the ancients, established the common point of the eccentrics not in the Sun, but near it; they still construct on that basis a calculation that corresponds to the heavens. By translating Brahe's numbers into the Ptolemaic form, Ptolemy might tell me that as long as he upheld and expressed the phenomena he could consider no other eccentric than the one that is described by the center of the epicycle about which the epicycle moves uniformly. So I had to watch out, over and over, so that by using a new method I would not fail to furnish something that had already been achieved by them with their ancient methods. To meet this objection, therefore, I have demonstrated in the first part of the work that the same results are obtained or can be set forth using this new method as were obtained through their old method.

In the second part of this work I take up the matter in question and I describe not less correctly, but rather much better by my method, the positions of Mars in apparent opposition with the Sun than they, using their old method, describe the positions of Mars in mean opposition with the Sun.

Meanwhile, throughout the entire second part (so far as it is devoted to geometric demonstrations based on the observations) I leave in suspense the question as to who is more correct, they or I, seeing that we both agree about certain observations (in fact, I preface this as a rule to our machinations). That my method is consistent with the physical causes and that their ancient method is inconsistent I have partly revealed in the first section, especially in chapter 6.

Finally, in chapter 52 of the fourth section of the work, using certain other observations no less reliable than the earlier ones and which their ancient method cannot fit while mine can perfectly, I have proven very firmly that the eccentric of Mars is so placed that its line of apsides intersects the very center of the solar body, not some nearby point; so all the eccentrics meet in the Sun itself. Moreover, that this holds true not only for the longitude but also for the latitude I have proven in the fifth part in chapter 67, where the same thing is derived from the observed latitudes.

Such things could not have been proven earlier in this work, since an exact knowledge of the causes of the second inequality in the motion of the planets enters into these astronomical demonstrations, and, similarly, not before something new, unknown to our predecessors, was disclosed in the third part.

As a matter of fact, I have demonstrated in the third part that regardless whether the so-called ancient method is right, which uses the mean motion of the Sun, or my new method, which uses the apparent motion, nevertheless, in either case something of the causes of the first inequality is mixed with the second inequality that is common to all the planets. In the case of Ptolemy, I have shown that his epicycles do not have as centers those points about which their motions are uniform. In the case of Copernicus, I have shown that the circle on which the Earth moves about the Sun does not have as a center that point about which its motion is regular and uniform. In the case of Tycho Brahe, I have shown that the circle on which the common center or the so-called node of the eccentrics revolves does not have as center the point about which its motion is regular and uniform. For if I concede to Brahe that the common point of the eccentrics does not coincide with the center of the Sun, it is necessary, as he says, for the course of that common point, which in size and period is obviously equal to the Sun's course, to be an eccentric and to tend toward Capricorn as the Sun's eccentric circuit tends toward Cancer. The same thing happens to Ptolemy's epicycles. But if I put the common point or node of the eccentrics at the center of the solar body, then the circuit common to both the node and the Sun is eccentric to the Earth and tends toward Cancer, although its eccentricity is only half that of the point about which the Sun's motion is regular and uniform.

And according to Copernicus: the Earth's eccentric lies toward Capricorn, but with only half the eccentricity of the point in Capricorn about which the Earth's motion is uniform.

So also in Ptolemy's theory: on the diameters of the epicycles that run from Capricorn to Cancer there are three points; the outermost two are equidistant from the middle one and distant from each other by an amount which, in proportion to the diameters, is as great as the total eccentricity of the Sun in comparison to the diameter of its circuit. Of these three points, the middle ones are the centers of the epicycles and those that lie toward Cancer are the points about which the epicycle's motions are uniform, and finally those which lie toward Capricorn are those whose eccentrics (as described by the points in question) we are seeking *so long as we follow the apparent motion of the Sun instead of the mean motion,* that is, as if the epicycles were attached to the eccentric at those points. Hence, the whole theory of the Sun appears completely in the epicycle of each planet along with all of its motions and all the properties of the orbits.

With these things thus shown by a reliable method, the first step toward the physical causes has now been confirmed, and the next one toward them is built very clearly in the theories of Copernicus and Brahe, and more obscurely but at least plausibly in the Ptolemaic scheme. For, whether it is the Earth which moves or the Sun, it has certainly been demonstrated that the body which moves does so in a nonuniform manner, that is, slowly when it is farther from the body at rest and faster when it is approaching closer to this body. Thus the difference between the three theories appears right away in physical terms, indeed by conjectures, but with no less certainty than the conjectures of doctors concerning physiology or to any other branch of physics.

First, Ptolemy is certainly exploded. Who would believe that there are as many theories of the Sun (resembling one another precisely, or actually equal) as there are planets? As Brahe saw, a single theory of the Sun was enough to perform the same functions; a very generally accepted axiom in physics is that nature uses as few principles as possible.

That Copernicus is more successful in dealing with celestial physics than Brahe is proven by many arguments.

First, Brahe actually constructed his five theories of the Sun from the planetary theories, then he brought them down to the centers of the eccentrics, concealed, and merged them into one; but the thing itself brought about by these theories he left in the universe. For Brahe no less than for Ptolemy, each planet is moved not only by its own motion but by the actual motion of the Sun, mixing the two into one and from this mixture effecting a coiled course; thence it follows that the spheres are not solid, as Brahe has very solidly demonstrated. Copernicus, however, stripped the five planets completely of this extraneous motion, which arises deceptively from the way they are observed. Thus the motions were vainly multiplied by Brahe as they were by Ptolemy before him.

Secondly, if there are no spheres, the conditions under which the intelligences and moving spirits operate will become very difficult because, in order to move a planet in two combined motions, they would have to look after so many things. At the very least, they would have to endeavor, at one and the same time, to look after the origins, centers, and periods of both motions. But if the Earth moves, it is shown that many of these things can be accomplished not by animate faculties, but by physical ones—undoubtedly magnetic. But these are the more general arguments; others follow that arise appropriately from the demonstrations upon which we now enter.

Assuming the Earth does in fact move, it is demonstrated that it adopts the rules governing its swiftness and slowness from a measure of its approach or recession from the Sun. But the same thing holds for the other planets as well, so that they are urged on or retarded according to this approach or recession from the Sun. The demonstration of these things is up to this point geometrical.

From this very reliable demonstration may now be drawn a physical conjecture, that the source of the motions of the five planets is in the Sun itself. Furthermore, it is very likely that the source of the Earth's motion is at the same place as that of the other five planets, namely, in the Sun. For this reason it is therefore very probable that the Earth moves, since there is an apparent, plausible cause for its motions.

On the other hand, many reasons render it likely that the Sun remains in one position at the center of the universe, most of all because in it is the source of motion for at least five of the planets. Whether you follow Copernicus or Brahe, the source of motion for the five planets is located in the Sun, although in Copernicus's theory, a sixth planet is included, that is to say, the Earth. However, it is more likely for the source of all motion to remain in one place than to move. But if we follow the theory of Brahe and claim that the Sun moves, this first condition still remains valid: the Sun moves slowly when it is farther from the Earth and quickly when it approaches the Earth, and this is true not only as an appearance, but in reality. This is the effect of the equant circle that I introduced into the theory of the Sun by an inescapable demonstration. Therefore, on the basis of this very sure conclusion established by the physical conjecture employed above, the following schema for physics would have to be set forth: the Sun with all this great burden of five eccentrics (to speak roughly) being moved by the Earth, or the source of the motion of the Sun and the five eccentrics attached to it residing in the Earth.

But let us consider the bodies of both the Sun and the Earth: which would be the better source of motion for the other? Does the Sun, which moves the other planets, move the Earth, or does the Earth move the Sun, itself the mover of the other planets and so many times larger than the Earth? Let us not be forced to concede that the Sun is moved by the Earth, which is absurd. We must concede immobility to the Sun and motion to the Earth.

What is there to say about the period of revolution of 365 days, which is midway between Mars's period of 687 days and that of Venus, which is 225 days? Does not nature proclaim loudly that the circuit requiring 365 days is located midway between the circuits of Mars and Venus around the Sun, and thus it too goes about the Sun? And that this is the circuit of the Earth about the Sun and not of the Sun about the Earth? But these matters are more appropriate for my *Mysterium cosmographicum* [1596], and I should not have mentioned here any arguments other than those that are relevant to this treatise.

There are other, metaphysical arguments that support the Sun's being in the center of the universe, namely, the dignity of the star or its brilliance. Read my little book just mentioned, or in Copernicus [*GBWW*, Vol. 16, pp. 526–28]. There is something about this in Aristotle, Book 2 of *De caelo* [*GBWW*, Vol. 8, pp. 384–85], where he mentions the Pythagoreans who by the name of fire signified the Sun. I touched on this somewhat in my *Astronomiae pars optica* [1604], chapter 1, page 7. Also in chapter 6, especially page 225. Indeed, you will find in chapter 9, page 322, of that work a metaphysical argument to the effect that it is appropriate for the Earth to revolve in some place other than in the middle of the universe.

Nevertheless, I hope the reader will pardon me if I here indicate some remedies for certain objections that prejudice the mind and steal the clarity from my arguments. They are not really different from the ones I discuss in my work, especially in the third and fourth parts, which deal with the physical causes of planetary motions.

The motion of heavy bodies prevents many from believing that the Earth is moved by an animate, or rather a magnetic, motion. Let them ponder the following propositions:

A mathematical point, whether it is the center of the universe or not, cannot move heavy bodies toward itself either as an efficient or as an objective cause. Let the physicists prove that a point has this force, although a point is neither a body nor is it comprehensible except in relation to something else.

It is impossible for the form of a stone in moving its body to seek a mathematical point or the center of the universe without seeing the body on which the point is located. Let the physicists prove that natural objects have a sort of sympathy to a thing that is actually nothing.

But heavy bodies do not fall in this same manner toward the center of the universe because they are fleeing from the outer boundaries of a round universe. For the proportion according to which they are distant from the center of the universe is indiscernible and inconsequential compared to the distance from the outer boundaries of the universe. What is the reason for this antipathy? With what force, with what wisdom must heavy bodies be endowed in order to escape so effectively from an enemy that surrounds them on all sides? And with what alertness must the outer boundaries of the universe be endowed in order to pursue their enemy so meticulously?

Nor are heavy bodies pushed into the middle by a rapid whirling, as in the case of a whirlpool. For such a motion, if we assume there is one, is not extended down to these lower regions; otherwise we would feel it and be drawn by it and the Earth itself along with us; actually we would be snatched off and the Earth would follow. My opponents consider all of this ridiculous. It appears, therefore, that the popular doctrine about gravity is wrong.

The true doctrine of gravity depends on the following axioms:

Every physical substance, insofar as it is physical, tends to remain at rest at every position in which it is placed in isolation, outside the sphere of influence of a related body.

Gravity is a physical effect operating mutually between related bodies to unite or join them (which, in the order of things, the magnetic capability [*facultas*] also is) with the result that the Earth draws a stone much more than the stone seeks the Earth.

Heavy bodies (especially if we place the Earth at the center of the universe) are not borne toward the center of the universe as such but toward the center of a related spherical body, such as the Earth. So, wherever the Earth is located or wherever it is carried by its animate capability, heavy bodies are always drawn toward it. If the Earth were not round, heavy bodies would not always be drawn straight to the midpoint of the Earth, but they would be drawn toward different points from different sides.

If two stones were placed near one another at some part of the universe outside the sphere of influence of a third related body, these stones would, like two magnetic bodies, move together at some intermediate position, each moving toward the other by an amount proportional to the bulk of the other body.

If the Moon and the Earth were not retained in their own orbits by an animate or some other equivalent force, the Earth would move upward toward the Moon by $\frac{1}{54}$ of the interval and the Moon would descend toward the Earth about 53 parts of the interval; there they would meet, assuming, however, that their substances have exactly the same density.

If the Earth should cease attracting its oceans, they would all rise up and would flow around the body of the Moon.

The sphere of attraction of the Moon reaches the Earth: it teases the water in the tropical zones and in fact assembles the water wherever it is at the zenith. This is imperceptible in inland waters, but is noticeable wherever there are very wide expanses of ocean and an ample freedom of movement for the water. Because of this, the shores of the surrounding climatic zones are left exposed, but yet even bays in the tropics effect a reduction in the nearby oceans. Furthermore, when the waters in the broader regions of the ocean rise, it can happen that in the narrower bays, if they are not too restricted, the water would seem to flee when the Moon is present; in fact, it subsides when the abundance of water is carried elsewhere.

Indeed, the Moon crosses the zenith quickly, and since the water cannot follow so quickly, it flows to the west in the tropics until it touches the opposite shores and is dammed by them. It withdraws when the Moon departs from the assembly of waters; that is, the army that was on the march against the tropics withdraws now that the attraction that set it in motion has deserted it. Once the attack has been made, just as in water carriers, the water ebbs and assaults its own shores and covers them; such an attack, in the absence of the Moon, generates another attack until the Moon returns to rein in the attack, restrain it and push it along with her own motion. So all the shores that are equally accessible are filled at the same time, while the more remote ones are filled later, some in different ways because of the various degrees of accessibility to the ocean.

I will point out in passing that the Syrtes [shoals off North Africa] are mounds of sand built up in this way; countless islands are created or destroyed in these spinning eddies (as for example, in the Gulf of Mexico); it seems that the soft, fertile, crumbly soil of the Indies was finally broken up and penetrated by this eternal flow and inundation, with the help of some sort of general movement of the Earth. It is asserted that India was once continuous from the golden Chersonnese to the east and the south, but now the ocean, which was once farther back between China and America, has flowed in; the shores of Moluccas and of other neighboring islands extend upward because the surface of the sea has subsided, which corroborates the truth of this thing.

Taprobane seems to have been submerged by it (as is consistent with the account of the Calcuttans that some of the places there were once submerged) when the Chinese Sea poured through the broken dikes into the Indian Ocean, to the extent that nothing of Taprobane remains today save some mountain tops that appear as the innumerable islands called the Maldives. According to geographers and Diodorus of Sicily, it is easy to prove that Taprobane was once situated in that place opposite the mouth of the Indus River and the promontory of Corium, and toward the south. It is attested also in an ecclesiastical history that there was the same bishop for Arabia and Taprobane, since it was nearby, not 500 German miles to the east (or indeed, because of the exaggeration common to that age, not more than a thousand). The island of Sumatra, which today is thought to have been Taprobane, I think was once the golden Chersonnese, joined to the isthmus of India at the city of Malacca. For Chersonesus [on Crete] cannot be called "Chersonnese," which today we believe was golden, any more than Italy can.

Although these things are appropriate to other places, I wanted to explain them all in one context in order to make more credible the marine tides and through them, the Moon's power of attraction.

Now it follows, if the Moon's power of attraction extends to the Earth, that the Earth's power of attraction must be much more likely to extend to the Moon and far beyond, and that nothing made of earthly matter and raised to some height can ever escape such a strong embrace of the attracting power.

Nothing made of physical matter is absolutely light [i.e., has a negative weight]. It is relatively lighter because it is less dense either as a result of its own nature or an outside heat. I call "rarified" not only that which is porous and gaping with many holes, but in general also that which contains a smaller amount of physical matter in the same amount of space that a heavier body might occupy.

The motion of light bodies follows from their definition. It must not be thought that they flee toward the outer surface of the universe when they are borne upward or that they are not attracted by the Earth; actually they are attracted less than heavy bodies are, and so they are displaced by heavy bodies until they come to rest and are held in their place by the Earth.

Even if the Earth's attracting power extends quite a distance upward, as we said, still, if a stone were at such a distance that it became comparable to the diameter of the Earth, it is true that, when the Earth moved, such a stone would not simply follow but would mix its own resisting forces with the attractive forces of the Earth and would thus partially extricate itself from the Earth's pull. This is not unlike the case when violent motion separates projectiles somewhat from the Earth's pull so that they either run ahead when flung toward the east, or are held back when flung toward the west; so they leave the spot from which they are projected with a concentrated force, and the Earth's pull cannot substantially impede this violence so long as the violent motion is in its full vigor.

But since no projectile is separated from the Earth's surface by even a hundred-thousandth of the Earth's radius, and even the clouds and smoke, which contain a slight amount of terrestrial matter, do not soar to a height of even a thousandth of the Earth's radius, it follows that even though the clouds, smoke, or bodies hurled upward perpendicularly are resistant and have a natural tendency to rest, I say no part of them can serve to hinder the Earth's pull since this resistance is negligible in proportional to that pull. So a body that is projected perpendicularly upward falls back to its place without any interference from the Earth's motion; the Earth cannot be moved out from under it but carries flying objects along with it in the air so that they are linked to it by a magnetic force no less than if they were actually in contact with it.

When these propositions are thoroughly understood and carefully weighed, not only does the absurdity and the falsely conceived physical impossibility of the Earth's motion vanish, but it will also become obvious how the physical objections, no matter how they are formulated, must be met.

However, Copernicus prefers to have the Earth and all terrestrial objects, even those detached from the Earth, informed by one and the same motive soul, so that the Earth turning its own body, also turns all those particles detached from it, with the result that through violent motions a force is produced for this soul that is diffused through all the particles—just as I say that a force is similarly produced for the physical capability (which we call gravity or magnetism) through violent motions.

Nevertheless for bodies removed from the Earth such a physical force suffices; the animate force is superfluous.

But if many people fear the worst for themselves and the Earth's creatures because of the swiftness of its motion, they have no reason for alarm. About this subject, see chapter 15 and 16 of my book on the star in Serpens [*De stella nova Serpentarii,* 1606], pages 82 and 84. In the same place you will learn also of the voyage under full sail through the immensity of the spheres of the universe—something that is often raised against Copernicus's theory, as being unnatural. It is shown in fact that this would be perfectly consistent, while, on the other hand, the speed of the heavens would be inconsistent and unnatural if the Earth were made simply to stand still in its place and position.

There are many more, however, who are moved by piety to disagree with Copernicus, fearing that falsehood would be charged against the Holy Spirit who speaks through the Scriptures if we were to declare that the Earth moves while the Sun stands still.

Indeed, let them consider this: since we learn very many and most important things through our sense of sight, it is impossible for us to separate our speech from this ocular sense. So it happens very frequently that we speak according to our visual perceptions, although we certainly know that in reality things are otherwise.

There is an example in Virgil's poetry: "We are leaving port and the land and cities recede" [*GBWW,* Vol. 13, p. 149, ll. 72–73]. So also when we emerge from the narrow boundaries of some valley, we say that a vast plain opens up before us.

Thus Christ said to Peter, "Launch forth into the deep [Latin: *altum* = height]" [Luke 5:4] as if the sea were higher than the shores. It appears thus to the eyes, but the study of optics reveals the reasons for this deception. Christ was making use of a perfectly acceptable expression, but one arising from a visual deception. So also we speak figuratively of the rising and setting of stars, that is, their ascent and descent; at the time when some are saying the Sun is setting, we say it is rising. See chapter 10, page 327, of the *Astronomiae pars optica.*

Likewise the followers of Ptolemy continue to say that the planets are standing still when they appear to remain for several days in succession in the vicinity of the same fixed starts, although they think that at the same time they are actually being moved upward or downward on a straight line from the Earth.

Thus writers of all nations use the word *solstice,* although they deny that the Sun is really standing still. Likewise no one will ever be so devoted to Copernicus that he would not say the Sun is entering Cancer or Leo, even if he means that the Earth is entering Capricorn or Aquarius. And other expressions similarly.

The sacred writings speak to men in a very human way about common matters (in which they were not intended for instruction) so that they can be understood by men; they use such expressions accepted by all in order to introduce other loftier and more divine matters.

Is it any wonder, then, that Scripture speaks in accord with human senses although, at the same time, the truth of the matter diverges from senses of all men, learned and unlearned? Who is unaware of the poetic allusion in Psalm 19? where, using the image of the Sun, the course of the gospel and the wandering of Christ the Lord over this Earth (undertaken for our sake) is being sung: the Sun is said to come forth from his tabernacle of the horizon like the bridegroom from his chamber or like the strong man rejoicing to run a race. Virgil imitates the simile, "Dawn leaving Tithonus's saffron couch" [*GBWW,* Vol. 13, p. 183, ll. 584–85]. Of course, poetry was earlier among the Hebrews.

The psalmist knew the Sun did not go forth from the horizon as if it were coming out of its tabernacle (even if it seemed thus to the eyes). Actually, he thought the Sun moved primarily because it appeared to do so. Nevertheless, he expresses both ideas, since both appear that way to the sight. He ought not to be judged false in either place. In fact, visual perception has its own truth, which is proper to the more arcane meaning of the psalmist in thus representing the course of the gospel and of the Son of God. Likewise, Joshua talks about the valleys toward which the Sun and Moon are moving, probably because it so appeared to him in Jordan [Joshua 10:12ff]. Nevertheless each achieves his purpose: the glory of the God of David (and Syracides with him) is made manifest, which causes these things to be represented this way to our eyes or even for a mystical sense visibly expressed.

Joshua wished that the Sun might be kept for a whole day in the middle of the sky with respect to his vantage point, while for other men it would be delayed under the Earth. Thoughtless people consider it only a contradiction of words: "the Sun stood still," and "the Earth stood still." They do not consider that this contradiction arose only within the boundaries of optics and astronomy, and for this reason it does not extend to common usage. They do not want to see that Joshua had only one thing in his prayers, that the mountains might not rob him of sunlight, and that he expressed this prayer in words conforming to his sense of sight. It would have been quite out of place at that time for him to think about astronomy and the errors of sight. If someone had suggested that the Sun was not really moving toward the valley of Ajalon but only seemed to be, would not Joshua have exclaimed that he was seeking to extend the daylight by any means whatever? He would have reacted the same way, therefore, if anyone had taken issue with him over the Sun's permanent immobility and the Earth's motion.

God easily understood from Joshua's words, however, what he wanted, and by arresting the Earth's motion made the Sun seem to stand still for him. The sum of Joshua's prayer came down to this, that it might so appear to him, regardless of the reality; to be sure, the appearance was not groundless and invalid but was related to the desired effect.

But see chapter 10 of the *Astronomiae pars optica.* Here you will discover the reasons why it is the Sun and not the Earth that seems to all men to move, namely, since the Sun appears to be small and the Earth large, and since the Sun's motion cannot be grasped by sight because of its apparent slowness but by reasoning alone, due to its changed proximity to mountains over a certain period of time. It is impossible for unforewarned reason to conceive of anything other than an immovable Earth, with the vault of heaven over it like a great house in which the Sun like a bird flying in the air, so small in appearance, passes from one region to another.

Such a conception of all mankind gave rise to the first line on the sacred pages: "In the beginning," says Moses, "God created the heaven and the Earth" [Genesis 1:1], evidently because these two parts are the most obvious to the sense of sight. It is as if Moses said to man, "This whole Earthly edifice which you see, with the light above and the vast darkness below, wherein you have your being and by which you are sheltered, was created by God."

Elsewhere man is asked whether he can find out the height of heaven above or the depth of the Earth beneath [Jeremiah 31:37], because it seems to the common man that each stretches equally into infinite space. Nevertheless no one in his right mind will by these words circumscribe the astronomers' diligent attempts either to show the Earth's contemptible smallness in comparison with the heavens or to investigate astronomical distances, since they are speaking not about a theoretical dimension, but about the real one that is utterly impossible for the human body so long as it is fixed to the Earth and breathing in the free air. Read the whole 38th chapter of Job and compare it with the matters discussed in astronomy and physics.

If someone were to allege on the basis of the 24th Psalm that the Earth is founded upon the seas in order to establish a new philosophical principle that the Earth does float on water—as absurd as it may sound—he should be told, and deservedly, to leave the Holy Spirit alone and not drag it with contempt into the schools of physics. For the psalmist wanted to express there nothing but what men knew long ago and what they experience daily, namely, that the Earth (having been raised up after the separation of the waters) has enormous rivers flowing through it and oceans surrounding it. Certainly the same expression was used elsewhere, when the Israelites sang that they sat above the waters of Babylon, that is to say, by the riverside, or on the banks of the Euphrates and Tigris.

If one willingly accepts this, why not accept that in places where objections to the Earth's motion are commonly found, we should likewise turn our eyes from physics to the meaning of scripture.?

A generation comes (says Ecclesiastes) and a generation passes away; but the Earth abides forever [Ecclesiastes 1:4]. Would Solomon have disputed the point with astronomers? No, rather he warned men of their transitory state, while the Earth, the dwelling place of mankind, remains forever the same; the Sun's movement is a perpetual revolution; the wind is driven in a circle and returns to the same spot; the rivers flow from their sources to the sea, and from the sea they return to their sources; and finally, while some men lie dying others are born. Life's tale is eternally the same; there is nothing new under the Sun.

This is no physical dogma you hear. The message is a moral one, about something self-evident, observed by the eyes of all men, but seldom considered. Therefore Solomon impresses it upon us. Who doesn't know that the Earth is eternally the same? Who doesn't see that the Sun rises daily from the east, that the rivers constantly rush to the sea, that the vicissitudes of the wind return again, that new men succeed the old? But who seriously considers the fact that the same drama of life is being eternally played out, with only a change in the actors, and that there is never anything new in human affairs? So, by mentioning what is evident to everyone, Solomon warns of something that the majority of men wrongly neglect.

It is generally thought that Psalm 104 contains a physical discussion, since it entirely concerns physical matters. There God is said to have laid the foundations of the Earth, that it should not be removed forever. But the psalmist is very far from speculating on the physical causes. He rejoices entirely in the greatness of God who has made all things; he composes a hymn to God the creator wherein he treats in order the creatures of the universe as it appears to his eyes.

If you pay close attention, this is actually a commentary on the six days of creation of Genesis. For, as in Genesis, the first three days are devoted to the separation of the realms, first of light from the outer darkness, second of the waters from the waters with a great expanse between them, and third of the land from the seas whereby the land is clothed with herbs and plants; the last three days were devoted to filling the regions thus distinguished, the fourth, of the heavens, the fifth, of the seas and air, the sixth of the land. Similarly in this psalm there are as many distinct parts as there are works of the six days.

In the second verse, the psalmist surrounds the creator with light, like a garment, as the first of his creations and the work of the first day.

The second part begins with the third verse, where he discusses the waters above the heavens, the expanse of the heavens and the atmospheric phenomena that he thinks arise from the upper waters, namely clouds, winds, whirlwinds, and lightning.

The third part begins from the sixth verse and celebrates the Earth as the foundation of the things being considered. Indeed, the psalmist relates everything to the Earth and the animals that inhabit it because, in the judgment of sight, there are two primary parts of the universe, the heavens and the Earth. Consequently he here contemplates the fact that after so many ages the Earth has not sunk, cracked, or decayed, even though no one has discovered on what foundations it stands.

The psalmist does not wish to teach what men do not know, but to bring to mind what they are neglecting, to wit, the greatness and the power of God in the creation of such a large mass, so strong and stable. If an astronomer teaches that the Earth is placed among the planets, he does not overthrow what the psalmist is saying here, nor does he contradict common experience. It is nonetheless true that the Earth, the work of God the architect, does not collapse (as our buildings are wont to do) when wasted with age and decay. The Earth does not lean to the side, the dwellings of living creatures are not disturbed, the mountains and shores stand firm, unmoved, against the onslaughts of wind and wave as they were from the beginning. The psalmist adds a very beautiful picture of the separation of the seas from the continents; he adorns it with a description of springs and the benefits that springs and cliffs render to birds and the beasts. He does not neglect the adornment of the Earth's surface recalled by Moses among the works of the third day, but for this he seeks a higher cause, the pure moistening of heaven. And he embellishes his account with a recital of the benefits rendered by such an adornment for the nurture and pleasure of men, and for the lairs of the beasts.

The fourth part begins with verse 20, celebrating the work of the fourth day, the Sun and Moon, but chiefly the usefulness that the seasonal division of time brings to man and living creatures—this being his subject matter; it is clearly evident that he is not playing the astronomer. Had he been, he would not have failed to mention the five planets, than whose motion there is nothing more admirable, nothing more beautiful, nothing that testifies more evidently to the wisdom of the Creator—to those who understand it.

The fifth part from the 26th verse concerns the work of the fifth day where he fills the seas with fish and decorates them with ships.

The sixth part is more obscurely connected from the 28th verse, where he discusses the land creatures that were created on the sixth day. Finally he declares in general the goodness of God, who sustains and creates things anew. All his remarks about the universe refer to living creatures; he says nothing that would not be granted, because his purpose is to extol those things that are known, not to inquire into the unknown, and in fact to urge men to reflect on the benefits accruing to them from the works of each of these days.

And I as well implore my reader not to forget the divine goodness conferred on mankind, and which the psalmist urges him especially to consider. When he has returned from the temple and entered upon the study of astronomy, may he praise and glorify with me the wisdom and greatness of the creator, which I have revealed in a deeper explication of the form of the universe, in an investigation of causes, and in my detection of the deceptiveness of sight. Let him not only extol the bounty of God in the preservation of living creatures of all kinds by the strength and stability of the Earth, but also let him acknowledge the wisdom of the creator in its motion, so abstruse, so admirable.

Whoever is so stupid that he cannot grasp the science of astronomy or so weak that he cannot believe Copernicus without offending his piety, I advise the man who dismisses the study of astronomy and damns whatever philosophical opinions he pleases to mind his own business, to quit this worldly pursuit, to stay at home and cultivate his own garden, and when he turns his eyes toward the visible heavens (the only way he sees them), let him with his whole heart pour forth praise and gratitude to God the creator. Let him assure himself that he is serving God no less than the astronomer to whom God has granted the privilege of seeing more clearly with the eyes of the mind, and of yet being willing and able to celebrate God even beyond his own discoveries.

Scholars ought to give some consideration to Brahe's theory of universe, for indeed it follows the middle of the road in certain respects, partly in freeing astronomers as much as possible from the useless baggage of too many epicycles and partly in embracing with Copernicus the causes of motion unknown to Ptolemy. Brahe also gives some place for physical speculations by admitting the Sun to the center of the planetary system. But on the other hand, he is a slave to the common breed of lettered men in that he eliminates the motion of the Earth because it is so hard to believe. In so doing, he entangles the planetary theories in many difficulties both with regard to astronomical speculations and demonstrations, and by quite upsetting celestial physics.

So much for the authority of scripture. Now, touching the opinions of the church fathers on natural science, I can reply in a word. In theology it is authority that must be taken seriously, but in philosophy it is reason. So it was Saint Lactantius who denied that the Earth is round, Saint Augustine who, in admitting its roundness, still denied the antipodes [*GBWW*, Vol. 18, p. 428], and it is the Sacred Office of today which, while conceding the Earth's smallness, denies its motion. But a greater saint to me is Truth: that the Earth is round, has antipodes on opposite sides, is contemptibly small and, lastly, is carried among the planets, which, with all due respect to the church fathers, I demonstrate from philosophy.

But enough about the truth of the Copernican hypothesis. Let us return to the plan with which I started this introduction.

I began by saying that in this work I would treat the whole of astronomy, not on the basis of fictitious hypotheses, but according to physical causes. In fact, I have striven toward this end in two steps; in the one, I discovered that the planetary eccentrics coincide at the body of the Sun, and in the other, that the theory of the Earth requires an equant circle and the bisection of its eccentricity.

Furthermore, this should be the third step, which was demonstrated very securely by a comparison of the second part of the plan with the fourth part, that the eccentricity of Mars's equant must also be bisected exactly—a fact that Brahe and Copernicus long held in doubt.

In the third part, by way of anticipation, it is established by induction from all the planets that since there are no solid spheres (as Brahe showed from the paths of comets), the Sun's body is the source of power that drives all the planets. I have reasoned that, although the Sun remains in one position, it still rotates as in a lathe, and indeed emits from itself throughout the extent of the universe an immaterial emanation [*species*] of its body, analogous to the immaterial emanation of the Sun's light. This emanation rotates with the solar body, like a very rapid whirlwind, covering the whole universe, and it carries around with it the bodies of the planets, with greater or lesser violence depending on whether it is denser or weaker there, according to the rules of its emission.

Once this mutual power has been explained whereby all the planets are carried about the Sun, each in its own circle, it follows logically from my arguments that, since I had already rejected solid spheres on Brahe's authority, individual movers should be assigned to the individual planets and located in their globes. This I have also done in the third part.

It is incredible to say how much labor it cost me to set up those movers according to this method of argument; this is revealed in the fourth part. For the equations of the eccentric gave the wrong distances of the planet from the Sun, disagreeing with the observations. This was not the result of my introducing them in error, but because, under the spell of the common opinion I had bound them into circles like donkeys in a mill. Restrained by such fetters, my movers could not do their work.

My exhausting task was not finished until I had devised the fourth step toward a physical hypothesis. After very laborious demonstrations and the analysis of a large number of observations, I noticed that the planet's route in the sky is not a circle, but an oval—perfectly elliptical.

Here geometry came to mind and taught me that such an orbit would result if to the mover of each planet we assign the job of oscillating the planet's body along a straight line extended toward the Sun. Not only this, but even the correct equations, consistent with the observations, are produced because of such an oscillation.

Finally, therefore, the roof has been constructed for the edifice; this sort of oscillation is shown geometrically to be the product of a physical, magnetic capability. So the specific movers of the planets are shown with great probability to be nothing other than planetary influences similar to what in a magnet seeks the pole and attracts iron. Thus the whole system of celestial motions is administered by purely physical capabilities, that is to say, magnetic ones, except for the rotation of the solar body as it stays in one place; here a vital capability seems to be needed.

Next, in the fifth part it is demonstrated that the physical hypotheses already introduced satisfy even the latitudes.

In parts three and four, however, a certain role was given Mind to play to the extent that the mover proper to each planet adds Reason to the animate capability that moves its globe; if anyone is put off by some strange, seemingly strong objections to the emanation and wants to distrust the nature of bodies, let him just accept the following, that Mind uses the apparent diameter of the Sun as the measure of its oscillation and has the sense of the angles that astronomers require.

Therefore, let only this much be said for the sake of the physicists; the astronomers and geometers will find everything else properly arranged in the following synopses of the chapters. These I wanted to be sufficiently detailed so that they could take the place of an index and so that the reader might seek some illumination of the arguments in the synoptic table when he gets stuck in the obscurity either of the subject matter or the style. Also, he might perceive the system of order and the coherence of subject matters when grouped under the same chapter heading and see with greater clarity the relationship of the arguments when set in their own paragraphs, since it might be perhaps less conspicuous in its context. Therefore, I ask the reader to consider it well.

Chapter 7

On the Occasion When I Took up the Theory of Mars

The divine voice that calls men to learn astronomy is, in truth, expressed in the universe itself, not by words or syllables, but by things themselves and by the agreement of the human intellect and senses with the ensemble of celestial bodies and phenomena. Nevertheless, there is a certain destiny that secretly drives men toward different arts and gives them the assurance that just as they are part of the works of creation, so also they participate in the divine Providence.

Thus when I was old enough to taste sweetness of philosophy, I embraced it all with an extreme passion, without taking a particular interest in astronomy. I have for this, certainly, a sufficient intelligence, and I understood without difficulty the geometry and astronomy imposed by the series of courses, which depend on figures, numbers, and proportions. But these were the prescribed studies, and nothing indicated to me a particular inclination for astronomy. Now I was supported by a scholarship from the Duke of Wurttemberg, and when I saw that my fellow students would excuse themselves when the Prince was soliciting for foreign countries, although in fact they simply refused for love of their native land, I fully decided, being of a tougher nature, to go immediately where I might be sent.

The first place offered to me was an astronomical position into which, frankly, I was pushed only because of the authority of my teachers, not that I was frightened by the distance of the place—a fear I had condemned in the others (as I have said)—but because of the unexpected character and lowness of the position as well as the weakness of my education in this part of philosophy. I accepted, therefore, being richer in ingenuity than in knowledge, and protesting strongly that I would by no means abandon my right to another kind of life, [an ecclesiastical position] that appeared to me much better. What was the success of my studies during the first two years appears in my *Mysterium cosmographicum,* and moreover, what stimulus my teacher Maestlin applied to me for taking up astronomy, you will read in the same little book and in his letter prefixed to the *Narratio prima* of Rheticus. I esteemed my discovery very highly, and much more so when I saw that it was so greatly commended by Maestlin. But he did not stimulate me as much by the untimely promise made by him to the readers, of what he described as a general astronomical work by me, inasmuch as I was eager to inquire into the restoration of astronomy and to see if my discovery could be exposed to the discrimination of observations. Indeed it was demonstrated in the book itself that it agreed within the accuracy of common astronomy.

Therefore at this time I began to think seriously of comparing it with observations. In 1597 I wrote to Tycho Brahe asking him to tell me what he thought of my little work, and when in his answer he mentioned, among other things, his observations, he fired me with an enormous desire to see them. Moreover, Tycho Brahe, himself an important part in my destiny, did not cease from then on to urge me to visit him. But since the distance of the two places would have deterred me, I ascribe it to Divine Providence that he came to Bohemia, where I arrived just before the beginning of the year 1600, with the hope of obtaining the correct eccentricities of the planetary orbits. When, in the first week, I learned that Brahe himself, along with Ptolemy and Copernicus, employed the mean motion of the Sun, but in fact the apparent motion agreed more with my little book (as shown by the book itself), I was authorized to use the observations in my manner.

Now at that time his personal aide, Christian Severinus [Longomontanus], had taken up the theory of Mars, which was placed in his hands so that they might study the observation of the acronycal place, or opposition of Mars, with the Sun in 9° of Leo. Had Christian been occupied with another planet, I would have started with that one.

This is why I consider it again an act of Divine Providence that I arrived at the time when he was studying Mars; because for us to arrive at the secret knowledge of astronomy, it is absolutely necessary to use the motion of Mars; otherwise it would remain eternally hidden.

The table of mean oppositions from the year 1580 was remade; a hypothesis was invented that managed to represent all of them within two minutes in longitude, and whose numbers were only a little different from those I have used in chapter 5. The apogee was placed in 23°45′ of Leo at the beginning of the year 1585; the maximum eccentricity, which is composed of the semidiameters of both small circles, was 20160 parts of the sort in which the radius of the major epicycle was 16380. Accordingly, the eccentricity of the equant point (in the form of the first inequality in the Ptolemaic theory) was 20160 or somewhat less.

On the basis of this hypothesis, the table of equations of the eccentric was laid out by single degrees as well as the corrected mean motion, which was made by the addition of 1¾′ to the mean motion of the *Prutenicae Tabulae.* Those of the mean motion, apogee, and similarly the node, were expanded through forty years like those made for the motion of the Sun and Moon in volume I of [Tycho's] *Progymnasmata.* Only for the latitudes at the oppositions and for the parallax of the annual orbit did Christian get stuck. To be sure, there was a hypothesis and a table for the latitudes, but it did not agree with the observed latitudes. These things were also a serious obstacle in the lunar motion.

When I therefore suspected on this account that the hypothesis was wrong, I equipped myself for the work according to the ideas and suppositions expressed in my *Mysterium cosmographicum.* At first it was much disputed among us whether by establishing some other hypothesis so many planetary places could be expressed by an eccentric within a hair's breadth, and whether that which performed so well for the circuit throughout the entire zodiac could be false.

But I have shown in the preceding Part I that even with a false eccentricity the observations can be satisfied to 5′ and even better, provided the equant point is right. Indeed, with respect to the parallaxes of the annual orbit and the latitudes, the prize was still to be awarded, nor was it obtained by their hypothesis; therefore it remains to inquire whether or not these calculations disagree anywhere by 5′.

I therefore began to explore the reliability of their procedures. What has followed as a result in this work would be too tedious and useless to repeat here. Hence I shall pursue only that part of this labor of four years that pertains to the understanding of our method.

Chapter 34

The Sun Is a Magnetic Body, and Rotates in Its Space

Concerning that power which is closely attached to, and draws, the bodies of the planets, we have already said how it is formed, how it is akin to light, and what it is in its metaphysical being. Next, we shall contemplate the deeper nature of the source [of power], shown by the outflowing emanation (or archetype). For it may appear that there lies hidden in the body of the Sun a sort of divinity, which may be compared to our soul, from which flows that emanation driving the planets around, just as from the soul of someone throwing pebbles an emanation of motion comes to inhere in the pebbles thrown by him, even when he who threw them removes his hand from them. And to those who proceed soberly, other reflections will soon be provided.

The power that is extended from the Sun to the planets moves them in a circular course around the immovable body of the Sun. This cannot happen, or be conceived in thought, in any other way than this, that the power moves in the same path along which it carries the other planets. This has been observed to some extent in catapults and other violent motions. Thus, Fracastoro and others, relying on a story told by the most ancient Egyptians, spoke with little probability when they said that some of the planets perchance would have their orbits deflected gradually beyond the poles of the world, and thus afterwards would move in a path opposite to the rest and to their modern course. For it is much more likely that the bodies of the planets are borne in that direction in which that power emanating from the Sun tends.

But this emanation is immaterial, flowing from its body out to this distance without the passing of any time, and is in all other respects like light. Therefore, it is not only required by the nature of the emanation, but likely in itself owing to this kinship with light, that along with the particles of its body or source it too is divided up, and when any particle of the solar body moves toward some part of the world, the particle of the immaterial emanation which from the beginning of creation corresponded to that particle of the body also always moves toward the same part. If this were not so, it would not be an emanation, and would come down from the body in curved rather than straight lines.

Since the emanation is moved in a circular course, in order thereby to confer motion upon the planets, the body of the Sun, or source, must move with it, not, of course, from space to space in the world,—for I have said, with Copernicus, that the body of the Sun remains in the center of the world,—but upon its center or axis, both immobile, its parts moving from place to place, while the whole body remains in the same place.

In order that the force of the argument from similitude may be that much more evident, I would like you, reader, to recall the demonstration in optics that vision occurs through the emanation of lucid particles toward the eye from the surfaces of the seen object. Now imagine that some orator in a great crowd of men, forming a circle around him, turns his face, or his whole body along with it, once about. Those of the audience to whom he turns his eyes directly will also see his eyes, but those who stand behind him then lack the view of his eyes. But when he turns himself around, he turns his eyes around to everyone in the orb. Therefore, in a very short interval of time, all get a glimpse of his eyes. This they get by the arrival of a lucid particle or emanation of color descending from the eyes of the orator to the eyes of the spectators. By turning his eyes around in the small space in which his head is located, he carries around along with it the rays of the lucid particle in the very large orb in which the eyes of the spectators all around are situated. For unless the lucid particle went around, his spectators would not be recipients of his eyes' glance. Here you see clearly that the immaterial emanation of light either is moved around or stands still depending upon whether that of which it is the emanation either moves or stands still.

Therefore, since the emanation of the source, or the power moving the planets, rotates about the center of the world, I conclude with good reason, following this example, that that of which it is the emanation, the Sun, also rotates.

However, the same thing is also shown by the following argument. Motion which is local and subjected to time cannot inhere in a bare immaterial emanation, since such an emanation is incapable of receiving an applied motion unless the received motion is non-temporal, just as the power is immaterial. Also, although it has been proved that this moving power rotates, it cannot be allowed to have infinite speed (for then it would seem that infinite speed would also have to be imposed upon the bodies), and therefore it completes its rotation in some period of time. Therefore, it cannot carry out this motion by itself, and it is as a consequence necessary that it is moved only because the body upon which it depends is moved.

By the same argument, it appears to be a correct conclusion that there does not exist within the boundaries of the solar body anything immaterial by whose rotation the emanation descending from that immaterial something also rotates. For again, local motion that takes time cannot correctly be attributed to anything immaterial. It therefore remains that the body of the Sun itself rotates in the manner described above, indicating the poles of the zodiac by the poles of its rotation (by extension to the fixed stars of the line from the center of the body through the poles), and indicating the ecliptic by the greatest circle of its body, thus furnishing a natural cause for these astronomical entities.

Further, we see that the individual planets are not carried along with equal swiftness at every distance from the Sun, nor is the speed of all of them at their various distances equal. For Saturn takes thirty years, Jupiter twelve, Mars twenty-three months, Earth twelve, Venus eight and one-half, and Mercury three. Nevertheless, it follows from what has been said that every orb of power emanating from the Sun (in the space embraced by the lowest, Mercury, as well as that embraced by the highest, Saturn) is twisted around with a whirl equal to that which spins the solar body, with an equal period. (There is nothing absurd in this statement, for the emanating power is immaterial, and by its own nature would be capable of infinite speed if it were possible to impress a motion upon it from elsewhere, for then it could be impeded neither by weight, which it lacks, nor by the obstruction of the corporeal medium.) It is consequently clear that the planets are not so constituted as to emulate the swiftness of the motive power. For Saturn is less receptive than Jupiter, since its returns are slower, while the orb of power at the path of Saturn returns with the same swiftness as the orb of power at the path of Jupiter, and so on in order, all the way to Mercury, which, by example of the superior planets, doubtless moves more slowly than the power that pulls it. It is therefore necessary that the nature of the planetary globes is material, from an inherent property, arising from the origin of things, to be inclined to rest or to the privation of motion. When the tension between these things leads to a fight, the power is more overcome by that planet which is placed in a weaker power, and is moved more slowly by it, and is less overcome by a planet which is closer to the Sun.

This analogy shows that there is in all planets, even in the lowest, Mercury, a material force of disengaging itself somewhat from the orb of the Sun's power.

From this it is concluded that the rotation of the solar body anticipates considerably the periodic times of all the planets; therefore, it must rotate in its space at least once in one-third of a year.

However, in my *Mysterium cosmographicum* I pointed out that there is about the same proportion between the semidiameters of the Sun's body and the orb of Mercury as there is between the semidiameters of the body of the Earth and the orb of the Moon. Hence, you may plausibly conclude that the period of the orb of Mercury would have the same ratio to the period of the body of the Sun as the period of the orb of the Moon has to the period of the body of the Earth. And the semidiameter of the orb of the Moon is sixty times the semidiameter of the body of the Earth, while the period of the orb of the Moon (or the month) is a little less than thirty times the period of the body of the Earth (or day), and thus the ratio of the distances is double the ratio of the periodic times. Therefore, if the doubled ratio also holds for the Sun and Mercury, since the diameter of the Sun's body is about one-sixtieth of the diameter of Mercury's orb, the time of rotation of the solar globe will be one-thirtieth of eighty-eight days, which is the period of Mercury's orb. Hence it is likely that the Sun rotates in about three days.

You may, on the other hand, prefer to prescribe the Sun's diurnal period in such a way that the diurnal rotation of the Earth is dispensed by the diurnal rotation of the Sun, by some sort of magnetic force. I would certainly not object. Such a rapid rotation appears not to be alien to that body in which lies the first impulse for all motion.

This opinion (on the rotation of the solar body as the cause of the motion for the other planets) is beautifully confirmed by the example of the Earth and the Moon. For the chief, monthly motion of the Moon, by the force of the demonstrations used in chapters 32 and 33, takes its origin entirely from the Earth (for what the Sun is for the rest of the planets there, the Earth is for the Moon in this demonstration). Consider, therefore, how our Earth occasions the motion of the Moon: while this our Earth, and its immaterial emanation along with it, rotates twenty-nine and one-half times about its axis, this emanation has only enough power at the Moon to drive it once around in the same time, in (of course) the same direction in which the Earth leads it.

Here, by the way, is a marvel: in any given time the center of the Moon traverses twice as long a line about the center of the Earth as any place on the surface of the Earth beneath the great circle of the equator. For if equal spaces were measured out in equal times, the Moon ought to return in sixty days, since the size of its orb is sixty times the size of the Earth's globe.

This is surely because there is so much force in the immaterial emanation of the Earth, while the lunar body is doubtless of great rarity and weak resistance. Thus, to remove your bewilderment, consider that on the principles we have supposed it would necessarily follow that if the Moon's material force had no resistance to the motion impressed from outside by the Earth, the Moon would be carried at exactly the same speed as the immaterial emanation, that is, with the Earth itself, and would complete its circuit in twenty-four hours, in which the Earth also completes its circuit. For even if the tenuity of the Earth's emanation is great at the distance of sixty semidiameters, the ratio of one to nothing is still the same as the ratio of sixty to nothing. Hence the immaterial emanation of the Earth would win out completely, if the Moon did not resist.

Here, one might inquire of me what sort of body I consider the Sun to be, from which this motive emanation descends. I would ask him to proceed under the guidance of a further analogy, and urge him to inspect more closely the example of the magnet brought up a little earlier, whose power resides in the entire body of the magnet when it grows in bulk, or when by being divided it is diminished. So in the Sun the moving power appears so much stronger that it seems likely that its body is of all [those in the world] the most dense.

And the power of attracting iron is spread out spherically from the magnet so that there exists a certain orb within which iron is attracted, but more strongly so as the iron comes nearer into the embrace of that orb. In exactly the same way the power moving the planets is propagated from the Sun in an orb, and is weaker in the more remote parts of the orb.

The magnet, however, does not attract with all its parts, but has filaments (so to speak) or straight fibers (seat of the motor power) extended through its length, so that if a little strip of iron is placed in a middle position between the heads of the magnet at the side, the magnet does not attract it, but only directs it parallel to its own fibers. Thus it is credible that there is in the Sun no force whatever attracting the planets, as there is in the magnet (for then they would approach the Sun until they were quite joined with it), but only a directing force, and consequently that it has circular fibers all set up in the same direction, which are indicated by the zodiac circle.

Therefore, as the Sun forever turns itself, the motive force or the outflowing of the emanation from the Sun's magnetic fibers, diffused through all the distances of the planets, also rotates in an orb, and does so in the same time as the Sun, just as when a magnet is moved about, the magnetic power is also moved, and the iron along with it, following the magnetic force.

The example of the magnet I have hit upon is a very pretty one, and entirely suited to the subject; indeed, it is little short of being the very truth. So why should I speak of the magnet as if it were an example? For, by the demonstration of the Englishman William Gilbert [*GBWW*, Vol. 28], the Earth itself is a big magnet, and is said by the same author, a defender of Copernicus, to rotate once a day, just as I conjecture of the Sun. And because of that rotation, and because it has magnetic fibers intersecting the line of its motion at right angles, those fibers lie in various circles about the poles of the Earth parallel to its motion. I am therefore absolutely within my rights to state that the Moon is carried along by the rotation of the Earth and the motion of its magnetic power, only thirty times slower.

I know that the filaments of the Earth, and its motion, indicate the equator, while the circuit of the Moon is generally related to the zodiac—on this point there will be more in chapter 37 and Part V. With this one exception, everything fits: the Earth is intimately related to the lunar period, just as the Sun is to that of the other planets. And just as the planets are eccentric with respect to the Sun, so is the Moon with respect to the Earth. So it is certain that the Earth is looked upon by the Moon's mover as its pole star (so to speak), just as the Sun is looked upon by the movers belonging to the rest of the planets, for which see chapter 38 [here omitted]. It is therefore plausible, since the Earth moves the Moon through its emanation, and is a magnetic body, while the Sun moves the planets similarly through a projected emanation, that the Sun is likewise a magnetic body.

Kepler's Abstract of Chapter 39

In What Orbit and by What Means the Motive Power Inherent in the Planets Ought to Move Them Through the Aethereal Heavens in Order to Effect, as Is Commonly Accepted, Circular Orbits

Initially, there are set forth six physical axioms necessary to an investigation of the power that is specifically ascribed to the individual planets.

Two preconceived notions, however, reign throughout this chapter: the first, that the path of a planet is arranged in a perfect circle, and the second, that its journey is administered by a Mind. There is a discussion, therefore, of how such a Mind can make a circle out of the planets. And it is demonstrated first that this can happen if the planet's own power tries to drive its body in a perfect epicycle while at the same time the planet is also being hastened along by the solar power. This method is opposed by five physical absurdities.

Second, it is then demonstrated that this can happen if the planet watches a certain point beyond the Sun and maintains an equal distance from it throughout its circuit about the Sun. Nevertheless, this observing of some empty point is refuted by three absurdities.

Third, it is shown that a perfect circle can occur if the planet's own power causes it to oscillate on the diameter of the epicycle directed toward the Sun, as if prescribed by laws of rhythmical movement from the epicycle's circumference. But at the same time, it is shown that the correct oscillation cannot be described by the planet if it remains on the diameter of the epicycle, nor do the oscillations correspond to the eccentric arcs traversed either with respect to time, or to the corrected anomaly, even assuming that a perfect circle must be made out of the planet's composite route.

Fourth, it is now even denied that a planet's own force, using some sort of Mind, can conceive an imaginary eccentric or epicycle and from such a rule regulate the distances required for a perfectly circular path. As long as we regard the planet's path to be perfectly circular, the standard to which the Mind of the planet relates these oscillations of its body remains in doubt.

Since the standard for this oscillation is being aired, I shall consider how the planet's Mind can comprehend this standard and the oscillation prescribed by it. Whether the epicycle, or its diameter, or the center of the eccentric, serves as a standard—all of these are rejected as being inappropriate to comprehend and lacking an easy-to-grasp means of measurement by which the Mind can comprehend it. Then it is brought out that the planet's Mind looks to the increasing and decreasing diameter of the Sun and uses that for determining the distance between its body and the Sun: this is drawn by analogy from the latitudes. Rebuttals are also made to the objections concerning the small size of the Sun and the lack of sensory perceptions in the planets. It is finally argued that the idea of administration by a Mind is not entirely contradictory.

But then a problem appears concerning the movement of the planetary body by an innate animate force. And with so many difficulties cropping up on all sides, a preconception held up to now must be especially called into question for physical reasons, namely, the idea that the path of the planet is perfectly circular (and also partly concerning the Mind as regulator of this oscillation); a little farther on, in chapter 44, such an idea will be thoroughly shredded up by geometry.

Kepler's Abstract of Chapter 40

An Imperfect Method for Computing Equations from the Physical Hypothesis, Which Suffices, However, for the Theory of the Sun and Earth

1. The method whereby the physical part of the equation (that is, the time the planet spends in some arc of the eccentric) is found from the distances between the points of this arc and the Sun.

Translator's note: Kepler here uses the traditional astronomical meaning of "equation," which is the difference between the mean motion of the planet and its true position, but he now distinguishes between the physical part, which he will shortly establish from the areas, and the optical part, which is the actual angle used in transforming the mean motion into the true longitude. He uses these terms again, for example, in chapter 59, and also in the *Epitome* [*GBWW*, Vol. 16, pp. 996-98].

2. There is a geometric demonstration showing that the distances between the infinite number of points of the arc and the Sun are contained approximately in the area between the arc and the lines connecting the Sun to the endpoints of the arc, and showing that one triangle between the Sun, the center of the eccentric, and the end of the arc gives both parts of the equation: the angle at the end of the arc gives the optical part and the area gives the physical part.

3. A demonstration: in the case of the Sun, the parts of the equation, both optical and physical, are virtually equal.

4. A preliminary demonstration is set forth: that triangles with equal bases are in the same proportion as their altitudes.

5. Using this theorem, it is shown that the area of the equatorial triangle increases with the sine of the eccentric anomaly, and

hence becomes a short-cut for computing this area. At the same time it is shown by a numerical test that the parts of the equation do not differ by any discernible amount—this first at 90 degrees and then at 45 degrees. There follows a very small exception, showing that the area is a little less than the distances of all degrees of the eccentric, and a little more than the distances of all degrees of the corrected anomaly.

7. A geometric representation of a quadrilateral conchoid, which is equivalent to the distances of all degrees of the eccentric from the Sun. Here geometers are challenged to square this space.

8. The space between two conchoids is shown not to have the same width at places equidistant from the middle. There is more about this in chapter 43.

Chapter 58

In What Manner the Oscillation Discovered and Demonstrated in Chapter 56 May Be Accepted, and Nevertheless an Error May Be Introduced in an Erroneous Application of the Oscillation, Whereby the Path of the Planet Is Made Puffy-cheeked

> Galatea seeks me mischievously,
> the lusty wench:
> She flees to the willows,
> but hopes I'll see her first.
> —Virgil, *Eclogues,* 3.64
> (cf. *GBWW,* Vol. 13, p. 11, ll. 64–65.)

It is perfectly fitting that I borrow Virgil's voice to sing this about Nature. For the closer the approach to her, the more petulant her games become, and the more she again and again sneaks out of the seeker's grasp just when he is about to seize her through some circuitous route. Nevertheless, she never ceases to invite me to seize her, as though delighting in my mistakes.

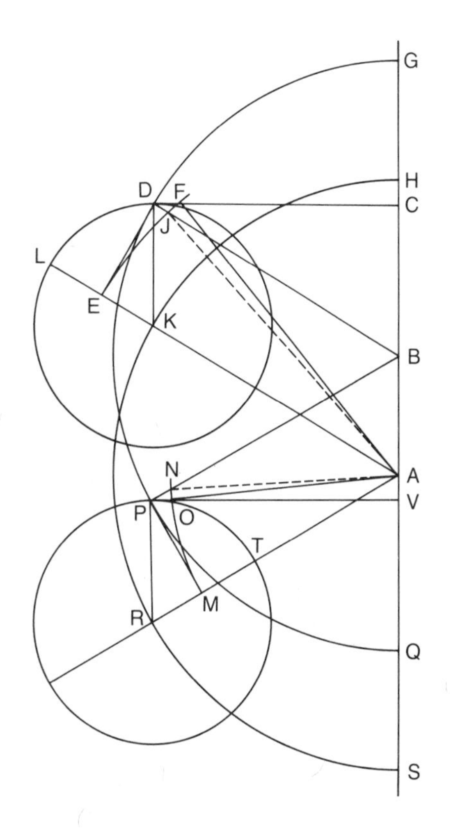

Throughout this entire work, my aim has been to find a physical hypothesis that not only will produce distances that are in agreement with those observed, but also, and at the same time, sound equations, which hitherto we have been forced to borrow from the vicarious hypothesis of chapter 16. So, while trying to use a false method to do the same thing through this hypothesis, which is itself perfectly correct, I began once again to fear for the whole undertaking.

On the line of apsides, about centers A and B, let the equal circles GD, HK be described. And let AB be the eccentricity of the circle GD. Also, let the eccentric anomaly, or its number of degrees, be the arc GD or HK, by the equivalence established in chap-

ter 3. Next, about center K, with radius KD equal to AB, let the epicycle LDF be described, which will intersect the circle GD at D, through the equivalence established in chapter 3. Let AK be drawn, and extended to intersect the epicycle at L, so that the arc LD is similar to the eccentric anomaly GD or HK. And let BD be joined. Now, from D let perpendiculars be drawn to GA, LA, and let these be DC, DE.

Therefore, by what has previously been demonstrated in chapter 56, AE will indubitably be the correct distance at this eccentric anomaly. The question remains how much time was taken to arrive at it. Now the versed sine of its arc, GC, which, after multiplication, becomes LE, when subtracted from GA, yields the correct distance AE. These indications persuaded me that the other end of AE should be sought, not on the line DC (which was actually perfectly correct), but at the point I of the line DB, such that if I drew the arc EIF about center A with radius AE, it would intersect DB at I. Thus, according to this persuasion, AI would be the correct distance, both in position and length, and IAG would be the true equalized anomaly. But it is manifest that the arc EIF intersects the line DC at a higher place, namely, at F. Thus the angles IAG and FAG differ by the quantity IAF.

I therefore erred in taking the line AI instead of AF. I first discovered the error empirically. For when I explored the quantity of the area DAG, either using all the distances or using the small area DAB, and then fitted the angle IAG, rather than FAG, to this area DAG, now converted into time, in the upper part of the semicircle I found $5\frac{1}{2}'$ more, and in the lower half $4'$ less, than the vicarious hypothesis gave with sufficient certainty. And so, since the equations disagreed with the truth, I began once more to accuse these perfectly correct distances AE, and the planet's oscillation LE, of the crime for which my false method, which took I in place of F, was to be blamed. What need is there for many words? The very truth, and the nature of things, though repudiated and ordered into exile, sneaked in again through the back door, to be received by me under an unwonted guise. That is, I rejected the oscillation on the diameter LE, and began by recalling the ellipses, quite convinced that I was thus following a hypothesis far, far different from the oscillation hypothesis, although they coincide exactly, as will be demonstrated in the following chapter. The only difference was that where I erred before in my method, I proceeded correctly this time, using F instead of I, as it should be.

My line of reasoning was like that presented in chapters 49, 50, and 56 [here omitted]. The circle of chapter 43 erred in excess, while the ellipse of chapter 45 erred in defect. And the excess of the former and the defect of the latter are equal. But the only figure occupying the middle between a circle and an ellipse is another ellipse. Therefore, the ellipse is the path of the planet, and the lunule cut off from the semicircle has half the breadth of the previous one, namely, 429.

If, moreover, the planet's path is an ellipse, it is clear enough that I cannot be taken in place of F, for if this were done, the planet's path is made to be puffy-cheeked.

For let the angles QBP, SAR in the lower part be equal to GBD, HAK, and about center R let the epicycle PT again be described, equal to the previous one, and from P, the intersection of the epicycle with the eccentric, let perpendiculars PV, PM, be dropped to BQ, AR [respectively], and let PB be joined. And about center A, with radius AM, let the arc MN be described, intersecting PV at O, and PB at N. So, by analogy with the above, just as we took I in place of F, let us now take N for O, and consider that just as AN is the correct distance in length, it is also correct in position. Now the points I, N, and the like do indeed make the planet's path puffy-cheeked. For the arcs GD and QP are equal. And BD, BP, projected from a common center, intersect the lunule which is cut off. But DI and PN, the breadths of the lunule as measured through the center, are unequal. And DI is smaller, and PN greater. For since ED and MP are equal, and EDI, MPN are right, while EI is a great er circle, since its radius AE is greater, and MN is a smaller circle, since its radius AM is smaller, therefore, PN will definitely be greater, and DI smaller. Therefore, the lunule cut off is narrower above, at D, and broader below, at P. In the ellipse, in contrast, this lunule is of equal breadth at points equally removed from the apsides G and Q.

So it is clear that the path is puffy-cheeked, so it is not an ellipse. And since the ellipse gives the correct equations, it is fitting that this puffy-cheeked path should give incorrect ones.

Nor was there any need to compute the equations anew from the ellipse. I knew they were going to perform their function without further prompting. I was only concerned about the distances, that if they were taken from the ellipse they might cause me trouble. But if this were to happen, I had already prepared a refuge, namely, the uncertainty of 200 units in the distances. Consequently, I did not hesitate much here, either. The greatest scruple by far, however, was that although I was almost driven to madness in considering and calculating this matter, I could not find why the planet, to which an oscillation on the diameter was attributed with such probability, and by so perfect an agreement with the observed distances, would rather go on an elliptical orbit as shown by the equations. O ridiculous me! As if the oscillation on the diameter could not be the way to the ellipse! So this notion brought me up short, that the ellipse exists because of the oscillation. With reasoning derived from physical principles agreeing with experience there is no figure left for the orbit except a perfect ellipse.

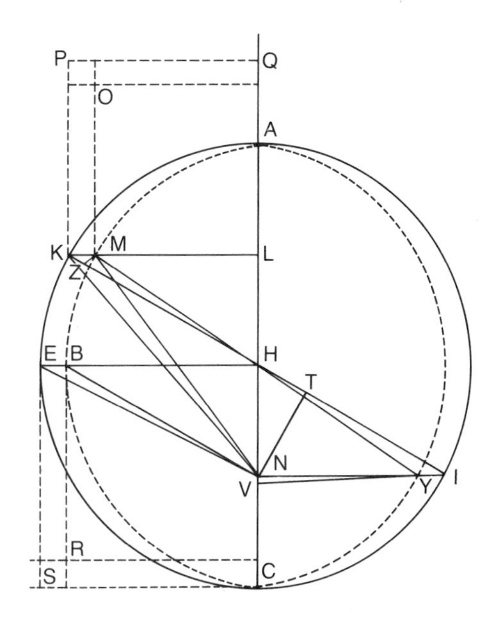

Chapter 59

A Demonstration That the Orbit of Mars Oscillating on the Diameter of the Epicycle Becomes a Perfect Ellipse, and That the Area of a Circle Measures the Sum of the Distances for Points on the Circumference of the Ellipse.

Preliminary theorems:

I.

If an ellipse is drawn inside a circle, touching the circle at its opposing endpoints, and if a diameter is drawn through the center and through the points of contact, and then if perpendiculars are dropped from any other points of the circle's circumference to this diameter, all these perpendiculars will be cut in the same ratio by the circumference of the ellipse.

Commandino proves this in his commentary on proposition 5 of Archimedes' On Spheroids *using proposition 21 of the first book of Apollonius'* Conics (*GBWW*, Vol. 11, p. 628).

Let AEC be a circle and in it the ellipse ABC touching the circle at A and C. Let a diameter be drawn through A and C, the points of contact, and through H, the center. Then from points of the circumference K and E, drop perpendiculars KL and EH, intersecting the circumference of the ellipse at M and B. There will be the same ratio between BH and HE as between ML and LK, and so on for all other sets of perpendiculars.

II.

The area of the ellipse thus inscribed within the circle has the same proportion to the area of the circle as the aforementioned lines.

Thus BH is to HE as the area of the ellipse ABC is to the area of the circle AEC. This is the fifth proposition of Archimedes' On Conoids and Spheroids (*GBWW,* Vol. 11, p. 460).

III.

If lines are drawn from some point of the diameter to the points on some perpendicular where the circumference of the el lipse and of the circle intersect it, then the areas cut out by these lines will again be proportional to the segments of the perpendicular.

Let N be the point on the diameter and KML the perpendicular. Then connect K and M with N. I say that as ML is to LK, or, according to preliminary theorem I above, as BH is to HE (or the minor to the major axis), so the area AMN is to the area AKN. For the area AML is to area AKL as ML is to LK, according to Archimedes' assumptions for the fifth proposition of On Spheroids, *which Commandino demonstrates in his commentaries on this proposition lettered C and D. For the right-angled triangles NLM and NLK, the altitude NL is the same, and the bases are LM and LK. Therefore, as ML is to LK, MLN is to KLN. By putting these together, the whole area AMN is to the whole area AKN as ML is to LK. Q.E.D.*

IV.

When the circle is divided into a certain number of equal arcs by perpendiculars such as these, the ellipse is divided into unequal arcs; those near the vertices have the largest ratio while those near the middle positions have the smallest ratio.

For near the vertices the ratio of the arcs is very close to the ratio of the sectioned perpendiculars, which they closely approximate according to their length, although they always remain smaller. Near the middle positions they become almost equal; nevertheless, the elliptical arcs remain smaller since they are curved less than the circular arcs. This is self-evident.

V.

The whole elliptical circumference is very close to the arithmetic mean between the circle of the major axis and the circle of the minor axis.

In fact, it was previously proven in chapter 48 that the circumference whose diameter is the mean proportional between the axes of the ellipse is longer than that of the circle whose area (according to the seventh proposition of Archimedes' On Conoids and Spheroids; *GBWW,* Vol. 11, p. 461) *equals the area of the ellipse. However, the arithmetic mean is longer than the mean proportional. Therefore, these are very nearly equal.*

VI.

The gnomons [L-shaped differences] of divided squares are in the same ratio to one another as the squares themselves.

Take two squares PL and SH. Let their sides KL and EH be divided proportionally at points M and B. Draw gnomons KOQ and CRE. Since ML is to LK as BH is to HE, OL will therefore be to LP as RH is to HS. But gnomons are the differences of the squares, so LP is to its own gnomon as HS is to its, and conversely, as PL is to HS, so the gnomon KOQ is to the gnomon CRE.

VII.

If a line equal to the semimajor axis is drawn from the end of the semiminor axis that lies on the circumference of the ellipse so that it is terminated at a point on the major axis itself, the square of the line that lies between this point and the center equals the gnomon that the square of the semimajor axis makes around the square of the semiminor axis.

From the endpoint B of the semiminor axis HB, draw a straight line BN equal in length to the semimajor axis AH. I say that HN squared equals the gnomon ERC, that is, it is the mean proportional between EB and the remainder of the circle's diameter. This has been proven earlier in chapter 46, but here it is shown more easily and readily in the pure case. The gnomon is the difference of squares BH and HE or HA according to theorem VI above. But HN squared is the difference of the squares BH and BN (that is, HE or AH) according to proposition 46 of the first book of Euclid (*GBWW*, Vol. 11, p. 28, prop. 47 [sic]). *Therefore the square of HN is equal to the gnomon ERC. Q.E.D.*

VIII.

If the circle is divided into a certain number or an infinity of parts, and the points of division are connected with some point other than the center within the area of the circle, and if they are also connected with the center, then the sum of those lines to the center will be less than the sum of those lines to the other point.

Moreover, two lines near the line of apsides, drawn to opposite points from the eccentric, will be almost equal to the two drawn from the center to opposite points; however, two lines in the intermediate positions will be much greater than those that are drawn from the center to the same points.

This was shown in chapter 40. So the excess does not increase uniformly with the number of lines counted, and much less so with

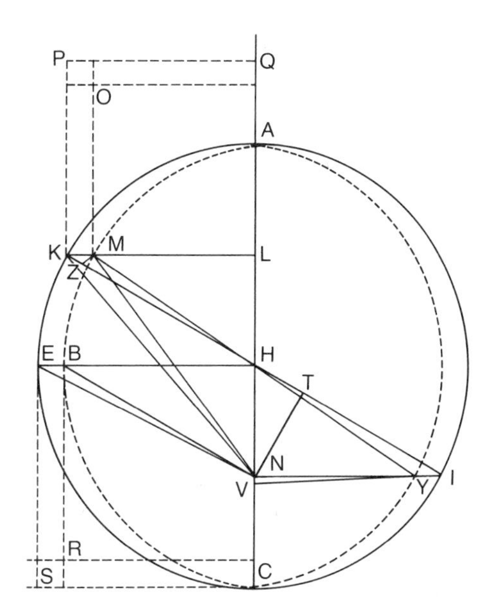

the sines. For the differences of the latter vanish at the end, whereas the differences of said excesses are greatest at the end. Now to have the area KNA of the circle increasing uniformly, surely the part KHA goes according to the number of lines, by the construction; however, the part KNH goes according to the sines of the arcs, that is, their corresponding lines multiplied by HN, according to chapter 40. Therefore, the area of the circle is not suited for measuring of the sum of the distances on its circumference.

IX.

But if instead of the lines from the eccentric point we take those lines determined by the perpendiculars dropped from that point to those going through the center, that is, if we take the diametral distances instead of the circumferential distances as defined in chapters 39 and 57, then their sum equals the sum of those lines drawn from the center.

Let some point be chosen on the circumference of the circle, say K, and from K through H draw a straight line to the opposite part of the circumfer-

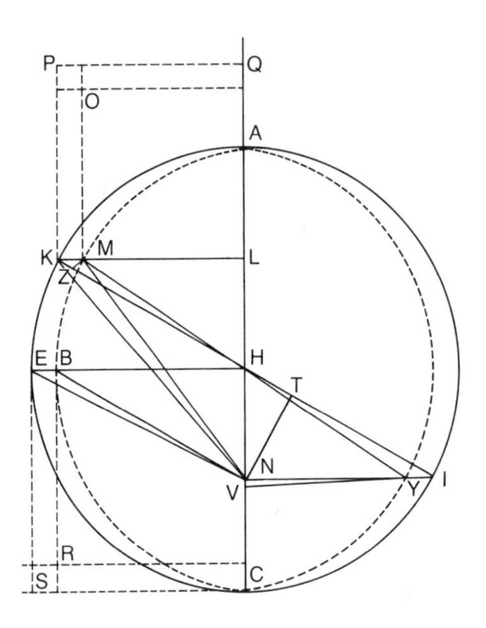

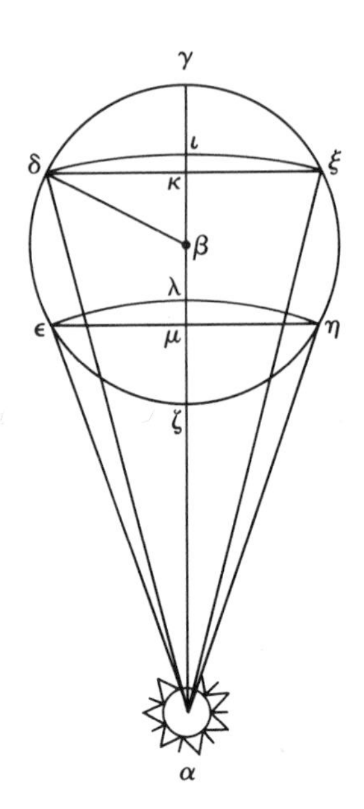

ence, I, and from N drop a perpendicular NT to KI. Then KH plus HI equals KT plus TI. And any sum of the conjoint lines KH and HI equals the equivalent sum of the conjoint lines KT and TI. Since, however, when AK is divided into any number of equal parts, the sum of the lines from AN to KT increases partly with respect to the number of lines HA and HK, and partly with respect to the sines multiplied by HN, it increases, therefore, uniformly with respect to the area KNA through our premise. Hence, the area of the circle and the parts KNA measure the sums of the diametral distances.

X.

The ratio of the distances drawn from the eccentric point of the ellipse to equal arcs of the ellipse, no less than for the circle in preliminary theorem VIII, is contrary to the ratio of the arcs of the circle and of the ellipse explained in preliminary theorem IV. For the two lines drawn from the eccentric point in opposite directions exceed the two drawn from the center in opposite directions, in a very small ratio that dwindles to nothing near the apsides; but in the middle longitudes they exceed the others by the largest ratio.

This appears in chapter 40. Again, therefore, as in preliminary theorem VIII, the area of the ellipse is unsuitable for measuring the sum of distances of equal arcs of its own elliptical circumference.

XI.

Using these premises, I will now reveal the proof.

If in the ellipse divided by perpendiculars dropped from equal arcs of the circle (as above in preliminary theorem IV), the points of division of the circle and ellipse are connected with the point that was found in preliminary theorem VII, then I say that those lines drawn to the circumference of the circle are the circumferential ones, while those drawn to the circumference of the ellipse are the diametral ones, which correspond to an equal number of degrees from the apsides in the epicycle.

From point I opposite K from the center H, drop perpendicular IV to AC, intersecting the elliptical circumference at Y. And from point N (found in preliminary theorem VII), lines are drawn to the intersection points K and M, and I and Y made from the same perpendicular on the other side; these are NK and NM, also NI and NY. Repeat the figure of chapters 39 and 57, and let the radius of the epicycle $\beta\gamma$ *be equal to the eccentricity HN. Arc* $\gamma\delta$ *begun from apsis* $\alpha\gamma$ *is similar to AK also begun from the apsis, and* $\alpha\beta$ *equals the radius HA. I say now that NK is the circumferential* $\alpha\delta$ *(proven in chapter 2) and NM is the diametral* $\alpha\kappa$.

First, KN is the hypotenuse of KL and LN. Likewise MN is the hypotenuse of ML and LN. Let LP be the square on LK, and LO the square on LM. Therefore with KL squared and LM squared (that is, the square LO) and subtracting what is common to both [LN squared], the gnomon LOQ is left by which KN squared exceeds MN squared. Now as KL is to EH so KM is to EB through the first of our theorems. Therefore, also as the square KQ (or KLsquared) is to the square EC (or EH squared), so is the gnomen KOQ to the gnomen ERC through the sixth of our theorems. But here in the eccentric circle as KL (the sine of arc AK) is to EH (or AH, the total sine) so in the epicycle is the perpendicular $\delta\kappa$ *(from point* κ *or arc* $\gamma\delta$*, which is similar to AK, to the diameter of the apsis* $\beta\gamma$ *to the radius of the epicycle* $\beta\gamma$*. Also as the gnomon KOQ is to the gnomon ERC, so is the square* $\delta\kappa$ *to the square* $\beta\gamma$*. But* $\beta\gamma$ *itself is equal to HN. Furthermore, HN squared equals the gnomon ERC by theorem VII. Therefore,* $\beta\gamma$ *squared equals the gnomon ERC, and hence* $\delta\kappa$ *squared (*$\delta\kappa$ *being the perpendicular from the aforementioned point of the epicycle), will be equal to the gnomon KOQ. But the square of that perpendicular* $\delta\kappa$ *is the excess of* $\delta\alpha$*, the circumferential distance, over* $\kappa\alpha$*, the diametral one. Therefore, the gnomon KOQ, equal to the above, is the excess of the square* $\delta\alpha$ *over the square* $\kappa\alpha$*. But KN is equal to* $\delta\alpha$*. Therefore, KN exceeds* $\kappa\alpha$ *by the gnomon KOQ. By the same gnomon, it exceeds also the square MN. Therefore, the diametral distances MN and* $\kappa\alpha$ *are equal. Q.E.D. Similarly, it can be shown for NY that it equals* $\alpha\mu$ *inasmuch as* $\zeta\eta$ *is similar to CI. And so on for all the others.*

XII.

Furthermore, for the same reason it is also clear that the area of the circle both totally and in single parts is the genuine measure of the sum of the lines representing the distances between the arcs of the elliptical path of the planets and the center of the sun.

For according to IX of these theorems, if the area of the whole circle is equivalent to all the diametral distances for all the arcs of the division undertaken, then the parts of that area such as KNA bounded at point N (whence the eccentricity originates) are equivalent to those diametral distances that coincide with arc KA enclosing that area.

According to XI previously set forth, the diametral distances KT and TI, that is, $\kappa\alpha$ *and* $\mu\alpha$ *in chapter 40, are the same as the distances MN and NY of the points of the ellipse M and Y.*

Therefore, as the area of the circle is to the sum of the distances of the ellipse so part of the area of the circle KNA bounded at the center of the sun N (whence the eccentricity originates) is to the sum of those distances of the ellipse belonging to the elliptical arc AM, which has just as many degrees as the arc of the circle AK enclosing the area.

XIII.

Here, however, some uncertainty creeps in: if the area AKN is equivalent to all the distances from N to the elliptical arc AM for just as many points as we put in AK, then what is the corresponding elliptical arc, that is, where should it end? For it seems that it should not end at the perpendicular line KL. The reason is that, according to preliminary theorem IV, unequal elliptical arcs correspond to the equal arcs of the circle. Thus there are smaller arcs near the vertices A and C, and the larger arcs near B. But in fact it seems necessary to take equal arcs of the elliptical orbit if we actually want to evaluate and compare the amounts of time the planet spends in them. To be specific, since it is certain that the end of this arc ought to be distant from N by the length

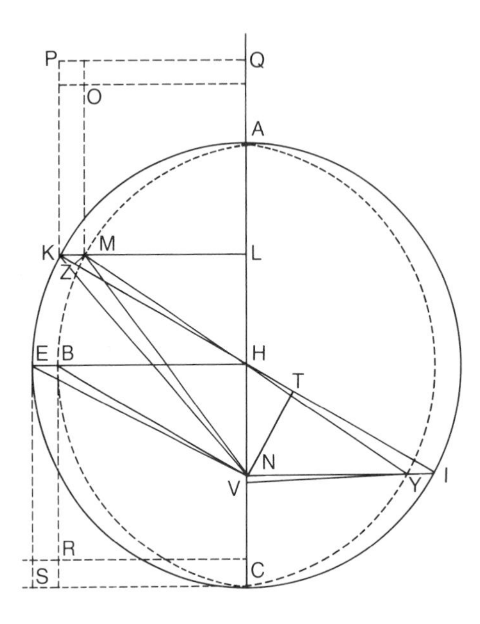

MN, therefore, as in chapter 58, the arc MZ drawn with the center N and length NM indicates some point that terminates the arc of the ellipse, and it seems that this point will not be M, but Z, where the arc intersects the line KH, so that the corresponding arc of the orbit would be AZ.

We might claim in any event that the arc of the ellipse whose time interval the area AKN measures ought to be divided into unequal parts whose smaller segments occur near the apsides.

Let us consider that the path of the planet ABC is divided into equal arcs. Since the planet spends a longer time in arc A than it does in C, proportional to how much longer NA is than NC, and both NA and NC together equal the major axis of the ellipse, and since HB is the semiminor axis of the ellipse, then the amount of time the planet spends in an arc at B and in the opposite arc conjointly will be shorter than in the equal arcs A and C conjointly. In order to make the amount of time spent near A and C shorter, and near B and its opposite point longer, and so that hence the combined time intervals in the two opposite arcs will always be equal, the arcs near A and C must be made shorter and those near B and its opposite longer. However, the perpendiculars KML cause just this effect, as is clear from the objection itself.

But using this solution we only know for sure that near A and C the arcs ought to be little short ones. Whether, however, the particular arcs that are determined by the perpendiculars KML are in fact the exact arcs required, does not yet follow. Now, however, it will be made clear in the following way.

XIV.

If someone would divide the ellipse AMC into a certain number of equal arcs and assign to each of them their distances from N, but if instead of the sums of distances to AM, AB, and ABC, he would use the areas AMN, ABN, and ABCNA, then according to preliminary theorem X the same error that happened before in chapter 40, when we tried this same thing for a perfect circle, would again happen here for the ellipse, namely, that the two distances MN and NY from the two points M and Y on the opposite sides of the center H are estimated to be shorter than the area MHY.

On the other hand, if he would divide the same ellipse AMC into just as many unequal arcs, not according to preliminary theorem X, but according to the procedure such that the circle AKC is first divided into equal arcs, and then perpendicular lines KL are drawn to AC from the ends of the individual arcs, thereby also cutting the ellipse AM into arcs, and if the elliptical area is used in place of the distances of these arcs from N, then this becomes a remedy compensating very exactly for the error that was made.

I will prove this for the initial points of the quadrants A and C, for their endpoints B, and for the intermediate stages.

If the two lines NA and NC are used for the line AHC at the beginnings of the quadrants A and C, then there is no error; at the endpoints, however, if for BN (that is, for EH) I take instead BH, the er-

ror or deficit turns out to be greatest, by the amount BE according to preliminary theorem X. And by preliminary theorem VII of this chapter, as HE is to EB, so the correct length is to the error that is made here. If, therefore, the total sum of all the distances (with their deficits) takes as its measure the area of what is evidently an ellipse, then, after distributing the deficit among the individual distances by the nature of our operation or computation, it turns out that NA and NC are made too short with respect to this measurement of all the distances. This falsifies our statement that all lines err equally in deficit, since NA and NC do not err. They contribute correctly to this sum, but when its distribution is made, they fail to receive the correct amount since the other lines near B have defrauded the sum.

See now how we remedy this error in the same proportion.

By means of preliminary theorem IV of this chapter, the smallest arcs AK and AM near apsides A or C are in the ratio of KL to LM, or EH to HB; earlier, the straight lines near B erred in deficit in this same ratio. And furthermore, the smallest arcs of the circle and ellipse, near B, say KE and MB, are equal, just as previously the straight lines AN and NC were together equal to the line AHC. Thus, just as before in the matter of the straight lines, so now in the matter of the arcs, when considering the mean and uniform size of the arcs, the arc near the apsides A or C will be small with respect to the long one at the middle longitudes near B.

And so, where (in the erroneous area of the ellipse in question) the distances were too short with respect to their faulty sum, there the arcs were too small with respect to their mean value, as in A and C; and where the distances were too long, there the arcs were too long, as in B.

So just as much less of a time interval is accumulated by our calculations through the small region near apsides, as is proportional to the greater number of distances used for such an arc, since it is cut into small sections, each part of which has its own assigned distance. On the other hand, more of a time interval than there ought to be is accumulated in our calculation through the individual distances near the middle longitudes at B, while part of the defect that occurs in this place we transferred to the blameless apsides, A and C, but exactly equivalent to the fewer distances our calculation collects since they are corrected by begging from the large portions of the arc. On the one hand, at A and C, although the individual distances cannot correct things because of their brevity in our calculation, they guarantee by their greater frequency that the correct amounts of time are spent there. On the other hand, where the distances err in length as they originate in our calculation, the error is removed by being dispersed more widely and extensively.

I have spoken about the beginning and end, that the arcs of the circle begin to differ from the ellipse at A and C in the same ratio (which is EH to HB) as do the correct distances from those that the area of the ellipse collects near B and its opposite; and surely the arcs near BE and the distances at A and C cease differing in the same ratio, undoubtedly with a ratio of equality.

Now we should say that it is also the same in the intermediate stages.

For indeed, the lines NA and NC at first differ little from the lines AHC, but the increments rapidly build up the differences to quite an appreciable amount. On the other hand, where they differ the most, as BN exceeds HB, there the increments gradually vanish. Thus, in the middle they are greatest, around an eccentric anomaly of 45°.

This is clear to a certain point from the angle and secants of the equation. The secant of the angle of the optical equation differs from the total sine by almost the same amount as BN differs from BH, with the opposite angles of the equations mutually lending their support to this proportion. But the increments of the secants of the optical equation are just about at a maximum around 45° but are small at the beginning and end of the quadrant. See the end of chapter 43 about this.

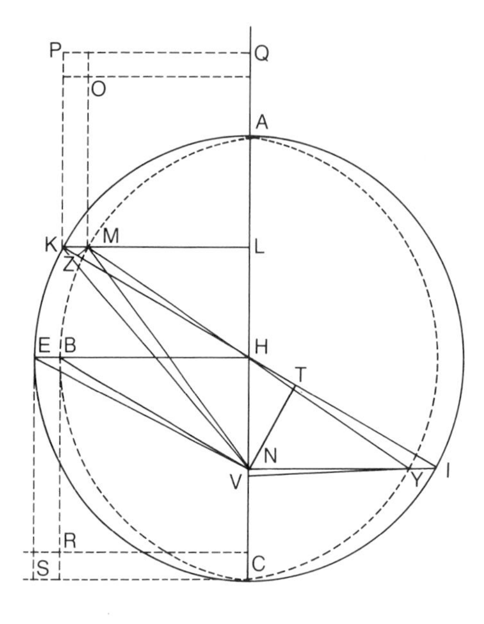

Likewise, the increases of the elliptical arcs marked off by the perpendiculars KL proceed also in the same ratio. For at the beginning of A or C the arc AK (always begun from A) is to its increment as LK is to KM. But the whole arc is small, so the increment is also small. At the end, near B, the ratio AE to AB is rendered almost equal so that although the arc AB is large since it is nearly a quadrant, its increment is again small. In the middle, therefore, around 45°, the increment of the arcs is most obvious.

It is therefore clear that even in the intermediate stages the ratios are equal, to the extent that one can inquire into such a subtle consideration.

The demonstration is about as certain as a non-technical or non-geometric one can be, insofar as it pertains to the part about the progression of the intermediate increases. I would hope, moreover, that this little part could also be treated geometrically and skillfully so that it would satisfy even an Apollonius. In the meantime, until someone finds this and works it out, we must be content with what we have.

XV.

But let us complete the demonstration.

The arc of the ellipse whose time intervals the area AKN measures ought to end at LK, so that it becomes AM.

Up to now we have been engaged in this fiction, that if someone had enough leisure so that he might be willing to compute the area of the ellipse, he would not go far wrong if he used the area of the ellipse AMN in place of as many distances of AM as there are equal arcs in AK. This is likely the most important proposition we have so far demonstrated.

Now I will add a lesser proposition from the third preliminary theorem of this chapter, in which it was shown that the area AKC is to the area AMC as the area AKN is to the area AMN. We conclude, therefore, since the ratio between equal multiples remains the same, that the area of the circle AKN also measures the sum of the diametral distances (say KT and TI) or as many elliptical distances of AM as there are parts in AK. Whence it is obvious that the more closely grouped distances are rightly attributed to the parts of the ellipse near A and C in the same number as the sections established on it by perpendiculars KL coming from equal arcs of AK.

Lest anyone doubt the truth of this matter, put off by the subtlety and complexity of the argument, it was originally discovered in the following practical way. I set up the diametral lines KT and TI for each degree of the eccentric anomaly instead of distances from N. Then I added the individual distances in order to find the running sum of the distances. They all added up to 36,000,000, as was right. Now by the rule of proportions, the sum 36,000,000 was to 360° (the nominal designation of the total periodic time) as the individual sums are to their designated time intervals; comparing the running sums with the total gave precisely the same thing, down to the last second, as if I had multiplied half the eccentricity by the sine of the eccentric anomaly and had compared it with the area of the circle, which is equivalent in the same way to 360° (the nominal designation of the periodic time).

Next, although I believed that the correct distance NM had to be applied to the line KH, so that it was ZN, and had thus found the corrected anomaly ZNA corresponding to the mean anomaly AKN, the equations obviously disagreed with my vicarious hypothesis of chapter 16. Near 45° there was a difference of $5\frac{1}{2}'$ between the corrected and the true values, the latter found from actual observations, and near 135° it was about 4′. But with AM arranged so that it ends at KL, then using the corrected anomaly MNA for the mean anomaly AKN finds perfect agreement with the vicarious hypothesis, that is, with the observations. When it was therefore well established, I was afterwards driven also to try to find as well from the principles (now laid down for the first time) the very cause of the matter, which I have revealed to the reader in this chapter as skillfully and clearly as possible. Because, unless the physical causes that I adopted from the outset in place of principles were valid, they could never have stood up through such a detailed examination.

If anyone thinks that the obscurity of this discussion springs out of the confusion of my mind, I will confess to him my guilt in this up to a point, because I did not want to leave untouched these matters, so very obscure as they are, nor are they really necessary for the practice of astrology, which many consider to be the sole end for this celestial philosophy. So far as the other matters are concerned, I ask anyone interested in them to read the *Conics* of Apollonius. He will see there certain matters that no ingenuity can treat so felicitously that they can be understood in a cursory reading. It is a work requiring thoughtfulness and continual pondering of the words.

Phaedra

Jean Racine

Editor's Introduction

In a book published some time ago called *The Idea of a Theatre,* Francis Fergusson, for many years head of the drama department at Bennington College, suggested that while the theatre is among the definitive art forms of our tradition, yet at only a few times and in a few places has it actually existed in such a way as to mirror the whole culture of which it was a part, to which it has therefore given a kind of unity such as Dante managed to give in the *Divine Comedy* to the Middle Ages. Among the examples cited by Mr. Fergusson, each of which had only a brief duration, one is perhaps less well known than the others outside the country in which it appeared, where productions of its plays are nevertheless still regularly given. It is the Baroque theatre of France in the seventeenth century, of which the preeminent playwrights in tragedy were first Corneille and then Racine, and of which the great comic genius was Molière.

Racine, who gave the tragic drama of his time in France its "classical" design, and who is perhaps the only Frenchman to have sounded the authentic tragic note in his plays—as the Greeks did in their time, and as Shakespeare did in his—was an unlikely figure to have achieved such importance. Especially was he so in the rigidly formal and pedigreed society of France in the age of Louis XIV, for which all of his works were written, and which had to approve of them if they were to survive. Of provincial birth, the playwright was a parvenu, indeed the first French writer born without position or money to rise to the rank of a courtier, even a nobleman, and to die possessed of both fortune and influence.

He was rigorously educated despite his circumstances at no less strict a place than the convent of Port-Royal, to which his grandmother repaired when she became a widow, where she and a sister and daughter all took vows. This caused difficulties. The Jansenist doctrine of Port-Royal, with its insistence on austere seclusion, was too severe for the Catholic Establishment of that day (which eventually caused the convent to be abandoned and pulled down), and among its stern proscriptions was the theatre, for his interest in which Racine, while still a young man and far from securely situated, was in effect turned out. Yet he remained devoted to the Jansenist teachings, and his religious commitment, which was always to some degree at odds with his dramatic formulations—his tragic sense of life, as one might say—never left him, indeed is sometimes thought to have brought his career to an abrupt and premature end.

Well schooled in Latin and Greek at Port-Royal, Racine also made the acquaintance of a number of literary figures and aristocratic pupils who taught and studied there. With these connections he was able to go on to college at Beauvais and eventually to study at Paris, where he developed an interest in literary pursuits which, despite the caution of his mentors, was to prove decisive. Sensing that drama offered the promise of worldly success, he commenced a career of authorship as a poet-playwright that included a widely read open letter defending theatrical productions against Jansenist condemnation in 1666. A friendship with Molière, begun in 1664, proved abortive—Racine did not like Molière's natural style of acting—and the two broke off a promising relationship from which, however, Racine acquired Molière's star actress, Du Parc, who became his mistress. For her he wrote his tragedy, *Andromaque* (1667), in which he dramatized a characteristic theme: the folly and blindness of passionate love. Among the tragedies that subsequently established him as the first playwright of his time, superseding the aging Corneille, were *Britannicus* (1670), *Bérénice* (1671), *Bejazet* (1672), and *Mithridate* (1673), all of which dealt with classical subjects, as the taste of that neoclassical age required.

Phaedra (1677), which is usually cited as the greatest of Racine's tragedies, was also his last, though why he at that point suddenly retired from the theatre (to which he returned briefly in 1689 with *Esther,* which was something like an opera) remains a mystery. Possibly the somber retelling of the *Hippolytus* of Euripides, which is what the play is, raised disturbing questions about his faith which he did not wish any longer to confront. More likely, at least in worldly terms, was the fact that he had been given an appointment as court historian which, dull though its duties were, promised him security and income for the rest of his life. He also married at that time a pious young woman wholly uninterested in the theatre and disapproving of the life that went with it.

In any case, although he continued to have an interest in letters and brought out editions of his plays, Racine was henceforth content to be a courtier, gentleman of the bedchamber (a gift bestowed by the king in 1690), and favorite of the king's mistress, Mme de Maintenon. His death came from an abscess of the liver, eight years after the last of his plays, *Athalie,* was written (but never performed). According to his wishes he was buried at Port-Royal, from which his remains were retrieved when in 1710 the convent was destroyed by papal edict.

Phaedra

CHARACTERS

Theseus, *son of Aegeus and King of Athens.*
Phaedra, *wife of Theseus and Daughter of Minos and Pasiphaë.*
Hippolytus, *son of Theseus and Antiope, Queen of the Amazons.*
Aricia, *Princess of the Blood Royal of Athens.*
Oenone, *nurse of Phaedra.*
Theramenes, *tutor of Hippolytus.*
Ismene, *bosom friend of Aricia.*
Panope, *waiting-woman of Phaedra.*
Guards

The scene is laid at Troezen, a town of the Peloponnesus.

ACT I

Scene I

HIPPOLYTUS, THERAMENES

Hippolytus

My mind is settled, dear Theramenes,
And I can stay no more in lovely Troezen.
In doubt that racks my soul with mortal anguish,
I grow ashamed of such long idleness.
Six months and more my father has been gone,
And what may have befallen one so dear
I know not, nor what corner of the earth
Hides him.

Theramenes

And where, prince, will you look for him?
Already, to content your just alarm,
Have I not cross'd the seas on either side
Of Corinth, ask'd if aught were known of Theseus
Where Acheron is lost among the Shades,
Visited Elis, doubled Toenarus,
And sail'd into the sea that saw the fall
Of Icarus? Inspired with what new hope,
Under what favour'd skies think you to trace
His footsteps? Who knows if the King, your father,
Wishes the secret of his absence known?
Perchance, while we are trembling for his life,
The hero calmly plots some fresh intrigue,
And only waits till the deluded fair—

Hippolytus

Cease, dear Theramenes, respect the name
Of Theseus. Youthful errors have been left
Behind, and no unworthy obstacle
Detains him. Phaedra long has fix'd a heart
Inconstant once, nor need she fear a rival.
In seeking him I shall but do my duty,
And leave a place I dare no longer see.

Theramenes

Indeed! When, prince, did you begin to dread
These peaceful haunts, so dear to happy childhood,
Where I have seen you oft prefer to stay,
Rather than meet the tumult and the pomp
Of Athens and the court? What danger shun you,
Or shall I say what grief?

Hippolytus

That happy time
Is gone, and all is changed, since to these shores
The gods sent Phaedra.

Theramenes

I perceive the cause
Of your distress. It is the queen whose sight
Offends you. With a step dame's spite she schemed
Your exile soon as she set eyes on you.
But if her hatred is not wholly vanish'd,
It has at least taken a milder aspect.
Besides, what danger can a dying woman,
One too who longs for death, bring on your head?
Can Phaedra, sick'ning of a dire disease
Of which she will not speak, weary of life
And of herself, form any plots against you?

Hippolytus

It is not her vain enmity I fear,
Another foe alarms Hippolytus.
I fly, it must be own'd, from young Aricia,
The sole survivor of an impious race.

Theramenes

What! You become her persecutor too!
The gentle sister of the cruel sons
Of Pallas shared not in their perfidy;
Why should you hate such charming innocence?

Hippolytus

I should not need to fly, if it were hatred.

Theramenes

May I, then, learn the meaning of your flight?
Is this the proud Hippolytus I see,
Than whom there breathed no fiercer foe to love
And to that yoke which Theseus has so oft
Endured? And can it be that Venus, scorn'd
So long, will justify your sire at last?
Has she, then, setting you with other mortals,
Forced e'en Hippolytus to offer incense
Before her? Can you love?

Hippolytus

Friend, ask me not.
You, who have known my heart from infancy
And all its feelings of disdainful pride,
Spare me the shame of disavowing all
That I profess'd. Born of an Amazon,
The wildness that you wonder at I suck'd
With mother's milk. When come to riper age,
Reason approved what Nature had implanted.
Sincerely bound to me by zealous service,
You told me then the story of my sire,
And know how oft, attentive to your voice,
I kindled when I heard his noble acts,
As you described him bringing consolation
To mortals for the absence of Alcides,
The highways clear'd of monsters and of robbers,
Procrustes, Cercyon, Sciro, Sinnis slain,
The Epidaurian giant's bones dispersed,
Crete reeking with the blood of Minotaur.
But when you told me of less glorious deeds,
Troth plighted here and there and everywhere,
Young Helen stolen from her home at Sparta,
And Periboea's tears in Salamis,
With many another trusting heart deceived
Whose very names have 'scaped his memory,
Forsaken Ariadne to the rocks
Complaining, last this Phaedra, bound to him
By better ties,—you know with what regret
I heard and urged you to cut short the tale,
Happy had I been able to erase
From my remembrance that unworthy part
Of such a splendid record. I, in turn,
Am I too made the slave of love, and brought
To stoop so low? The more contemptible
That no renown is mine such as exalts
The name of Theseus, that no monsters quell'd
Have given me a right to share his weakness.

And if my pride of heart must needs be humbled,
Aricia should have been the last to tame it.
Was I beside myself to have forgotten
Eternal barriers of separation
Between us? By my father's stern command
Her brethren's blood must ne'er be reinforced
By sons of hers; he dreads a single shoot
From stock so guilty, and would fain with her
Bury their name, that, even to the tomb
Content to be his ward, for her no torch
Of Hymen may be lit. Shall I espouse
Her rights against my sire, rashly provoke
His wrath, and launch upon a mad career—

Theramenes

The gods, dear prince, if once your hour is come,
Care little for the reasons that should guide us.
Wishing to shut your eyes, Theseus unseals them;
His hatred, stirring a rebellious flame
Within you, lends his enemy new charms.
And, after all, why should a guiltless passion
Alarm you? Dare you not essay its sweetness,
But follow rather a fastidious scruple?
Fear you to stray where Hercules has wander'd?
What heart so stout that Venus has not vanquish'd?
Where would you be yourself, so long her foe,
Had your own mother, constant in her scorn
Of love, ne'er glowed with tenderness for Theseus?
What boots it to affect a pride you feel not?
Confess it, all is changed; for some time past
You have been seldom seen with wild delight
Urging the rapid car along the strand,
Or, skilful in the art that Neptune taught,
Making th' unbroken steed obey the bit;
Less often have the woods return'd our shouts;
A secret burden on your spirits cast
Has dimm'd your eye. How can I doubt you love?
Vainly would you conceal the fatal wound.
Has not the fair Aricia touch'd your heart?

Hippolytus

Theramenes, I go to find my father.

Theramenes

Will you not see the queen before you start,
My prince?

Hippolytus

That is my purpose: you can tell her.

Yes, I will see her; duty bids me do it.
But what new ill vexes her dear Oenone?

Scene II

Hippolytus, Oenone, Theramenes

Oenone

Alas, my lord, what grief was e'er like mine?
The queen has almost touch'd the gates of death.
Vainly close watch I keep by day and night,
E'en in my arms a secret malady
Slays her, and all her senses are disorder'd.
Weary yet restless from her couch she rises,
Pants for the outer air, but bids me see
That no one on her misery intrudes.
She comes.

Hippolytus

Enough. She shall not be disturb'd,
Nor be confronted with a face she hates.

Scene III

Phaedra, Oenone

Phaedra

We have gone far enough. Stay, dear Oenone;
Strength fails me, and I needs must rest awhile.
My eyes are dazzled with this glaring light
So long unseen, my trembling knees refuse
Support. Ah me!

Oenone

Would Heaven that our tears
Might bring relief!

Phaedra

Ah, how these cumbrous gauds,
These veils oppress me! What officious hand
Has tied these knots, and gather'd o'er my brow
These clustering coils? How all conspires to add
To my distress!

Oenone

What is one moment wish'd,
The next, is irksome. Did you not just now,
Sick of inaction, bid us deck you out,
And, with your former energy recall'd,

Ariadne is abandoned by Theseus. Engraving, F. Ehrmann

Desire to go abroad, and see the light
Of day once more? You see it, and would fain
Be hidden from the sunshine that you sought.

Phaedra

Thou glorious author of a hapless race,
Whose daughter 'twas my mother's boast to be,
Who well may'st blush to see me in such plight,
For the last time I come to look on thee,
O Sun!

Oenone

What! Still are you in love with death?
Shall I ne'er see you, reconciled to life,
Forego these cruel accents of despair?

Phaedra

Would I were seated in the forest's shade!
When may I follow with delighted eye,
Thro' glorious dust flying in full career,
A chariot—

Oenone

Madam?

Phaedra

Have I lost my senses?
What said I? and where am I? Whither stray
Vain wishes? Ah! The gods have made me mad.

I blush, Oenone, and confusion covers
My face, for I have let you see too clearly
The shame of grief that, in my own despite,
O'erflows these eyes of mine.

Oenone

If you must blush,
Blush at a silence that inflames your woes.
Resisting all my care, deaf to my voice,
Will you have no compassion on yourself,
But let your life be ended in mid course?
What evil spell has drain'd its fountain dry?
Thrice have the shades of night obscured the heav'ns
Since sleep has enter'd thro' your eyes, and thrice
The dawn has chased the darkness thence, since food
Pass'd your wan lips, and you are faint and languid.
To what dread purpose is your heart inclined?
How dare you make attempts upon your life,
And so offend the gods who gave it you,
Prove false to Theseus and your marriage vows,
Ay, and betray your most unhappy children,
Bending their necks yourself beneath the yoke?
That day, be sure, which robs them of their mother,
Will give high hopes back to the stranger's son,
To that proud enemy of you and yours,
To whom an Amazon gave birth, I mean
Hippolytus—

Phaedra

Ye gods!

Oenone

Ah, this reproach
Moves you!

Phaedra

Unhappy woman, to what name
Gave your mouth utterance?

Oenone

Your wrath is just.
'Tis well that that ill-omen'd name can rouse
Such rage. Then live. Let love and duty urge
Their claims. Live, suffer not this son of Scythia,
Crushing your children 'neath his odious sway,
To rule the noble offspring of the gods,
The purest blood of Greece. Make no delay;
Each moment theatens death; quickly restore
Your shatter'd strength, while yet the torch of life

Holds out, and can be fann'd into a flame.

Phaedra

Too long have I endured its guilt and shame!

Oenone

Why? What remorse gnaws at your heart? What crime
Can have disturb'd you thus? Your hands are not
Polluted with the blood of innocence?

Phaedra

Thanks be to Heav'n, my hands are free from stain.
Would that my soul were innocent as they!

Oenone

What awful project have you then conceived,
Whereat your conscience should be still alarm'd?

Phaedra

Have I not said enough? Spare me the rest.
I die to save myself a full confession.

Oenone

Die then, and keep a silence so inhuman;
But seek some other hand to close your eyes.
Tho' but a spark of life remains within you,
My soul shall go before you to the Shades.
A thousand roads are always open thither;
Pain'd at your want of confidence, I'll choose
The shortest. Cruel one, when has my faith
Deceived you! Think how in my arms you lay
New born. For you, my country and my children
I have forsaken. Do you thus repay
My faithful service?

Phaedra

What do you expect
From words so bitter? Were I to break silence,
Horror would freeze your blood.

Oenone

What can you say
To horrify me more than to behold
You die before my eyes?

Phaedra

When you shall know
My crime, my death will follow none the less,
But with the added stain of guilt.

Oenone

Dear Madam,
By all the tears that I have shed for you,
By these weak knees I clasp, relieve my mind
From torturing doubt.

Phaedra

It is your wish. Then rise.

Oenone

I hear you. Speak.

Phaedra

Heav'ns! How shall I begin?

Oenone

Dismiss vain fears, you wound me with distrust.

Phaedra

O fatal animosity of Venus!
Into what wild distractions did she cast
My mother!

Oenone

Be they blotted from remembrance,
And for all time to come buried in silence.

Phaedra

My sister Ariadne, by what love
Were you betray'd to death, on lonely shores
Forsaken!

Oenone

Madam, what deep-seated pain
Prompts these reproaches against all your kin?

Phaedra

It is the will of Venus, and I perish,
Last, most unhappy of a family
Where all were wretched.

Oenone

Do you love?

Phaedra

I feel
All its mad fever.

Oenone

Ah! for whom?

Phaedra

Hear now
The crowning horror. Yes, I love—my lips
Tremble to say his name.

Oenone

Whom?

Phaedra

Know you him,
Son of the Amazon, whom I've oppress'd
So long?

Oenone

Hippolytus? Great gods!

Phaedra

'Tis you
Have named him.

Oenone

All my blood within my veins
Seems frozen. O despair! O cursèd race!
Ill-omen'd journey! Land of misery!
Why did we ever reach thy dangerous shores?

Phaedra

My wound is not so recent. Scarcely had I
Been bound to Theseus by the marriage yoke,
And happiness and peace seem'd well secured,
When Athens show'd me my proud enemy.
I look'd, alternately turn'd pale and blush'd
To see him, and my soul grew all distraught;
A mist obscured my vision, and my voice
Falter'd, my blood ran cold, then burn'd like fire;
Venus I felt in all my fever'd frame,
Whose fury had so many of my race
Pursued. With fervent vows I sought to shun
Her torments, built and deck'd for her a shrine,
And there, 'mid countless victims did I seek
The reason I had lost; but all for naught,
No remedy could cure the wounds of love!
In vain I offer'd incense on her altars;
When I invoked her name my heart adored
Hippolytus, before me constantly;
And when I made her altars smoke with victims,

'Twas for a god whose name I dared not utter.
I fled his presence everywhere, but found him—
O crowning horror!—in his father's features.
Against myself, at last, I raised revolt,
And stirr'd my courage up to persecute
The enemy I loved. To banish him
I wore a step-dame's harsh and jealous carriage,
With ceaseless cries I clamour'd for his exile,
Till I had torn him from his father's arms.
I breathed once more, Oenone; in his absence
My days flow'd on less troubled than before,
And innocent. Submissive to my husband,
I hid my grief, and of our fatal marriage
Cherish'd the fruits. Vain caution! Cruel Fate!
Brought hither by my spouse himself, I saw
Again the enemy whom I had banish'd,
And the old wound too quickly bled afresh.
No longer is it love hid in my heart,
But Venus in her might seizing her prey.
I have conceived just terror for my crime;
I hate my life, and hold my love in horror.
Dying I wish'd to keep my fame unsullied,
And bury in the grave a guilty passion;
But I have been unable to withstand
Tears and entreaties, I have told you all;
Content, if only, as my end draws near,
You do not vex me with unjust reproaches,
Nor with vain efforts seek to snatch from death
The last faint lingering sparks of vital breath.

Scene IV

Phaedra, Oenone, Panope

Panope

Fain would I hide from you tidings so sad,
But 'tis my duty, Madam, to reveal them.
The hand of death has seized your peerless husband,
And you are last to hear of this disaster.

Oenone

What say you, Panope?

Panope

The queen, deceived
By a vain trust in Heav'n, begs safe return
For Theseus, while Hippolytus his son
Learns of his death from vessels that are now
In port.

Phaedra

Ye gods!

Panope

Divided counsels sway
The choice of Athens; some would have the prince,
Your child, for master; other, disregarding
The laws, dare to support the stranger's son.
'Tis even said that a presumptuous faction
Would crown Aricia and the house of Pallas.
I deem'd it right to warn you of this danger.
Hippolytus already is prepared
To start, and should he show himself at Athens,
'Tis to be fear'd the fickle crowd will all
Follow his lead.

Oenone

Enough. The queen, who hears you,
By no means will neglect this timely warning.

Scene V

Phaedra, Oenone

Oenone

Dear lady, I had almost ceased to urge
The wish that you should live, thinking to follow
My mistress to the tomb, from which my voice
Had fail'd to turn you; but this new misfortune
Alters the aspect of affairs, and prompts
Fresh measures. Madam, Theseus is no more,
You must supply his place. He leaves a son,
A slave, if you should die, but, if you live,
A King. On whom has he to lean but you?
No hand but yours will dry his tears. Then live
For him, or else the tears of innocence
Will move the gods, his ancestors, to wrath
Against his mother. Live, your guilt is gone,
No blame attaches to your passion now.
The King's decease has freed you from the bonds
That made the crime and horror of your love.
Hippolytus no longer need be dreaded,
Him you may see henceforth without reproach.
It may be, that, convinced of your aversion,
He means to head the rebels. Undeceive him,
Soften his callous heart, and bend his pride.
King of this fertile land, in Troezen here
His portion lies; but as he knows, the laws

Give to your son the ramparts that Minerva
Built and protects. A common enemy
Threatens you both, unite them to oppose
Aricia.

Phaedra

To your counsel I consent.
Yes, I will live, if life can be restored,
If my affection for a son has pow'r
To rouse my sinking heart at such a dangerous hour.

ACT II

Scene I

Aricia, Ismene

Aricia

Hippolytus request to see me here!
Hippolytus desire to bid farewell!
Is't true, Ismene? Are you not deceived?

Ismene

This is the first result of Theseus' death.
Prepare yourself to see from every side
Hearts turn towards you that were kept away
By Theseus. Mistress of her lot at last,
Aricia soon shall find all Greece fall low,
To do her homage.

Aricia

'Tis not then, Ismene,
An idle tale? Am I no more a slave?
Have I no enemies?

Ismene

The gods oppose
Your peace no longer, and the soul of Theseus
Is with your brothers.

Aricia

Does the voice of fame
Tell how he died?

Ismene

Rumours incredible
Are spread. Some say that, seizing a new bride,
The faithless husband by the waves was swallow'd.

Others affirm, and this report prevails,
That with Pirithoüs to the world below
He went, and saw the shores of dark Cocytus,
Showing himself alive to the pale ghosts;
But that he could not leave those gloomy realms,
Which whoso enters there abides for ever.

Aricia

Shall I believe that ere his destined hour
A mortal may descend into the gulf
Of Hades? What attraction could o'ercome
Its terrors?

Ismene

He is dead, and you alone
Doubt it. The men of Athens mourn his loss.
Troezen already hails Hippolytus
As King. And Phaedra, fearing for her son,
Asks counsel of the friends who share his trouble,
Here in this palace.

Aricia

Will Hippolytus,
Think you, prove kinder than his sire, make light
My chains, and pity my misfortunes?

Ismene

Yes,
I think so, Madam.

Aricia

Ah, you know him not
Or you would never deem so hard a heart
Can pity feel, or me alone except
From the contempt in which he holds our sex.
Has he not long avoided every spot
Where we resort?

Ismene

I know what tales are told
Of proud Hippolytus, but I have seen
Him near you, and have watch'd with curious eye
How one esteem'd so cold would bear himself.
Little did his behaviour correspond
With what I look'd for; in his face confusion
Appear'd at your first glance, he could not turn
His languid eyes away, but gazed on you.
Love is a word that may offend his pride,
But what the tongue disowns, looks can betray.

Aricia

How eagerly my heart hears what you say,
Tho' it may be delusion, dear Ismene!
Did it seem possible to you, who know me,
That I, sad sport of a relentless Fate,
Fed upon bitter tears by night and day,
Could ever taste the maddening draught of love?
The last frail offspring of a royal race,
Children of Earth, I only have survived
War's fury. Cut off in the flow'r of youth,
Mown by the sword, six brothers have I lost,
The hope of an illustrious house, whose blood
Earth drank with sorrow, near akin to his
Whom she herself produced. Since then, you know
How thro' all Greece no heart has been allow'd
To sigh for me, lest by a sister's flame
The brothers' ashes be perchance rekindled.
You know, besides, with what disdain I view'd
My conqueror's suspicions and precautions,
And how, oppos'd as I have ever been
To love, I often thank'd the King's injustice
Which happily confirm'd my inclination.
But then I never had beheld his son.
Not that, attracted merely by the eye,
I love him for his beauty and his grace,
Endowments which he owes to Nature's bounty,
Charms which he seems to know not or to scorn.
I love and prize in him riches more rare,
The virtues of his sire, without his faults.
I love, as I must own, that generous pride
Which ne'er has stoop'd beneath the amorous yoke.
Phaedra reaps little glory from a lover
So lavish of his sighs; I am too proud
To share devotion with a thousand others,
Or enter where the door is always open.
But to make one who ne'er has stoop'd before
Bend his proud neck, to pierce a heart of stone,
To bind a captive whom his chains astonish,
Who vainly 'gainst a pleasing yoke rebels,—
That piques my ardour, and I long for that.
'Twas easier to disarm the god of strength
Than this Hippolytus, for Hercules
Yielded so often to the eyes of beauty,
As to make triumph cheap. But, dear Ismene,
I take too little heed of opposition
Beyond my pow'r to quell, and you may hear me,
Humbled by sore defeat, upbraid the pride
I now admire. What! Can he love? and I
Have had the happiness to bend—

Ismene

He comes.

Yourself shall hear him.

SCENE II

HIPPOLYTUS, ARICIA, ISMENE

Hippolytus

Lady, ere I go
My duty bids me tell you of your change
Of fortune. My worst fears are realized;
My sire is dead. Yes, his protracted absence
Was caused as I foreboded. Death alone,
Ending his toils, could keep him from the world
Conceal'd so long. The gods at last have doom'd
Alcides' friend, companion, and successor.
I think your hatred, tender to his virtues,
Can hear such terms of praise without resentment,
Knowing them due. One hope have I that soothes
My sorrow: I can free you from restraint.
Lo, I revoke the laws whose rigour moved
My pity; you are at your own disposal,
Both heart and hand; here, in my heritage,
In Troezen, where my grandsire Pittheus reign'd
Of yore and I am now acknowledged King,
I leave you free, free as myself,—and more.

Aricia

Your kindness is too great, 'tis overwhelming.
Such generosity, that pays disgrace
With honour, lends more force than you can think
To those harsh laws from which you would release me.

Hippolytus

Athens, uncertain how to fill the throne
Of Theseus, speaks of you, anon of me,
And then of Phaedra's son.

Aricia

Of me, my lord?

Hippolytus

I know myself excluded by strict law:
Greece turns to my reproach a foreign mother.
But if my brother were my only rival,
My rights prevail o'er his clearly enough
To make me careless of the law's caprice.
My forwardness is check'd by juster claims:

To you I yield my place, or, rather, own
That it is yours by right, and yours the sceptre,
As handed down from Earth's great son, Erechtheus.
Adoption placed it in the hands of Aegeus:
Athens, by him protected and increased,
Welcomed a king so generous as my sire,
And left your hapless brothers in oblivion.
Now she invites you back within her walls:
Protracted strife has cost her groans enough,
Her fields are glutted with your kinsmen's blood
Fatt'ning the furrows out of which it sprung
At first. I rule this Troezen; while the son
Of Phaedra has in Crete a rich domain.
Athens is yours. I will do all I can
To join for you the votes divided now
Between us.

Aricia

Stunn'd at all I hear, my lord,
I fear, I almost fear a dream deceives me.
Am I indeed awake? Can I believe
Such generosity? What god has put it
Into your heart? Well is the fame deserved
That you enjoy! That fame falls short of truth!
Would you for me prove traitor to yourself?
Was it not boon enough never to hate me,
So long to have abstain'd from harbouring
The enmity—

Hippolytus

To hate you? I, to hate you?
However darkly my fierce pride was painted,
Do you suppose a monster gave me birth?
What savage temper, what envenom'd hatred
Would not be mollified at sight of you?
Could I resist the soul-bewitching charm—

Aricia

Why, what is this, Sir?

Hippolytus

I have said too much
Not to say more. Prudence in vain resists
The violence of passion. I have broken
Silence at last, and I must tell you now
The secret that my heart can hold no longer.
You see before you an unhappy instance
Of hasty pride, a prince who claims compassion
I, who, so long the enemy of Love,

Mock'd at his fetters and despised his captives,
Who, pitying poor mortals that were shipwreck'd,
In seeming safety view'd the storms from land,
Now find myself to the same fate exposed,
Toss'd to and fro upon a sea of troubles!
My boldness has been vanquish'd in a moment,
And humbled is the pride wherein I boasted.
For nearly six months past, ashamed, despairing,
Bearing where'er I go the shaft that rends
My heart, I struggle vainly to be free
From you and from myself; I shun you, present;
Absent, I find you near; I see your form
In the dark forest depths; the shades of night,
Nor less broad daylight, bring back to my view
The charms that I avoid; all things conspire
To make Hippolytus your slave. For fruit
Of all my bootless sighs, I fail to find
My former self. My bow and javelins
Please me no more, my chariot is forgotten,
With all the Sea God's lessons; and the woods
Echo my groans instead of joyous shouts
Urging my fiery steeds.
Hearing this tale
Of passion so uncouth, you blush perchance
At your own handiwork. With what wild words
I offer you my heart, strange captive held
By silken jess! But dearer in your eyes
Should be the offering, that this language comes
Strange to my lips; reject not vows express'd
So ill, which but for you had ne'er been form'd.

Scene III

Hippolytus, Aricia, Theramenes, Ismene

Theramenes

Prince, the Queen comes. I herald her approach.
'Tis you she seeks.

Hippolytus

Me?

Theramenes

What her thought may be
I know not. But I speak on her behalf.
She would converse with you ere you go hence.

Hippolytus

What shall I say to her? Can she expect—

Aricia

You cannot, noble Prince, refuse to hear her,
Howe'er convinced she is your enemy,
Some shade of pity to her tears is due.

Hippolytus

Shall we part thus? and will you let me go,
Not knowing if my boldness has offended
The goddess I adore? Whether this heart,
Left in your hands—

Aricia

Go, Prince, pursue the schemes
Your generous soul dictates, make Athens own
My sceptre. All the gifts you offer me
Will I accept, but this high throne of empire
Is not the one most precious in my sight.

SCENE IV

HIPPOLYTUS, THERAMENES

Hippolytus

Friend, is all ready?
But the Queen approaches.
Go, see the vessel in fit trim to sail.
Haste, bid the crew aboard, and hoist the signal:
Then soon return, and so deliver me
From interview most irksome.

SCENE V

PHAEDRA, HIPPOLYTUS, OENONE

Phaedra (to Oenone)

There I see him!
My blood forgets to flow, my tongue to speak
What I am come to say.

Oenone

Think of your son,
How all his hopes depend on you.

Phaedra

I hear
You leave us, and in haste. I come to add
My tears to your distress, and for a son
Plead my alarm. No more has he a father,
And at no distant day my son must witness

My death. Already do a thousand foes
Threaten his youth. You only can defend him
But in my secret heart remorse awakes,
And fear lest I have shut your ears against
His cries. I tremble lest your righteous anger
Visit on him ere long the hatred earn'd
By me, his mother.

Hippolytus

No such base resentment,
Madam, is mine.

Phaedra

I could not blame you, Prince,
If you should hate me. I have injured you:
So much you know, but could not read my heart.
T' incur your enmity has been mine aim.
The self-same borders could not hold us both;
In public and in private I declared
Myself your foe, and found no peace till seas
Parted us from each other. I forbade
Your very name to be pronounced before me.
And yet if punishment should be proportion'd
To the offence, if only hatred draws
Your hatred, never woman merited
More pity, less deserved your enmity.

Hippolytus

A mother jealous of her children's rights
Seldom forgives the offspring of a wife
Who reign'd before her. Harassing suspicions
Are common sequels of a second marriage.
Of me would any other have been jealous
No less than you, perhaps more violent.

Phaedra

Ah, Prince, how Heav'n has from the general law
Made me exempt, be that same Heav'n my witness!
Far different is the trouble that devours me!

Hippolytus

This is no time for self-reproaches, Madam.
It may be that your husband still beholds
The light, and Heav'n may grant him safe return,
In answer to our prayers. His guardian god
Is Neptune, ne'er by him invoked in vain.

Phaedra

He who has seen the mansions of the dead
Returns not thence. Since to those gloomy shores

Theseus is gone, 'tis vain to hope that Heav'n
May send him back. Prince, there is no release
From Acheron's greedy maw. And yet, methinks,
He lives, and breathes in you. I see him still
Before me, and to him I seem to speak;
My heart—
Oh! I am mad; do what I will,
I cannot hide my passion.

Hippolytus

Yes, I see
The strange effects of love. Theseus, tho' dead,
Seems present to your eyes, for in your soul
There burns a constant flame.

Phaedra

Ah, yes, for Theseus
I languish and I long, not as the Shades
Have seen him, of a thousand different forms
The fickle lover, and of Pluto's bride
The would-be ravisher, but faithful, proud
E'en to a slight disdain, with youthful charms
Attracting every heart, as gods are painted,
Or like yourself. He had your mien, your eyes,
Spoke and could blush like you, when to the isle
Of Crete, my childhood's home, he cross'd the waves,
Worthy to win the love of Minos' daughters.
What were you doing then? Why did he gather
The flow'r of Greece, and leave Hippolytus?
Oh, why were you too young to have embark'd
On board the ship that brought thy sire to Crete?
At your hands would the monster then have perish'd,
Despite the windings of his vast retreat.
To guide your doubtful steps within the maze
My sister would have arm'd you with the clue.
But no, therein would Phaedra have forestall'd her,
Love would have first inspired me with the thought;
And I it would have been whose timely aid
Had taught you all the labyrinth's crooked ways.
What anxious care a life so dear had cost me!
No threat had satisfied your lover's fears:
I would myself have wish'd to lead the way,
And share the peril you were bound to face;
Phaedra with you would have explored the maze,
With you emerged in safety, or have perish'd.

Hippolytus

Gods! What is this I hear? Have you forgotten
That Theseus is my father and your husband?

Phaedra

Why should you fancy I have lost remembrance
Thereof, and am regardless of mine honour?

Hippolytus

Forgive me, Madam. With a blush I own
That I misconstrued words of innocence.
For very shame I cannot bear your sight
Longer. I go—

Phaedra

Ah! cruel Prince, too well
You understood me, I have said enough
To save you from mistake. I love. But think not
That at the moment when I love you most
I do not feel my guilt; no weak compliance
Has fed the poison that infects my brain.
The ill-starr'd object of celestial vengeance,
I am not so detestable to you
As to myself. The gods will bear me witness,
Who have within my veins kindled this fire,
The gods, who take a barbarous delight
In leading a poor mortal's heart astray.
Do you yourself recall to mind the past:
'Twas not enough for me to fly, I chased you
Out of the country, wishing to appear
Inhuman, odious; to resist you better,
I sought to make you hate me. All in vain!
Hating me more I loved you none the less:
New charms were lent to you by your misfortunes.
I have been drown'd in tears, and scorch'd by fire;
Your own eyes might convince you of the truth,
If for one moment you could look at me.
What is't I say? Think you this vile confession
That I have made is what I meant to utter?
Not daring to betray a son for whom
I trembled, 'twas to beg you not to hate him
I came. Weak purpose of a heart too full
Of love for you to speak of aught besides!
Take your revenge, punish my odious passion;
Prove yourself worthy of your valiant sire,
And rid the world of an offensive monster!
Does Theseus' widow dare to love his son?
The frightful monster! Let her not escape you!
Here is my heart. This is the place to strike.
Already prompt to expiate its guilt,
I feel it leap impatiently to meet
Your arm. Strike home. Or, if it would disgrace you

To steep your hand in such polluted blood,
If that were punishment too mild to slake
Your hatred, lend me then your sword, if not
Your arm. Quick, give't.

Oenone

What, Madam, will you do?
Just gods! But someone comes. Go, fly from shame,
You cannot 'scape if seen by any thus.

SCENE VI

HIPPOLYTUS, THERAMENES

Theramenes

Is that the form of Phaedra that I see
Hurried away? What mean these signs of sorrow?
Where is your sword? Why are you pale, confused?

Hippolytus

Friend, let us fly. I am, indeed, confounded
With horror and astonishment extreme.
Phaedra—but no; gods; let this dreadful secret
Remain for ever buried in oblivion.

Theramenes

The ship is ready if you wish to sail.
But Athens has already giv'n her vote;
Their leaders have consulted all her tribes;
Your brother is elected, Phaedra wins.

Hippolytus

Phaedra?

Theramenes

A herald, charged with a commission
From Athens, has arrived to place the reins
Of power in her hands. Her son is King.

Hippolytus

Ye gods, who know her, do ye thus reward
Her virtue?

Theramenes

A faint rumour meanwhile whispers
That Theseus is not dead, but in Epirus
Has shown himself. But, after all my search,
I know too well—

Hippolytus

Let nothing be neglected.
This rumour must be traced back to its source.
If it be found unworthy of belief,
Let us set sail, and cost whate'er it may,
To hands deserving trust the sceptre's sway.

ACT III

Scene I

Phaedra, Oenone

Phaedra

Ah! Let them take elsewhere the worthless honours
They bring me. Why so urgent I should see them?
What flattering balm can soothe my wounded heart?
Far rather hide me: I have said too much.
My madness has burst forth like streams in flood,
And I have utter'd what should ne'er have reach'd
His ear. Gods! How he heard me! How reluctant
To catch my meaning, dull and cold as marble,
And eager only for a quick retreat!
How oft his blushes made my shame the deeper!
Why did you turn me from the death I sought?
Ah! When his sword was pointed to my bosom,
Did he grow pale, or try to snatch it from me?
That I had touch'd it was enough for him
To render it for ever horrible,
Leaving defilement on the hand that holds it.

Oenone

Thus brooding on your bitter disappointment,
You only fan a fire that must be stifled.
Would it not be more worthy of the blood
Of Minos to find peace in nobler cares,
And, in defiance of a wretch who flies
From what he hates, reign, mount the proffer'd throne?

Phaedra

I reign! Shall I the rod of empire sway,
When reason reigns no longer o'er myself?
When I have lost control of all my senses?
When 'neath a shameful yoke I scarce can breathe?
When I am dying?

Oenone

Fly.

Phaedra

I cannot leave him.

Oenone

Dare you not fly from him you dared to banish?

Phaedra

The time for that is past. He knows my frenzy.
I have o'erstepp'd the bounds of modesty,
And blazon'd forth my shame before his eyes.
Hope stole into my heart against my will.
Did you not rally my declining pow'rs?
Was it not you yourself recall'd my soul
When fluttering on my lips, and with your counsel,
Lent me fresh life, and told me I might love him?

Oenone

Blame me or blame me not for your misfortunes,
Of what was I incapable, to save you?
But if your indignation e'er was roused
By insult, can you pardon his contempt?
How cruelly his eyes, severely fix'd,
Survey'd you almost prostrate at his feet!
How hateful then appear'd his savage pride!
Why did not Phaedra see him then as I
Beheld him?

Phaedra

This proud mood that you resent
May yield to time. The rudeness of the forests
Where he was bred, insured to rigorous laws,
Clings to him still; love is a word he ne'er
Had heard before. It may be his surprise
Stunn'd him, and too much vehemence was shown
In all I said.

Oenone

Remember that his mother
Was a barbarian.

Phaedra

Scythian tho' she was,
She learned to love.

Oenone

He has for all the sex
Hatred intense.

Phaedra

Then in his heart no rival

Shall ever reign. Your counsel comes too late
Oenone, serve my madness, not my reason.
His heart is inaccessible to love.
Let us attack him where he has more feeling.
The charms of sovereignty appear'd to touch him;
He could not hide that he was drawn to Athens;
His vessels' prows were thither turn'd already,
All sail was set to scud before the breeze.
Go you on my behalf, to his ambition
Appeal, and let the prospect of the crown
Dazzle his eyes. The sacred diadem
Shall deck his brow, no higher honour mine
Than there to bind it. His shall be the pow'r
I cannot keep; and he shall teach my son
How to rule men. It may be he will deign
To be to him a father. Son and mother
He shall control. Try ev'ry means to move him;
Your words will find more favour than can mine.
Urge him with groans and tears; show Phaedra dying.
Nor blush to use the voice of supplication.
In you is my last hope; I'll sanction all
You say; and on the issue hangs my fate.

Scene II

Phaedra (alone)

Venus implacable, who seest me shamed
And sore confounded, have I not enough
Been humbled? How can cruelty be stretch'd
Farther? Thy shafts have all gone home, and thou
Hast triumph'd. Would'st thou win a new renown?
Attack an enemy more contumacious:
Hippolytus neglects thee, braves thy wrath,
Nor ever at thine altars bow'd the knee.
Thy name offends his proud, disdainful ears.
Our interests are alike: avenge thyself,
Force him to love—
But what is this? Oenone
Return'd already? He detests me then,
And will not hear you.

Scene III

Phaedra, Oenone

Oenone

Madam, you must stifle
A fruitless love. Recall your former virtue:

The king who was thought dead will soon appear
Before your eyes, Theseus has just arrived,
Theseus is here. The people flock to see him
With eager haste. I went by your command
To find the prince, when with a thousand shouts
The air was rent—

Phaedra

My husband is alive,
That is enough, Oenone. I have own'd
A passion that dishonours him. He lives:
I ask to know no more.

Oenone

What?

Phaedra

I foretold it,
But you refuse to hear. Your tears prevail'd
Over my just remorse. Dying this morn,
I had deserved compassion; your advice
I took, and die dishonour'd.

Oenone

Die?

Phaedra

Just Heav'ns!
What have I done to-day? My husband comes,
With him his son: and I shall see the witness
Of my adulterous flame watch with what face
I greet his father, while my heart is big
With sighs he scorn'd, and tears that could not move him
Moisten mine eyes. Think you that his respect
For Theseus will induce him to conceal
My madness, nor disgrace his sire and king?
Will he be able to keep back the horror
He has for me? His silence would be vain.
I know my treason, and I lack the boldness
Of those abandon'd women who can taste
Tranquillity in crime, and show a forehead
All unabash'd. I recognize my madness,
Recall it all. These vaulted roofs, methinks,
These walls can speak, and, ready to accuse me,
Wait but my husband's presence to reveal
My perfidy. Death only can remove
This weight of horror. Is it such misfortune
To cease to live? Death causes no alarm
To misery. I only fear the name

That I shall leave behind me. For my sons
How sad a heritage! The blood of Jove
Mighty justly swell the pride that boasts descent
From Heav'n, but heavy weighs a mother's guilt
Upon her offspring. Yes, I dread the scorn
That will be cast on them, with too much truth,
For my disgrace. I tremble when I think
That, crush'd beneath that curse, they'll never dare
To raise their eyes.

Oenone

Doubt not I pity both;
Never was fear more just than yours. Why, then,
Expose them to this ignominy? Why
Will you accuse yourself? You thus destroy
The only hope that's left; it will be said
That Phaedra, conscious of her perfidy,
Fled from her husband's sight. Hippolytus
Will be rejoiced that, dying, you should lend
His charge support. What can I answer him?
He'll find it easy to confute my tale,
And I shall hear him with an air of triumph
To every open ear repeat your shame.
Sooner than that may fire from heav'n consume me!
Deceive me not. Say, do you love him still?
How look you now on this contemptuous prince?

Phaedra

As on a monster frightful to mine eyes.

Oenone

Why yield him, then, an easy victory?
You fear him? Venture to accuse him first,
As guilty of the charge which he may bring
This day against you. Who can say 'tis false?
All tells against him: in your hands his sword
Happily left behind, your present trouble,
Your past distress, your warnings to his father,
His exile which your earnest pray'rs obtain'd.

Phaedra

What! Would you have me slander innocence?

Oenone

My zeal has need of naught from you but silence.
Like you I tremble, and am loath to do it;
More willingly I'd face a thousand deaths,
But since without this bitter remedy
I lose you, and to me your life outweighs

All else, I'll speak. Theseus, howe'er enraged
Will do no worse than banish him again.
A father, when he punishes, remains
A father, and his ire is satisfied
With a light sentence. But if guiltless blood
Should flow, is not your honour of more moment?
A treasure far too precious to be risk'd?
You must submit, whatever it dictates;
For, when our reputation is at stake,
All must be sacrificed, conscience itself.
But someone comes. 'Tis Theseus.

Phaedra

And I see
Hippolytus, my ruin plainly written
In his stern eyes. Do what you will; I trust
My fate to you. I cannot help myself.

SCENE IV

THESEUS, HIPPOLYTUS, PHAEDRA, OENONE, THERAMENES

Theseus

Fortune no longer fights against my wishes,
Madam, and to your arms restores—

Phaedra

Stay, Theseus!
Do not profane endearments that were once
So sweet, but which I am unworthy now
To taste. You have been wrong'd. Fortune has proved
Spiteful, nor in your absence spared your wife.
I am unfit to meet your fond caress,
How I may bear my shame my only care
Henceforth.

SCENE V

THESEUS, HIPPOLYTUS, THERAMENES

Theseus

Strange welcome for your father, this!
What does it mean, my son?

Hippolytus

Phaedra alone
Can solve this mystery. But if my wish
Can move you, let me never see her more;

Suffer Hippolytus to disappear
For ever from the home that holds your wife.

Theseus

You, my son! Leave me?

Hippolytus

'Twas not I who sought her:
'Twas you who led her footsteps to these shores.
At your departure you thought meet, my lord,
To trust Aricia and the Queen to this
Troezenian land, and I myself was charged
With their protection. But what cares henceforth
Need keep me here? My youth of idleness
Has shown its skill enough o'er paltry foes
That range the woods. May I not quit a life
Of such inglorious ease, and dip my spear
In nobler blood? Ere you had reach'd my age
More than one tyrant, monster more than one
Had felt the weight of your stout arm. Already,
Successful in attacking insolence,
You had removed all dangers that infested
Our coasts to east and west. The traveller fear'd
Outrage no longer. Hearing of your deeds,
Already Hercules relied on you,
And rested from his toils. While I, unknown
Son of so brave a sire, am far behind
Even my mother's footsteps. Let my courage
Have scope to act, and if some monster yet
Has 'scaped you, let me lay the glorious spoils
Down at your feet; or let the memory
Of death faced nobly keep my name alive,
And prove to all the world I was your son.

Theseus

Why, what is this? What terror has possess'd
My family to make them fly before me?
If I return to find myself so fear'd,
So little welcome, why did Heav'n release me
From prison? My sole friend, misled by passion,
Was bent on robbing of his wife the tyrant
Who ruled Epirus. With regret I lent
The lover aid, but Fate had made us blind,
Myself as well as him. The tyrant seized me
Defenceless and unarm'd. Pirithoüs
I saw with tears cast forth to be devour'd
By savage beasts that lapp'd the blood of men.
Myself in gloomy caverns he inclosed,
Deep in the bowels of the earth, and nigh

To Pluto's realms. Six months I lay ere Heav'n
Had pity, and I 'scaped the watchful eyes
That guarded me. Then did I purge the world
Of a foul foe, and he himself has fed
His monsters. But when with expectant joy
To all that is most precious I draw near
Of what the gods have left me, when my soul
Looks for full satisfaction in a sight
So dear, my only welcome is a shudder,
Embrace rejected, and a hasty flight.
Inspiring, as I clearly do, such terror,
Would I were still a prisoner in Epirus!
Phaedra complains what I have suffer'd outrage.
Who has betray'd me? Speak. Why was I not
Avenged? Has Greece, to whom mine arm so oft
Brought useful aid, shelter'd the criminal?
You make no answer. Is my son, mine own
Dear son, confederate with mine enemies?
I'll enter. This suspense is overwhelming.
I'll learn at once the culprit and the crime,
And Phaedra must explain her troubled state.

Scene VI

Hippolytus, Theramenes

Hippolytus

What do these words portend, which seem'd to freeze
My very blood? Will Phaedra, in her frenzy
Accuse herself, and seal her own destruction?
What will the King say? Gods! What fatal poison
Has love spread over all his house! Myself,
Full of a fire his hatred disapproves,
How changed he finds me from the son he knew!
With dark forebodings in my mind alarm'd,
But innocence has surely naught to fear.
Come, let us to, and in some other place
Consider how I best may move my sire
To tenderness, and tell him of a flame
Vex'd but not vanquish'd by a father's blame.

ACT IV

Scene I

Theseus, Oenone

Theseus

Ah! What is this I hear? Presumptuous traitor!
And would he have disgraced his father's honour?
With what relentless footsteps Fate pursues me!
Whither I go I know not, nor where know
I am. O kind affection ill repaid!
Audacious scheme! Abominable thought!
To reach the object of his foul desire
The wretch disdain'd not to use violence.
I know this sword that served him in his fury.
The sword I gave him for a nobler use.
Could not the sacred ties of blood restrain him?
And Phaedra,—was she loath to have him punish'd?
She held her tongue. Was that to spare the culprit?

Oenone

Nay, but to spare a most unhappy father.
O'erwhelm'd with shame that her eyes should have kindled
So infamous a flame and prompted him
To crime so heinous, Phaedra would have died.
I saw her raise her arm, and ran to save her.
To me alone you owe it that she lives;
And, in my pity both for her and you,
Have I against my will interpreted
Her tears.

Theseus

The traitor! He might well turn pale.
'Twas fear that made him tremble when he saw me.
I was astonish'd that he show'd no pleasure;
His frigid greeting chill'd my tenderness.
But was this guilty passion that devours him
Declared already ere I banish'd him
From Athens?

Oenone

Sire, remember how the Queen
Urged you. Illicit love caused all her hatred.

Theseus

And then this fire broke out again at Troezen?

Oenone

Sire, I have told you all. Too long the Queen

Has been allow'd to bear her grief alone.
Let me now leave you and attend to her.

Scene II

Theseus, Hippolytus

Theseus

Ah! There he is. Great gods! That noble mien
Might well deceive an eye less fond than mine!
Why should the sacred stamp of virtue gleam
Upon the forehead of an impious wretch?
Ought not the blackness of a traitor's heart
To show itself by sure and certain signs?

Hippolytus

My father, may I ask what fatal cloud
Has troubled your majestic countenance?
Dare you not trust this secret to your son?

Theseus

Traitor, how dare you show yourself before me?
Monster, whom Heaven's bolts have spared too long!
Survivor of that robber crew whereof
I cleansed the earth. After your brutal lust
Scorn'd even to respect my marriage bed,
You venture—you, my hated foe—to come
Into my presence, here, where all is full
Of your foul infamy, instead of seeking
Some unknown land that never heard my name.
Fly, traitor, fly! Stay not to tempt the wrath
That I can scarce restrain, nor brave my hatred.
Disgrace enough have I incurr'd for ever
In being father of so vile a son,
Without your death staining indelibly
The glorious record of my noble deeds.
Fly, and unless you wish quick punishment
To add you to the criminals cut off
By me, take heed this sun that lights us now
Ne'er see you more set foot upon this soil.
I tell you once again,—fly, haste, return not,
Rid all my realms of your atrocious presence.
  To thee, to thee, great Neptune, I appeal;
If erst I clear'd thy shores of foul assassins,
Recall thy promise to reward those efforts,
Crown'd with success, by granting my first pray'r.
Confined for long in close captivity,

Hippolytus, after being accused by Phaedra, defends himself before Theseus. Painting, P. Guerin.

I have not yet call'd on thy pow'rful aid,
Sparing to use the valued privilege
Till at mine utmost need. The time is come,
I ask thee now. Avenge a wretched father!
I leave this traitor to thy wrath; in blood
Quench his outrageous fires, and by thy fury
Theseus will estimate thy favour tow'rds him.

Hippolytus

Phaedra accuses me of lawless passion!
This crowning horror all my soul confounds;
Such unexpected blows, falling at once,
O'erwhelm me, choke my utterance, strike me dumb.

Theseus

Traitor, you reckon'd that in timid silence
Phaedra would bury your brutality.
You should not have abandon'd in your flight
The sword that in her hands helps to condemn you;
Or rather, to complete your perfidy,
You should have robb'd her both of speech and life.

Hippolytus

Justly indignant at a lie so black
I might be pardon'd if I told the truth;
But it concerns your honour to conceal it.
Approve the reverence that shuts my mouth;
And, without wishing to increase your woes,
Examine closely what my life has been.
Great crimes are never single, they are link'd
To former faults. He who has once transgress'd
May violate at last all that men hold
Most sacred; vice, like virtue, has degrees
Of progress; innocence was never seen
To sink at once into the lowest depths
Of guilt. No virtuous man can in a day
Turn traitor, murderer, an incestuous wretch.
The nursling of a chaste, heroic mother,
I have not proved unworthy of my birth.
Pittheus, whose wisdom is by all esteem'd,
Deign'd to instruct me when I left her hands.
It is no wish of mine to vaunt my merits,
But, if I may lay claim to any virtue,
I think beyond all else I have display'd
Abhorrence of those sins with which I'm charged.
For this Hippolytus is known in Greece,
So continent that he is deem'd austere.
All know my abstinence inflexible:
The daylight is not purer than my heart.
How, then, could I, burning with fire profane—

Theseus

Yes, dastard, 'tis that very pride condemns you.
I see the odious reason of your coldness:
Phaedra alone bewitch'd your shameless eyes;
Your soul, to other's charms indifferent,
Disdain'd the blameless fires of lawful love.

Hippolytus

No, father, I have hidden it too long,
This heart has not disdain'd a sacred flame.
Here at your feet I own my real offence:
I love, and love in truth where you forbid me;
Bound to Aricia by my heart's devotion,
The child of Pallas has subdued your son.
A rebel to your laws, her I adore,
And breathe forth ardent sighs for her alone.

Theseus

You love her? Heav'ns!

But no, I see the trick.

You feign a crime to justify yourself.

Hippolytus

Sir, I have shunn'd her for six months, and still
Love her. To you yourself I came to tell it,
Trembling the while. Can nothing clear your mind
Of your mistake? What oath can reassure you?
By heav'n and earth and all the pow'rs of nature—

Theseus

The wicked never shrink from perjury.
Cease, cease, and spare me irksome protestations,
If your false virtue has no other aid.

Hippolytus

Tho' it to you seem false and insincere,
Phaedra has secret cause to know it true.

Theseus

Ah! how your shamelessness excites my wrath!

Hippolytus

What is my term and place of banishment?

Theseus

Were you beyond the Pillars of Alcides,
Your perjured presence were too near me yet.

Hippolytus

What friends will pity me, when you forsake
And think me guilty of a crime so vile?

Theseus

Go, look you out for friends who hold in honour
Adultery and clap their hands at incest,
Low, lawless traitors, steep'd in infamy,
The fit protectors of a knave like you.

Hippolytus

Are incest and adultery the words
You cast at me? I hold my tongue. Yet think
What mother Phaedra had; too well you know
Her blood, not mine, is tainted with those horrors.

Theseus

What! Does your rage before my eyes lose all
Restraint? For the last time,—out of my sight!
Hence, traitor! Wait not till a father's wrath
Force thee away 'mid general execration.

Scene III

Theseus (alone)

Wretch! Thou must meet inevitable ruin.
Neptune has sworn by Styx—to gods themselves
A dreadful oath,—and he will execute
His promise. Thou canst not escape his vengeance.
I loved thee; and, in spite of thine offence,
My heart is troubled by anticipation
For thee. But thou hast earn'd thy doom too well.
Had father ever greater cause for rage?
Just gods, who see the grief that overwhelms me,
Why was I cursed with such a wicked son?

Scene IV

Phaedra, Theseus

Phaedra

My lord, I come to you, fill'd with just dread.
Your voice raised high in anger reach'd mine ears,
And much I fear that deeds have follow'd threats.
Oh, if there yet is time, spare your own offspring.
Respect your race and blood, I do beseech you.
Let me not hear that blood cry from the ground;
Save me the horror and perpetual pain
Of having caused his father's hand to shed it.

Theseus

No, Madam, from that stain my hand is free.
But, for all that, the wretch has not escaped me.
The hand of an Immortal now is charged
With his destruction. 'Tis a debt that Neptune
Owes me, and you shall be avenged.

Phaedra

A debt
Owed you? Pray'rs made in anger—

Theseus

Never fear
That they will fail. Rather join yours to mine.
In all their blackness paint for me his crimes,
And fan my tardy passion to white heat.
But yet you know not all his infamy;
His rage against you overflows in slanders;
Your mouth, he says, is full of all deceit,
He says Aricia has his heart and soul,
That her alone he loves.

Phaedra

Aricia?

Theseus

Aye,
He said it to my face! an idle pretext!
A trick that gulls me not! Let us hope Neptune
Will do him speedy justice. To his altars
I go, to urge performance of his oaths.

Scene V

Phaedra (alone)

Ah, he is gone! What tidings struck mine ears?
What fire, half smother'd, in my heart revives?
What fatal stroke falls like a thunderbolt?
Stung by remorse that would not let me rest,
I tore myself out of Oenone's arms,
And flew to help Hippolytus with all
My soul and strength. Who knows if that repentance
Might not have moved me to accuse myself?
And, if my voice had not been choked with shame,
Perhaps I had confess'd the frightful truth.
Hippolytus can feel, but not for me!
Aricia has his heart, his plighted troth.
Ye gods, when, deaf to all my sighs and tears,
He arm'd his eye with scorn, his brow with threats,
I deem'd his heart, impregnable to love,
Was fortified 'gainst all my sex alike.
And yet another has prevail'd to tame
His pride, another has secured his favour.
Perhaps he has a heart easily melted;
I am the only one he cannot bear!
And shall I charge myself with his defence?

Scene VI

Phaedra, Oenone

Phaedra

Know you, dear Nurse, what I have learn'd just now?

Oenone

No; but I come in truth with trembling limbs.
I dreaded with what purpose you went forth,
The fear of fatal madness made me pale.

Phaedra

Who would have thought it, Nurse? I had a rival.

Oenone

A rival?

Phaedra

Yes, he loves. I cannot doubt it.
This wild untamable Hippolytus,
Who scorn'd to be admired, whom lovers' sighs
Wearied, this tiger, whom I fear'd to rouse,
Fawns on a hand that has subdued his pride:
Aricia has found entrance to his heart.

Oenone

Aricia?

Phaedra

Ah! anguish as yet untried!
For what new tortures am I still reserved?
All I have undergone, transports of passion,
Longings and fears, the horrors of remorse,
The shame of being spurn'd with contumely,
Were feeble foretastes of my present torments.
They love each other! By what secret charm
Have they deceived me? Where, and when, and how
Met they? You knew it all. Why was I cozen'd?
You never told me of those stolen hours
Of amorous converse. Have they oft been seen
Talking together? Did they seek the shades
Of thickest woods? Alas! full freedom had they
To see each other. Heav'n approved their sighs;
They loved without the consciousness of guilt;
And every morning's sun for them shone clear,
While I, an outcast from the face of Nature,
Shunn'd the bright day, and sought to hide myself.
Death was the only god whose aid I dared
To ask: I waited for the grave's release.
Water'd with tears, noursh'd with gall, my woe
Was all too closely watch'd; I did not dare
To weep without restraint. In mortal dread
Tasting this dangerous solace, I disguised
My terror 'neath a tranquil countenance,
And oft had I to check my tears, and smile.

Oenone

What fruit will they enjoy of their vain love?
They will not see each other more.

Phaedra

That love
Will last for ever. Even while I speak,

Ah, fatal thought, they laugh to scorn the madness
Of my distracted heart. In spite of exile
That soon must part them, with a thousand oaths
They seal yet closer union. Can I suffer
A happiness, Oenone, which insults me?
I crave your pity. She must be destroy'd.
My husband's wrath against a hateful stock
Shall be revived, nor must the punishment
Be light: the sister's guilt passes the brothers'.
I will entreat him in my jealous rage.
  What am I saying? Have I lost my senses?
Is Phaedra jealous, and will she implore
Theseus for help? My husband lives, and yet
I burn. For whom? Whose heart is this I claim
As mine? At every word I say, my hair
Stands up with horror. Guilt henceforth has pass'd
All bounds. Hypocrisy and incest breathe
At once thro' all. My murderous hands are ready
To spill the blood of guileless innocence.
Do I yet live, wretch that I am, and dare
To face this holy Sun from whom I spring?
My father's sire was king of all the gods;
My ancestors fill all the universe.
Where can I hide? In the dark realms of Pluto?
But there my father holds the fatal urn;
His hand awards th' irrevocable doom:
Minos is judge of all the ghosts in hell.
Ah! how his awful shade will start and shudder
When he shall see his daughter brought before him,
Forced to confess sins of such varied dye,
Crimes it may be unknown to hell itself!
What wilt thou say, my father, at a sight
So dire? I think I see thee drop the urn,
And, seeking some unheard-of punishment,
Thyself become my executioner.
Spare me! A cruel goddess has destroy'd
Thy race; and in my madness recognize
Her wrath. Alas! My aching heart has reap'd
No fruit of pleasure from the frightful crime
The shame of which pursues me to the grave,
And ends in torment life-long misery.

Oenone

Ah, Madam, pray dismiss a groundless dread:
Look less severely on a venial error.
You love. We cannot conquer destiny.
You were drawn on as by a fatal charm.
Is that a marvel without precedent

Among us? Has love triumph'd over you,
And o'er none else? Weakness is natural
To man. A mortal, to a mortal's lot
Submit. You chafe against a yoke that others
Have long since borne. The dwellers in Olympus,
The gods themselves, who terrify with threats
The sins of men, have burn'd with lawless fires.

Phaedra

What words are these I hear? What counsel this
You dare to give me? Will you to the end
Pour poison in mine ears? You have destroy'd me.
You brought me back when I should else have quitted
The light of day, made me forget my duty
And see Hippolytus, till then avoided.
What hast thou done? Why did your wicked mouth
With blackest lies slander his blameless life?
Perhaps you've slain him, and the impious pray'r
Of an unfeeling father has been answer'd.
No, not another word! Go, hateful monster;
Away, and leave me to my piteous fate.
May Heav'n with justice pay you your deserts!
And may your punishment for ever be
A terror to all those who would, like you,
Nourish with artful wiles the weaknesses
Of princes, push them to the brink of ruin
To which their heart inclines, and smooth the path
Of guilt. Such flatterers doth the wrath of Heav'n
Bestow on kings as its most fatal gift.

Oenone (alone)

O gods! to serve her what have I not done?
This is the due reward that I have won.

ACT V

Scene I

Hippolytus, Aricia

Aricia

Can you keep silent in this mortal peril?
Your father loves you. Will you leave him thus
Deceived? If in your cruel heart you scorn
My tears, content to see me nevermore,
Go, part from poor Aricia; but at least,
Going, secure the safety of your life.

Defend your honour from a shameful stain,
And force your father to recall his pray'rs.
There yet is time. Why out of mere caprice
Leave the field free to Phaedra's calumnies?
Let Theseus know the truth.

Hippolytus

Could I say more,
Without exposing him to dire disgrace?
How should I venture, by revealing all,
To make a father's brow grow red with shame?
The odious mystery to you alone
Is known. My heart has been outpour'd to none
Save you and Heav'n. I could not hide from you
(Judge if I love you) all I fain would hide
E'en from myself. But think under what seal
I spoke. Forget my words, if that may be;
And never let so pure a mouth disclose
This dreadful secret. Let us trust to Heav'n
My vindication, for the gods are just;
For their own honour will they clear the guiltless;
Sooner or later punish'd for her crime,
Phaedra will not escape the shame she merits.
I ask no other favour than your silence;
In all besides I give my wrath free scope.
Make your escape from this captivity,
Be bold to bear me company in flight;
Linger not here on this accursèd soil,
Where virtue breathes a pestilential air.
To cover your departure take advantage
Of this confusion, caused by my disgrace.
The means of flight are ready, be assured;
You have as yet no other guards than mine.
Pow'rful defenders will maintain our quarrel;
Argos spreads open arms, and Sparta calls us.
Let us appeal for justice to our friends,
Nor suffer Phaedra, in a common ruin
Joining us both, to hunt us from the throne,
And aggrandize her son by robbing us.
Embrace this happy opportunity:
What fear retrains? You seem to hesitate.
Your interest alone prompts me to urge
Boldness. When I am all on fire, how comes it
That you are ice? Fear you to follow then
A banish'd man?

Aricia

Ah, dear to me would be
Such exile! With what joy, my fate to yours

United, could I live, by all the world
Forgotten! But not yet has that sweet tie
Bound us together. How then can I steal
Away with you? I know the strictest honour
Forbids me not out of your father's hands
To free myself; this is no parent's home,
And flight is lawful when one flies from tyrants.
But you, Sir, love me; and my virtue shrinks—

Hippolytus

No, no, your reputation is to me
As dear as to yourself. A nobler purpose
Brings me to you. Fly from your foes, and follow
A husband. Heav'n, that sends us these misfortunes,
Sets free from human instruments the pledge
Between us. Torches do not always light
The face of Hymen.
At the gates of Troezen,
'Mid ancient tombs where princes of my race
Lie buried, stands a temple ne'er approach'd
By perjurers, where mortals dare not make
False oaths, for instant punishment befalls
The guilty. Falsehood knows no stronger check
Than what is present there—the fear of death
That cannot be avoided. Thither then
We'll go, if you consent, and swear to love
For ever, take the guardian god to witness
Our solemn vows, and his paternal care
Entreat. I will invoke the name of all
The holiest Pow'rs, chaste Dian, and the Queen
Of Heav'n, yea all the gods who know my heart
Will guarantee my sacred promises.

Aricia

The King draws near. Depart,—make no delay.
To mask my flight, I linger yet one moment.
Go you; and leave with me some trusty guide,
To lead my timid footsteps to your side.

SCENE II

THESEUS, ARICIA, ISMENE

Theseus

Ye gods, throw light upon my troubled mind,
Show me the truth which I am seeking here.

Aricia (*aside to* ISMENE)

Get ready, dear Ismene, for our flight.

Scene III

Theseus, Aricia

Theseus

Your colour comes and goes, you seem confused,
Madam! What business had my son with you?

Aricia

Sire, he was bidding me farewell for ever.

Theseus

Your eyes, it seems, can tame that stubborn pride;
And the first sighs he breathes are paid to you.

Aricia

I can't deny the truth; he has not, Sire,
Inherited your hatred and injustice;
He did not treat me like a criminal.

Theseus

That is to say, he swore eternal love.
Do not rely on that inconstant heart;
To others has he sworn as much before.

Aricia

He, Sire?

Theseus

You ought to check his roving taste.
How could you bear a partnership so vile?

Aricia

And how can you endure that vilest slanders
Should make a life so pure as black as pitch?
Have you so little knowledge of his heart?
Do you so ill distinguish between guilt
And innocence? What mist before your eyes
Blinds them to virtue so conspicuous?
Ah! 'tis too much to let false tongues defame him.
Repent; call back your murderous wishes, Sire;
Fear, fear lest Heav'n in its severity
Hate you enough to hear and grant your pray'rs.
Oft in their wrath the gods accept our victims,
And oftentimes chastise us with their gifts.

Theseus

No, vainly would you cover up his guilt.
Your love is blind to his depravity.

But I have witness irreproachable:
Tears have I seen, true tears, that may be trusted.

Aricia

Take heed, my lord. Your hands invincible
Have rid the world of monsters numberless;
But all are not destroy'd, one you have left
Alive—Your son forbids me to say more.
Knowing with what respect he still regards you,
I should too much distress him if I dared
Complete my sentence. I will imitate
His reverence, and, to keep silence, leave you.

SCENE IV

Theseus (alone)

What is there in her mind? What meaning lurks
In speech begun but to be broken short?
Would both deceive me with a vain pretence?
Have they conspired to put me to the torture?
And yet, despite my stern severity,
What plaintive voice cries deep within my heart?
A secret pity troubles and alarms me.
Oenone shall be questioned once again,
I must have clearer light upon this crime.
Guards, bid Oenone come, and come alone.

SCENE V

THESEUS, PANOPE

Panope

I know not what the Queen intends to do,
But from her agitation dread the worst.
Fatal despair is painted on her features;
Death's pallor is already in her face.
Oenone, shamed and driven from her sight,
Has cast herself into the ocean depths.
None knows what prompted her to deed so rash;
And now the waves hide her from us for ever.

Theseus

What say you?

Panope

Her sad fate seems to have added
Fresh trouble to the Queen's tempestuous soul.
Sometimes, to soothe her secret pain, she clasps

Her children close, and bathes them with her tears;
Then suddenly, the mother's love forgotten,
She thrusts them from her with a look of horror.
She wanders to and fro with doubtful steps;
Her vacant eye no longer knows us. Thrice
She wrote, and thrice did she, changing her mind,
Destroy the letter ere 'twas well begun.
Vouchsafe to see her, Sire: vouchsafe to help her.

Theseus

Heav'ns! Is Oenone dead, and Phaedra bent
On dying too? Oh, call me back my son!
Let him defend himself, and I am ready
To hear him. Be not hasty to bestow
Thy fatal bounty, Neptune; let my pray'rs
Rather remain ever unheard. Too soon
I lifted cruel hands, believing lips
That may have lied! Ah! What despair may follow!

Scene VI

Theseus, Theramenes

Theseus

Theramenes, is't thou? Where is my son?
I gave him to thy charge from tenderest childhood.
But whence these tears that overflow thine eyes?
How is it with my son?

Theramenes

Concern too late!
Affection vain! Hippolytus is dead.

Theseus

Gods!

Theramenes

I have seen the flow'r of all mankind
Cut off, and I am bold to say that none
Deserved it less.

Theseus

What! My son dead! When I
Was stretching out my arms to him, has Heav'n
Hasten'd his end? What was this sudden stroke?

Theramenes

Scarce had we pass'd out of the gates of Troezen,
He silent in his chariot, and his guards,

Downcast and silent too, around him ranged;
To the Mycenian road he turn'd his steeds,
Then, lost in thought, allow'd the reins to lie
Loose on their backs. His noble chargers, erst
So full of ardour to obey his voice,
With head depress'd and melancholy eye
Seem'd now to mark his sadness and to share it.
A frightful eye, that issues from the deep,
With sudden discord rends the troubled air;
And from the bosom of the earth a groan
Is heard in answer to that voice of terror.
Our blood is frozen at our very hearts;
With bristling manes the list'ning steeds stand still.
Meanwhile upon the watery plain there rises
A mountain billow with a mighty crest
Of foam, that shoreward rolls, and, as it breaks,
Before our eyes vomits a furious monster.
With formidable horns its brow is arm'd,
And all its body clothed with yellow scales,
In front a savage bull, behind a dragon
Turning and twisting in impatient rage.
Its long continued bellowings make the shore
Tremble; the sky seems horror-struck to see it;

Hippolytus is dragged to his death. Engraving after a painting by P. Rubens.

The earth with terror quakes; its poisonous breath
Infects the air. The wave that brought it ebbs
In fear. All fly, forgetful of the courage
That cannot aid, and in a neighbouring temple
Take refuge—all save bold Hippolytus.
A hero's worthy son, he stays his steeds,
Seizes his darts, and, rushing forward, hurls
A missile with sure aim that wounds the monster
Deep in the flank. With rage and pain it springs
E'en to the horses' feet, and, roaring, falls,
Writhes in the dust, and shows a fiery throat
That covers them with flames, and blood, and smoke.
Fear lends them wings; deaf to his voice for once,
And heedless of the curb, they onward fly.
Their master wastes his strength in efforts vain;
With foam and blood each courser's bit is red.
Some say a god, amid this wild disorder,
Was seen with goads pricking their dusty flanks.
O'er jagged rocks they rush urged on by terror;
Crash! goes the axle-tree. Th' intrepid youth
Sees his car broken up, flying to pieces;
He falls himself entangled in the reins.
Pardon my grief. That cruel spectacle
Will be for me a source of endless tears.
I saw thy hapless son, I saw him, Sire,
Dragg'd by the horses that his hands had fed,
Pow'rless to check their fierce career, his voice
But adding to their fright, his body soon
One mass of wounds. Our cries of anguish fill
The plain. At last they slacken their swift pace,
Then stop, not far from those old tombs that mark
Where lie the ashes of his royal sires.
Panting I thither run, and after me
His guard, along the track stain'd with fresh blood
That reddens all the rocks; caught in the briers
Locks of his hair hang dripping, gory spoils!
I come, I call him. Stretching forth his hand,
He opes his dying eyes, soon closed again.
"The gods have robb'd me of a guiltless life,"
I hear him say: "Take care of sad Aricia
When I am dead. Dear friend, if e'er my father
Mourn, undeceived, his son's unhappy fate
Falsely accused; to give my spirit peace,
Tell him to treat his captive tenderly,
And to restore—" With that the hero's breath
Fails, and a mangled corpse lies in my arms,
A piteous object, trophy of the wrath
Of Heav'n—so changed, his father would not know him.

Theseus

Alas, my son! Dear hope for ever lost!
The ruthless gods have served me but too well.
For what a life of anguish and remorse
Am I reserved!

Theramenes

Aricia at that instant,
Flying from you, comes timidly, to take him
For husband, there, in presence of the gods.
Thus drawing nigh, she sees the grass all red
And reeking, sees (sad sight for lover's eye!)
Hippolytus stretch'd there, pale and disfigured.
But, for a time doubtful of her misfortune,
Unrecognized the hero she adores,
She looks, and asks—"Where is Hippolytus?"
Only too sure at last that he lies there
Before her, with sad eyes that silently
Reproach the gods, she shudders, groans, and falls
Swooning and all but lifeless, at his feet.
Ismene, all in tears, kneels down beside her,
And calls her back to life—life that is naught
But sense of pain. And I, to whom this light
Is darkness now, come to discharge the duty
The hero has imposed on me, to tell thee
His last request—a melancholy task.
But hither comes his mortal enemy.

Scene VII

Theseus, Phaedra, Theramenes, Panope, Guards

Theseus

Madam, you've triumph'd, and my son is kill'd!
Ah, but what room have I for fear! How justly
Suspicion racks me that in blaming him
I err'd! But he is dead; accept your victim;
Rightly or wrongly slain, let your heart leap
For joy. My eyes shall be for ever blind:
Since you accuse him, I'll believe him guilty.
His death affords me cause enough for tears,
Without a foolish search for further light
Which, pow'rless to restore him to my grief,
Might only serve to make me more unhappy.
Far from this shore and far from you I'll fly,
For here the image of my mangled son
Would haunt my memory and drive me mad.
From the whole world I fain would banish me,

For all the world seems to rise up in judgment
Against me; and my very glory weights
My punishment; for, were my name less known
'Twere easier to hide me. All the favours
The gods have granted me I mourn and hate,
Nor will I importune them with vain pray'rs
Henceforth for ever. Give me what they may,
What they have taken will all else outweigh.

Phaedra

Theseus, I cannot hear you and keep silence:
I must repair the wrong that he has suffer'd—
Your son was innocent.

Theseus

Unhappy father!
And it was on your word that I condemn'd him!
Think you such cruelty can be excused—

Phaedra

Moments to me are precious; hear me, Theseus.
'Twas I who cast an eye of lawless passion
On chaste and dutiful Hippolytus.
Heav'n in my bosom kindled baleful fire,
And vile Oenone's cunning did the rest.
She fear'd Hippolytus, knowing my madness
Would make that passion known which he regarded
With horror; so advantage of my weakness
She took, and hasten'd to accuse him first.
For that she has been punish'd, tho' too mildly;
Seeking to shun my wrath she cast herself
Beneath the waves. The sword ere now had cut
My thread of life, but slander'd innocence
Made its cry heard, and I resolved to die
In a more lingering way, confessing first
My penitence to you. A poison, brought
To Athens by Medea, runs thro' my veins.
Already in my heart the venom works,
Infusing there a strange and fatal chill;
Already as thro' thickening mists I see
The spouse to whom my presence is an outrage;
Death, from mine eyes veiling the light of heav'n,
Restores its purity that they defiled.

Panope

She dies, my lord!

Theseus

Would that the memory

Of her disgraceful deed could perish with her!
Ah, disabused too late! Come, let us go,
And with the blood of mine unhappy son
Mingle our tears, clasping his dear remains,
In deep repentance for a pray'r detested.
Let him be honour'd as he well deserves;
And, to appease his sore offended ghost,
Be her near kinsmen's guilt whate'er it may,
Aricia shall be held my daughter from to-day.

The Birth of Tragedy

Friedrich Nietzsche

Editor's Introduction

Driven in mind, tortured in heart, dying insane, for the most part unread in his lifetime and misunderstood after it, Nietzsche has come to be regarded in the century following his death as a major influence in the creation of the modern temper. This is so, not so much despite his limitations as because of them. Nietzsche's scorn of traditional wisdom, his furious anger at what he conceived to be the moral and intellectual hypocrisies of his age, his despair of the culture in which he found himself, even the broken eloquence with which he expressed himself, whereby he spoke for the most part in aphorisms rather than sustained argument, of which he was incapable, are all traits of an important witness to a cultural crisis of which such distraction has been among the characteristic signs. And in certain of his insights—or, one might better say, in the passion with which he held to certain insights (which themselves were not always original), as that the moral will cannot prevail without becoming destructive of itself—he is a figure of all but tragic dimensions.

His life suggests the strain of his moral and intellectual concerns. Born in 1844 in Saxony, which was part of Prussia, Nietzsche was named after the king, Friedrich Wilhelm, who died mad, as did Nietzsche himself. He was well educated in classical studies and especially in philology. In 1869, though by then he despised that discipline as pedantry, preferring philosophy, he became professor of philology at the University of Basel, in Switzerland, where he took citizenship. A disciple at first of Schopenhauer, whose resignation for a time attracted him, he formed a liaison with Wagner, then self-exiled from Germany, in whom Nietzsche felt a kindred spirit, and to whom *The Birth of Tragedy* (1872), the first of his books, in which he attacked the idea of the Greek mind as something serene, was dedicated. Subsequently he broke with Wagner, whose *Parsifal* he thought a pseudo-religious betrayal of atheistic principles, and whose hatred of the Jews and the French, as well as his strong German nationalism, which had begun to be evident, were all to Nietzsche offensive.

Nietzsche's health was never good; apparently he contracted syphilis while a student, he was severely injured while riding a horse in the Franco-Prussian War, and while serving as a medical orderly he became ill with both dysentery and diphtheria, the effects of which were lasting. In spite of these physical defects he forced himself to work, and in 1879, feeling confined by an academic situation, he resigned his professorship to devote full time to writing.

For the next ten years, until insanity overcame him, he wrote the books for which he was to become famous, among them *Thus Spake Zarathustra* (1883–84; not published until 1892); *Beyond Good and Evil* (1886); *The Genealogy of Morals* (1887); and *The Anti-Christ* (1895). These works established him as the proponent of moral and intellectual positions—concerning the Superman capable of enduring his own will, against Christianity (we owe to Nietzsche the dictum "God is dead"), and as a believer in nihilism, or the meaninglessness of life—that are by now familiar. Yet almost nothing of his writing in this most productive period of his life was noticed or even read at the time. His books were turned out in nearly complete isolation at the town of Sils Maria in Switzerland, where he had gone to live. Not until 1888, when the Danish critic Georg Brandes called attention to him, was Nietzsche recognized, though interest in him grew rapidly after that, and well before his death his reputation had begun to grow.

Unhappily for Nietzsche, this response came too late for him to appreciate or even perceive. At the beginning of 1889 it was apparent that he was suffering from a delusion that he was celebrated as only later he would come to be, and by the end of the year, following a collapse in the street, it was apparent that his mind was gone. For the remaining decade of his life, which ended on August 25, 1900, he sat for the most part in silence, uttering only senseless remarks. His condition is thought to have been a consequence of his syphilis, notwithstanding that for most of his adult life he had been a virtual ascetic.

The misunderstanding of his doctrines and the misinterpretation of his work was the result not only of their frenetic expression but, more blatantly, of the misguided attempts of Nietzsche's sister, Elizabeth, to edit his writings and advance his reputation. It was she who, having married a notorious anti-Semite, Bernhard Förster, whose opinions she espoused, made it appear that her brother was of the same mind, which in fact he was not, as she otherwise, too, contrived to present him, sometimes with altogether fictitious "unpublished works," as the proto-fascist he has sometimes been thought to be. She seems not to have realized the impropriety of these distortions, being ignorant of what her brother really thought and believed. But the effect of her efforts was to obscure a mind that, while often harsh was never hateful, and that, far from taking satisfaction in the moral consequences of its positions, was so deeply disturbed by these as finally to shatter the personality of which it was a part.

The Birth of Tragedy

An Attempt at Self-Criticism

1.

Whatever may lie at the bottom of this doubtful book must be a question of the first rank and attractiveness, moreover a deeply personal question,—in proof thereof observe the time in which it originated, in spite of which it originated, the exciting period of the Franco-German war of 1870–71. While the thunder of the battle of Wörth rolled over Europe, the ruminator and riddle-lover, who had to be the parent of this book, sat somewhere in a nook of the Alps, lost in riddles and ruminations, consequently very much concerned and unconcerned at the same time, and wrote down his meditations on the Greeks,—the kernel of the curious and almost inaccessible book, to which this belated prologue (or epilogue) is to be devoted. A few weeks later: and he found himself under the walls of Metz, still wrestling with the notes of interrogation he had set down concerning the alleged "cheerfulness" of the Greeks and of Greek art; till at last, in that month of deep suspense, when peace was debated at Versailles, he too attained to peace with himself, and, slowly recovering from a disease brought home from the field, made up his mind definitely regarding the "Birth of Tragedy from the Spirit of Music."—From music? Music and Tragedy? Greeks and tragic music? Greeks and the Artwork of pessimism? A race of men, well-fashioned, beautiful, envied, life-inspiring, like no other race hitherto, the Greeks—indeed? The Greeks were in need of tragedy? Yea—of art? Wherefore—Greek art? . . .

We can thus guess where the great note of interrogation concerning the value of existence had been set. Is pessimism necessarily the sign of decline, of decay, of failure, of exhausted and weakened instincts?—as was the case with the Indians, as is, to all appearance, the case with us "modern" men and Europeans? Is there a pessimism of strength? An intellectual predilection for what is hard, awful, evil, problematical in existence, owing to well-being, to exuberant health, to fullness of existence? Is there perhaps suffering in overfullness itself? A seductive fortitude with the keenest of glances, which yearns for the terrible, as for the enemy, the worthy enemy, with whom it may try its strength? from whom it is willing to learn what "fear" is? What means tragic myth to the Greeks of the best, strongest, bravest era? And the prodigious phenomenon of the Dionysian? And that which was born thereof, tragedy?—And again: that of which tragedy died, the Socratism of morality, the dialectics, contentedness and cheerfulness of the theoretical man—indeed? might not this very Socratism be a sign of decline, of weariness, of disease, of anarchically disintegrating instincts? And the "Hellenic cheerfulness" of the later Hellenism merely a glowing sunset? The Epicurean will counter to pessimism merely a precaution of the sufferer? And science itself, our science—ay, viewed as a symptom of life, what really signifies all science? Whither, worse still, whence—all science? Well? Is scientism perhaps only fear and evasion of pessimism? A subtle defence against—truth? Morally speaking, something like falsehood and cowardice? And, unmorally speaking, an artifice? O Socrates, Socrates, was this perhaps thy secret? Oh mysterious ironist, was this perhaps thine—irony? . . .

2.

What I then laid hands on, something terrible and dangerous, a problem with horns, not necessarily a bull itself, but at all events a new problem: I should say to-day it was the problem of science itself—science conceived for the first time as problematic, as questionable. But the book, in which my youthful ardour and suspicion then discharged themselves—what an impossible book must needs grow out of a task so disagreeable to youth. Constructed of nought but precocious, unripened self-experiences, all of which lay close to the threshold of the communicable, based on the groundwork of art—for the problem of science cannot be discerned on the groundwork of science,—a book perhaps for artists, with collateral analytical and retrospective aptitudes (that is, an exceptional kind of artists, for whom one must seek and does not even care to seek . . .), full of psychological innovations and artists' secrets, with an artists' metaphysics in the background, a work of youth, full of youth's mettle and youth's melancholy, independent, defiantly self-sufficient even when it seems to bow to some authority and self-veneration; in short, a firstling-work, even in every bad sense of the term; in spite of its senile problem, affected with every fault of youth, above all with youth's prolixity and youth's "storm and stress": on the other hand, in view of the success it had (especially with the great artist to whom it addressed itself, as it were, in a duologue, Richard Wagner) a demonstrated book, I mean a book which, at any rate, sufficed "for the best of its time." On this account, if for no other reason, it should be treated with some consideration and reserve; yet I shall not altogether conceal how disagreeable it now appears to me, how after sixteen years it stands a total stranger before me,—before an eye which is more mature, and a hundred times more fastidious, but which has by no means grown colder nor lost any of its interest in that self-same task essayed for the first time by this daring book,—to view science through the optics of the artist, and art moreover through the optics of life. . . .

3.

I say again, to-day it is an impossible book to me,—I call it badly written, heavy, painful, image-angling and image-entangling, maudlin, sugared at times even to femininism, uneven in tempo, void of the will to logical cleanliness, very convinced and therefore rising above the necessity of demonstration, distrustful even of the propriety of demonstration, as being a book for initiates, as "music" for those who are baptised with the name of Music, who are united from the beginning of things by common ties of rare experiences in art, as a countersign for blood-relations *in artibus*,—a haughty and fantastic book, which from the very first withdraws even more from the *profanum vulgus* of the "cultured" than from the "people," but which also, as its effect has shown and still shows, knows very well how to seek fellow-enthusiasts and lure them to new by-ways and dancing-grounds. Here, at any rate—thus much was acknowledged with curiosity as well as with aversion—a strange voice spoke, the disciple of a still "unknown God," who for the time being had hidden himself under the hood of the scholar, under the German's gravity and disinclination for dialectics, even under the bad manners of the Wagnerian; here was a spirit with strange and still nameless needs, a memory bristling with questions, experiences and obscurities, beside which stood the name Dionysos like one more note of interrogation; here spoke—people said to themselves with misgivings—something like a mystic and almost mænadic soul, which, undecided whether it should disclose or conceal itself, stammers with an effort and capriciously as in a strange tongue. It should have sung, this "new soul"—and not spoken! What a pity, that I did not dare to say what I then had to say, as a poet: I could have done so perhaps! Or at least as a philologist:—for even at the present day well-nigh everything in this domain remains to be discovered and disinterred by the philologist! Above all the problem, that here there is a problem before us,—and that, so long as we have no answer to the question "what is Dionysian?" the Greeks are now as ever wholly unknown and inconceivable . . .

4.

Ay, what is Dionysian?—In this book may be found an answer,—a "knowing one" speaks here, the votary and disciple of his god. Perhaps I should now speak more guardedly and less eloquently of a psychological question so difficult as the origin of tragedy among the Greeks. A fundamental question is the relation of the Greek to pain, his degree of sensibility,—did this relation remain constant? or did it veer about?—the question, whether his ever-increasing longing for beauty, for festivals, gaieties, new cults, did really grow out of want, privation, melancholy, pain? For suppose even this to be true—and Pericles (or Thucydides) intimates as much in the great Funeral Speech:—whence then the opposite longing, which appeared first in the order of time, the longing for the ugly, the good, resolute desire of the Old Hellene for pessimism, for tragic myth, for the picture of all that is terrible, evil, enigmatical, destructive, fatal at the basis of existence,—whence then must tragedy have sprung? Perhaps from joy, from strength, from exuberant health, from over-fullness. And what then, physiologically speaking, is the meaning of that madness, out of which comic as well as tragic art has grown, the Dionysian madness? What? perhaps madness is not necessarily the symptom of degeneration, of decline, of belated culture? Perhaps there are—a question for alienists—neuroses of health? of folk-youth and -youthfulness? What does that synthesis of god and goat in the Satyr point to? What self-experience, what "stress," made the Greek think of the Dionysian reveller and primitive man as a satyr? And as regards the origin of the tragic chorus: perhaps there were endemic ecstasies in the eras when the Greek body bloomed and the Greek soul brimmed over with life? Visions and hallucinations, which took hold of entire communities, entire cult-assem-blies? What if the Greeks in the very wealth of their youth had the will to be tragic and were pessimists? What if it was madness itself, to use a word of Plato's which brought the greatest blessings upon Hellas? And what if, on the other hand and conversely, at the very time of their dissolution and weakness, the Greeks became always more optimistic, more superficial, more histrionic, also more ardent for logic and the logicising of the world,—consequently at the same time more "cheerful" and more "scientific"? Ay, despite all "modern ideas" and prejudices of the democratic taste, may not the triumph of optimism, the common sense that has gained the upper hand, the practical and theoretical utilitarianism, like democracy itself, with which it is synchronous—be symptomatic of declining vigour, of approaching age, of physiological weariness? And not at all—pessimism? Was Epicurus an optimist—because a sufferer? . . . We see it is a whole bundle of weighty questions which this book has taken upon itself,—let us not fail to add its weightiest question! Viewed through the optics of life, what is the meaning of—morality? . . .

5.

Already in the foreword to Richard Wagner, art—and not morality—is set down as the properly metaphysical activity of man; in the book itself the piquant proposition recurs time and again, that the existence of the world is justified only as an æsthetic phenomenon. Indeed, the entire book recognises only an artist-thought and artist-afterthought behind all occurrences,—a "God," if you will, but certainly only an altogether thoughtless and unmoral artist-God, who, in construction as in destruction, in good as in evil, desires to become conscious of his own equable joy and sovereign glory; who, in creating worlds, frees himself from the anguish of fullness and overfullness, from the suffering of the contradictions concentrated with him. The world, that is, the redemption of God attained at every moment, as the perpetually changing, perpetually new vision of the most suffering, most antithetical, most contradictory being, who contrives to redeem himself only in appearance: this entire artist-metaphysics, call it arbitrary, idle, fantastic, if you will,—the point is, that it already betrays a spirit, which is determined some day, at all hazards, to make a stand against the moral interpretation and significance of life. Here, perhaps for the first time, a pessimism "Beyond Good and Evil" announces itself, here that "perverseness of disposition" obtains expression and formulation, against which Schopenhauer never grew tired of hurling beforehand his angriest imprecations and thunderbolts,—a philosophy which dares to put, derogatorily put, morality itself in the world of phenomena, and not only among "phenomena" (in the sense of the idealistic *terminus technicus*), but among the "illusions," as appearance, semblance, error, interpretation, accommodation, art. Perhaps the depth of this antimoral tendency may be best estimated from the guarded and hostile silence with which Christianity is treated throughout this book,—Christianity, as being the most extravagant burlesque of the moral theme to which mankind has hitherto been obliged to listen. In fact, to the purely æsthetic world-interpretation and justification taught in this book, there is no greater antithesis than the Christian dogma, which is only and will be only moral, and which, with its absolute standards, for instance, its truthfulness of God, relegates—that is, disowns, convicts, condemns—art, all art, to the realm of falsehood. Behind such a mode of thought and valuation, which, if at all genuine, must be hostile to art, I always experienced what was hostile to life, the wrathful, vindictive counterwill to life itself: for all life rests on appearance, art, illusion, optics, necessity of perspective and error. From the very first Christianity was, essentially and thoroughly, the nausea and surfeit of Life for Life, which only disguised, concealed and decked itself out under the belief in "another" or "better" life. The hatred of the "world," the curse on the affections, the fear of beauty and sensuality, another world, invented for the purpose of slandering this world the more, at bottom a longing for Nothingness, for the end, for rest, for the "Sabbath of Sabbaths"—all this, as also the unconditional will of Christianity to recognise only moral values, has always appeared to me as the most dangerous and ominous of all possible forms of a "will to perish"; at the least, as the symptom of a most fatal disease, of profoundest weariness, despondency, exhaustion, impoverishment of life,—for before the tribunal of morality (especially Christian, that is, unconditional morality) life must constantly and inevitably be the loser, because life is something essentially unmoral,—indeed, oppressed with the weight of contempt and the everlasting No, life must finally be regarded as unworthy of desire, as in itself unworthy. Morality itself what?—may not morality be a "will to disown life," a secret instinct for annihilation, a principle of decay, of depreciation, of slander, a beginning of the end? And, consequently, the danger of dangers? . . . It was against morality, therefore, that my instinct, as an intercessory instinct for life, turned in this questionable book, inventing for itself a fundamental counter-dogma and counter-valuation of life, purely artistic, purely anti-Christian. What should I call it? As a philologist and man of words I baptised it, not without some liberty—for who could be sure of the proper name of the Antichrist?—with the name of a Greek god: I called it Dionysian.

6.

You see which problem I ventured to touch upon in this early work? . . . How I now regret, that I had not then the courage (or immodesty?) to allow myself, in all respects, the use of an individual language for such individual contemplations and ventures in the field of thought—that I laboured to express, in Kantian and Schopenhauerian formulæ, strange and new valuations, which ran fundamentally counter to the spirit of Kant and Schopenhauer, as well as to their taste! What, forsooth, were Schopenhauer's views on tragedy? "What gives"—he says in *Welt als Wille und Vorstellung,*[1] II. 495—"to all tragedy that singular swing towards elevation, is the awakening of the knowledge that the world, that life, cannot satisfy us thoroughly, and consequently is not worthy of our attachment. In this consists the tragic spirit: it therefore leads to resignation." Oh, how differently Dionysos spoke to me! Oh how far from me then was just this entire resignationism!—But there is something far worse in this book, which I now regret even more than having obscured and spoiled Dionysian anticipations with Schopenhauerian formalæ: to wit, that, in general, I spoiled the grand Hellenic problem, as it had opened up before me, by the admixture of the most modern things! that I entertained hopes, where nothing was to be hoped for, where everything pointed all-too-clearly to an approaching end! That, on the basis of our latter-day German music, I began to fable about the "spirit of Teutonism," as if it were on the point of discovering and returning to itself,—ay, at the very time that the German spirit which not so very long before had had the will to the lordship over Europe, the strength to lead and govern Europe, testamentarily and conclusively resigned and, under the pompous pretence of empire-founding, effected its transition to mediocritisation, democracy, and "modern ideas." In very fact, I have since learned to regard this "spirit of Teutonism" as something to be despaired of and unsparingly treated, as also our present German music, which is Romanticism through and through and the most un-Grecian of all possible forms of art: and moreover a first-rate nerve-destroyer, doubly dangerous for a people given to drinking and revering the unclear as a virtue, namely, in its two-fold capacity of an intoxicating and stupefying narcotic. Of course, apart from all precipitate hopes and faulty applications to matters specially modern, with which I then spoiled my first book, the great Dionysian note of interrogation, as set down therein, continues standing on and on, even with reference to music: how must we conceive of a music, which is no longer of Romantic origin, like the German; but of Dionysian? . . .

7.

But, my dear Sir, if your book is not Romanticism, what in the world is? Can the deep hatred of the present, of "reality" and "modern ideas" be pushed farther than has been done in your artist-metaphysics?—which would rather believe in Nothing, or in the devil, than in the "Now"? Does not a radical bass of wrath and annihilative pleasure growl on beneath all your contrapuntal vocal art and aural seduction, a mad determination to oppose all that "now" is, a will which is not so very far removed from practical nihilism and which seems to say: "rather let nothing be true, than that you should be in the right, than that your truth should prevail!" Hear, yourself, my dear Sir Pessimist and art-deifier, with ever so unlocked ears, a single select passage of your own book, that not ineloquent dragon-slayer passage, which may sound insidiously rat-charming to young ears and hearts. What? is not that the true blue romanticist-confession of 1830 under the mask of the pessimism of 1850? After which, of course, the usual romanticist finale at once strikes up,—rupture, collapse, return and prostration before an old belief, before the old God. . . . What? is not your pessimist book itself a piece of anti-Hellenism and Romanticism, something "equally intoxicating and befogging," a narcotic at all events, ay, a piece of music, of German music? But listen:

Let us imagine a rising generation with this undauntedness of vision, with this heroic impulse towards the prodigious, let us imagine the bold step of these dragon-slayers, the proud daring with which they turn their backs on all the effeminate doctrines of optimism, in order "to live resolutely" in the Whole and in the Full: would it not be necessary for the tragic man of this culture, with his self-discipline to earnestness and terror, to desire a new art, the art of metaphysical comfort, tragedy as the Helena belonging to him, and that he should exclaim with Faust:

"Und sollt ich nicht, sehnsüchtigster Gewalt,
In's Leben ziehn die einzigste Gestalt?"[2]

"Would it not be necessary?" . . . No, thrice no! ye young romanticists: it would not be necessary! But it is very probable, that things may end thus, that ye may end thus, namely "comforted," as it is written, in spite of all self-discipline to earnestness and terror; metaphysically comforted, in short, as Romanticists are wont to end, as Christians. . . . No! ye should first of all learn the art of earthly comfort, ye should learn to laugh, my young friends, if ye are at all determined to remain pessimists: if so, you will perhaps, as laughing ones, eventually send all metaphysical comfortism to the devil—and metaphysics first of all! Or, to say it in the language of that Dionysian ogre, called Zarathustra:

"Lift up your hearts, my brethren, high, higher! And do not forget your legs! Lift up also your legs, ye good dancers—and better still if ye stand also on your heads!

"This crown of the laughter, this rose-garland crown—I myself have put on this crown; I myself have consecrated my laughter. No one else have I found to-day strong enough for this.

"Zarathustra the dancer, Zarathustra the light one, who beckoneth with his pinions, one ready for flight, beckoning unto all birds, ready and prepared, a blissfully light-spirited one:—

"Zarathustra the soothsayer, Zarathustra the soothlaugher, no impatient one, no absolute one, one who loveth leaps and side-leaps: I myself have put on this crown!

"This crown of the laughter, this rose-garland crown—to you my brethren do I cast this crown! Laughing have I consecrated: ye higher men, learn, I pray you—to laugh!"

—Sils-Maria, Oberengadin, August 1886.

Foreword to Richard Wagner

In order to keep at a distance all the possible scruples, excitements, and misunderstandings to which the thoughts gathered in this essay will give occasion, considering the peculiar character of our æsthetic publicity, and to be able also to write the introductory remarks with the same contemplative delight, the impress of which, as the petrifaction of good and elevating hours, it bears on every page, I form a conception of the moment when you, my highly honoured friend, will receive this essay; how you, say after an evening walk in the winter snow, will behold the unbound Prometheus on the title-page, read my name, and be forthwith convinced that, whatever this essay may contain, the author has something earnest and impressive to say, and, moreover, that in all his meditations he communed with you as with one present and could thus write only what befitted your presence. You will thus remember that it was at the same time as your magnificent dissertation on

Beethoven originated, viz., amidst the horrors and sublimities of the war which had just then broken out, that I collected myself for these thoughts. But those persons would err, to whom this collection suggests no more perhaps than the antithesis of patriotic excitement and æsthetic revelry, of gallant earnestness and sportive delight. Upon a real perusal of this essay, such readers will, rather to their surprise, discover how earnest is the German problem we have to deal with, which we properly place, as a vortex and turning-point, in the very midst of German hopes. Perhaps, however, this same class of readers will be shocked at seeing an æsthetic problem taken so seriously, especially if they can recognise in art no more than a merry diversion, a readily dispensable court-jester to the "earnestness of existence": as if no one were aware of the real meaning of this confrontation with the "earnestness of existence." These earnest ones may be informed that I am convinced that art is the highest task and the properly metaphysical activity of this life, as it is understood by the man, to whom, as my sublime protagonist on this path, I would now dedicate this essay.

—BASEL, end of the year 1871.

The Birth of Tragedy

1.

We shall have gained much for the science of æsthetics, when once we have perceived not only by logical inference, but by the immediate certainty of intuition, that the continuous development of art is bound up with the duplexity of the Apollonian and the Dionysian: in like manner as procreation is dependent on the duality of the sexes, involving perpetual conflicts with only periodically intervening reconciliations. These names we borrow from the Greeks, who disclose to the intelligent observer the profound mysteries of their view of art, not indeed in concepts, but in the impressively clear figures of their world of deities. It is in connection with Apollo and Dionysus, the two art-deities of the Greeks, that we learn that there existed in the Grecian world a wide antithesis, in origin and aims, between the art of the shaper, the Apollonian, and the non-plastic art of music, that of Dionysus: both these so heterogeneous tendencies run parallel to each other, for the most part openly at variance, and continually inciting each other to new and more powerful births, to perpetuate in them the strife of this antithesis, which is but seemingly bridged over by their mutual term "Art"; till at last, by a metaphysical miracle of the Hellenic will, they appear paired with each other, and through this pairing eventually generate the equally Dionysian and Apollonian art-work of Attic tragedy.

In order to bring these two tendencies within closer range, let us conceive them first of all as the separate art-worlds of dreamland and drunkenness; between which physiological phenomena a contrast may be observed analogous to that existing between the Apollonian and the Dionysian. In dreams, according to the conception of Lucretius, the glorious divine figures first appeared to the souls of men, in dreams the great shaper beheld the charming corporeal structure of superhuman beings, and the Hellenic poet, if consulted on the mysteries of poetic inspiration, would likewise have suggested dreams and would have offered an explanation resembling that of Hans Sachs in the Meistersingers:—

Mein Freund, das grad' ist Dichters Werk,
dass er sein Träumen deut' und merk'.
Glaubt mir, des Menschen wahrster Wahn
wird ihm im Traume aufgethan:
all' Dichtkunst und Poëterei
ist nichts als Wahrtraum-Deuterei.[3]

The beauteous appearance of the dream-worlds, in the production of which every man is a perfect artist, is the presupposition of all plastic art, and in fact, as we shall see, of an important half of poetry also. We take delight in the immediate apprehension of form; all forms speak to us; there is nothing indifferent, nothing superfluous. But, together with the highest life of this dream-reality we also have, glimmering through it, the sensation of its appearance: such at least is my experience, as to the frequency, ay, normality of which I could adduce many proofs, as also the sayings of the poets. Indeed, the man of philosophic turn has a foreboding that underneath this reality in which we live and have our being, another and altogether different reality lies concealed, and that therefore it is also an appearance; and Schopenhauer actually designates the gift of occasionally regarding men and things as mere phantoms and dream-pictures as the criterion of philosophical ability. Accordingly, the man susceptible to art stands in the same relation to the reality of dreams as the philosopher to the reality of existence; he is a close and willing observer, for from these pictures he reads the meaning of life, and by these processes he trains himself for life. And it is perhaps not only the agreeable and friendly pictures that he realises in himself with such perfect understanding: the earnest, the troubled, the dreary, the gloomy, the sudden checks, the tricks of fortune, the uneasy presentiments, in short, the whole "Divine Comedy" of life, and the Inferno, also pass before him, not merely like pictures on the wall—for he too lives and suffers in these scenes,—and yet not without that fleeting sensation of appearance. And perhaps many a one will, like myself, recollect having sometimes called out cheeringly and not without success amid the dangers and terrors of dream-life: "It is a dream! I will dream on!" I have likewise been told of persons capable of continuing the causality of one and the same dream for three and even more successive nights: all of which facts clearly testify that our innermost being, the common substratum of all of us, experiences our dreams with deep joy and cheerful acquiescence.

This cheerful acquiescence in the dream-experience has likewise been embodied by the Greeks in their Apollo: for Apollo, as the god of all shaping energies, is also the soothsaying god. He, who (as the etymology of the name indicates) is the "shining one," the deity of light, also rules over the fair appearance of the inner world of fantasies. The higher truth, the perfection of these states in contrast to the only partially intelligible everyday world, ay, the deep consciousness of nature, healing and helping in sleep and dream, is at the same time the symbolical analogue of the faculty of soothsaying and, in general, of the arts, through which life is made possible and worth living. But also that delicate line, which the dream-picture must not overstep—lest it act pathologically (in which case appearance, being reality pure and simple, would impose upon us)—must not be wanting in the picture of Apollo: that measured limitation, that freedom from the wilder emotions, that philosophical calmness of the sculptor-god. His eye must be "sunlike," according to his origin; even when it is angry and looks displeased, the sacredness of his beauteous appearance is still there. And so we might apply to Apollo, in an eccentric sense, what Schopenhauer in *The World as Will and Idea* says of the man wrapt in the veil of Mâyâ: "Just as in a stormy sea, unbounded in every direction, rising and falling with howling mountainous waves, a sailor sits in a boat and trusts in his frail barque: so in the midst of a world of sorrows the individual sits quietly supported by and trusting in his *principium individuationis.*" Indeed, we might say of Apollo, that in him the unshaken faith in this *principium* and the quiet sitting of the man wrapt therein have received their sublimest expression; and we might even designate Apollo as the glorious divine image of the *principium individuationis,* from out of the gestures and looks of which all the joy and wisdom of "appearance," together with its beauty, speak to us.

In the same work Schopenhauer has described to us the stupendous awe which seizes upon man, when of a sudden he is at a loss to account for the cognitive forms of a phenomenon, in that the principle of reason, in some one of its manifestations, seems to admit of an exception. Add to this awe the blissful ecstasy which rises from the innermost depths of man, ay, of nature, at this same collapse of the *principium individuationis,* and we shall gain an insight into the being of the Dionysian, which is brought within closest ken perhaps by the analogy of drunkenness. It is either under the influence of the narcotic draught, of which the hymns of all primitive men and peoples tell us, or by the powerful approach of spring penetrating all nature with joy, that those Dionysian emotions awake, in the augmentation of which the subjective vanishes to complete self-forgetfulness. So also in the German Middle Ages singing and dancing crowds, ever increasing in number, were borne from place to place under this same Dionysian power. In these St. John's and St. Vitus's dancers we again perceive the Bacchic choruses of the Greeks, with their previous history in Asia Minor, as far back as Babylon and the orgiastic Sacæa. There are some, who, from lack of experience or obtuseness, will turn away from such phenomena as "folk-diseases" with a smile of contempt or pity prompted by the consciousness of their own health: of course, the poor wretches do not divine what a cadaverous-looking and ghastly aspect this very "Health" of theirs presents when the glowing life of the Dionysian revellers rushes past them.

Under the charm of the Dionysian not only is the covenant between man and man again established, but also estranged, hostile or subjugated nature again celebrates her reconciliation with her lost son, man. Of her own accord earth proffers her gifts, and peacefully the beasts of prey approach from the desert and the rocks. The chariot of Dionysus is bedecked with flowers and garlands: panthers and tigers pass beneath his yoke. Change Beethoven's "jubilee-song" into a painting, and, if your imagination be equal to the occasion when the awe-struck millions sink into the dust, you will then be able to approach the Dionysian. Now is the slave a free man, now all the stubborn, hostile barriers, which necessity, caprice, or "shameless fashion" has set up between man and man, are broken down. Now, at the evangel of cosmic harmony, each one feels himself not only united, reconciled, blended with his neighbour, but as one with him, as if the veil of Mâyâ had been torn and were now merely fluttering in tatters before the mysterious Primordial Unity. In song and in dance man exhibits himself as a member of a higher community: he has forgotten how to walk and speak, and is on the point of taking a dancing flight into the air. His gestures bespeak enchantment. Even as the animals now talk, and as the earth yields milk, and honey, so also something supernatural sounds forth from him: he feels himself a god, he himself now walks about enchanted and elated even as the gods whom he saw walking about in his dreams. Man is no longer an artist, he has become a work of art: the artistic power of all nature here reveals itself in the tremors of drunkenness to the highest gratification of the Primordial Unity. The noblest clay, the costliest marble, namely man, is here kneaded and cut, and the chisel strokes of the Dionysion world-artist are accompanied with the cry of the Eleusinian mysteries: "Ihr stürzt nieder, Millionen? Ahnest du den Schöpfer, Welt?"[4]

2.

Thus far we have considered the Apollonian and his antithesis, the Dionysian, as artistic powers, which burst forth from nature herself, without the mediation of the human artist, and in which her art-impulses are satisfied in the most immediate and direct way: first, as the pictorial world of dreams, the perfection of which has no connection whatever with the intellectual height or artistic culture of the unit man, and again, as drunken reality, which likewise does not heed the unit man, but even seeks to destroy the individual and redeem him by a mystic feeling of Oneness. Anent these immediate art-states of nature every artist is either an "imitator," to wit, either an Apollonian, an artist in dreams, or a Dionysian, an artist in ecstasies, or finally—as for instance in Greek tragedy—an artist in both dreams and ecstasies: so we may perhaps picture him, as in his Dionysian drunkenness and mystical self-abnegation, lonesome and apart from the revelling choruses, he sinks down, and how now, through Apollonian dream-inspiration, his own state, *i.e.,* his oneness with the primal source of the universe, reveals itself to him in a symbolical dream-picture.

After these general premisings and contrastings, let us now approach the Greeks in order to learn in what degree and to what height these art-impulses of nature were developed in them: whereby we shall be enabled to understand and appreciate more deeply the relation of the Greek artist to his archetypes, or, according to the Aristotelian expression, "the imitation of nature." In spite of all the dream-literature and the numerous dream-anecdotes of the Greeks, we can speak only conjecturally, though with a fair degree of certainty, of their dreams. Considering the incredibly precise and unerring plastic power of their eyes, as also their manifest and sincere delight in colours, we can hardly refrain (to the shame of every one born later) from assuming for their very dreams a logical causality of lines and contours, colours and groups, a sequence of scenes resembling their best reliefs, the perfection of which would certainly justify us, if a comparison were possible, in designating the dreaming Greeks as Homers and Homer as a dreaming Greek: in a deeper sense than when modern man, in respect to his dreams, ventures to compare himself with Shakespeare.

On the other hand, we should not have to speak conjecturally, if asked to disclose the immense gap which separated the Dionysian Greek from the Dionysian barbarian. From all quarters of the Ancient World—to say nothing of the modern—from Rome as far as Babylon, we can prove the existence of Dionysian festivals, the type of which bears, at best, the same relation to the Greek festivals as the bearded satyr, who borrowed his name and attributes from the goat, does to Dionysus himself. In nearly every instance the centre of these festivals lay in extravagant sexual licentiousness, the waves of which overwhelmed all family life and its venerable traditions; the very wildest beasts of nature were let loose here, including that detestable mixture of lust and cruelty which has always seemed to me the genuine "witches' draught." For some time, however, it would seem that the Greeks were perfectly secure and guarded against the feverish agitations of these festivals (—the knowledge of which entered Greece by all the channels of land and sea) by the figure of Apollo himself rising here in full pride, who could not have held out the Gorgon's head to a more dangerous power than this grotesquely uncouth Dionysian. It is in Doric art that this majestically-reject-ing attitude of Apollo perpetuated itself. This opposition became more precarious and even impossible, when, from out of the deepest root of the Hellenic nature, similar impulses finally broke forth and made way for themselves: the Delphic god, by a seasonably effected reconciliation, was now contented with taking the destructive arms from the hands of his powerful antagonist. This reconciliation marks the most important moment in the history of the Greek cult: wherever we turn our eyes we may observe the revolutions resulting from this event. It was the reconciliation of two antagonists, with the sharp demarcation of the boundary-lines to be thenceforth observed by each, and with periodical transmission of testimonials;—in reality, the chasm was not bridged over. But if we observe how, under the pressure of this conclusion of peace, the Dionysian power manifested itself, we shall now recognise in the Dionysian orgies of the Greeks, as compared with the Babylonian Sacæa and their retrogression of man to the tiger and the ape, the significance of festivals of world-redemption and days of transfiguration. Not till then does nature attain her artistic jubilee; not till then does the rapture of the *principium individuationis* become an artistic phenomenon. That horrible "witches' draught" of sensuality and cruelty was here powerless: only the curious blending and duality in the emotions of the Dionysian revellers reminds one of it—just as medicines remind one of deadly poisons,—that phenomenon, to wit, that pains beget joy, that jubilation wrings painful sounds out of the breast. From the highest joy sounds the cry of horror or the yearning wail over an irretrievable loss. In these Greek festivals a sentimental trait, as it were, breaks forth from nature, as if she must sigh over her dismemberment into individuals. The song and pantomime of such dually-minded revellers was something new and unheard-of in the Homeric-Grecian world: and the Dionysian music in particular excited awe and horror. If music, as it would seem, was previously known as an Apollonian art, it was, strictly speaking, only as the wave-beat of rhythm, the formative power of which was developed to the representation of Apollonian conditions. The music of Apollo was Doric architectonics in tones, but in merely suggested tones, such as those of the cithara. The very element which forms the essence of Dionysian music (and hence of music in general) is carefully excluded as un-Apollonian; namely the thrilling power of the tone, the uniform stream of the melos, and the thoroughly incomparable world of harmony. In the Dionysian dithyramb man is incited to the highest exaltation of all his symbolic faculties; something never before experienced struggles for utterance—the annihilation of the veil of Mâyâ, Oneness as genius of the race, ay, of nature. The essence of nature is now to be expressed symbolically; a new world of symbols is required; for once the entire symbolism of the body, not only the symbolism of the lips, face, and speech, but the whole pantomime of dancing which sets all the members into rhythmical motion. Thereupon the other symbolic powers, those of music, in rhythmics, dynamics, and harmony, suddenly become impetuous. To comprehend this collective discharge of all the symbolic powers, a man must have already attained that height of self-abnegation, which wills to express itself symbolically through these powers: the Dithyrambic votary of Dionysus is therefore understood only by those like himself! With what astonishment must the Apollonian Greek have beheld him! With an astonishment, which was all the greater the more it was mingled with the shuddering suspicion that all this was in reality not so very foreign to him, yea, that, like unto a veil, his Apollonian consciousness only hid this Dionysian world from his view.

3.

In order to comprehend this, we must take down the artistic structure of the Apollonian culture, as it were, stone by stone, till we behold the foundations on which it rests. Here we observe first of all the glorious Olympian figures of the gods, standing on the gables of this structure, whose deeds, represented in far-shining reliefs, adorn its friezes. Though Apollo stands among them as an individual deity, side by side with others, and without claim to priority of rank, we must not suffer this fact to mislead us. The same impulse which embodied itself in Apollo has, in general, given birth to this whole Olympian world, and in this sense we may regard Apollo as the father thereof. What was the enormous need from which proceeded such an illustrious group of Olympian beings?

Whosoever, with another religion in his heart, approaches these Olympians and seeks among them for moral elevation, even for sanctity, for incorporeal spiritualisation, for sympathetic looks of love, will soon be obliged to turn his back on them, discouraged and disappointed. Here nothing suggests asceticism, spirituality, or duty: here only an exuberant, even triumphant life speaks to us, in which everything existing is deified, whether good or bad. And so the spectator will perhaps stand quite bewildered before this fantastic exuberance of life, and ask himself what magic potion these madly merry men could have used for enjoying life, so that, wherever they turned their eyes, Helena, the ideal image of their own existence "floating in sweet sensuality," smiled upon them. But to this spectator, already turning backwards, we must call out: "depart not hence, but hear rather what Greek folk-wisdom says of this same life, which with such inexplicable cheerfulness spreads out before thee. There is an ancient story that king Midas hunted in the forest a long time for the wise Silenus, the companion of Dionysus, without capturing him. When at last he fell into his hands, the king asked what was best of all and most desirable for man. Fixed and immovable, the demon remained silent; till at last, forced by the king, he broke out with shrill laughter into these words: "Oh, wretched race of a day, children of chance and misery, why do ye compel me to say to you what it were most expedient for you not to hear? What is best of all is for ever beyond your reach: not to be born, not to be, to be nothing. The second best for you, however, is soon to die."

How is the Olympian world of deities related to this folk-wisdom? Even as the rapturous vision of the tortured martyr to his sufferings.

Now the Olympian magic mountain opens, as it were, to our view and shows to us its roots. The Greek knew and felt the terrors and horrors of existence: to be able to live at all, he had to interpose the shining dream-birth of the Olympian world between himself and them. The excessive distrust of the titanic powers of nature, the Moira throning inexorably over all knowledge, the vulture of the great philanthropist Prometheus, the terrible fate of the wise Œdipus, the family curse of the Atridæ which drove Orestes to matricide; in short, that entire philosophy of the sylvan god, with its mythical exemplars, which wrought the ruin of the melancholy Etruscans—was again and again surmounted anew by the Greeks through the artistic middle world of the Olympians, or at least veiled and withdrawn from sight. To be able to live, the Greeks had, from direst necessity, to create these gods: which process we may perhaps picture to ourselves in this manner: that out of the original Titan thearchy of terror the Olympian thearchy of joy was evolved, by slow transitions, through the Apollonian impulse to beauty, even as roses break forth from thorny bushes. How else could this so sensitive people, so vehement in its desires, so singularly qualified for suffering, have endured existence, if it had not been exhibited to them in their gods, surrounded with a higher glory? The same impulse which calls art into being, as the complement and consummation of existence, seducing to a continuation of life, caused also the Olympian world to arise, in which the Hellenic "will" held up before itself a transfiguring mirror. Thus do the gods justify the life of man, in that they themselves live it—the only satisfactory Theodicy! Existence under the bright sunshine of such gods is regarded as that which is desirable in itself, and the real grief of the Homeric men has reference to parting from it, especially to early parting: so that we might now say of them, with a reversion of the Silenian wisdom, that "to die early is worst of all for them, the second worst is—some day to die at all." If once the lamentation is heard, it will ring out again, of the short-lived Achilles, of the leaf-like change and vicissitude of the human race, of the decay of the heroic age. It is not unworthy of the greatest hero to long for a continuation of life, ay, even as a day-labourer. So vehemently does the "will," at the Apollonian stage of development, long for this existence, so completely at one does the Homeric man feel himself with it, that the very lamentation becomes its song of praise.

Here we must observe that this harmony which is so eagerly contemplated by modern man, in fact, this oneness of man with nature, to express which Schiller introduced the technical term "naïve," is by no means such a simple, naturally resulting and, as it were, inevitable condition, which must be found at the gate of every culture leading to a paradise of man: this could be believed only by an age which sought to picture to itself Rousseau's Émile also as an artist, and imagined it had found in Homer such an artist Émile, reared at Nature's bosom. Wherever we meet with the "naïve" in art, it behoves us to recognise the highest effect of the Apollonian culture, which in the first place has always to overthrow some Titanic empire and slay monsters, and which, through powerful dazzling representations and pleasurable illusions, must have triumphed over a terrible depth of world-contemplation and a most keen susceptibility to suffering. But how seldom is the naïve—that complete absorption in the beauty of appearance—attained! And hence how inexpressibly sublime is Homer, who, as unit being, bears the same relation to this Apollonian folk-culture as the unit dream-artist does to the dream-faculty of the people and of Nature in general. The Homeric "naïveté" can be comprehended only as the complete triumph of the Apollonian illusion: it is the same kind of illusion as Nature so frequently employs to compass her ends. The true goal is veiled by a phantasm: we stretch out our hands for the latter, while Nature attains the former through our illusion. In the Greeks the "will" desired to contemplate itself in the transfiguration of the genius and the world of art; in order to glorify themselves, its creatures had to feel themselves worthy of glory; they had to behold themselves again in a higher sphere, without this consummate world of contemplation acting as an imperative or reproach. Such is the sphere of beauty, in which, as in a mirror, they saw their images, the Olympians. With this mirroring of beauty the Hellenic will combated its talent—correlative to the artistic—for suffering and for the wisdom of suffering: and, as a monument of its victory, Homer, the naïve artist, stands before us.

4.

Concerning this naïve artist the analogy of dreams will enlighten us to some extent. When we realise to ourselves the dreamer, as, in the midst of the illusion of the dream-world and without disturbing it, he calls out to himself: "it is a dream, I will dream on"; when we must thence infer a deep inner joy in dream-contemplation; when, on the other hand, to be at all able to dream with this inner joy in contemplation, we must have completely forgotten the day and its terrible obtrusiveness, we may, under the direction of the dream-reading Apollo, interpret all these phenomena to ourselves somewhat as follows. Though it is certain that of the two halves of life, the waking and the dreaming, the former appeals to us as by far the more preferred, important, excellent and worthy of being lived, indeed, as that which alone is lived: yet, with reference to that mysterious ground of our being of which we are the phenomenon, I should, paradoxical as it may seem, be inclined to maintain the very opposite estimate of the value of dream life. For the more clearly I perceive in nature those all-powerful art impulses, and in them a fervent longing for appearance, for redemption through appearance, the more I feel myself driven to the metaphysical assumption that the Verily-Existent and Primordial Unity, as the Eternally Suffering and Self-Contradictory, requires the rapturous vision, the joyful appearance, for its continuous salvation: which appearance we, who are completely wrapt in it and composed of it, must regard as the Verily Non-existent,—i.e., as a perpetual unfolding in time, space and causality,—in other words, as empiric reality. If we therefore waive the consideration of our own "reality" for the present, if we conceive our empiric existence, and that of the world generally, as a representation of the Primordial Unity generated every moment, we shall then have to regard the dream as an appearance of appearance, hence as a still higher gratification of the primordial desire for appearance. It is for this same reason that the innermost heart of Nature experiences that indescribable joy in the naïve artist and in the naïve work of art, which is likewise only "an appearance of appearance." In a symbolic painting, Raphael, himself one of these immortal "naïve" ones, has represented to us this depotentiating of appearance to appearance, the primordial process of the naïve artist and at the same time of Apollonian culture. In his *Transfiguration,* the lower half, with the possessed boy, the despairing bearers, the helpless, terrified disciples, shows to us the reflection of eternal primordial pain, the sole basis of the world: the "appearance" here is the counter-appearance of eternal Contradiction, the father of things. Out of this appearance then arises, like an ambrosial vapour, a visionlike new world of appearances, of which those wrapt in the first appearance see nothing—a radiant floating in purest bliss and painless Contemplation beaming from wide-open eyes. Here there is presented to our view, in the highest symbolism of art, that Apollonian world of beauty and its substratum, the terrible wisdom of Silenus, and we comprehend, by intuition, their necessary interdependence. Apollo, however, again appears to us as the apotheosis of the *principium individuationis,* in which alone the perpetually attained end of the Primordial Unity, its redemption through appearance, is consummated: he shows us, with sublime attitudes, how the entire world of torment is necessary, that thereby the individual may be impelled to realise the redeeming vision, and then, sunk in contemplation thereof, quietly sit in his fluctuating barque, in the midst of the sea.

This apotheosis of individuation, if it be at all conceived as imperative and laying down precepts, knows but one law—the individual, i.e., the observance of the boundaries of the individual, measure in the Hellenic sense. Apollo, as ethical deity, demands due proportion of his disciples, and, that this may be observed, he demands self-knowledge. And thus, parallel to the æsthetic necessity for beauty, there run the demands "know thyself" and "not too much," while presumption and undueness are regarded as the truly hostile demons of the non-Apollonian sphere, hence as characteristics of the pre-Apollonian age, that of the Titans, and of the extra-Apollonian world, that of the barbarians. Because of his Titan-like love for man, Prometheus had to be torn to pieces by vultures; because of his excessive wisdom, which solved the riddle of the Sphinx, Œdipus had to plunge into a bewildering vortex of monstrous crimes: thus did the Delphic god interpret the Grecian past.

So also the effects wrought by the Dionysian appeared "titanic" and "barbaric" to the Apollonian Greek: while at the same time he could not conceal from himself that he too was inwardly related to these overthrown Titans and heroes. Indeed, he had to recognise still more than this: his entire existence, with all its beauty and moderation, rested on a hidden substratum of suffering and of knowledge, which was again disclosed to him by the Dionysian. And lo! Apollo could not live without Dionysus! The "titanic" and the "barbaric" were in the end not less necessary than the Apollonian. And now let us imagine to ourselves how the ecstatic tone of the Dionysian festival sounded in ever more luring and bewitching strains into this artificially confined world built on appearance and moderation, how in these strains all the undueness of nature, in joy, sorrow, and knowledge, even to the transpiercing shriek, became audible: let us ask ourselves what meaning could be attached to the psalmodising artist of Apollo, with the phantom harp-sound, as compared with this demonic folk-song! The muses of the arts of "appearance" paled before an art which, in its intoxication, spoke the truth, the wisdom of Silenus cried "woe! woe!" against the cheerful Olympians. The individual, with all his boundaries and due proportions, went under in the self-oblivion of the Dionysian states and forgot the Apollonian precepts. The Undueness revealed itself as truth, contradiction, the bliss born of pain, declared itself out of the heart of nature. And thus, wherever the Dionysian prevailed, the Apollonian was routed and annihilated. But it is quite as certain that, where the first assault was successfully withstood, the authority and majesty of the Delphic god exhibited itself as more rigid and menacing than ever. For I can only explain to myself the Doric state and Doric art as a permanent war-camp of the Apollonian: only by incessant opposition to the titanic-barbaric nature of the Dionysian was it possible for an art so defiantly-prim, so encompassed with bulwarks, a training so warlike and rigorous, a constitution so cruel and relentless, to last for any length of time.

Up to this point we have enlarged upon the observation made at the beginning of this essay: how the Dionysian and the Apollonian, in ever new births succeeding and mutually augmenting one another, controlled the Hellenic genius: how from out the age of "bronze," with its Titan struggles and rigorous folk-philosophy, the Homeric world develops under the fostering sway of the Apollonian impulse to beauty, how this "naïve" splendour is again overwhelmed by the inbursting flood of the Dionysian, and how against this new power the Apollonian rises to the austere majesty of Doric art and the Doric view of things. If, then, in this way, in the strife of these two hostile principles, the older Hellenic history falls into four great periods of art, we are now driven to inquire after the ulterior purpose of these unfoldings and processes, unless perchance we should regard the last-attained period, the period of Doric art, as the end and aim of these artistic impulses: and here the sublime and highly celebrated art-work of Attic tragedy and dramatic dithyramb presents itself to our view as the common goal of both these impulses, whose mysterious union, after many and long precursory struggles, found its glorious consummation in such a child,—which is at once Antigone and Cassandra.

5.

We now approach the real purpose of our investigation, which aims at acquiring a knowledge of the Dionyso-Apollonian genius and his artwork, or at least an anticipatory understanding of the mystery of the aforesaid union. Here we shall ask first of all where that new germ which subsequently developed into tragedy and dramatic dithyramb first makes itself perceptible in the Hellenic world. The ancients themselves supply the answer in symbolic form, when they place Homer and Archilochus as the forefathers and torch-bearers of Greek poetry side by side on gems, sculptures, etc., in the sure conviction that only these two thoroughly original compeers, from whom a stream of fire flows over the whole of Greek posterity, should be taken into consideration. Homer, the aged dreamer sunk in himself, the type of the Apollonian naïve artist, beholds now with astonishment the impassioned genius of the warlike votary of the muses, Archilochus, violently tossed to and fro on the billows of existence: and modern æsthetics could only add by way of interpretation, that here the "objective" artist is confronted by the first "subjective" artist. But this interpretation is of little service to us, because we know the subjective artist only as the poor artist, and in every type and elevation of art we demand specially and first of all the conquest of the Subjective, the redemption from the "ego" and the cessation of every individual will and desire; indeed, we find it impossible to believe in any truly artistic production, however insignificant, without objectivity, without pure, interestless contemplation. Hence our æsthetics must first solve the problem as to how the "lyrist" is possible as an artist: he who according to the experience of all ages continually says "I" and sings off to us the entire chromatic scale of his passions and desires. This very Archilochus appals us, alongside of Homer, by his cries of hatred and scorn, by the drunken outbursts of his desire. Is not just he then, who has been called the first subjective artist, the non-artist proper? But whence then the reverence which was shown to him—the poet—in very remarkable utterances by the Delphic oracle itself, the focus of "objective" art?

Schiller has enlightened us concerning his poetic procedure by a psychological observation, inexplicable to himself, yet not apparently open to any objection. He acknowledges that as the preparatory state to the act of poetising he had not perhaps before him or within him a series of pictures with co-ordinate causality of thoughts, but rather a musical mood ("The perception with me is at first without a clear and definite object; this forms itself later. A certain musical mood of mind precedes, and only after this does the poetical idea follow with me."). Add to this the most important phenomenon of all ancient lyric poetry, the union, regarded everywhere as natural, of the lyrist with the musician, their very identity, indeed,—compared with which our modern lyric poetry is like the statue of a god without a head,—and we may now, on the basis of our metaphysics of æsthetics set forth above, interpret the lyrist to ourselves as follows. As Dionysian artist he is in the first place become altogether one with the Primordial Unity, its pain and contradiction, and he produces the copy of this Primordial Unity as music, granting that music has been correctly termed a repetition and a recast of the world; but now, under the Apollonian dream-inspiration, this music again becomes visible to him as in a symbolic dream-picture. The formless and intangible reflection of the primordial pain in music, with its redemption in appearance, then generates a second mirroring as a concrete symbol or example. The artist has already surrendered his subjectivity in the Dionysian process: the picture which now shows to him his oneness with the heart of the world, is a dream-scene, which embodies the primordial contradiction and primordial pain, together with the primordial joy, of appearance. The "I" of the lyrist sounds therefore from the abyss of being: its "subjectivity," in the sense of the modern æsthetes, is a fiction. When Archilochus, the first lyrist of the Greeks, makes known both his mad love and his contempt to the daughters of Lycambes, it is not his passion which dances before us in orgiastic frenzy: we see Dionysus and the Mænads, we see the drunken reveller Archilochus sunk down to sleep—as Euripides depicts it in the Bacchæ, the sleep on the high Alpine pasture, in the noonday sun:—and now Apollo approaches and touches him with the laurel. The Dionyso-musical enchantment of the sleeper now emits, as it were, picture sparks, lyrical poems, which in their highest development are called tragedies and dramatic dithyrambs.

The plastic artist, as also the epic poet, who is related to him, is sunk in the pure contemplation of pictures. The Dionysian musician is, without any picture, himself just primordial pain and the primordial reechoing thereof. The lyric genius is conscious of a world of pictures and symbols—growing out of the state of mystical self-abnegation and oneness,—which has a colouring causality and velocity quite different from that of the world of the plastic artist and epic poet. While the latter lives in these pictures, and only in them, with joyful satisfaction, and never grows tired of contemplating them with love, even in their minutest characters, while even the picture of the angry Achilles is to him but a picture, the angry expression of which he enjoys with the dream-joy in appearance—so that, by this mirror of appearance, he is guarded against being unified and blending with his figures;—the pictures of the lyrist on the other hand are nothing but his very self and, as it were, only different projections of himself, on account of which he as the moving centre of this world is entitled to say "I": only of course this self is not the same as that of the waking, empirically real man, but the only verily existent and eternal self resting at the basis of things, by means of the images whereof the lyric genius sees through even to this basis of things. Now let us suppose that he beholds himself also among these images as non-genius, i.e., his subject, the whole throng of subjective passions and impulses of the will directed to a definite object which appears real to him; if now it seems as if the lyric genius and the allied non-genius were one, and as if the former spoke the little word "I" of his own accord, this appearance will no longer be able to lead us astray, as it certainly led those astray who designated the lyrist as the subjective poet. In truth, Archilochus, the passionately inflamed, loving and hating man, is but a vision of the genius, who by this time is no longer Archilochus, but a genius of the world, who expresses his primordial pain symbolically in the figure of the man Archilochus: while the subjectively willing and desiring man, Archilochus, can never at any time be a poet. It is by no means necessary, however, that the lyrist should see nothing but the phenomenon of the man Archilochus before him as a reflection of eternal being; and tragedy shows how far the visionary world of the lyrist may depart from this phenomenon, to which, of course, it is most intimately related.

Schopenhauer, who did not shut his eyes to the difficulty presented by the lyrist in the philosophical contemplation of art, thought he had found a way out of it, on which, however, I cannot accompany him; while he alone, in his profound metaphysics of music, held in his hands the means whereby this difficulty could be definitely removed: as I believe I have removed it here in his spirit and to his honour. In contrast to our view, he describes the peculiar nature of song as follows: "It is the subject of the will, i.e., his own volition, which fills the consciousness of the singer; often as an unbound and satisfied desire (joy), but still more often as a restricted desire (grief), always as an emotion, a passion, or an agitated frame of mind. Besides this, however, and along with it, by the sight of surrounding nature, the singer becomes conscious of himself as the subject of pure will-less knowing, the unbroken, blissful peace of which now appears, in contrast to the stress of desire, which is always restricted and always needy. The feeling of this contrast, this alternation, is really what the song as a whole expresses and what principally constitutes the lyrical state of mind. In it pure knowing comes to us as it were to deliver us from desire and the stress thereof: we follow, but only for an instant; for desire, the remembrance of our personal ends, tears us anew from peaceful contemplation; yet ever again the next beautiful surrounding in which the pure will-less knowledge presents itself to us, allures us away from desire. Therefore, in song and in the lyrical mood, desire (the personal interest of the ends) and the pure perception of the surrounding which presents itself, are wonderfully mingled with each other; connections between them are sought for and imagined; the subjective disposition, the affection of the will, imparts its own hue to the contemplated surrounding, and conversely, the surroundings communicate the reflex of their colour to the will. The true song is the expression of the whole of this mingled and divided state of mind."[5]

Who could fail to see in this description that lyric poetry is here characterised as an imperfectly attained art, which seldom and only as it were in leaps arrives at its goal, indeed, as a semi-art, the essence of which is said to consist in this, that desire and pure contemplation, i.e., the unæsthetic and the æsthetic condition, are wonderfully mingled with each other? We maintain rather, that this entire antithesis, according to which, as according to some standard of value, Schopenhauer, too, still classifies the arts, the antithesis between the subjective and the objective, is quite out of place in æsthetics, inasmuch as the subject, i.e., the desiring individual who furthers his own egoistic ends, can be conceived only as the adversary, not as the origin of art. In so far as the subject is the artist, however, he has already been released from his individual will, and has become as it were the medium, through which the one verily existent Subject celebrates his redemption in appearance. For this one thing must above all be clear to us, to our humiliation and exaltation, that the entire comedy of art is not at all performed, say, for our betterment and culture, and that we are just as little the true authors of this art-world: rather we may assume with regard to ourselves, that its true author uses us as pictures and artistic projections, and that we have our highest dignity in our significance as works of art—for only as an æsthetic phenomenon is existence and the world eternally justified:—while of course our consciousness of this our specific significance hardly differs from the kind of consciousness which the soldiers painted on canvas have of the battle represented thereon. Hence all our knowledge of art is at bottom quite illusory, because, as knowing persons we are not one and identical with the Being who, as the sole author and spectator of this comedy of art, prepares a perpetual entertainment for himself. Only in so far as the genius in the act of artistic production coalesces with this primordial artist of the world, does he get a glimpse of the eternal essence of art, for in this state he is, in a marvellous manner, like the weird picture of the fairy-tale which can at will turn its eyes and behold itself; he is now at once subject and object, at once poet, actor, and spectator.

6.

With reference to Archilochus, it has been established by critical research that he introduced the folk-song into literature, and, on account thereof, deserved, according to the general estimate of the Greeks, his unique position alongside of Homer. But what is this popular folk-song in contrast to the wholly Apollonian epos? What else but the *perpetuum vestigium* of a union of the Apollonian and the Dionysian? Its enormous diffusion among all peoples, still further enhanced by ever new births, testifies to the power of this artistic double impulse of nature: which leaves its vestiges in the popular song in like manner as the orgiastic movements of a people perpetuate themselves in its music. Indeed, one might also furnish historical proofs, that every period which is highly productive in popular songs has been most violently stirred by Dionysian currents, which we must always regard as the substratum and prerequisite of the popular song.

First of all, however, we regard the popular song as the musical mirror of the world, as the original melody, which now seeks for itself a parallel dream-phenomenon and expresses it in poetry. Melody is therefore primary and universal, and as such may admit of several objectivations, in several texts. Likewise, in the naïve estimation of the people, it is regarded as by far the more important and necessary. Melody generates the poem out of itself by an ever-recurring process. The strophic form of the popular song points to the same phenomenon, which I always beheld with astonishment, till at last I found this explanation. Any one who in accordance with this theory examines a collection of popular songs, such as "Des Knaben Wunderhorn," will find innumerable instances of the perpetually productive melody scattering picture sparks all around: which in their variegation, their abrupt change, their mad precipitance, manifest a power quite unknown to the epic appearance and its steady flow. From the point of view of the epos, this unequal and irregular pictorial world of lyric poetry must be simply condemned: and the solemn epic rhapsodists of the Apollonian festivals in the age of Terpander have certainly done so.

Accordingly, we observe that in the poetising of the popular song, language is strained to its utmost to imitate music; and hence a new world of poetry begins with Archilochus, which is fundamentally opposed to the Homeric. And in saying this we have pointed out the only possible relation between poetry and music, between word and tone: the word, the picture, the concept here seeks an expression analogous to music and now experiences in itself the power of music. In this sense we may discriminate between two main currents in the history of the language of the Greek people, according as their language imitated either the world of phenomena and of pictures, or the world of music. One has only to reflect seriously on the linguistic difference with regard to colour, syntactical structure, and vocabulary in Homer and Pindar, in order to comprehend the significance of this contrast; indeed, it becomes palpably clear to us that in the period between Homer and Pindar the orgiastic flute tones of Olympus must have sounded forth, which, in an age as late as Aristotle's, when music was infinitely more developed, transported people to drunken enthusiasm, and which, when their influence was first felt, undoubtedly incited all the poetic means of expression of contemporaneous man to imitation. I here call attention to a familiar phenomenon of our own times, against which our æsthetics raises many objections. We again and again have occasion to observe how a symphony of Beethoven compels the individual hearers to use figurative speech, though the appearance presented by a collocation of the different pictorial world generated by a piece of music may be never so fantastically diversified and even contradictory. To practise its small wit on such compositions, and to overlook a phenomenon which is certainly worth explaining, is quite in keeping with this æsthetics. Indeed, even if the tone-poet has spoken in pictures concerning a composition, when for instance he designates a certain symphony as the "pastoral" symphony, or a passage therein as "the scene by the brook," or another as the "merry gathering of rustics," these are likewise only symbolical representations born out of music—and not perhaps the imitated objects of music—representations which can give us no information whatever concerning the Dionysian content of music, and which in fact have no distinctive value of their own alongside of other pictorical expressions. This process of a discharge of music in pictures we have now to transfer to some youthful, linguistically productive people, to get a notion as to how the strophic popular song originates, and how the entire faculty of speech is stimulated by this new principle of imitation of music.

If, therefore, we may regard lyric poetry as the effulguration of music in pictures and concepts, we can now ask: "how does music appear in the mirror of symbolism and conception?" It appears as will, taking the word in the Schopenhauerian sense, i.e., as the antithesis of the æsthetic, purely contemplative, and passive frame of mind. Here, however, we must discriminate as sharply as possible between the concept of essentiality and the concept of phenominality; for music, according to its essence, cannot be will, because as such it would have to be wholly banished from the domain of art—for the will is the unæsthetic-in-itself;—yet it appears as will. For in order to express the phenomenon of music in pictures, the lyrist requires all the stirrings of passion, from the whispering of infant desire to the roaring of madness. Under the impulse to speak of music in Apollonian symbols, he conceives of all nature, and himself therein, only as the eternally willing, desiring, longing existence. But in so far as he interprets music by means of pictures, he himself rests in the quiet calm of Apollonian contemplation, however much all around him which he beholds through the medium of music is in a state of confused and violent motion. Indeed, when he beholds himself through this same medium, his own image appears to him in a state of unsatisfied feeling: his own willing, longing, moaning and rejoicing are to him symbols by which he interprets music. Such is the phenomenon of the lyrist: as Apollonian genius he interprets music through the image of the will, while he himself, completely released from the avidity of the will, is the pure, undimmed eye of day.

Our whole disquisition insists on this, that lyric poetry is dependent on the spirit of music just as music itself in its absolute sovereignty does not require the picture and the concept, but only endures them as accompaniments. The poems of the lyrist can express nothing which has not already been contained in the vast universality and absoluteness of the music which compelled him to use figurative speech. By no means is it possible for language adequately to render the cosmic symbolism of music, for the very reason that music stands in symbolic relation to the primordial contradiction and primordial pain in the heart of the Primordial Unity, and therefore symbolises a sphere which is above all appearance and before all phenomena. Rather should we say that all phenomena, compared with it, are but symbols: hence language, as the organ and symbol of phenomena, cannot at all disclose the innermost essence of music; language can only be in superficial contact with music when it attempts to imitate music; while the profoundest significance of the latter cannot be brought one step nearer to us by all the eloquence of lyric poetry.

7.

We shall now have to avail ourselves of all the principles of art hitherto considered, in order to find our way through the labyrinth, as we must designate the origin of Greek tragedy. I shall not be charged with absurdity in saying that the problem of this origin has as yet not even been seriously stated, not to say solved, however often the fluttering tatters of ancient tradition have been sewed together in sundry combinations and torn asunder again. This tradition tells us in the most unequivocal terms, that tragedy sprang from the tragic chorus, and was originally only chorus and nothing but chorus: and hence we feel it our duty to look into the heart of this tragic chorus as being the real proto-drama, without in the least contenting ourselves with current art-phraseology—according to which the chorus is the ideal spectator, or represents the people in contrast to the regal side of the scene. The latter explanatory notion, which sounds sublime to many a politician—that the immutable moral law was embodied by the democratic Athenians in the popular chorus, which always carries its point over the passionate excesses and extravagances of kings—may be ever so forcibly suggested by an observation of Aristotle: still it has no bearing on the original formation of tragedy, inasmuch as the entire antithesis of king and people, and, in general, the whole politico-social sphere, is excluded from the purely religious beginnings of tragedy; but, considering the well-known classical form of the chorus in Æschylus and Sophocles, we should even deem it blasphemy to speak here of the anticipation of a "constitutional representation of the people," from which blasphemy others have not shrunk, however. The ancient governments knew of no constitutional representation of the people *in praxi,* and it is to be hoped that they did not even so much as "anticipate" it in tragedy.

Much more celebrated than this political explanation of the chorus is the notion of A. W. Schlegel, who advises us to regard the chorus, in a manner, as the essence and extract of the crowd of spectators,—as the "ideal spectator." This view, when compared with the historical tradition that tragedy was originally only chorus, reveals itself in its true character, as a crude, unscientific, yet brilliant assertion, which, however, has acquired its brilliancy only through its concentrated form of expression, through the truly Germanic bias in favour of whatever is called "ideal," and through our momentary astonishment. For we are indeed astonished the moment we compare our well-known theatrical public with this chorus, and ask ourselves if it could ever be possible to idealise something analogous to the Greek chorus out of such a public. We tacitly deny this, and now wonder as much at the boldness of Schlegel's assertion as at the totally different nature of the Greek public. For hitherto we always believed that the true spectator, be he who he may, had always to remain conscious of having before him a work of art, and not an empiric reality: whereas the tragic chorus of the Greeks is compelled to recognise real beings in the figures of the stage. The chorus of the Oceanides really believes that it sees before it the Titan Prometheus, and considers itself as real as the god of the scene. And are we to own that he is the highest and purest type of spectator, who, like the Oceanides, regards Prometheus as real and present in body? And is it characteristic of the ideal spectator that he should run on the stage and free the god from his torments? We had believed in an æsthetic public, and considered the individual spectator the better qualified the more he was capable of viewing a work of art as art, that is, æsthetically; but now the Schlegelian expression has intimated to us, that the perfect ideal spectator does not at all suffer the world of the scenes to act æsthetically on him, but corporeo-empirically. Oh, these Greeks! we have sighed; they will upset our æsthetics! But once accustomed to it, we have reiterated the saying of Schlegel, as often as the subject of the chorus has been broached.

But the tradition which is so explicit here speaks against Schlegel: the chorus as such, without the stage,—the primitive form of tragedy,—and the chorus of ideal spectators do not harmonise. What kind of art would that be which was extracted from the concept of the spectator, and whereof we are to regard the "spectator as such" as the true form? The spectator without the play is something absurd. We fear that the birth of tragedy can be explained neither by the high esteem for the moral intelligence of the multitude nor by the concept of the spectator without the play; and we regard the problem as too deep to be even so much as touched by such superficial modes of contemplation.

An infinitely more valuable insight into the signification of the chorus had already been displayed by Schiller in the celebrated Preface to his Bride of Messina, where he regarded the chorus as a living wall which tragedy draws round herself to guard her from contact with the world of reality, and to preserve her ideal domain and poetical freedom.

It is with this, his chief weapon, that Schiller combats the ordinary conception of the natural, the illusion ordinarily required in dramatic poetry. He contends that while indeed the day on the stage is merely artificial, the architecture only symbolical, and the metrical dialogue purely ideal in character, nevertheless an erroneous view still prevails in the main: that it is not enough to tolerate merely as a poetical license that which is in reality the essence of all poetry. The introduction of the chorus is, he says, the decisive step by which war is declared openly and honestly against all naturalism in art.—It is, methinks, for disparaging this mode of contemplation that our would-be superior age has coined the disdainful catchword "pseudo-idealism." I fear, however, that we on the other hand with our present worship of the natural and the real have landed at the nadir of all idealism, namely in the region of cabinets of wax-figures. An art indeed exists also here, as in certain novels much in vogue at present: but let no one pester us with the claim that by this art the Schiller-Goethian "Pseudo-idealism" has been vanquished.

It is indeed an "ideal" domain, as Schiller rightly perceived, upon which the Greek satyric chorus, the chorus of primitive tragedy, was wont to walk, a domain raised far above the actual path of mortals. The Greek framed for this chorus the suspended scaffolding of a fictitious natural state and placed thereon fictitious natural beings. It is on this foundation that tragedy grew up, and so it could of course dispense from the very first with a painful portrayal of reality. Yet it is not an arbitrary world placed by fancy betwixt heaven and earth; rather is it a world possessing the same reality and trustworthiness that Olympus with its dwellers possessed for the believing Hellene. The satyr, as being the Dionysian chorist, lives in a religiously acknowledged reality under the sanction of the myth and cult. That tragedy begins with him, that the Dionysian wisdom of tragedy speaks through him, is just as surprising a phenomenon to us as, in general, the derivation of tragedy from the chorus. Perhaps we shall get a starting-point for our inquiry, if I put forward the proposition that the satyr, the fictitious natural being, is to the man of culture what Dionysian music is to civilization. Concerning this latter, Richard Wagner says that it is neutralised by music even as lamplight by daylight. In like manner, I believe, the Greek man of culture felt himself neutralised in the presence of the satyric chorus: and this is the most immediate effect of the Dionysian tragedy, that the state and society, and, in general, the gaps between man and man give way to an overwhelming feeling of oneness, which leads back to the heart of nature. The metaphysical comfort,—with which, as I have here intimated, every true tragedy dismisses us—that, in spite of the perpetual change of phenomena, life at bottom is indestructibly powerful and pleasurable, this comfort appears with corporeal lucidity as the satyric chorus, as the chorus of natural beings, who live ineradicable as it were behind all civilisation, and who, in spite of the ceaseless change of generations and the history of nations, remain for ever the same.

With this chorus the deep-minded Hellene, who is so singularly qualified for the most delicate and severe suffering, consoles himself:—he who has glanced with piercing eye into the very heart of the terrible destructive processes of so-called universal history, as also into the cruelty of nature, and is in danger of longing for a Buddhistic negation of the will. Art saves him, and through art life saves him—for herself.

For we must know that in the rapture of the Dionysian state, with its annihilation of the ordinary bounds and limits of existence, there is a lethargic element, wherein all personal experiences of the past are submerged. It is by this gulf of oblivion that the everyday world and the world of Dionysian reality are separated from each other. But as soon as this everyday reality rises again in consciousness, it is felt as such, and nauseates us; an ascetic will-paralysing mood is the fruit of these states. In this sense the Dionysian man may be said to resemble Hamlet: both have for once seen into the true nature of things,—they have perceived, but they are loath to act; for their action cannot change the eternal nature of things; they regard it as shameful or ridiculous that one should require of them to set aright the time which is out of joint. Knowledge kills action, action requires the veil of illusion—it is this lesson which Hamlet teaches, and not the cheap wisdom of John-a-Dreams who from too much reflection, as it were from a surplus of possibilities, does not arrive at action at all. Not reflection, no!—true knowledge, insight into appalling truth, preponderates over all motives inciting to action, in Hamlet as well as in the Dionysian man. No comfort avails any longer; his longing goes beyond a world after death, beyond the gods themselves; existence with its glittering reflection in the gods, or in an immortal other world is abjured. In the consciousness of the truth he has perceived, man now sees everywhere only the awfulness or the absurdity of existence, he now understands the symbolism in the fate of Ophelia, he now discerns the wisdom of the sylvan god Silenus: and loathing seizes him.

Here, in this extremest danger of the will, art approaches, as a saving and healing enchantress; she alone is able to transform these nauseating reflections on the awfulness or absurdity of existence into representations wherewith it is possible to live: these are the representations of the sublime as the artistic subjugation of the awful, and the comic as the artistic delivery from the nausea of the absurd. The satyric chorus of dithyramb is the saving deed of Greek art; the paroxysms described above spent their force in the intermediary world of these Dionysian followers.

8.

The satyr, like the idyllic shepherd of our more recent time, is the offspring of a longing after the Primitive and the Natural; but mark with what firmness and fearlessness the Greek embraced the man of the woods, and again, how coyly and mawkishly the modern man dallied with the flattering picture of a tender, flute-playing, soft-natured shepherd! Nature, on which as yet no knowledge has been at work, which maintains unbroken barriers to culture—this is what the Greek saw in his satyr, which still was not on this account supposed to coincide with the ape. On the contrary: it was the archetype of man, the embodiment of his highest and strongest emotions, as the enthusiastic reveller enraptured by the proximity of his god, as the fellow-suffering companion in whom the suffering of the god repeats itself, as the herald of wisdom speaking from the very depths of nature, as the emblem of the sexual omnipotence of nature, which the Greek was wont to contemplate with reverential awe. The satyr was something sublime and godlike: he could not but appear so, especially to the sad and wearied eye of the Dionysian man. He would have been offended by our spurious tricked-up shepherd, while his eye dwelt with sublime satisfaction on the naked and unstuntedly magnificent characters of nature: here the illusion of culture was brushed away from the archetype of man; here the true man, the bearded satyr, revealed himself, who shouts joyfully to his god. Before him the cultured man shrank to a lying caricature. Schiller is right also with reference to these beginnings of tragic art: the chorus is a living bulwark against the onsets of reality, because it—the satyric chorus—portrays existence more truthfully, more realistically, more perfectly than the cultured man who ordinarily considers himself as the only reality. The sphere of poetry does not lie outside the world, like some fantastic impossibility of a poet's imagination: it seeks to be the very opposite, the unvarnished expression of truth, and must for this very reason cast aside the false finery of that supposed reality of the cultured man. The contrast between this intrinsic truth of nature and the falsehood of culture, which poses as the only reality, is similar to that existing between the eternal kernel of things, the thing in itself, and the collective world of phenomena. And even as tragedy, with its metaphysical comfort, points to the eternal life of this kernel of existence, notwithstanding the perpetual dissolution of phenomena, so the symbolism of the satyric chorus already expresses figuratively this primordial relation between the thing in itself and phenomenon. The idyllic shepherd of the modern man is but a copy of the sum of the illusions of culture which he calls nature; the Dionysian Greek desires truth and nature in their most potent form;—he sees himself metamorphosed into the satyr.

The revelling crowd of the votaries of Dionysus rejoices, swayed by such moods and perceptions, the power of which transforms them before their own eyes, so that they imagine they behold themselves as reconstituted genii of nature, as satyrs. The later constitution of the tragic chorus is the artistic imitation of this natural phenomenon, which of course required a separation of the Dionysian spectators from the enchanted Dionysians. However, we must never lose sight of the fact that the public of the Attic tragedy rediscovered itself in the chorus of the orchestra, that there was in reality no antithesis of public and chorus: for all was but one great sublime chorus of dancing and singing satyrs, or of such as allowed themselves to be represented by the satyrs. The Schlegelian observation must here reveal itself to us in a deeper sense. The chorus is the "ideal spectator" in so far as it is the only beholder, the beholder of the visionary world of the scene. A public of spectators, as known to us, was unknown to the Greeks. In their theatres the terraced structure of the spectators' space rising in concentric arcs enabled every one, in the strictest sense, to overlook the entire world of culture around him, and in surfeited contemplation to imagine himself a chorist. According to this view, then, we may call the chorus in its primitive stage in proto-tragedy, a self-mirroring of the Dionysian man: a phenomenon which may be best exemplified by the process of the actor, who, if he be truly gifted, sees hovering before his eyes with almost tangible perceptibility the character he is to represent. The satyric chorus is first of all a vision of the Dionysian throng, just as the world of the stage is, in turn, a vision of the satyric chorus: the power of this vision is great enough to render the eye dull and insensible to the impression of "reality," to the presence of the cultured men occupying the tiers of seats on every side. The form of the Greek theatre reminds one of a lonesome mountain-valley: the architecture of the scene appears like a luminous cloud-picture which the Bacchants swarming on the mountains behold from the heights, as the splendid encirclement in the midst of which the image of Dionysus is revealed to them.

Owing to our learned conception of the elementary artistic processes, this artistic proto-phenomenon, which is here introduced to explain the tragic chorus, is almost shocking: while nothing can be more certain then that the poet is a poet only in that he beholds himself surrounded by forms which live and act before him, into the innermost being of which his glance penetrates. By reason of a strange defeat in our capacities, we modern men are apt to represent to ourselves the æsthetic proto-phenomenon as too complex and abstract. For the true poet the metaphor is not a rhetorical figure, but a vicarious image which actually hovers before him in place of a concept. The character is not for him an aggregate composed of a studied collection of particular traits, but an irrepressibly live person appearing before his eyes, and differing only from the corresponding vision of the painter by its ever continued life and action. Why is it that Homer sketches much more vividly than all the other poets? Because he contemplates much more. We talk so abstractly about poetry, because we are all wont to be bad poets. At bottom the æsthetic phenomenon is simple: let a man but have the faculty of perpetually seeing a lively play and of constantly living surrounded by hosts of spirits, then he is a poet: let him but feel the impulse to transform himself and to talk from out the bodies and souls of others, then he is a dramatist.

The Dionysian excitement is able to impart to a whole mass of men this artistic faculty of seeing themselves surrounded by such a host of spirits, with whom they know themselves to be inwardly one. This function of the tragic chorus is the dramatic proto-phenomenon: to see one's self transformed before one's self, and then to act as if one had really entered into another body, into another character. This function stands at the beginning of the development of the drama. Here we have something different from the rhapsodist, who does not blend with his pictures, but only sees them, like the painter, with contemplative eye outside of him; here we actually have a surrender of the individual by his entering into another nature. Moreover this phenomenon appears in the form of an epidemic: a whole throng feels itself metamorphosed in this wise. Hence it is that the dithyramb is essentially different from every other variety of the choric song. The virgins, who with laurel twigs in their hands solemnly proceed to the temple of Apollo and sing a processional hymn, remain what they are and retain their civic names: the dithyrambic chorus is a chorus of transformed beings, whose civic past and social rank are totally forgotten: they have become the timeless servants of their god that live aloof from all the spheres of society. Every other variety of the choric lyric of the Hellenes is but an enormous enhancement of the Apollonian unit-singer: while in the dithyramb we have before us a community of unconscious actors, who mutually regard themselves as transformed among one another.

This enchantment is the prerequisite of all dramatic art. In this enchantment the Dionysian reveller sees himself as a satyr, and as satyr he in turn beholds the god, that is, in his transformation he sees a new vision outside him as the Apollonian consummation of his state. With this new vision the drama is complete.

According to this view, we must understand Greek tragedy as the Dionysian chorus, which always disburdens itself anew in an Apollonian world of pictures. The choric parts, therefore, with which tragedy is interlaced, are in a manner the motherwomb of the entire so-called dialogue, that is, of the whole stage-world, of the drama proper. In several successive outbursts does this primordial basis of tragedy beam forth the vision of the drama, which is a dream-phenomenon throughout, and, as such, epic in character: on the other hand, however, as objectivation of a Dionysian state, it does not represent the Apollonian redemption in appearance, but, conversely, the dissolution of the individual and his unification with primordial existence. Accordingly, the drama is the Apollonian embodiment of Dionysian perceptions and influences, and is thereby separated from the epic as by an immense gap.

The chorus of Greek tragedy, the symbol of the mass of the people moved by Dionysian excitement, is thus fully explained by our conception of it as here set forth. Whereas, being accustomed to the position of a chorus on the modern stage, especially an operatic chorus, we could never comprehend why the tragic chorus of the Greeks should be older, more primitive, indeed, more important than the "action" proper,—as has been so plainly declared by the voice of tradition; whereas, furthermore, we could not reconcile with this traditional paramount importance and primitiveness the fact of the chorus' being composed only of humble, ministering beings; indeed, at first only of goatlike satyrs; whereas, finally, the orchestra before the scene was always a riddle to us; we have learned to comprehend at length that the scene, together with the action, was fundamentally and originally conceived only as a vision, that the only reality is just the chorus, which of itself generates the vision and speaks thereof with the entire symbolism of dancing, tone, and word. This chorus beholds in the vision its lord and master Dionysus, and is thus for ever the serving chorus: it sees how he, the god, suffers and glorifies himself, and therefore does not itself act. But though its attitude towards the god is throughout the attitude of ministration, this is nevertheless the highest expression, the Dionysian expression of Nature, and therefore, like Nature herself, the chorus utters oracles and wise sayings when transported with enthusiasm: as fellow-sufferer it is also the sage proclaiming truth from out the heart of Nature. Thus, then, originates the fantastic figure, which seems so shocking, of the wise and enthusiastic satyr, who is at the same time "the dumb man" in contrast to the god: the image of Nature and her strongest impulses, yea, the symbol of Nature, and at the same time the herald of her art and wisdom: musician, poet, dancer, and visionary in one person.

Agreeably to this view, and agreeably to tradition, Dionysus, the proper stage-hero and focus of vision, is not at first actually present in the oldest period of tragedy, but is only imagined as present: i.e., tragedy is originally only "chorus" and not "drama." Later on the attempt is made to exhibit the god as real and to display the visionary figure together with its glorifying encirclement before the eyes of all; it is here that the "drama" in the narrow sense of the term begins. To the dithyrambic chorus is now assigned the task of exciting the minds of the hearers to such a pitch of Dionysian frenzy, that, when the tragic hero appears on the stage, they do not behold in him, say, the unshapely masked man, but a visionary figure, born as it were of their own ecstasy. Let us picture Admetes thinking in profound meditation of his lately departed wife Alcestis, and quite consuming himself in spiritual contemplation thereof—when suddenly the veiled figure of a woman resembling her in form and gait is led towards him: let us picture his sudden trembling anxiety, his agitated comparisons, his instinctive conviction—and we shall have an analogon to the sensation with which the spectator, excited to Dionysian frenzy, saw the god approaching on the stage, a god with whose sufferings he had already become identified. He involuntarily transferred the entire picture of the god, fluttering magically before his soul, to this masked figure and resolved its reality as it were into a phantasmal unreality. This is the Apollonian dream-state, in which the world of day is veiled, and a new world, clearer, more intelligible, more striking than the former, and nevertheless more shadowy, is ever born anew in perpetual change before our eyes. We accordingly recognise in tragedy a thorough-going stylistic contrast: the language, colour, flexibility and dynamics of the dialogue fall apart in the Dionysian lyrics of the chorus on the one hand, and in the Apollonian dream-world of the scene on the other, into entirely separate spheres of expression. The Apollonian appearances, in which Dionysus objectifies himself, are no longer "ein ewiges Meer, ein wechselnd Weben, ein glühend Leben" ("An eternal sea, A weaving, flowing, Life, all glowing"), as is the music of the chorus, they are no longer the forces merely felt, but not condensed into a picture, by which the inspired votary of Dionysus divines the proximity of his god: the clearness and firmness of epic form now speak to him from the scene, Dionysus now no longer speaks through forces, but as an epic hero, almost in the language of Homer.

9.

Whatever rises to the surface in the dialogue of the Apollonian part of Greek tragedy, appears simple, transparent, beautiful. In this sense the dialogue is a copy of the Hellene, whose nature reveals itself in the dance, because in the dance the greatest energy is merely potential, but betrays itself nevertheless in flexible and vivacious movements. The language of the Sophoclean heroes, for instance, surprises us by its Apollonian precision and clearness, so that we at once imagine we see into the innermost recesses of their being, and marvel not a little that the way to these recesses is so short. But if for the moment we disregard the character of the hero which rises to the surface and grows visible—and which at bottom is nothing but the light-picture cast on a dark wall, that is, appearance through and through,—if rather we enter into the myth which projects itself in these bright mirror-ings, we shall of a sudden experience a phenomenon which bears a reverse relation to one familiar in optics. When, after a vigorous effort to gaze into the sun, we turn away blinded, we have dark-coloured spots before our eyes as restoratives, so to speak; while, on the contrary, those light-picture phenomena of the Sophoclean hero,—in short, the Apollonian of the mask,—are the necessary productions of a glance into the secret and terrible things of nature, as it were shining spots to heal the eye which dire night has seared. Only in this sense can we hope to be able to grasp the true meaning of the serious and significant notion of "Greek cheerfulness"; while of course we encounter the misunderstood notion of this cheerfulness, as resulting from a state of unendangered comfort, on all the ways and paths of the present time.

The most sorrowful figure of the Greek stage, the hapless Œdipus, was understood by Sophocles as the noble man, who in spite of his wisdom was destined to error and misery, but nevertheless through his extraordinary sufferings ultimately exerted a magical, wholesome influence on all around him, which continues effective even after his death. The noble man does not sin; this is what the thoughtful poet wishes to tell us: all laws, all natural order, yea, the moral world itself, may be destroyed through his action, but through this very action a higher magic circle of influences is brought into play, which establish a new world on the ruins of the old that has been overthrown. This is what the poet, in so far as he is at the same time a religious thinker, wishes to tell us: as poet, he shows us first of all a wonderfully complicated legal mystery, which the judge slowly unravels, link by link, to his own destruction. The truly Hellenic delight at this dialectical loosening is so great, that a touch of surpassing cheerfulness is thereby communicated to the entire play, which everywhere blunts the edge of the horrible presuppositions of the procedure. In the *Œdipus at Colonus* we find the same cheerfulness, elevated, however, to an infinite transfiguration: in contrast to the aged king, subjected to an excess of misery, and exposed solely as a sufferer to all that befalls him, we have here a supermundane cheerfulness, which descends from a divine sphere and intimates to us that in his purely passive attitude the hero attains his highest activity, the influence of which extends far beyond his life, while his earlier conscious musing and striving led him only to passivity. Thus, then, the legal knot of the fable of Œdipus, which to mortal eyes appears indissolubly entangled, is slowly unravelled—and the profoundest human joy comes upon us in the presence of this divine counterpart of dialectics. If this explanation does justice to the poet, it may still be asked whether the substance of the myth is thereby exhausted; and here it turns out that the entire conception of the poet is nothing but the light-picture which healing nature holds up to us after a glance into the abyss. Œdipus, the murderer of his father, the husband of his mother, Œdipus, the interpreter of the riddle of the Sphinx! What does the mysterious triad of these deeds of destiny tell us? There is a primitive popular belief, especially in Persia, that a wise Magian can be born only of incest: which we have forthwith to interpret to ourselves with reference to the riddle-solving and mother-marrying Œdipus, to the effect that when the boundary of the present and future, the rigid law of individuation and, in general, the intrinsic spell of nature, are broken by prophetic and magical powers, an extraordinary counter-naturalness—as, in this case, incest—must have preceded as a cause; for how else could one force nature to surrender her secrets but by victoriously opposing her, i.e., by means of the Unnatural? It is this intuition which I see imprinted in the awful triad of the destiny of Œdipus: the very man who solves the riddle of nature—that double-constituted Sphinx—must also, as the murderer of his father and husband of his mother, break the holiest laws of nature. Indeed, it seems as if the myth sought to whisper into our ears that wisdom, especially Dionysian wisdom, is an unnatural abomination, and that whoever, through his knowledge, plunges nature into an abyss of annihilation, must also experience the dissolution of nature in himself. "The sharpness of wisdom turns round upon the sage: wisdom is a crime against nature": such terrible expressions does the myth call out to us: but the Hellenic poet touches like a sunbeam the sublime and formidable Memnonian statue of the myth, so that it suddenly begins to sound—in Sophoclean melodies.

With the glory of passivity I now contrast the glory of activity which illuminates the *Prometheus* of Æschylus. That which Æschylus the thinker had to tell us here, but which as a poet he only allows us to surmise by his symbolic picture, the youthful Goethe succeeded in disclosing to us in the daring words of his Prometheus:—

"Hier sitz' ich, forme Menschen
Nach meinem Bilde,
Ein Geschlecht, das mir gleich sei,
Zu leiden, zu weinen,
Zu geniessen und zu freuen sich,
Und dein nicht zu achten,
Wie ich!"[6]

Man, elevating himself to the rank of the Titans, acquires his culture by his own efforts, and compels the gods to unite with him, because in his self-sufficient wisdom he has their existence and their limits in his hand. What is most wonderful, however, in this Promethean form, which according to its fundamental conception is the specific hymn of impiety, is the profound Æschylean yearning for justice: the untold sorrow of the bold "single-handed being" on the one hand, and the divine need, ay, the foreboding of a twilight of the gods, on the other, the power of these two worlds of suffering constraining to reconciliation, to metaphysical oneness—all this suggests most forcibly the central and main position of the Æschylean view of things, which sees Moira as eternal justice enthroned above gods and men. In view of the astonishing boldness with which Æschylus places the Olympian world on his scales of justice, it must be remembered that the deep-minded Greek had an immovably firm substratum of metaphysical thought in his mysteries, and that all his sceptical paroxysms could be discharged upon the Olympians. With reference to these deities, the Greek artist, in particular, had an obscure feeling as to mutual dependency: and it is just in the Prometheus of Æschylus that this feeling is symbolised. The Titanic artist found in himself the daring belief that he could create men and at least destroy Olympian deities: namely, by his superior wisdom, for which, to be sure, he had to atone by eternal suffering. The splendid "can-ing" of the great genius, bought too cheaply even at the price of eternal suffering, the stern pride of the artist: this is the essence and soul of Æschylean poetry, while Sophocles in his Œdipus preludingly strikes up the victory-song of the saint. But even this interpretation which Æschylus has given to the myth does not fathom its astounding depth of terror; the fact is rather that the artist's delight in unfolding, the cheerfulness of artistic creating bidding defiance to all calamity, is but a shining stellar and nebular image reflected in a black sea of sadness. The tale of Prometheus is an original possession of the entire Aryan family of races, and documentary evidence of their capacity for the profoundly tragic; indeed, it is not improbable that this myth has the same characteristic significance for the Aryan race that the myth of the fall of man has for the Semitic, and that there is a relationship between the two myths like that of brother and sister. The presupposition of the Promethean myth is the transcendent value which a naïve humanity attach to fire as the true palladium of every ascending culture: that man, however, should dispose at will of this fire, and should not receive it only as a gift from heaven, as the igniting lightning or the warming solar flame, appeared to the contemplative primordial men as crime and robbery of the divine nature. And thus the first philosophical problem at once causes a painful, irreconcilable antagonism between man and God, and puts as it were a mass of rock at the gate of every culture. The best and highest that men can acquire they obtain by a crime, and must now in their turn take upon themselves its consequences, namely the whole flood of sufferings and sorrows with which the offended celestials must visit the nobly aspiring race of man: a bitter reflection, which, by the dignity it confers on crime, contrasts strangely with the Semitic myth of the fall of man, in which curiosity, beguilement, seducibility, wantonness,—in short, a whole series of pre-eminently feminine passions,—were regarded as the origin of evil. What distinguishes the Aryan representation is the sublime view of active sin as the properly Promethean virtue, which suggests at the same time the ethical basis of pessimistic tragedy as the justification of human evil—of human guilt as well as of the suffering incurred thereby. The misery in the essence of things—which the contemplative Aryan is not disposed to explain away—the antagonism in the heart of the world, manifests itself to him as a medley of different worlds, for instance, a Divine and a human world, each of which is in the right individually, but as a separate existence alongside of another has to suffer for its individuation. With the heroic effort made by the individual for universality, in his attempt to pass beyond the bounds of individuation and become the one universal being, he experiences in himself the primordial contradiction concealed in the essence of things, i.e., he trespasses and suffers. Accordingly crime is understood by the Aryans to be a man, sin by the Semites a woman; as also, the original crime is committed by man, the original sin by woman. Besides, the witches' chorus says:

> "Wir nehmen das nicht so genau:
> Mit tausend Schritten macht's die Frau;
> Doch wie sie auch sich eilen kann
> Mit einem Sprunge macht's der Mann."[7]

He who understands this innermost core of the tale of Prometheus—namely, the necessity of crime imposed on the titanically striving individual—will at once be conscious of the un-Apollonian nature of this pessimistic representation: for Apollo seeks to pacify individual beings precisely by drawing boundary-lines between them, and by again and again calling attention thereto, with his requirements of self-knowledge and due proportion, as the holiest laws of the universe. In order, however, to prevent the form from congealing to Egyptian rigidity and coldness in consequence of this Apollonian tendency, in order to prevent the extinction of the motion of the entire lake in the effort to prescribe to the individual wave its path and compass, the high tide of the Dionysian tendency destroyed from time to time all the little circles in which the one-sided Apollonian "will" sought to confine the Hellenic world. The suddenly swelling tide of the Dionysian then takes the separate little wave-mountains of individuals on its back, just as the brother of Prometheus, the Titan Atlas, does with the earth. This Titanic impulse, to become as it were the Atlas of all individuals, and to carry them on broad shoulders higher and higher, farther and farther, is what the Promethean and the Dionysian have in common. In this respect the Æschylean Prometheus is a Dionysian mask, while, in the afore-mentioned profound yearning for justice, Æschylus betrays to the intelligent observer his paternal descent from Apollo, the god of individuation and of the boundaries of justice. And so the double-being of the Æschylean Prometheus, his conjoint Dionysian and Apollonian nature, might be thus expressed in an abstract formula: "Whatever exists is alike just and unjust, and equally justified in both."

Das ist deine Welt! Das heisst eine Welt![8]

10.

It is an indisputable tradition that Greek tragedy in its earliest form had for its theme only the sufferings of Dionysus, and that for some time the only stage-hero therein was simply Dionysus himself. With the same confidence, however, we can maintain that not until Euripides did Dionysus cease to be the tragic hero, and that in fact all the celebrated figures of the Greek stage—Prometheus, Œdipus, etc.—are but masks of this original hero, Dionysus. The presence of a god behind all these masks is the one essential cause of the typical "ideality," so oft exciting wonder, of these celebrated figures. Some one, I know not whom, has maintained that all individuals are comic as individuals and are consequently un-tragic: from whence it might be inferred that the Greeks in general could not endure individuals on the tragic stage. And they really seem to have had these sentiments: as, in general, it is to be observed that the Platonic discrimination and valuation of the "idea" in contrast to the "eidolon," the image, is deeply rooted in the Hellenic being. Availing ourselves of Plato's terminology, however, we should have to speak of the tragic figures of the Hellenic stage somewhat as follows. The one truly real Dionysus appears in a multiplicity of forms, in the mask of a fighting hero and entangled, as it were, in the net of an individual will. As the visibly appearing god now talks and acts, he resembles an erring, striving, suffering individual: and that, in general, he appears with such epic precision and clearness, is due to the dream-reading Apollo, who reads to the chorus its Dionysian state through this symbolic appearance. In reality, however, this hero is the suffering Dionysus of the mysteries, a god experiencing in himself the sufferings of individuation, of whom wonderful myths tell that as a boy he was dismembered by the Titans and has been worshipped in this state as Zagreus: whereby is intimated that this dismemberment, the properly Dionysian suffering, is like a transformation into air, water, earth, and fire, that we must therefore regard the state of individuation as the source and primal cause of all suffering, as something objectionable in itself. From the smile of this Dionysus sprang the Olympian gods, from his tears sprang man. In his existence as a dismembered god, Dionysus has the dual nature of a cruel barbarised demon, and a mild pacific ruler. But the hope of the epopts looked for a new birth of Dionysus, which we have now to conceive of in anticipation as the end of individuation: it was for this coming third Dionysus that the stormy jubilation-hymns of the epopts resounded. And it is only this hope that sheds a ray of joy upon the features of a world torn asunder and shattered into individuals: as is symbolised in the myth by Demeter sunk in eternal sadness, who rejoices again only when told that she may once more give birth to Dionysus. In the views of things here given we already have all the elements of a profound and pessimistic contemplation of the world, and along with these we have the mystery doctrine of tragedy: the fundamental knowledge of the oneness of all existing things, the consideration of individuation as the primal cause of evil, and art as the joyous hope that the spell of individuation may be broken, as the augury of a restored oneness.

It has already been intimated that the Homeric epos is the poem of Olympian culture, wherewith this culture has sung its own song of triumph over the terrors of the war of the Titans. Under the predominating influence of tragic poetry, these Homeric myths are now reproduced anew, and show by this metempsychosis that meantime the Olympian culture also has been vanquished by a still deeper view of things. The haughty Titan Prometheus has announced to his Olympian tormentor that the extremest danger will one day menace his rule, unless he ally with him betimes. In Æschylus we perceive the terrified Zeus, apprehensive of his end, in alliance with the Titan. Thus, the former age of the Titans is subsequently brought from Tartarus once more to the light of day. The philosophy of wild and naked nature beholds with the undissembled mien of truth the myths of the Homeric world as they dance past: they turn pale, they tremble before the lightning glance of this goddess—till the powerful fist of the Dionysian artist forces them into the service of the new deity. Dionysian truth takes over the entire domain of myth as symbolism of its knowledge, which it makes known partly in the public cult of tragedy and partly in the secret celebration of the dramatic mysteries, always, however, in the old mythical garb. What was the power, which freed Prometheus from his vultures and transformed the myth into a vehicle of Dionysian wisdom? It is the Heracleian power of music: which, having reached its highest manifestness in tragedy, can invest myths with a new and most profound significance, which we have already had occasion to characterise as the most powerful faculty of music. For it is the fate of every myth to insinuate itself into the narrow limits of some alleged historical reality, and to be treated by some later generation as a solitary fact with historical claims: and the Greeks were already fairly on the way to restamp the whole of their mythical juvenile dream sagaciously and arbitrarily into a historico-pragmatical juvenile history. For this is the manner in which religions are wont to die out: when of course under the stern, intelligent eyes of an orthodox dogmatism, the mythical presuppositions of a religion are systematised as a completed sum of historical events, and when one begins apprehensively to defend the credibility of the myth, while at the same time opposing all continuation of their natural vitality and luxuriance; when, accordingly, the feeling for myth dies out, and its place is taken by the claim of religion to historical foundations. This dying myth was now seized by the new-born genius of Dionysian music, in whose hands it bloomed once more, with such colours as it had never yet displayed, with a fragrance that awakened a longing anticipation of a metaphysical world. After this final effulgence it collapses, its leaves wither, and soon the scoffing Lucians of antiquity catch at the discoloured and faded flowers which the winds carry off in every direction. Through tragedy the myth attains its profoundest significance, its most expressive form; it rises once more like a wounded hero, and the whole surplus of vitality, together with the philosophical calmness of the Dying, burns in its eyes with a last powerful gleam.

What meantest thou, oh impious Euripides, in seeking once more to enthral this dying one? It died under thy ruthless hands: and then thou madest use of counterfeit, masked myth, which like the ape of Heracles could only trick itself out in the old finery. And as myth died in thy hands, so also died the genius of music; though thou couldst covetously plunder all the gardens of music—thou didst only realise a counterfeit, masked music. And because thou hast forsaken Dionysus, Apollo hath also forsaken thee; rout up all the passions from their haunts and conjure them into thy sphere, sharpen and polish a sophistical dialectics for the speeches of thy heroes—thy very heroes have only counterfeit, masked passions, and speak only counterfeit, masked music.

11.

Greek tragedy had a fate different from that of all her older sister arts: she died by suicide, in consequence of an irreconcilable conflict; accordingly she died tragically, while they all passed away very calmly and beautifully in ripe old age. For if it be in accordance with a happy state of things to depart this life without a struggle, leaving behind a fair posterity, the closing period of these older arts exhibits such a happy state of things: slowly they sink out of sight, and before their dying eyes already stand their fairer progeny, who impatiently lift up their heads with courageous mien. The death of Greek tragedy, on the other hand, left an immense void, deeply felt everywhere. Even as certain Greek sailors in the time of Tiberius once heard upon a lonesome island the thrilling cry, "great Pan is dead": so now as it were sorrowful wailing sounded through the Hellenic world: "Tragedy is dead! Poetry itself has perished with her! Begone, begone, ye stunted, emaciated epigones! Begone to Hades, that ye may for once eat your fill of the crumbs of your former masters!"

But when after all a new Art blossomed forth which revered tragedy as her ancestress and mistress, it was observed with horror that she did indeed bear the features of her mother, but those very features the latter had exhibited in her long death-struggle. It was Euripides who fought this death-struggle of tragedy; the later art is known as the New Attic Comedy. In it the degenerate form of tragedy lived on as a monument of the most painful and violent death of tragedy proper.

This connection between the two serves to explain the passionate attachment to Euripides evinced by the poets of the New Comedy, and hence we are no longer surprised at the wish of Philemon, who would have got himself hanged at once, with the sole design of being able to visit Euripides in the lower regions: if only he could be assured generally that the deceased still had his wits. But if we desire, as briefly as possible, and without professing to say aught exhaustive on the subject, to characterise what Euripides has in common with Menander and Philemon, and what appealed to them so strongly as worthy of imitation: it will suffice to say that the spectator was brought upon the stage by Euripides. He who has perceived the material of which the Promethean tragic writers prior to Euripides formed their heroes, and how remote from their purpose it was to bring the true mask of reality on the stage, will also know what to make of the wholly divergent tendency of Euripides. Through him the commonplace individual forced his way from the spectators' benches to the stage itself; the mirror in which formerly only great and bold traits found expression now showed the painful exactness that conscientiously reproduces even the abortive lines of nature. Odysseus, the typical Hellene of the Old Art, sank, in the hands of the new poets, to the figure of the Græculus, who, as the good-naturedly cunning domestic slave, stands henceforth in the centre of dramatic interest. What Euripides takes credit for in the Aristophanean "Frogs," namely, that by his household remedies he freed tragic art from its pompous corpulency, is apparent above all in his tragic heroes. The spectator now virtually saw and heard his double on the Euripidean stage, and rejoiced that he could talk so well. But this joy was not all: one even learned of Euripides how to speak: he prides himself upon this in his contest with Æschylus: how the people have learned from him how to observe, debate, and draw conclusions according to the rules of art and with the cleverest sophistications. In general it may be said that through this revolution of the popular language he made the New Comedy possible. For it was henceforth no longer a secret, how—and with what saws—the commonplace could represent and express itself on the stage. Civic mediocrity, on which Euripides built all his political hopes, was now suffered to speak, while heretofore the demigod in tragedy and the drunken satyr, or demiman, in comedy, had determined the character of the language. And so the Aristophanean Euripides prides himself on having portrayed the common, familiar, everyday life and dealings of the people, concerning which all are qualified to pass judgment. If now the entire populace philosophises, manages land and goods with unheard-of circumspection, and conducts law-suits, he takes all the credit to himself, and glories in the splendid results of the wisdom with which he inoculated the rabble.

It was to a populace prepared and enlightened in this manner that the New Comedy could now address itself, of which Euripides had become as it were the chorus-master; only that in this case the chorus of spectators had to be trained. As soon as this chorus was trained to sing in the Euripidean key, there arose that chess-like variety of the drama, the New Comedy, with its perpetual triumphs of cunning and artfulness. But Euripides—the chorus-master—was praised incessantly: indeed, people would have killed themselves in order to learn yet more from him, had they not known that tragic poets were quite as dead as tragedy. But with it the Hellene had surrendered the belief in his immortality; not only the belief in an ideal past, but also the belief in an ideal future. The saying taken from the well-known epitaph, "as an old man, frivolous and capricious," applies also to aged Hellenism. The passing moment, wit, levity, and caprice, are its highest deities; the fifth class, that of the slaves, now attains to power, at least in sentiment: and if we can still speak at all of "Greek cheerfulness," it is the cheerfulness of the slave who has nothing of consequence to answer for, nothing great to strive for, and cannot value anything of the past or future higher than the present. It was this semblance of "Greek cheerfulness" which so revolted the deep-minded and formidable natures of the first four centuries of Christianity: this womanish flight from earnestness and terror, this cowardly contentedness with easy pleasure, was not only contemptible to them, but seemed to be a specifically anti-Christian sentiment. And we must ascribe it to its influence that the conception of Greek antiquity, which lived on for centuries, preserved with almost enduring persistency that peculiar hectic colour of cheerfulness—as if there had never been a Sixth Century with its birth of tragedy, its Mysteries, its Pythagoras and Heraclitus, indeed as if the art-works of that great period did not at all exist, which in fact—each by itself—can in no wise be explained as having sprung from the soil of such a decrepit and slavish love of existence and cheerfulness, and point to an altogether different conception of things as their source.

The assertion made a moment ago, that Euripides introduced the spectator on the stage to qualify him the better to pass judgment on the drama, will make it appear as if the old tragic art was always in a false relation to the spectator: and one would be tempted to extol the radical tendency of Euripides to bring about an adequate relation between art-work and public as an advance on Sophocles. But, as things are, "public" is merely a word, and not at all a homogeneous and constant quantity. Why should the artist be under obligations to accommodate himself to a power whose strength is merely in numbers? And if by virtue of his endowments and aspirations he feels himself superior to every one of these spectators, how could he feel greater respect for the collective expression of all these subordinate capacities than for the relatively highest-endowed individual spectator? In truth, if ever a Greek artist treated his public throughout a long life with presumptuousness and self-sufficiency, it was Euripides, who, even when the masses threw themselves at his feet, with sublime defiance made an open assault on his own tendency, the very tendency with which he had triumphed over the masses. If this genius had had the slightest reverence for the pandemonium of the public, he would have broken down long before the middle of his career beneath the weighty blows of his own failures. These considerations here make it obvious that our formula—namely, that Euripides brought the spectator upon the stage in order to make him truly competent to pass judgment—was but a provisional one, and that we must seek for a deeper understanding of his tendency. Conversely, it is undoubtedly well known that Æschylus and Sophocles during all their lives, indeed, far beyond their lives, enjoyed the full favour of the people, and that therefore in the case of these predecessors of Euripides the idea of a false relation between art-work and public was altogether excluded. What was it that thus forcibly diverted this highly gifted artist, so incessantly impelled to production, from the path over which shone the sun of the greatest names in poetry and the cloudless heaven of popular favour? What strange consideration for the spectator led him to defy the spectator? How could he, owing to too much respect for the public—dis-respect the public?

Euripides—and this is the solution of the riddle just propounded—felt himself, as a poet, undoubtedly superior to the masses, but not to two of his spectators: he brought the masses upon the stage; these two spectators he revered as the only competent judges and masters of his art: in compliance with their directions and admonitions, he transferred the entire world of sentiments, passions, and experiences, hitherto present at every festival representation as the invisible chorus on the spectators' benches, into the souls of his stage-heroes; he yielded to their demands when he also sought for these new characters the new word and the new tone; in their voices alone he heard the conclusive verdict on his work, as also the cheering promise of triumph when he found himself condemned as usual by the justice of the public.

Of these two spectators the one is—Euripides himself, Euripides as thinker, not as poet. It might be said of him, that his unusually large fund of critical ability, as in the case of Lessing, if it did not create, at least constantly fructified a productively artistic collateral impulse. With this faculty, with all the clearness and dexterity of his critical thought, Euripides had sat in the theatre and striven to recognise in the masterpieces of his great predecessors, as in faded paintings, feature and feature, line and line. And here had happened to him what one initiated in the deeper arcana of Æschylean tragedy must needs have expected: he observed something incommensurable in every feature and in every line, a certain deceptive distinctness and at the same time an enigmatic profundity, yea an infinitude, of background. Even the clearest figure had always a comet's tail attached to it, which seemed to suggest the uncertain and the inexplicable. The same twilight shrouded the structure of the drama, especially the significance of the chorus. And how doubtful seemed the solution of the ethical problems to his mind! How questionable the treatment of the myths! How unequal the distribution of happiness and misfortune! Even in the language of the Old Tragedy there was much that was objectionable to him, or at least enigmatical; he found especially too much pomp for simple affairs, too many tropes and immense things for the plainness of the characters. Thus he sat restlessly pondering in the theatre, and as a spectator he acknowledged to himself that he did not understand his great predecessors. If, however, he thought the understanding the root proper of all enjoyment and productivity, he had to inquire and look about to see whether any one else thought as he did, and also acknowledged this incommensurability. But most people, and among them the best individuals, had only a distrustful smile for him, while none could explain why the great masters were still in the right in face of his scruples and objections. And in this painful condition he found that other spectator, who did not comprehend, and therefore did not esteem, tragedy. In alliance with him he could venture, from amid his lonesomeness, to begin the prodigious struggle against the art of Æschylus and Sophocles—not with polemic writings, but as a dramatic poet, who opposed his own conception of tragedy to the traditional one.

12.

Before we name this other spectator, let us pause here a moment in order to recall our own impression, as previously described, of the discordant and incommensurable elements in the nature of Æschylean tragedy. Let us think of our own astonishment at the chorus and the tragic hero of that type of tragedy, neither of which we could reconcile with our practices any more than with tradition—till we rediscovered this duplexity itself as the origin and essence of Greek tragedy, as the expression of two interwoven artistic impulses, the Apollonian and the Dionysian.

To separate this primitive and all-powerful Dionysian element from tragedy, and to build up a new and purified form of tragedy on the basis of a non-Dionysian art, morality, and conception of things—such is the tendency of Euripides which now reveals itself to us in a clear light.

In a myth composed in the eve of his life, Euripides himself most urgently propounded to his contemporaries the question as to the value and signification of this tendency. Is the Dionysian entitled to exist at all? Should it not be forcibly rooted out of the Hellenic soil? Certainly, the poet tells us, if only it were possible: but the god Dionysus is too powerful; his most intelligent adversary—like Pentheus in the "Bacchæ"—is unwittingly enchanted by him, and in this enchantment meets his fate. The judgment of the two old sages, Cadmus and Tiresias, seems to be also the judgment of the aged poet: that the reflection of the wisest individuals does not overthrow old popular traditions, nor the perpetually propagating worship of Dionysus, that in fact it behoves us to display at least a diplomatically cautious concern in the presence of such strange forces: where however it is always possible that the god may take offence at such lukewarm participation, and finally change the diplomat—in this case Cadmus—into a dragon. This is what a poet tells us, who opposed Dionysus with heroic valour throughout a long life—in order finally to wind up his career with a glorification of his adversary, and with suicide, like one staggering from giddiness, who, in order to escape the horrible vertigo he can no longer endure, casts himself from a tower. This tragedy—the Bacchæ—is a protest against the practicability of his own tendency; alas, and it has already been put into practice! The surprising thing had happened: when the poet recanted, his tendency had already conquered. Dionysus had already been scared from the tragic stage, and in fact by a demonic power which spoke through Euripides. Even Euripides was, in a certain sense, only a mask: the deity that spoke through him was neither Dionysus nor Apollo, but an altogether new-born demon, called Socrates. This is the new antithesis: the Dionysian and the Socratic, and the art-work of Greek tragedy was wrecked on it. What if even Euripides now seeks to comfort us by his recantation? It is of no avail: the most magnificent temple lies in ruins. What avails the lamentation of the destroyer, and his confession that it was the most beautiful of all temples? And even that Euripides has been changed into a dragon as a punishment by the art-critics of all ages—who could be content with this wretched compensation?

Let us now approach this Socratic tendency with which Euripides combated and vanquished Æschylean tragedy.

We must now ask ourselves, what could be the ulterior aim of the Euripidean design, which, in the highest ideality of its execution, would found drama exclusively on the non-Dionysian? What other form of drama could there be, if it was not to be born of the womb of music, in the mysterious twilight of the Dionysian? Only the dramatised epos: in which Apollonian domain of art the tragic effect is of course unattainable. It does not depend on the subject-matter of the events here represented; indeed, I venture to assert that it would have been impossible for Goethe in his projected "Nausikaa" to have rendered tragically effective the suicide of the idyllic being with which he intended to complete the fifth act; so extraordinary is the power of the epic-Apollonian representation, that it charms, before our eyes, the most terrible things by the joy in appearance and in redemption through appearance. The poet of the dramatised epos cannot completely blend with his pictures any more than the epic rhapsodist. He is still just the calm, unmoved embodiment of Contemplation whose wide eyes see the picture before them. The actor in this dramatised epos still remains intrinsically rhapsodist: the consecration of inner dreaming is on all his actions, so that he is never wholly an actor.

How, then, is the Euripidean play related to this ideal of the Apollonian drama? Just as the younger rhapsodist is related to the solemn rhapsodist of the old time. The former describes his own character in the Platonic "Ion" as follows: "When I am saying anything sad, my eyes fill with tears; when, however, what I am saying is awful and terrible, then my hair stands on end through fear, and my heart leaps." Here we no longer observe anything of the epic absorption in appearance, or of the unemotional coolness of the true actor, who precisely in his highest activity is wholly appearance and joy in appearance. Euripides is the actor with leaping heart, with hair standing on end; as Socratic thinker he designs the plan, as passionate actor he executes it. Neither in the designing nor in the execution is he an artist pure and simple. And so the Euripidean drama is a thing both cool and fiery, equally capable of freezing and burning; it is impossible for it to attain the Apollonian effect of the epos, while, on the other hand, it has severed itself as much as possible from Dionysian elements, and now, in order to act at all, it requires new stimulants, which can no longer lie within the sphere of the two unique art-impulses, the Apollonian and the Dionysian. The stimulants are cool, paradoxical thoughts, in place of Apollonian intuitions—and fiery passions—in place of Dionysian ecstasies; and in fact, thoughts and passions very realistically copied, and not at all steeped in the ether of art.

Accordingly, if we have perceived this much, that Euripides did not succeed in establishing the drama exclusively on the Apollonian, but that rather his non-Dionysian inclinations deviated into a naturalistic and inartistic tendency, we shall now be able to approach nearer to the character of æsthetic Socratism, the supreme law of which reads about as follows: "to be beautiful everything must be intelligible," as the parallel to the Socratic proposition, "only the knowing one is virtuous." With this canon in his hands Euripides measured all the separate elements of the drama, and rectified them according to his principle: the language, the characters, the dramaturgic structure, and the choric music. The poetic deficiency and retrogression, which we are so often wont to impute to Euripides in comparison with Sophoclean tragedy, is for the most part the product of this penetrating critical process, this daring intelligibility. The Euripidean prologue may serve us as an example of the productivity of this rationalistic method. Nothing could be more opposed to the technique of our stage than the prologue in the drama of Euripides. For a single person to appear at the outset of the play telling us who he is, what precedes the action, what has happened thus far, yea, what will happen in the course of the play, would be designated by a modern playwright as a wanton and unpardonable abandonment of the effect of suspense. Everything that is about to happen is known beforehand; who then cares to wait for it actually to happen?—considering, moreover, that here there is not by any means the exciting relation of a predicting dream to a reality taking place later on. Euripides speculated quite differently. The effect of tragedy never depended on epic suspense, on the fascinating uncertainty as to what is to happen now and afterwards: but rather on the great rhetoro-lyric scenes in which the passion and dialectics of the chief hero swelled to a broad and mighty stream. Everything was arranged for pathos, not for action: and whatever was not arranged for pathos was regarded as objectionable. But what interferes most with the hearer's pleasurable satisfaction in such scenes is a missing link, a gap in the texture of the previous history. So long as the spectator has to divine the meaning of this or that person, or the presuppositions of this or that conflict of inclinations and intentions, his complete absorption in the doings and sufferings of the chief persons is impossible, as is likewise breathless fellow-feeling and fellow-fearing. The Æschyleo-Sophoclean tragedy employed the most ingenious devices in the first scenes to place in the hands of the spectator as if by chance all the threads requisite for understanding the whole: a trait in which that noble artistry is approved, which as it were masks the inevitably formal, and causes it to appear as something accidental. But nevertheless Euripides thought he observed that during these first scenes the spectator was in a strange state of anxiety to make out the problem of the previous history, so that the poetic beauties and pathos of the exposition were lost to him. Accordingly he placed the prologue even before the exposition, and put it in the mouth of a person who could be trusted: some deity had often as it were to guarantee the particulars of the tragedy to the public and remove every doubt as to the reality of the myth: as in the case of Descartes, who could only prove the reality of the empiric world by an appeal to the truthfulness of God and His inability to utter falsehood. Euripides makes use of the same divine truthfulness once more at the close of his drama, in order to ensure to the public the future of his heroes; this is the task of the notorious deus ex machina. Between the preliminary and the additional epic spectacle there is the dramatico-lyric present, the "drama" proper.

Thus Euripides as a poet echoes above all his own conscious knowledge; and it is precisely on this account that he occupies such a notable position in the history of Greek art. With reference to his critico-productive activity, he must often have felt that he ought to actualise in the drama the words at the beginning of the essay of Anaxagoras: "In the beginning all things were mixed together; then came the understanding and created order." And if Anaxagoras with his "*νουσ*" seemed like the first sober person among nothing but drunken philosophers, Euripides may also have conceived his relation to the other tragic poets under a similar figure. As long as the sole ruler and disposer of the universe, the *νουσ*, was still excluded from artistic activity, things were all mixed together in a chaotic, primitive mess;—it is thus Euripides was obliged to think, it is thus he was obliged to condemn the "drunken" poets as the first "sober" one among them. What Sophocles said of Æschylus, that he did what was right, though unconsciously, was surely not in the mind of Euripides: who would have admitted only thus much, that Æschylus, because he wrought unconsciously, did what was wrong. So also the divine Plato speaks for the most part only ironically of the creative faculty of the poet, in so far as it is not conscious insight, and places it on a par with the gift of the soothsayer and dream-interpreter; insinuating that the poet is incapable of composing until he has become unconscious and reason has deserted him. Like Plato, Euripides undertook to show to the world the reverse of the "unintelligent" poet; his æsthetic principle that "to be beautiful everything must be known" is, as I have said, the parallel to the Socratic "to be good everything must be known." Accordingly we may regard Euripides as the poet of æsthetic Socratism. Socrates, however, was the second spectator who did not comprehend and therefore did not esteem the

Old Tragedy; in alliance with him Euripides ventured to be the herald of a new artistic activity. If, then, the Old Tragedy was here destroyed, it follows that æsthetic Socratism was the murderous principle; but in so far as the struggle is directed against the Dionysian element in the old art, we recognise in Socrates the opponent of Dionysus, the new Orpheus who rebels against Dionysus; and although destined to be torn to pieces by the Mænads of the Athenian court, yet puts to flight the overpowerful god himself, who, when he fled from Lycurgus, the king of Edoni, sought refuge in the depths of the ocean—namely, in the mystical flood of a secret cult which gradually overspread the earth.

13.

That Socrates stood in close relationship to Euripides in the tendency of his teaching, did not escape the notice of contemporaneous antiquity; the most eloquent expression of this felicitous insight being the tale current in Athens, that Socrates was accustomed to help Euripides in poetising. Both names were mentioned in one breath by the adherents of the "good old time," whenever they came to enumerating the popular agitators of the day: to whose influence they attributed the fact that the old Marathonian stalwart capacity of body and soul was more and more being sacrificed to a dubious enlightenment, involving progressive degeneration of the physical and mental powers. It is in this tone, half indignantly and half contemptuously, that Aristophanic comedy is wont to speak of both of them—to the consternation of modern men, who would indeed be willing enough to give up Euripides, but cannot suppress their amazement that Socrates should appear in Aristophanes as the first and head sophist, as the mirror and epitome of all sophistical tendencies; in connection with which it offers the single consolation of putting Aristophanes himself in the pillory, as a rakish, lying Alcibiades of poetry. Without here defending the profound instincts of Aristophanes against such attacks, I shall now indicate, by means of the sentiments of the time, the close connection between Socrates and Euripides. With this purpose in view, it is especially to be remembered that Socrates, as an opponent of tragic art, did not ordinarily patronise tragedy, but only appeared among the spectators when a new play of Euripides was performed. The most noted thing, however, is the close juxtaposition of the two names in the Delphic oracle, which designated Socrates as the wisest of men, but at the same time decided that the second prize in the contest of wisdom was due to Euripides.

Sophocles was designated as the third in this scale of rank; he who could pride himself that, in comparison with Æschylus, he did what was right, and did it, moreover, because he knew what was right. It is evidently just the degree of clearness of this knowledge, which distinguishes these three men in common as the three "knowing ones" of their age.

The most decisive word, however, for this new and unprecedented esteem of knowledge and insight was spoken by Socrates when he found that he was the only one who acknowledged to himself that he knew nothing; while in his critical pilgrimage through Athens, and calling on the greatest statesmen, orators, poets, and artists, he discovered everywhere the conceit of knowledge. He perceived, to his astonishment, that all these celebrities were without a proper and accurate insight, even with regard to their own callings, and practised them only by instinct. "Only by instinct": with this phrase we touch upon the heart and core of the Socratic tendency. Socratism condemns therewith existing art as well as existing ethics; wherever Socratism turns its searching eyes it beholds the lack of insight and the power of illusion; and from this lack infers the inner perversity and objectionableness of existing conditions. From this point onwards, Socrates believed that he was called upon to correct existence; and, with an air of disregard and superiority, as the precursor of an altogether different culture, art, and morality, he enters single-handed into a world, of which, if we reverently touched the hem, we should count it our greatest happiness.

Here is the extraordinary hesitancy which always seizes upon us with regard to Socrates, and again and again invites us to ascertain the sense and purpose of this most questionable phenomenon of antiquity. Who is it that ventures single-handed to disown the Greek character, which, as Homer, Pindar, and Æschylus, as Phidias, as Pericles, as Pythia and Dionysus, as the deepest abyss and the highest height, is sure of our wondering admiration? What demoniac power is it which would presume to spill this magic draught in the dust? What demigod is it to whom the chorus of spirits of the noblest of mankind must call out: "Weh! Weh! Du hast sie zerstört, die schöne Welt, mit mächtiger Faust; sie stürzt, sie zerfällt!"[9]

A key to the character of Socrates is presented to us by the surprising phenomenon designated as the "daimonion" of Socrates. In special circumstances, when his gigantic intellect began to stagger, he got a secure support in the utterances of a divine voice which then spake to him. This voice, whenever it comes, always dissuades. In this totally abnormal nature instinctive wisdom only appears in order to hinder the progress of conscious perception here and there. While in all productive men it is instinct which is the creatively affirmative force, consciousness only comporting itself critically and dissuasively; with Socrates it is instinct which becomes critic, it is consciousness which becomes creator—a perfect monstrosity *per defectum!* And we do indeed observe here a monstrous *defectus* of all mystical aptitude, so that Socrates might be designated as the specific non-mystic, in whom the logical nature is developed, through a superfoetation, to the same excess as instinctive wisdom is developed in the mystic. On the other hand, however, the logical instinct which appeared in Socrates was absolutely prohibited from turning against itself; in its unchecked flow it manifests a native power such as we meet with, to our shocking surprise, only among the very greatest instinctive forces. He who has experienced even a breath of the divine naïveté and security of the Socratic course of life in the Platonic writings, will also feel that the enormous driving-wheel of logical Socratism is in motion, as it were, behind Socrates, and that it must be viewed through Socrates as through a shadow. And that he himself had a boding of this relation is apparent from the dignified earnestness with which he everywhere, and even before his judges, insisted on his divine calling. To refute him here was really as impossible as to approve of his instinct-disintegrating influence. In view of this indissoluble conflict, when he had at last been brought before the forum of the Greek state, there was only one punishment demanded, namely exile; he might have been sped across the borders as something thoroughly enigmatical, irrubricable and inexplicable, and so posterity would have been quite unjustified in charging the Athenians with a deed of ignominy. But that the sentence of death, and not mere exile, was pronounced upon him, seems to have been brought about by Socrates himself, with perfect knowledge of the circumstances, and without the natural fear of death: he met his death with the calmness with which, according to the description of Plato, he leaves the symposium at break of day, as the last of the revellers, to begin a new day; while the sleepy companions remain behind on the benches and the floor, to dream of Socrates, the true eroticist. The dying Socrates became the new ideal of the noble Greek youths,—an ideal they had never yet beheld,—and above all, the typical Hellenic youth, Plato, prostrated himself before this scene with all the fervent devotion of his visionary soul.

14.

Let us now imagine the one great Cyclopean eye of Socrates fixed on tragedy, that eye in which the fine frenzy of artistic enthusiasm had never glowed—let us think how it was denied to this eye to gaze with pleasure into the Dionysian abysses—what could it not but see in the "sublime and greatly lauded" tragic art, as Plato called it? Something very absurd, with causes that seemed to be without effects, and effects apparently without causes; the whole, moreover, so motley and diversified that it could not but be repugnant to a thoughtful mind, a dangerous incentive, however, to sensitive and irritable souls. We know what was the sole kind of poetry which he comprehended: the Æsopian fable: and he did this no doubt with that smiling complaisance with which the good honest Gellert sings the praise of poetry in the fable of the bee and the hen:—

"Du siehst an mir, wozu sie nützt,
Dem, der nicht viel Verstand besitzt,
Die Wahrheit durch ein Bild zu sagen."[10]

But then it seemed to Socrates that tragic art did not even "tell the truth": not to mention the fact that it addresses itself to him who "hath but little wit"; consequently not to the philosopher: a twofold reason why it should be avoided. Like Plato, he reckoned it among the seductive arts which only represent the agreeable, not the useful, and hence he required of his disciples abstinence and strict separation from such unphilosophical allurements; with such success that the youthful tragic poet Plato first of all burned his poems to be able to become a scholar of Socrates. But where unconquerable native capacities bore up against the Socratic maxims, their power, together with the momentum of his mighty character, still sufficed to force poetry itself into new and hitherto unknown channels.

An instance of this is the aforesaid Plato: he, who in the condemnation of tragedy and of art in general certainly did not fall short of the naïve cynicism of his master, was nevertheless constrained by sheer artistic necessity to create a form of art which is inwardly related even to the then existing forms of art which he repudiated. Plato's main objection to the old art—that it is the imitation of a phantom, and hence belongs to a sphere still lower than the empiric world—could not at all apply to the new art: and so we find Plato endeavouring to go beyond reality and attempting to represent the idea which underlies this pseudo-reality. But Plato, the thinker, thereby arrived by a roundabout road just at the point where he had always been at home as poet, and from which Sophocles and all the old artists had solemnly protested against that objection. If tragedy absorbed into itself all the earlier varieties of art, the same could again be said in an unusual sense of Platonic dialogue, which, engendered by a mixture of all the then existing forms and styles, hovers midway between narrative, lyric and drama, between prose and poetry, and has also thereby broken loose from the older strict law of unity of linguistic form; a movement which was carried still farther by the cynic writers, who in the most promiscuous style, oscillating to and fro betwixt prose and metrical forms, realised also the literary picture of the "raving Socrates" whom they were wont to represent in life. Platonic dialogue was as it were the boat in which the shipwrecked ancient poetry saved herself together with all her children: crowded into a narrow space and timidly obsequious to the one steersman, Socrates, they now launched into a new world, which never tired of looking at the fantastic spectacle of this procession. In very truth, Plato has given to all posterity the prototype of a new form of art, the prototype of the novel: which must be designated as the infinitely evolved Æsopian fable, in which poetry holds the same rank with reference to dialectic philosophy as this same philosophy held for many centuries with reference to theology: namely, the rank of ancilla. This was the new position of poetry into which Plato forced it under the pressure of the demon-inspired Socrates.

Here philosophic thought overgrows art and compels it to cling close to the trunk of dialectics. The Apollonian tendency has chrysalised in the logical schematism; just as something analogous in the case of Euripides (and moreover a translation of the Dionysian into the naturalistic emotion) was forced upon our attention. Socrates, the dialectical hero in Platonic drama, reminds us of the kindred nature of the Euripidean hero, who has to defend his actions by arguments and counter-arguments, and thereby so often runs the risk of forfeiting our tragic pity; for who could mistake the optimistic element in the essence of dialectics, which celebrates a jubilee in every conclusion, and can breathe only in cool clearness and consciousness: the optimistic element, which, having once forced its way into tragedy, must gradually overgrow its Dionysian regions, and necessarily impel it to self-destruction—even to the death-leap into the bourgeois drama. Let us but realise the consequences of the Socratic maxims: "Virtue is knowledge; man only sins from ignorance; he who is virtuous is happy": these three fundamental forms of optimism involve the death of tragedy. For the virtuous hero must now be a dialectician; there must now be a necessary, visible connection between virtue and knowledge, between belief and morality; the transcendental justice of the plot in Æschylus is now degraded to the superficial and audacious principle of "poetic justice" with its usual deus ex machina.

How does the chorus, and, in general, the entire Dionyso-musical substratum of tragedy, now appear in the light of this new Socrato-optimistic stage-world? As something accidental, as a readily dispensable reminiscence of the origin of tragedy; while we have in fact seen that the chorus can be understood only as the cause of tragedy, and of the tragic generally. This perplexity with respect to the chorus first manifests itself in Sophocles—an important sign that the Dionysian basis of tragedy already begins to disintegrate with him. He no longer ventures to entrust to the chorus the main share of the effect, but limits its sphere to such an extent that it now appears almost co-ordinate with the actors, just as if it were elevated from the orchestra into the scene: whereby of course its character is completely destroyed, notwithstanding that Aristotle countenances this very theory of the chorus. This alteration of the position of the chorus, which Sophocles at any rate recommended by his practice, and, according to tradition, even by a treatise, is the first step towards the annihilation of the chorus, the phases of which follow one another with alarming rapidity in Euripides, Agathon, and the New Comedy. Optimistic dialectics drives music out of tragedy with the scourge of its syllogisms: that is, it destroys the essence of tragedy, which can be explained only as a manifestation and illustration of Dionysian states, as the visible symbolisation of music, as the dream-world of Dionysian ecstasy.

If, therefore, we are to assume an anti-Dionysian tendency operating even before Socrates, which received in him only an unprecedentedly grand expression, we must not shrink from the question as to what a phenomenon like that of Socrates indicates: whom in view of the Platonic dialogues we are certainly not entitled to regard as a purely disintegrating, negative power. And though there can be no doubt whatever that the most immediate effect of the Socratic impulse tended to the dissolution of Dionysian tragedy, yet a profound experience of Socrates' own life compels us to ask whether there is necessarily only an antipodal relation between Socratism and art, and whether the birth of an "artistic Socrates" is in general something contradictory in itself.

For that despotic logician had now and then the feeling of a gap, or void, a sentiment of semi-reproach, as of a possibly neglected duty with respect to art. There often came to him, as he tells his friends in prison, one and the same dream-apparition, which kept constantly repeating to him: "Socrates, practise music." Up to his very last days he solaces himself with the opinion that his philosophising is the highest form of poetry, and finds it hard to believe that a deity will remind him of the "common, popular music." Finally, when in prison, he consents to practise also this despised music, in order thoroughly to unburden his conscience. And in this frame of mind he composes a poem on Apollo and turns a few Æsopian fables into verse. It was something similar to the demonian warning voice which urged him to these practices; it was because of his Apollonian insight that, like a barbaric king, he did not understand the noble image of a god and was in danger of sinning against a deity—through ignorance. The prompting voice of the Socratic dream-vision is the only sign of doubtfulness as to the limits of logical nature. "Perhaps"—thus he had to ask himself—"what is not intelligible to me is not therefore unreasonable? Perhaps there is a realm of wisdom from which the logician is banished? Perhaps art is even a necessary correlative of and supplement to science?"

15.

In the sense of these last portentous questions it must now be indicated how the influence of Socrates (extending to the present moment, indeed, to all futurity) has spread over posterity like an ever-increasing shadow in the evening sun, and how this influence again and again necessitates a regeneration of art,—yea, of art already with metaphysical, broadest and profoundest sense,—and its own eternity guarantees also the eternity of art.

Before this could be perceived, before the intrinsic dependence of every art on the Greeks, the Greeks from Homer to Socrates, was conclusively demonstrated, it had to happen to us with regard to these Greeks as it happened to the Athenians with regard to Socrates. Nearly every age and stage of culture has at some time or other sought with deep displeasure to free itself from the Greeks, because in their presence everything self-achieved, sincerely admired and apparently quite original, seemed all of a sudden to lose life and colour and shrink to an abortive copy, even to caricature. And so hearty indignation breaks forth time after time against this presumptuous little nation, which dared to designate as "barbaric" for all time everything not native: who are they, one asks one's self, who, though they possessed only an ephemeral historical splendour, ridiculously restricted institutions, a dubious excellence in their customs, and were even branded with ugly vices, yet lay claim to the dignity and singular position among the peoples to which genius is entitled among the masses. What a pity one has not been so fortunate as to find the cup of hemlock with which such an affair could be disposed of without ado: for all the poison which envy, calumny, and rankling resentment engendered within themselves have not sufficed to destroy that self-sufficient grandeur! And so one feels ashamed and afraid in the presence of the Greeks: unless one prize truth above all things, and dare also to acknowledge to one's self this truth, that the Greeks, as charioteers, hold in their hands the reins of our own and of every culture, but that almost always chariot and horses are of too poor material and incommensurate with the glory of their guides, who then will deem it sport to run such a team into an abyss: which they themselves clear with the leap of Achilles.

In order to assign also to Socrates the dignity of such a leading position, it will suffice to recognise in him the type of an unheard-of form of existence, the type of the theoretical man, with regard to whose meaning and purpose it will be our next task to attain an insight. Like the artist, the theorist also finds an infinite satisfaction in what is, and, like the former, he is shielded by this satisfaction from the practical ethics of pessimism with its lynx eyes which shine only in the dark. For if the artist in every unveiling of truth always cleaves with raptured eyes only to that which still remains veiled after the unveiling, the theoretical man, on the other hand, enjoys and contents himself with the cast-off veil, and finds the consummation of his pleasure in the process of a continuously successful unveiling through his own unaided efforts. There would have been no science if it had only been concerned about that one naked goddess and nothing else. For then its disciples would have been obliged to feel like those who purposed to dig a hole straight through the earth: each one of whom perceives that with the utmost lifelong exertion he is able to excavate only a very little of the enormous depth, which is again filled up before his eyes by the labours of his successor, so that a third man seems to do well when on his own account he selects a new spot for his attempts at tunnelling. If now some one proves conclusively that the antipodal goal cannot be attained in this direct way, who will still care to toil on in the old depths, unless he has learned to content himself in the meantime with finding precious stones or discovering natural laws? For that reason Lessing, the most honest theoretical man, ventured to say that he cared more for the search after truth than for truth itself: in saying which he revealed the fundamental secret of science, to the astonishment, and indeed, to the vexation of scientific men. Well, to be sure, there stands alongside of this detached perception, as an excess of honesty, if not of presumption, a profound illusion which first came to the world in the person of Socrates, the imperturbable belief that, by means of the clue of causality, thinking reaches to the deepest abysses of being, and that thinking is able not only to perceive being but even to correct it. This sublime metaphysical illusion is added as an instinct to science and again and again leads the latter to its limits, where it must change into art; which is really the end to be attained by this mechanism.

If we now look at Socrates in the light of this thought, he appears to us as the first who could not only live, but—what is far more—also die under the guidance of this instinct of science: and hence the picture of the dying Socrates, as the man delivered from the fear of death by knowledge and argument, is the escutcheon above the entrance to science which reminds every one of its mission, namely, to make existence appear to be comprehensible, and therefore to be justified: for which purpose, if arguments do not suffice, myth also must be used, which I just now designated even as the necessary consequence, yea, as the end of science.

He who once makes intelligible to himself how, after the death of Socrates, the mystagogue of science, one philosophical school succeeds another, like wave upon wave,—how an entirely unforeshadowed universal development of the thirst for knowledge in the widest compass of the cultured world (and as the specific task for every one highly gifted) led science on to the high sea from which since then it has never again been able to be completely ousted; how through the universality of this movement a common net of thought was first stretched over the entire globe, with prospects, moreover, of conformity to law in an entire solar system;—he who realises all this, together with the amazingly high pyramid of our present-day knowledge, cannot fail to see in Socrates the turning-point and vortex of so-called universal history. For if one were to imagine the whole incalculable sum of energy which has been used up by that universal tendency,—employed, not in the service of knowledge, but for the practical, i.e., egoistical ends of individuals and peoples,—then probably the instinctive love of life would be so much weakened in universal wars of destruction and incessant migrations of peoples, that, owing to the practice of suicide, the individual would perhaps feel the last remnant of a sense of duty, when, like the native of the Fiji Islands, as son he strangles his parents and, as friend, his friend: a practical pessimism which might even give rise to a horrible ethics of general slaughter out of pity—which, for the rest, exists and has existed wherever art in one form or another, especially as science and religion, has not appeared as a remedy and preventive of that pestilential breath.

In view of this practical pessimism, Socrates is the archetype of the theoretical optimist, who in the above-indicated belief in the fathomableness of the nature of things, attributes to knowledge and perception the power of a universal medicine, and sees in error evil in itself. To penetrate into the depths of the nature of things, and to separate true perception from error and illusion, appeared to the Socratic man the noblest and even the only truly human calling: just as from the time of Socrates onwards the mechanism of concepts, judgments, and inferences was prized above all other capacities as the highest activity and the most admirable gift of nature. Even the sublimest moral acts, the stirrings of pity, of self-sacrifice, of heroism, and that tranquillity of soul, so difficult of attainment, which the Apollonian Greek called Sophrosyne, were derived by Socrates, and his like-minded successors up to the present day, from the dialectics of knowledge, and were accordingly designated as teachable. He who has experienced in himself the joy of a Socratic perception, and felt how it seeks to embrace, in constantly widening circles, the entire world of phenomena, will thenceforth find no stimulus which could urge him to existence more forcible than the desire to complete that conquest and to knit the net impenetrably close. To a person thus minded the Platonic Socrates then appears as the teacher of an entirely new form of "Greek cheerfulness" and felicity of existence, which seeks to discharge itself in actions, and will find its discharge for the most part in maieutic and pedagogic influences on noble youths, with a view to the ultimate production of genius.

But now science, spurred on by its powerful illusion, hastens irresistibly to its limits, on which its optimism, hidden in the essence of logic, is wrecked. For the periphery of the circle of science has an infinite number of points, and while there is still no telling how this circle can ever be completely measured, yet the noble and gifted man, even before the middle of his career, inevitably comes into contact with those extreme points of the periphery where he stares at the inexplicable. When he here sees to his dismay how logic coils round itself at these limits and finally bites its own tail—then the new form of perception discloses itself, namely tragic perception, which, in order even to be endured, requires art as a safeguard and remedy.

If, with eyes strengthened and refreshed at the sight of the Greeks, we look upon the highest spheres of the world that surrounds us, we behold the avidity of the insatiate optimistic knowledge, of which Socrates is the typical representative, transformed into tragic resignation and the need of art: while, to be sure, this same avidity, in its lower stages, has to exhibit itself as antagonistic to art, and must especially have an inward detestation of Dionyso-tragic art, as was exemplified in the opposition of Socratism to Æschylean tragedy.

Here then with agitated spirit we knock at the gates of the present and the future: will that "transforming" lead to ever new configurations of genius, and especially of the music-practising Socrates? Will the net of art which is spread over existence, whether under the name of religion or of science, be knit always more closely and delicately, or is it destined to be torn to shreds under the restlessly barbaric activity and whirl which is called "the present day"?—Anxious, yet not disconsolate, we stand aloof for a little while, as the spectators who are permitted to be witnesses of these tremendous struggles and transitions. Alas! It is the charm of these struggles that he who beholds them must also fight them!

16.

By this elaborate historical example we have endeavoured to make it clear that tragedy perishes as surely by the evanescence of the spirit of music as it can be born only out of this spirit. In order to qualify the singularity of this assertion, and, on the other hand, to disclose the source of this insight of ours, we must now confront with clear vision the analogous phenomena of the present time; we must enter into the midst of these struggles, which, as I said just now, are being carried on in the highest spheres of our present world between the insatiate optimistic perception and the tragic need of art. In so doing I shall leave out of consideration all other antagonistic tendencies which at all times oppose art, especially tragedy, and which at present again extend their sway triumphantly, to such an extent that of the theatrical arts only the farce and the ballet, for example, put forth their blossoms, which perhaps not every one cares to smell, in tolerably rich luxuriance. I will speak only of the Most Illustrious Opposition to the tragic conception of things—and by this I mean essentially optimistic science, with its ancestor Socrates at the head of it. Presently also the forces will be designated which seem to me to guarantee a re-birth of tragedy—and who knows what other blessed hopes for the German genius!

Before we plunge into the midst of these struggles, let us array ourselves in the armour of our hitherto acquired knowledge. In contrast to all those who are intent on deriving the arts from one exclusive principle, as the necessary vital source of every work of art, I keep my eyes fixed on the two artistic deities of the Greeks, Apollo and Dionysus, and recognise in them the living and conspicuous representatives of two worlds of art which differ in their intrinsic essence and in their highest aims. Apollo stands before me as the transfiguring genius of the *principium individuationis* through which alone the redemption in appearance is to be truly attained, while by the mystical cheer of Dionysus the spell of individuation is broken, and the way lies open to the Mothers of Being, to the innermost heart of things. This extraordinary antithesis, which opens up yawningly between plastic art as the Apollonian and music as the Dionysian art, has become manifest to only one of the great thinkers, to such an extent that, even without this key to the symbolism of the Hellenic divinities, he allowed to music a different character and origin in advance of all the other arts, because, unlike them, it is not a copy of the phenomenon, but a direct copy of the will itself, and therefore represents the metaphysical of everything physical in the world, the thing-in-itself of every phenomenon. (Schopenhauer, *Welt als Wille und Vorstellung,* I. 310.) To this most important perception of æsthetics (with which, taken in a serious sense, æsthetics properly commences), Richard Wagner, by way of confirmation of its eternal truth, affixed his seal, when he asserted in his *Beethoven* that music must be judged according to æsthetic principles quite different from those which apply to the plastic arts, and not, in general, according to the category of beauty: although an erroneous æsthetics, inspired by a misled and degenerate art, has by virtue of the concept of beauty prevailing in the plastic domain accustomed itself to demand of music an effect analogous to that of the works of plastic art, namely the suscitating of delight in beautiful forms. Upon perceiving this extraordinary antithesis, I felt a strong inducement to approach the essence of Greek tragedy, and, by means of it, the profoundest revelation of Hellenic genius: for I at last thought myself to be in possession of a charm to enable me—far beyond the phraseology of our usual æsthetics—to represent vividly to my mind the primitive problem of tragedy: whereby such an astounding insight into the Hellenic character was afforded me that it necessarily seemed as if our proudly comporting classico-Hellenic science had thus far contrived to subsist almost exclusively on phantasmagoria and externalities.

Perhaps we may lead up to this primitive problem with the question: what æsthetic effect results when the intrinsically separate art-powers, the Apollonian and the Dionysian, enter into concurrent actions? Or, in briefer form: how is music related to image and concept?—Schopenhauer, whom Richard Wagner, with especial reference to this point, accredits with an unsurpassable clearness and perspicuity of exposition, expresses himself most copiously on the subject in the following passage which I shall cite here at full length from *The World as Will and Idea:* "According to all this, we may regard the phenomenal world, or nature, and music as two different expressions of the same thing, which is therefore itself the only medium of the analogy between these two expressions, so that a knowledge of this medium is required in order to understand that analogy. Music, therefore, if regarded as an expression of the world, is in the highest degree a universal language, which is related indeed to the universality of concepts, much as these are related to the particular things. Its universality, however, is by no means the empty universality of abstraction, but of quite a different kind, and is united with thorough and distinct definiteness. In this respect it resembles geometrical figures and numbers, which are the universal forms of all possible objects of experience and applicable to them all *a priori,* and yet are not abstract but perceptible and thoroughly determinate. All possible efforts, excitements and manifestations of will, all that goes on in the heart of man and that reason includes in the wide, negative concept of feeling, may be expressed by the infinite number of possible melodies, but always in the universality of mere form, without the material, always according to the thing-in-itself, not the phenomenon,—of which they reproduce the very soul and essence as it were, without the body. This deep relation which music bears to the true nature of all things also explains the fact that suitable music played to any scene, action, event, or surrounding seems to disclose to us its most secret meaning, and appears as the most accurate and distinct commentary upon it; as also the fact that whoever gives himself up entirely to the impression of a symphony seems to see all the possible events of life and the world take place in himself: nevertheless upon reflection he can find no likeness between the music and the things that passed before his mind. For, as we have said, music is distinguished from all the other arts by the fact that it is not a copy of the phenomenon, or, more accurately, the adequate objectivity of the will, but is the direct copy of the will itself, and therefore represents the metaphysical of everything physical in the world, and the thing-in-itself of every phenomenon. We might, therefore, just as well call the world embodied music as embodied will: and this is the reason why music makes every picture, and indeed every scene of real life and of the world, at once appear with higher significance; all the more so, to be sure, in proportion as its melody is analogous to the inner spirit of the given phenomenon. It rests upon this that we are able to set a poem to music as a song, or a perceptible representation as a pantomime, or both as an opera. Such particular pictures of human life, set to the universal language of music, are never bound to it or correspond to it with stringent necessity, but stand to it only in the relation of an example chosen at will to a general concept. In the determinateness of the real they represent that which music expresses in the universality of mere form. For melodies are to a certain extent, like general concepts, an abstraction from the actual. This actual world, then, the world of particular things, affords the object of perception, the special and the individual, the particular case, both to the universality of concepts and to the universality of the melodies. But these two universalities are in a certain respect opposed to each other; for the concepts contain only the forms, which are first of all abstracted from perception,—the separated outward shell of things, as it were,—and hence they are, in the strictest sense of the term, *abstracta;* music, on the other hand, gives the inmost kernel which precedes all forms, or the heart of things. This relation may be very well expressed in the language of the schoolmen, by saying: the concepts are the *universalia post rem,* but music gives the *universalia ante rem,* and the real world the *universalia in re.*—But that in general a relation is possible between a composition and a perceptible representation rests, as we have said, upon the fact that both are simply different expressions of the same inner being of the world. When now, in the particular case, such a relation is actually given, that is to say, when the composer has been able to express in the universal language of music the emotions of will which constitute the heart of an event, then the melody of the song, the music of the opera, is expressive. But the analogy discovered by the composer between the two must have proceeded from the direct knowledge of the nature of the world unknown to his reason, and must not be an imitation produced with conscious intention by means of conceptions; otherwise the music does not express the inner nature of the will itself, but merely gives an inadequate imitation of its phenomenon: all specially imitative music does this."

We have therefore, according to the doctrine of Schopenhauer, an immediate understanding of music as the language of the will, and feel our imagination stimulated to give form to this invisible and yet so actively stirred spirit-world which speaks to us, and prompted to embody it in an analogous example. On the other hand, image and concept, under the influence of a truly conformable music, acquire a higher significance. Dionysian art therefore is wont to exercise two kinds of influences on the Apollonian art-faculty: music firstly incites to the symbolic intuition of Dionysian universality, and, secondly, it causes the symbolic image to stand forth in its fullest significance. From these facts, intelligible in themselves and not inaccessible to profounder observation, I infer the capacity of music to give birth to myth, that is to say, the most significant exemplar, and precisely tragic myth: the myth which speaks of Dionysian knowledge in symbols. In the phenomenon of the lyrist, I have set forth that in him music strives to express itself with regard to its nature in Apollonian images. If now we reflect that music in its highest potency must seek to attain also to its highest symbolisation, we must deem it possible that it also knows how to find the symbolic expression of its inherent Dionysian wisdom; and where shall we have to seek for this expression if not in tragedy and, in general, in the conception of the tragic?

From the nature of art, as it is ordinarily conceived according to the single category of appearance and beauty, the tragic cannot be honestly deduced at all; it is only through the spirit of music that we understand the joy in the annihilation of the individual. For in the particular examples of such annihilation only is the eternal phenomenon of Dionysian art made clear to us, which gives expression to the will in its omnipotence, as it were, behind the *principium individuationis,* the eternal life beyond all phenomena, and in spite of all annihilation. The metaphysical delight in the tragic is a translation of the instinctively unconscious Dionysian wisdom into the language of the scene: the hero, the highest manifestation of the will, is disavowed for our pleasure, because he is only phenomenon, and because the eternal life of the will is not affected by his annihilation. "We believe in eternal life," tragedy exclaims; while music is the proximate idea of this life. Plastic art has an altogether different object: here Apollo vanquishes the suffering of the individual by the radiant glorification of the eternity of the phenomenon; here beauty triumphs over the suffering inherent in life; pain is in a manner surreptitiously obliterated from the features of nature. In Dionysian art and its tragic symbolism the same nature speaks to us with its true undissembled voice: "Be as I am! Amidst the ceaseless change of phenomena the eternally creative primordial mother, eternally impelling to existence, self-satisfying eternally with this change of phenomena!"

17.

Dionysian art, too, seeks to convince us of the eternal joy of existence: only we are to seek this joy not in phenomena, but behind phenomena. We are to perceive how all that comes into being must be ready for a sorrowful end; we are compelled to look into the terrors of individual existence—yet we are not to become torpid: a metaphysical comfort tears us momentarily from the bustle of the transforming figures. We are really for brief moments Primordial Being itself, and feel its indomitable desire for being and joy in existence; the struggle, the pain, the destruction of phenomena, now appear to us as something necessary, considering the surplus of innumerable forms of existence which throng and push one another into life, considering the exuberant fertility of the universal will. We are pierced by the maddening sting of these pains at the very moment when we have become, as it were, one with the immeasurable primordial joy in existence, and when we anticipate, in Dionysian ecstasy, the indestructibility and eternity of this joy. In spite of fear and pity, we are the happy living beings, not as individuals, but as the one living being, with whose procreative joy we are blended.

The history of the rise of Greek tragedy now tells us with luminous precision that the tragic art of the Greeks was really born of the spirit of music: with which conception we believe we have done justice for the first time to the original and most astonishing significance of the chorus. At the same time, however, we must admit that the import of tragic myth as set forth above never became transparent with sufficient lucidity to the Greek poets, let alone the Greek philosophers; their heroes speak, as it were, more superficially than they act; the myth does not at all find its adequate objectification in the spoken word. The structure of the scenes and the conspicuous images reveal a deeper wisdom than the poet himself can put into words and concepts: the same being also observed in Shakespeare, whose Hamlet, for instance, in an analogous manner talks more superficially than he acts, so that the previously mentioned lesson of Hamlet is to be gathered not from his words, but from a more profound contemplation and survey of the whole. With respect to Greek tragedy, which of course presents itself to us only as word-drama, I have even intimated that the incongruence between myth and expression might easily tempt us to regard it as shallower and less significant than it really is, and accordingly to postulate for it a more superficial effect than it must have had according to the testimony of the ancients: for how easily one forgets that what the word-poet did not succeed in doing, namely realising the highest spiritualisation and ideality of myth, he might succeed in doing every moment as creative musician! We require, to be sure, almost by philological method to reconstruct for ourselves the ascendency of musical influence in order to receive something of the incomparable comfort which must be characteristic of true tragedy. Even this musical ascendency, however, would only have been felt by us as such had we been Greeks: while in the entire development of Greek music—as compared with the infinitely richer music known and familiar to us—we imagine we hear only the youthful song of the musical genius intoned with a feeling of diffidence. The Greeks are, as the Egyptian priests say, eternal children, and in tragic art also they are only children who do not know what a sublime plaything has originated under their hands and—is being demolished.

That striving of the spirit of music for symbolic and mythical manifestation, which increases from the beginnings of lyric poetry to Attic tragedy, breaks off all of a sudden immediately after attaining luxuriant development, and disappears, as it were, from the surface of Hellenic art: while the Dionysian view of things born of this striving lives on in Mysteries and, in its strangest metamorphoses and debasements, does not cease to attract earnest natures. Will it not one day rise again as art out of its mystic depth?

Here the question occupies us, whether the power by the counteracting influence of which tragedy perished, has for all time strength enough to prevent the artistic reawaking of tragedy and of the tragic view of things. If ancient tragedy was driven from its course by the dialectical desire for knowledge and the optimism of science, it might be inferred that there is an eternal conflict between the theoretic and the tragic view of things, and only after the spirit of science has been led to its boundaries, and its claim to universal validity has been destroyed by the evidence of these boundaries, can we hope for a re-birth of tragedy: for which form of culture we should have to use the symbol of the music-practising Socrates in the sense spoken of above. In this contrast, I understand by the spirit of science the belief which first came to light in the person of Socrates,—the belief in the fathomableness of nature and in knowledge as a panacea.

He who recalls the immediate consequences of this restlessly onward-pressing spirit of science will realise at once that myth was annihilated by it, and that, in consequence of this annihilation, poetry was driven as a homeless being from her natural ideal soil. If we have rightly assigned to music the capacity to reproduce myth from itself, we may in turn expect to find the spirit of science on the path where it inimically opposes this mythopoeic power of music. This takes place in the development of the New Attic Dithyramb, the music of which no longer expressed the inner essence, the will itself, but only rendered the phenomenon, insufficiently, in an imitation by means of concepts; from which intrinsically degenerate music the truly musical natures turned away with the same repugnance that they felt for the art-destroying tendency of Socrates. The unerring instinct of Aristophanes surely did the proper thing when it comprised Socrates himself, the tragedy of Euripides, and the music of the new Dithyrambic poets in the same feeling of hatred, and perceived in all three phenomena the symptoms of a degenerate culture. By this New Dithyramb, music has in an outrageous manner been made the imitative portrait of phenomena, for instance, of a battle or a storm at sea, and has thus, of course, been entirely deprived of its mythopoeic power. For if it endeavours to excite our delight only by compelling us to seek external analogies between a vital or natural process and certain rhythmical figures and characteristic sounds of music; if our understanding is expected to satisfy itself with the perception of these analogies, we are reduced to a frame of mind in which the reception of the mythical is impossible; for the myth as a unique exemplar of generality and truth towering into the infinite, desires to be conspicuously perceived. The truly Dionysian music presents itself to us as such a general mirror of the universal will: the conspicuous event which is refracted in this mirror expands at once for our consciousness to the copy of an eternal truth. Conversely, such a conspicuous event is at once divested of every mythical character by the tone-painting of the New Dithyramb; music has here become a wretched copy of the phenomenon, and therefore infinitely poorer than the phenomenon itself: through which poverty it still further reduces even the phenomenon for our consciousness, so that now, for instance, a musically imitated battle of this sort exhausts itself in marches, signal-sounds, etc., and our imagination is arrested precisely by these superficialities. Tone-painting is therefore in every respect the counterpart of true music with its mythopoeic power: through it the phenomenon, poor in itself, is made still poorer, while through an isolated Dionysian music the phenomenon is evolved and expanded into a picture of the world. It was an immense triumph of the non-Dionysian spirit, when, in the development of the New Dithyramb, it had estranged music from itself and reduced it to be the slave of phenomena. Euripides, who, albeit in a higher sense, must be designated as a thoroughly unmusical nature, is for this very reason a passionate adherent of the New Dithyrambic Music, and with the liberality of a freebooter employs all its effective turns and mannerisms.

In another direction also we see at work the power of this un-Dionysian, myth-opposing spirit, when we turn our eyes to the prevalence of character representation and psychological refinement from Sophocles onwards. The character must no longer be expanded into an eternal type, but, on the contrary, must operate individually through artistic by-traits and shadings, through the nicest precision of all lines, in such a manner that the spectator is in general no longer conscious of the myth, but of the mighty nature-myth and the imitative power of the artist. Here also we observe the victory of the phenomenon over the Universal, and the delight in the particular quasi-anatomical preparation; we actually breathe the air of a theoretical world, in which scientific knowledge is valued more highly than the artistic reflection of a universal law. The movement along the line of the representation of character proceeds rapidly: while Sophocles still delineates complete characters and employs myth for their refined development, Euripides already delineates only prominent individual traits of character, which can express themselves in violent bursts of passion; in the New Attic Comedy, however, there are only masks with one expression: frivolous old men, duped panders, and cunnings slaves in untiring repetition. Where now is the mythopoeic spirit of music? What is still left now of music is either excitatory music or souvenir music, that is, either a stimulant for dull and used-up nerves, or tone-painting. As regards the former, it hardly matters about the text set to it: the heroes and choruses of Euripides are already dissolute enough when once they begin to sing; to what pass must things have come with his brazen successors?

The new un-Dionysian spirit, however, manifests itself most clearly in the dénouements of the new dramas. In the Old Tragedy one could feel at the close the metaphysical comfort, without which the delight in tragedy cannot be explained at all; the conciliating tones from another world sound purest, perhaps, in the Œdipus at Colonus. Now that the genius of music has fled from tragedy, tragedy is, strictly speaking, dead: for from whence could one now draw the metaphysical comfort? One sought, therefore, for an earthly unravelment of the tragic dissonance; the hero, after he had been sufficiently tortured by fate, reaped a well-deserved reward through a superb marriage or divine tokens of favour. The hero had turned gladiator, on whom, after being liberally battered about and covered with wounds, freedom was occasionally bestowed. The deus ex machina took the place of metaphysical comfort. I will not say that the tragic view of things was everywhere completely destroyed by the intruding spirit of the un-Dionysian: we only know that it was compelled to flee from art into the under-world as it were, in the degenerate form of a secret cult. Over the widest extent of the Hellenic character, however, there raged the consuming blast of this spirit, which manifests itself in the form of "Greek cheerfulness," which we have already spoken of as a senile, unproductive love of existence; this cheerfulness is the counterpart of the splendid "naïveté" of the earlier Greeks, which, according to the characteristic indicated above, must be conceived as the blossom of the Apollonian culture growing out of a dark abyss, as the victory which the Hellenic will, through its mirroring of beauty, obtains over suffering and the wisdom of suffering. The noblest manifestation of that other form of "Greek cheerfulness," the Alexandrine, is the cheerfulness of the theoretical man: it exhibits the same symptomatic characteristics as I have just inferred concerning the spirit of the un-Dionysian:—it combats Dionysian wisdom and art, it seeks to dissolve myth, it substitutes for metaphysical comfort an earthly consonance, in fact, a deus ex machina of its own, namely the god of machines and crucibles, that is, the powers of the genii of nature recognised and employed in the service of higher egoism; it believes in amending the world by knowledge, in guiding life by science, and that it can really confine the individual within a narrow sphere of solvable problems, where he cheerfully says to life: "I desire thee: it is worth while to know thee."

18.

It is an eternal phenomenon: the avidious will can always, by means of an illusion spread over things, detain its creatures in life and compel them to live on. One is chained by the Socratic love of knowledge and the vain hope of being able thereby to heal the eternal wound of existence; another is ensnared by art's seductive veil of beauty fluttering before his eyes; still another by the metaphysical comfort that eternal life flows on indestructibly beneath the whirl of phenomena: to say nothing of the more ordinary and almost more powerful illusions which the will has always at hand. These three specimens of illusion are on the whole designed only for the more nobly endowed natures, who in general feel profoundly the weight and burden of existence, and must be deluded into forgetfulness of their displeasure by exquisite stimulants. All that we call culture is made up of these stimulants; and, according to the proportion of the ingredients, we have either a specially Socratic or artistic or tragic culture: or, if historical exemplifications are wanted, there is either an Alexandrine or a Hellenic or a Buddhistic culture.

Our whole modern world is entangled in the meshes of Alexandrine culture, and recognises as its ideal the theorist equipped with the most potent means of knowledge, and labouring in the service of science, of whom the archetype and progenitor is Socrates. All our educational methods have originally this ideal in view: every other form of existence must struggle onwards wearisomely beside it, as something tolerated, but not intended. In an almost alarming manner the cultured man was here found for a long time only in the form of the scholar: even our poetical arts have been forced to evolve from learned imitations, and in the main effect of the rhyme we still recognise the origin of our poetic form from artistic experiments with a non-native and thoroughly learned language. How unintelligible must Faust, the modern cultured man, who is in himself intelligible, have appeared to a true Greek,—Faust, storming discontentedly through all the faculties, devoted to magic and the devil from a desire for knowledge, whom we have only to place alongside of Socrates for the purpose of comparison, in order to see that modern man begins to divine the boundaries of this Socratic love of perception and longs for a coast in the wide waste of the ocean of knowledge. When Goethe on one occasion said to Eckermann with reference to Napoleon: "Yes, my good friend, there is also a productiveness of deeds," he reminded us in a charmingly naïve manner that the non-theorist is something incredible and astounding to modern man; so that the wisdom of Goethe is needed once more in order to discover that such a surprising form of existence is comprehensible, nay even pardonable.

Now, we must not hide from ourselves what is concealed in the heart of this Socratic culture: Optimism, deeming itself absolute! Well, we must not be alarmed if the fruits of this optimism ripen,—if society, leavened to the very lowest strata by this kind of culture, gradually begins to tremble through wanton agitations and desires, if the belief in the earthly happiness of all, if the belief in the possibility of such a general intellectual culture is gradually transformed into the threatening demand for such an Alexandrine earthly happiness, into the conjuring of a Euripidean deus ex machina. Let us mark this well: the Alexandrine culture requires a slave class, to be able to exist permanently: but, in its optimistic view of life, it denies the necessity of such a class, and consequently, when the effect of its beautifully seductive and tranquillising utterances about the "dignity of man" and the "dignity of labour" is spent, it gradually drifts towards a dreadful destination. There is nothing more terrible than a barbaric slave class, who have learned to regard their existence as an injustice, and now prepare to take vengeance, not only for themselves, but for all generations. In the face of such threatening storms, who dares to appeal with confident spirit to our pale and exhausted religions, which even in their foundations have degenerated into scholastic religions?—so that myth, the necessary prerequisite of every religion, is already paralysed everywhere, and even in this domain the optimistic spirit—which we have just designated as the annihilating germ of society—has attained the mastery.

While the evil slumbering in the heart of theoretical culture gradually begins to disquiet modern man, and makes him anxiously ransack the stores of his experience for means to avert the danger, though not believing very much in these means; while he, therefore, begins to divine the consequences his position involves: great, universally gifted natures have contrived, with an incredible amount of thought, to make use of the apparatus of science itself, in order to point out the limits and the relativity of knowledge generally, and thus definitely to deny the claim of science to universal validity and universal ends: with which demonstration the illusory notion was for the first time recognised as such, which pretends, with the aid of causality, to be able to fathom the innermost essence of things. The extraordinary courage and wisdom of Kant and Schopenhauer have succeeded in gaining the most difficult victory, the victory over the optimism hidden in the essence of logic, which optimism in turn is the basis of our culture. While this optimism, resting on apparently unobjectionable *aeternae veritates,* believed in the intelligibility and solvability of all the riddles of the world, and treated space, time, and causality as totally unconditioned laws of the most universal validity, Kant, on the other hand, showed that these served in reality only to elevate the mere phenomenon, the work of Mâyâ, to the sole and highest reality, putting it in place of the innermost and true essence of things, thus making the actual knowledge of this essence impossible, that is, according to the expression of Schopenhauer, to lull the dreamer still more soundly asleep. With this knowledge a culture is inaugurated which I venture to designate as a tragic culture; the most important characteristic of which is that wisdom takes the place of science as the highest end,—wisdom, which, uninfluenced by the seductive distractions of the sciences, turns with unmoved eye to the comprehensive view of the world, and seeks to apprehend therein the eternal suffering as its own with sympathetic feelings of love. Let us imagine a rising generation with this undauntedness of vision, with this heroic desire for the prodigious, let us imagine the bold step of these dragon-slayers, the proud and daring spirit with which they turn their backs on all the effeminate doctrines of optimism in order "to live resolutely" in the Whole and in the Full: would it not be necessary for the tragic man of this culture, with his self-discipline to earnestness and terror, to desire a new art, the art of metaphysical comfort,—namely, tragedy, as the Helena belonging to him, and that he should exclaim with Faust:

> Und sollt' ich nicht, sehnsüchtigster Gewalt,
> In's Leben ziehn die einzigste Gestalt?[11]

But now that the Socratic culture has been shaken from two directions, and is only able to hold the sceptre of its infallibility with trembling hands,—once by the fear of its own conclusions which it at length begins to surmise, and again, because it is no longer convinced with its former naïve trust of the eternal validity of its foundation,—it is a sad spectacle to behold how the dance of its thought always rushes longingly on new forms, to embrace them, and then, shuddering, lets them go of a sudden, as Mephistopheles does the seductive Lamiæ. It is certainly the symptom of the "breach" which all are wont to speak of as the primordial suffering of modern culture that the theoretical man, alarmed and dissatisfied at his own conclusions, no longer dares to entrust himself to the terrible ice-stream of existence: he runs timidly up and down the bank. He no longer wants to have anything entire, with all the natural cruelty of things, so thoroughly has he been spoiled by his optimistic contemplation. Besides, he feels that a culture built up on the principles of science must perish when it begins to grow illogical, that is, to avoid its own conclusions. Our art reveals this universal trouble: in vain does one seek help by imitating all the great productive periods and natures, in vain does one accumulate the entire "world-literature" around modern man for his comfort, in vain does one place one's self in the midst of the art-styles and artists of all ages, so that one may give names to them as Adam did to the beasts: one still continues the eternal hungerer, the "critic" without joy and energy, the Alexandrine man, who is in the main a librarian and corrector of proofs, and who, pitiable wretch, goes blind from the dust of books and printers' errors.

19.

We cannot designate the intrinsic substance of Socratic culture more distinctly than by calling it the culture of the opera: for it is in this department that culture has expressed itself with special naïveté concerning its aims and perceptions, which is sufficiently surprising when we compare the genesis of the opera and the facts of operatic development with the eternal truths of the Apollonian and Dionysian. I call to mind first of all the origin of the *stilo rappresentativo* and the recitative. Is it credible that this thoroughly externalised operatic music, incapable of devotion, could be received and cherished with enthusiastic favour, as a re-birth, as it were, of all true music, by the very age in which the ineffably sublime and sacred music of Palestrina had originated? And who, on the other hand, would think of making only the diversion-craving luxuriousness of those Florentine circles and the vanity of their dramatic singers responsible for the love of the opera which spread with such rapidity? That in the same age, even among the same people, this passion for a half-musical mode of speech should awaken alongside of the vaulted structure of Palestrine harmonies which the entire Christian Middle Age had been building up, I can explain to myself only by a co-operating extra-artistic tendency in the essence of the recitative.

The listener, who insists on distinctly hearing the words under the music, has his wishes met by the singer in that he speaks rather than sings, and intensifies the pathetic expression of the words in this half-song: by this intensification of the pathos he facilitates the understanding of the words and surmounts the remaining half of the music. The specific danger which now threatens him is that in some unguarded moment he may give undue importance to music, which would forthwith result in the destruction of the pathos of the speech and the distinctness of the words: while, on the other hand, he always feels himself impelled to musical delivery and to virtuose exhibition of vocal talent. Here the "poet" comes to his aid, who knows how to provide him with abundant opportunities for lyrical interjections, repetitions of words and sentences, etc.,—at which places the singer, now in the purely musical element, can rest himself without minding the words. This alternation of emotionally impressive, yet only half-sung speech and wholly sung interjections, which is characteristic of the *stilo rappresentativo,* this rapidly changing endeavour to operate now on the conceptional and representative faculty of the hearer, now on his musical sense, is something so thoroughly unnatural and withal so intrinsically contradictory both to the Apollonian and Dionysian artistic impulses, that one has to infer an origin of the recitative foreign to all artistic instincts. The recitative must be defined, according to this description, as the combination of epic and lyric delivery, not indeed as an intrinsically stable combination which could not be attained in the case of such totally disparate elements, but an entirely superficial mosaic conglutination, such as is totally unprecedented in the domain of nature and experience. But this was not the opinion of the inventors of the recitative: they themselves, and their age with them, believed rather that the mystery of antique music had been solved by this *stilo rappresentativo,* in which, as they thought, the only explanation of the enormous influence of an Orpheus, an Amphion, and even of Greek tragedy was to be found. The new style was regarded by them as the re-awakening of the most effective music, the Old Greek music: indeed, with the universal and popular conception of the Homeric world as the primitive world, they could abandon themselves to the dream of having descended once more into the paradisiac beginnings of mankind, wherein music also must needs have had the unsurpassed purity, power, and innocence of which the poets could give such touching accounts in their pastoral plays. Here we see into the internal process of development of this thoroughly modern variety of art, the opera: a powerful need here acquires an art, but it is a need of an unæsthetic kind: the yearning for the idyll, the belief in the prehistoric existence of the artistic, good man. The recitative was regarded as the rediscovered language of this primitive man; the opera as the recovered land of this idyllically or heroically good creature, who in every action follows at the same time a natural artistic impulse, who sings a little along with all he has to say, in order to sing immediately with full voice on the slightest emotional excitement. It is now a matter of indifference to us that the humanists of those days combated the old ecclesiastical representation of man as naturally corrupt and lost, with this new-created picture of the paradisiac artist: so that opera may be understood as the oppositional dogma of the good man, whereby however a solace was at the same time found for the pessimism to which precisely the seriously-disposed men of that time were most strongly incited, owing to the frightful uncertainty of all conditions of life. It is enough to have perceived that the intrinsic charm, and therefore the genesis, of this new form of art lies in the gratification of an altogether unæsthetic need, in the optimistic glorification of man as such, in the conception of the primitive man as the man naturally good and artistic: a principle of the opera which has gradually changed into a threatening and terrible demand, which, in face of the socialistic movements of the present time, we can no longer ignore. The "good primitive man" wants his rights: what paradisiac prospects!

I here place by way of parallel still another equally obvious confirmation of my view that opera is built up on the same principles as our Alexandrine culture. Opera is the birth of the theoretical man, of the critical layman, not of the artist: one of the most surprising facts in the whole history of art. it was the demand of thoroughly unmusical hearers that the words must above all be understood, so that according to them a re-birth of music is only to be expected when some mode of singing has been discovered in which the text-word lords over the counterpoint as the master over the servant. For the words, it is argued, are as much nobler than the accompanying harmonic system as the soul is nobler than the body. It was in accordance with the laically unmusical crudeness of these views that the combination of music, picture and expression was effected in the beginnings of the opera: in the spirit of this æsthetics the first experiments were also made in the leading laic circles of Florence by the poets and singers patronised there. The man incapable of art creates for himself a species of art precisely because he is the inartistic man as such. Because he does not divine the Dionysian depth of music, he changes his musical taste into appreciation of the understandable word-and-tone-rhetoric of the passions in the *stilo rappresentativo,* and into the voluptuousness of the arts of song; because he is unable to behold a vision, he forces the machinist and the decorative artist into his service; because he cannot apprehend the true nature of the artist, he conjures up the "artistic primitive man" to suit his taste, that is, the man who sings and recites verses under the influence of passion. He dreams himself into a time when passion suffices to generate songs and poems: as if emotion had ever been able to create anything artistic. The postulate of the opera is a false belief concerning the artistic process, in fact, the idyllic belief that every sentient man is an artist. In the sense of this belief, opera is the expression of the taste of the laity in art, who dictate their laws with the cheerful optimism of the theorist.

Should we desire to unite in one the two conceptions just set forth as influential in the origin of opera, it would only remain for us to speak of an idyllic tendency of the opera: in which connection we may avail ourselves exclusively of the phraseology and illustration of Schiller in his "Essay on Elegiac Poetry." "Nature and the ideal," he says, "are either objects of grief, when the former is represented as lost, the latter unattained; or both are objects of joy, in that they are represented as real. The first case furnishes the elegy in its narrower signification, the second the idyll in its widest sense." Here we must at once call attention to the common characteristic of these two conceptions in operatic genesis, namely, that in them the ideal is not regarded as unattained or nature as lost. Agreeably to this sentiment, there was a primitive age of man when he lay close to the heart of nature, and, owing to this naturalness, had attained the ideal of mankind in a paradisiac goodness and artist-organisation: from which perfect primitive man all of us were supposed to be descended; whose faithful copy we were in fact still said to be: only we had to cast off some few things in order to recognise ourselves once more as this primitive man, on the strength of a voluntary renunciation of superfluous learnedness, of super-abundant culture. It was to such a concord of nature and the ideal, to an idyllic reality, that the cultured man of the Renaissance suffered himself to be led back by his operatic imitation of Greek tragedy; he made use of this tragedy, as Dante made use of Vergil, in order to be led up to the gates of paradise: while from this point he went on without assistance and passed over from an imitation of the highest form of Greek art to a "restoration of all things," to an imitation of man's original art-world. What delightfully naïve hopefulness of these daring endeavours, in the very heart of theoretical culture!—solely to be explained by the comforting belief, that "man-in-himself" is the eternally virtuous hero of the opera, the eternally fluting or singing shepherd, who must always in the end rediscover himself as such, if he has at any time really lost himself; solely the fruit of the optimism, which here rises like a sweetishly seductive column of vapour out of the depth of the Socratic conception of the world.

The features of the opera therefore do not by any means exhibit the elegiac sorrow of an eternal loss, but rather the cheerfulness of eternal rediscovery, the indolent delight in an idyllic reality which one can at least represent to one's self each moment as real: and in so doing one will perhaps surmise some day that this supposed reality is nothing but a fantastically silly dawdling, concerning which every one, who could judge it by the terrible earnestness of true nature and compare it with the actual primitive scenes of the beginnings of mankind, would have to call out with loathing: Away with the phantom! Nevertheless one would err if one thought it possible to frighten away merely by a vigorous shout such a dawdling thing as the opera, as if it were a spectre. He who would destroy the opera must join issue with Alexandrine cheerfulness, which expresses itself so naïvely therein concerning its favourite representation; of which in fact it is the specific form of art. But what is to be expected for art itself from the operation of a form of art, the beginnings of which do not at all lie in the æsthetic province; which has rather stolen over from a half-moral sphere into the artistic domain, and has been able only now and then to delude us concerning this hybrid origin? By what sap is this parasitic opera-concern nourished, if not by that of true art? Must we not suppose that the highest and indeed the truly serious task of art—to free the eye from its glance into the horrors of night and to deliver the "subject" by the healing balm of appearance from the spasms of volitional agitations—will degenerate under the influence of its idyllic seductions and Alexandrine adulation to an empty dissipating tendency, to pastime? What will become of the eternal truths of the Dionysian and Apollonian in such an amalgamation of styles as I have exhibited in the character of the *stilo rappresentativo?* where music is regarded as the servant, the text as the master, where music is compared with the body, the text with the soul? where at best the highest aim will be the realisation of a paraphrastic tone-painting, just as formerly in the New Attic Dithyramb? where music is completely alienated from its true dignity of being, the Dionysian mirror of the world, so that the only thing left to it is, as a slave of phenomena, to imitate the formal character thereof, and to excite an external pleasure in the play of lines and proportions. On close observation, this fatal influence of the opera on music is seen to coincide absolutely with the universal development of modern music; the optimism lurking in the genesis of the opera and in the essence of culture represented thereby, has, with alarming rapidity, succeeded in divesting music of its Dionyso-cosmic mission and in impressing on it a playfully formal and pleasurable character: a change with which perhaps only the metamorphosis of the Æschylean man into the cheerful Alexandrine man could be compared.

If, however, in the exemplification herewith indicated we have rightly associated the evanescence of the Dionysian spirit with a most striking, but hitherto unexplained transformation and degeneration of the Hellene—what hopes must revive in us when the most trustworthy auspices guarantee the reverse process, the gradual awakening of the Dionysian spirit in our modern world! It is impossible for the divine strength of Herakles to languish for ever in voluptuous bondage to Omphale. Out of the Dionysian root of the German spirit a power has arisen which has nothing in common with the primitive conditions of Socratic culture, and can neither be explained nor excused thereby, but is rather regarded by this culture as something terribly inexplicable and overwhelmingly hostile,—namely, German music as we have to understand it, especially in its vast solar orbit from Bach to Beethoven, from Beethoven to Wagner. What even under the most favourable circumstances can the knowledge-craving Socratism of our days do with this demon rising from unfathomable depths? Neither by means of the zig-zag and arabesque work of operatic melody, nor with the aid of the arithmetical counting board of fugue and contrapuntal dialectics is the formula to be found, in the trebly powerful light of which one could subdue this demon and compel it to speak. What a spectacle, when our æsthetes, with a net of "beauty" peculiar to themselves, now pursue and clutch at the genius of music romping about before them with incomprehensible life, and in so doing display activities which are not to be judged by the standard of eternal beauty any more than by the standard of the sublime. Let us but observe these patrons of music as they are, at close range, when they call out so indefatigably "beauty! beauty!" to discover whether they have the marks of nature's darling children who are fostered and fondled in the lap of the beautiful, or whether they do not rather seek a disguise for their own rudeness, an æsthetical pretext for their own unemotional insipidity: I am thinking here, for instance, of Otto Jahn. But let the liar and the hypocrite beware of our German music: for in the midst of all our culture it is really the only genuine, pure and purifying fire-spirit from which and towards which, as in the teaching of the great Heraclitus of Ephesus, all things move in a double orbit: all that we now call culture, education, civilisation, must appear some day before the unerring judge, Dionysus.

Let us recollect furthermore how Kant and Schopenhauer made it possible for the spirit of German philosophy streaming from the same sources to annihilate the satisfied delight in existence of scientific Socratism by the delimitation of the boundaries thereof; how through this delimitation an infinitely profounder and more serious view of ethical problems and of art was inaugurated, which we may unhesitatingly designate as Dionysian wisdom comprised in concepts. To what then does the mystery of this oneness of German music and philosophy point, if not to a new form of existence, concerning the substance of which we can only inform ourselves presentiently from Hellenic analogies? For to us who stand on the boundary line between two different forms of existence, the Hellenic prototype retains the immeasurable value, that therein all these transitions and struggles are imprinted in a classically instructive form: except that we, as it were, experience analogically in reverse order the chief epochs of the Hellenic genius, and seem now, for instance, to pass backwards from the Alexandrine age to the period of tragedy. At the same time we have the feeling that the birth of a tragic age betokens only a return to itself of the German spirit, a blessed self-rediscovering after excessive and urgent external influences have for a long time compelled it, living as it did in helpless barbaric formlessness, to servitude under their form. It may at last, after returning to the primitive source of its being, venture to stalk along boldly and freely before all nations without hugging the leading-strings of a Romanic civilisation: if only it can learn implicitly of one people—the Greeks, of whom to learn at all is itself a high honour and a rare distinction. And when did we require these highest of all teachers more than at present, when we experience a re-birth of tragedy and are in danger alike of not knowing whence it comes, and of being unable to make clear to ourselves whither it tends.

20.

It may be weighed some day before an impartial judge, in what time and in what men the German spirit has thus far striven most resolutely to learn of the Greeks: and if we confidently assume that this unique praise must be accorded to the noblest intellectual efforts of Goethe, Schiller, and Winkelmann, it will certainly have to be added that since their time, and subsequently to the more immediate influences of these efforts, the endeavour to attain to culture and to the Greeks by this path has in an incomprehensible manner grown feebler and feebler. In order not to despair altogether of the German spirit, must we not infer therefrom that possibly, in some essential matter, even these champions could not penetrate into the core of the Hellenic nature, and were unable to establish a permanent friendly alliance between German and Greek culture? So that perhaps an unconscious perception of this shortcoming might raise also in more serious minds the disheartening doubt as to whether after such predecessors they could advance still farther on this path of culture, or could reach the goal at all. Accordingly, we see the opinions concerning the value of Greek contribution to culture degenerate since that time in the most alarming manner; the expression of compassionate superiority may be heard in the most heterogeneous intellectual and non-intellectual camps, and elsewhere a totally ineffective declamation dallies with "Greek harmony," "Greek beauty," "Greek cheerfulness." And in the very circles whose dignity it might be to draw indefatigably from the Greek channel for the good of German culture, in the circles of the teachers in the higher educational institutions, they have learned best to compromise with the Greeks in good time and on easy terms, to the extent often of a sceptical abandonment of the Hellenic ideal and a total perversion of the true purpose of antiquarian studies. If there be any one at all in these circles who has not completely exhausted himself in the endeavour to be a trustworthy corrector of old texts or a natural-history microscopist of language, he perhaps seeks also to appropriate Grecian antiquity "historically" along with other antiquities, and in any case according to the method and with the supercilious air of our present cultured historiography. When, therefore, the intrinsic efficiency of the higher educational institutions has never perhaps been lower or feebler than at present, when the "journalist," the paper slave of the day, has triumphed over the academic teacher in all matters pertaining to culture, and there only remains to the latter the often previously experienced metamorphosis of now fluttering also, as a cheerful cultured butterfly, in the idiom of the journalist, with the "light elegance" peculiar thereto—with what painful confusion must the cultured persons of a period like the present gaze at the phenomenon (which can perhaps be comprehended analogically only by means of the profoundest principle of the hitherto unintelligible Hellenic genius) of the reawakening of the Dionysian spirit and the re-birth of tragedy? Never has there been another art-period in which so-called culture and true art have been so estranged and opposed, as is so obviously the case at present. We understand why so feeble a culture hates true art; it fears destruction thereby. But must not an entire domain of culture, namely the Socratic-Alexandrine, have exhausted its powers after contriving to culminate in such a daintily-tapering point as our present culture? When it was not permitted to heroes like Goethe and Schiller to break open the enchanted gate which leads into the Hellenic magic mountain, when with their most dauntless striving they did not get beyond the longing gaze which the Goethean Iphigenia cast from barbaric Tauris to her home across the ocean, what could the epigones of such heroes hope for, if the gate should not open to them suddenly of its own accord, in an entirely different position, quite overlooked in all endeavours of culture hitherto—amidst the mystic tones of reawakened tragic music.

Let no one attempt to weaken our faith in an impending re-birth of Hellenic antiquity; for in it alone we find our hope of a renovation and purification of the German spirit through the fire-magic of music. What else do we know of amidst the present desolation and languor of culture, which could awaken any comforting expectation for the future? We look in vain for one single vigorously-branching root, for a speck of fertile and healthy soil: there is dust, sand, torpidness and languishing everywhere! Under such circumstances a cheerless solitary wanderer could choose for himself no better symbol than the Knight with Death and the Devil, as Dürer has sketched him for us, the mail-clad knight, grim and stern of visage, who is able, unperturbed by his gruesome companions, and yet hopelessly, to pursue his terrible path with horse and hound alone. Our Schopenhauer was such a Dürerian knight: he was destitute of all hope, but he sought the truth. There is not his equal.

But how suddenly this gloomily depicted wilderness of our exhausted culture changes when the Dionysian magic touches it! A hurricane seizes everything decrepit, decaying, collapsed, and stunted; wraps it whirlingly into a red cloud of dust; and carries it like a vulture into the air. Confused thereby, our glances seek for what has vanished: for what they see is something risen to the golden light as from a depression, so full and green, so luxuriantly alive, so ardently infinite. Tragedy sits in the midst of this exuberance of life, sorrow and joy, in sublime ecstasy; she listens to a distant doleful song—it tells of the Mothers of Being, whose names are: *Wahn, Wille, Wehe* (whim, will, woe)—Yes, my friends, believe with me in Dionysian life and in the re-birth of tragedy. The time of the Socratic man is past: crown yourselves with ivy, take in your hands the thyrsus, and do not marvel if tigers and panthers lie down fawning at your feet. Dare now to be tragic men, for ye are to be redeemed! Ye are to accompany the Dionysian festive procession from India to Greece! Equip yourselves for severe conflict, but believe in the wonders of your god!

21.

Gliding back from these hortative tones into the mood which befits the contemplative man, I repeat that it can only be learnt from the Greeks what such a sudden and miraculous awakening of tragedy must signify for the essential basis of a people's life. It is the people of the tragic mysteries who fight the battles with the Persians: and again, the people who waged such wars required tragedy as a necessary healing potion. Who would have imagined that there was still such a uniformly powerful effusion of the simplest political sentiments, the most natural domestic instincts and the primitive manly delight in strife in this very people after it had been shaken to its foundations for several generations by the most violent convulsions of the Dionysian demon? If at every considerable spreading of the Dionysian commotion one always perceives that the Dionysian loosing from the shackles of the individual makes itself felt first of all in an increased encroachment on the political instincts, to the extent of indifference, yea even hostility, it is certain, on the other hand, that the state-forming Apollo is also the genius of the *principium individuationis,* and that the state and domestic sentiment cannot live without an assertion of individual personality. There is only one way from orgasm for a people,—the way to Indian Buddhism, which, in order to be at all endured with its longing for nothingness, requires the rare ecstatic states with their elevation above space, time, and the individual; just as these in turn demand a philosophy which teaches how to overcome the indescribable depression of the intermediate states by means of a fancy. With the same necessity, owing to the unconditional dominance of political impulses, a people drifts into a path of extremest secularisation, the most magnificent, but also the most terrible expression of which is the Roman *imperium*.

Placed between India and Rome, and constrained to a seductive choice, the Greeks succeeded in devising in classical purity still a third form of life, not indeed for long private use, but just on that account for immortality. For it holds true in all things that those whom the gods love die young, but, on the other hand, it holds equally true that they then live eternally with the gods. One must not demand of what is most noble that it should possess the durable toughness of leather; the staunch durability, which, for instance, was inherent in the national character of the Romans, does not probably belong to the indispensable predicates of perfection. But if we ask by what physic it was possible for the Greeks, in their best period, notwithstanding the extraordinary strength of their Dionysian and political impulses, neither to exhaust themselves by ecstatic brooding, nor by a consuming scramble for empire and worldly honour, but to attain the splendid mixture which we find in a noble, inflaming, and contemplatively disposing wine, we must remember the enormous power of tragedy, exciting, purifying, and disburdening the entire life of a people; the highest value of which we shall divine only when, as in the case of the Greeks, it appears to us as the essence of all the prophylactic healing forces, as the mediator arbitrating between the strongest and most inherently fateful characteristics of a people.

Tragedy absorbs the highest musical orgasm into itself, so that it absolutely brings music to perfection among the Greeks, as among ourselves; but it then places alongside thereof tragic myth and the tragic hero, who, like a mighty Titan, takes the entire Dionysian world on his shoulders and disburdens us thereof; while, on the other hand, it is able by means of this same tragic myth, in the person of the tragic hero, to deliver us from the intense longing for this existence, and reminds us with warning hand of another existence and a higher joy, for which the struggling hero prepares himself presentiently by his destruction, not by his victories. Tragedy sets a sublime symbol, namely the myth between the universal authority of its music and the receptive Dionysian hearer, and produces in him the illusion that music is only the most effective means for the animation of the plastic world of myth. Relying upon this noble illusion, she can now move her limbs for the dithyrambic dance, and abandon herself unhesitatingly to an orgiastic feeling of freedom, in which she could not venture to indulge as music itself, without this illusion. The myth protects us from the music, while, on the other hand, it alone gives the highest freedom thereto. By way of return for this service, music imparts to tragic myth such an impressive and convincing metaphysical significance as could never be attained by word and image, without this unique aid; and the tragic spectator in particular experiences thereby the sure presentiment of supreme joy to which the path through destruction and negation leads; so that he thinks he hears, as it were, the innermost abyss of things speaking audibly to him.

If in these last propositions I have succeeded in giving perhaps only a preliminary expression, intelligible to few at first, to this difficult representation, I must not here desist from stimulating my friends to a further attempt, or cease from beseeching them to prepare themselves, by a detached example of our common experience, for the perception of the universal proposition. In this example I must not appeal to those who make use of the pictures of the scenic processes, the words and the emotions of the performers, in order to approximate thereby to musical perception; for none of these speak music as their mother-tongue, and, in spite of the aids in question, do not get farther than the precincts of musical perception, without ever being allowed to touch its innermost shrines; some of them, like Gervinus, do not even reach the precincts by this path. I have only to address myself to those who, being immediately allied to music, have it as it were for their mother's lap, and are connected with things almost exclusively by unconscious musical relations. I ask the question of these genuine musicians: whether they can imagine a man capable of hearing the third act of *Tristan und Isolde* without any aid of word or scenery, purely as a vast symphonic period, without expiring by a spasmodic distention of all the wings of the soul? A man who has thus, so to speak, put his ear to the heart-chamber of the cosmic will, who feels the furious desire for existence issuing therefrom as a thundering stream or most gently dispersed brook, into all the veins of the world, would he not collapse all at once? Could he endure, in the wretched fragile tenement of the human individual, to hear the re-echo of countless cries of joy and sorrow from the "vast void of cosmic night," without flying irresistibly towards his primitive home at the sound of this pastoral dance-song of metaphysics? But if, nevertheless, such a work can be heard as a whole, without a renunciation of individual existence, if such a creation could be created without demolishing its creator—where are we to get the solution of this contradiction?

Here there interpose between our highest musical excitement and the music in question the tragic myth and the tragic hero—in reality only as symbols of the most universal facts, of which music alone can speak directly. If, however, we felt as purely Dionysian beings, myth as a symbol would stand by us absolutely ineffective and unnoticed, and would never for a moment prevent us from giving ear to the re-echo of the *universalia ante rem.* Here, however, the Apollonian power, with a view to the restoration of the well-nigh shattered individual, bursts forth with the healing balm of a blissful illusion: all of a sudden we imagine we see only Tristan, motionless, with hushed voice saying to himself: "the old tune, why does it wake me?" And what formerly interested us like a hollow sigh from the heart of being, seems now only to tell us how "waste and void is the sea." And when, breathless, we thought to expire by a convulsive distention of all our feelings, and only a slender tie bound us to our present existence, we now hear and see only the hero wounded to death and still not dying, with his despairing cry: "Longing! Longing! In dying still longing! for longing not dying!" And if formerly, after such a surplus and superabundance of consuming agonies, the jubilation of the born rent our hearts almost like the very acme of agony, the rejoicing Kurwenal now stands between us and the "jubilation as such," with face turned toward the ship which carries Isolde. However powerfully fellow-suffering encroaches upon us, it nevertheless delivers us in a manner from the primordial suffering of the world, just as the symbol-image of the myth delivers us from the immediate perception of the highest cosmic idea, just as the thought and word deliver us from the unchecked effusion of the unconscious will. The glorious Apollonian illusion makes it appear as if the very realm of tones presented itself to us as a plastic cosmos, as if even the fate of Tristan and Isolde had been merely formed and moulded therein as out of some most delicate and impressible material.

Thus does the Apollonian wrest us from Dionysian universality and fill us with rapture for individuals; to these it rivets our sympathetic emotion, through these it satisfies the sense of beauty which longs for great and sublime forms; it brings before us biographical portraits, and incites us to a thoughtful apprehension of the essence of life contained therein. With the immense potency of the image, the concept, the ethical teaching and the sympathetic emotion—the Apollonian influence uplifts man from his orgiastic self-annihilation, and beguiles him concerning the universality of the Dionysian process into the belief that he is seeing a detached picture of the world, for instance, Tristan and Isolde, and that, through music, he will be enabled to see it still more clearly and intrinsically. What can the healing magic of Apollo not accomplish when it can even excite in us the illusion that the Dionysian is actually in the service of the Apollonian, the effects of which it is capable of enhancing; yea, that music is essentially the representative art for an Apollonian substance?

With the pre-established harmony which obtains between perfect drama and its music, the drama attains the highest degree of conspicuousness, such as is usually unattainable in mere spoken drama. As all the animated figures of the scene in the independently evolved lines of melody simplify themselves before us to the distinctness of the catenary curve, the coexistence of these lines is also audible in the harmonic change which sympathises in a most delicate manner with the evolved process: through which change the relations of things become immediately perceptible to us in a sensible and not at all abstract manner, as we likewise perceive thereby that it is only in these relations that the essence of a character and of a line of melody manifests itself clearly. And while music thus compels us to see more extensively and more intrinsically than usual, and makes us spread out the curtain of the scene before ourselves like some delicate texture, the world of the stage is as infinitely expanded for our spiritualised, introspective eye as it is illumined outwardly from within. How can the word-poet furnish anything analogous, who strives to attain this internal expansion and illumination of the visible stage-world by a much more imperfect mechanism and an indirect path, proceeding as he does from word and concept? Albeit musical tragedy likewise avails itself of the word, it is at the same time able to place alongside thereof its basis and source, and can make the unfolding of the word, from within outwards, obvious to us.

Of the process just set forth, however, it could still be said as decidedly that it is only a glorious appearance, namely the aforementioned Apollonian illusion, through the influence of which we are to be delivered from the Dionysian obtrusion and excess. In point of fact, the relation of music to drama is precisely the reverse; music is the adequate idea of the world, drama is but the reflex of this idea, a detached umbrage thereof. The identity between the line of melody and the living form, between the harmony and the character-relations of this form, is true in a sense antithetical to what one would suppose on the contemplation of musical tragedy. We may agitate and enliven the form in the most conspicuous manner, and enlighten it from within, but it still continues merely phenomenon, from which there is no bridge to lead us into the true reality, into the heart of the world. Music, however, speaks out of this heart; and though countless phenomena of the kind might be passing manifestations of this music, they could never exhaust its essence, but would always be merely its externalised copies. Of course, as regards the intricate relation of music and drama, nothing can be explained, while all may be confused by the popular and thoroughly false antithesis of soul and body; but the unphilosophical crudeness of this antithesis seems to have become—who knows for what reason—a readily accepted Article of Faith with our æstheticians, while they have learned nothing concerning an antithesis of phenomenon and thing-in-itself, or perhaps, for reasons equally unknown, have not cared to learn anything thereof.

Should it have been established by our analysis that the Apollonian element in tragedy has by means of its illusion gained a complete victory over the Dionysian primordial element of music, and has made music itself subservient to its end, namely, the highest and clearest elucidation of the drama, it would certainly be necessary to add the very important restriction: that at the most essential point this Apollonian illusion is dissolved and annihilated. The drama, which, by the aid of music, spreads out before us with such inwardly illumined distinctness in all its movements and figures, that we imagine we see the texture unfolding on the loom as the shuttle flies to and fro,—attains as a whole an effect which transcends all Apollonian artistic effects. In the collective effect of tragedy, the Dionysian gets the upper hand once more; tragedy ends with a sound which could never emanate from the realm of Apollonian art. And the Apollonian illusion is thereby found to be what it is,—the assiduous veiling during the performance of tragedy of the intrinsically Dionysian effect: which, however, is so powerful, that it finally forces the Apollonian drama itself into a sphere where it begins to talk with Dionysian wisdom, and even denies itself and its Apollonian conspicuousness. Thus then the intricate relation of the Apollonian and the Dionysian in tragedy must really be symbolised by a fraternal union of the two deities: Dionysus speaks the language of Apollo; Apollo, however, finally speaks the language of Dionysus; and so the highest goal of tragedy and of art in general is attained.

22.

Let the attentive friend picture to himself purely and simply, according to his experiences, the effect of a true musical tragedy. I think I have so portrayed the phenomenon of this effect in both its phases that he will now be able to interpret his own experiences. For he will recollect that with regard to the myth which passed before him he felt himself exalted to a kind of omniscience, as if his viusal faculty were no longer merely a surface faculty, but capable of penetrating into the interior, and as if he now saw before him, with the aid of music, the ebullitions of the will, the conflict of motives, and the swelling stream of the passions, almost sensibly visible, like a plenitude of actively moving lines and figures, and could thereby dip into the most tender secrets of unconscious emotions. While he thus becomes conscious of the highest exaltation of his instincts for conspicuousness and transfiguration, he nevertheless feels with equal definitiveness that this long series of Apollonian artistic effects still does not generate the blissful continuance in will-less contemplation which the plasticist and the epic poet, that is to say, the strictly Apollonian artists, produce in him by their artistic productions: to wit, the justification of the world of the *individuatio* attained in this contemplation,—which is the object and essence of Apollonian art. He beholds the transfigured world of the stage and nevertheless denies it. He sees before him the tragic hero in epic clearness and beauty, and nevertheless delights in his annihilation. He comprehends the incidents of the scene in all their details, and yet loves to flee into the incomprehensible. He feels the actions of the hero to be justified, and is nevertheless still more elated when these actions annihilate their originator. He shudders at the sufferings which will befall the hero, and yet anticipates therein a higher and much more overpowering joy. He sees more extensively and profoundly than ever, and yet wishes to be blind. Whence must we derive this curious internal dissension, this collapse of the Apollonian apex, if not from the Dionysian spell, which, though apparently stimulating the Apollonian emotions to their highest pitch, can nevertheless force this superabundance of Apollonian power into its service? Tragic myth is to be understood only as a symbolisation of Dionysian wisdom by means of the expedients of Apollonian art: the mythus conducts the world of phenomena to its boundaries, where it denies itself, and seeks to flee back again into the bosom of the true and only reality; where it then, like Isolde, seems to strike up its metaphysical swan-song:—

In des Wonnemeeres
wogendem Schwall,
in der Duft-Wellen
tönendem Schall,
in des Waltathems
wehendem All—
ertrinken—versinken—
unbewusst—höchste Lust![12]

We thus realise to ourselves in the experiences of the truly æsthetic hearer the tragic artist himself when he proceeds like a luxuriously fertile divinity of individuation to create his figures (in which sense his work can hardly be understood as an "imitation of nature")—and when, on the other hand, his vast Dionysian impulse then absorbs the entire world of phenomena, in order to anticipate beyond it, and through its annihilation, the highest artistic primal joy, in the bosom of the Primordial Unity. Of course, our æsthetes have nothing to say about this return in fraternal union of the two art-deities to the original home, nor of either the Apollonian or Dionysian excitement of the hearer, while they are indefatigable in characterising the struggle of the hero with fate, the triumph of the moral order of the world, or the disburdenment of the emotions through tragedy, as the properly Tragic: an indefatigableness which makes me think that they are perhaps not æsthetically excitable men at all, but only to be regarded as moral beings when hearing tragedy. Never since Aristotle has an explanation of the tragic effect been proposed, by which an æsthetic activity of the hearer could be inferred from artistic circumstances. At one time fear and pity are supposed to be forced to an alleviating discharge through the serious procedure, at another time we are expected to feel elevated and inspired at the triumph of good and noble principles, at the sacrifice of the hero in the interest of a moral conception of things; and however certainly I believe that for countless men precisely this, and only this, is the effect of tragedy, it as obviously follows therefrom that all these, together with their interpreting æsthetes, have had no experience of tragedy as the highest art. The pathological discharge, the catharsis of Aristotle, which philologists are at a loss whether to include under medicinal or moral phenomena, recalls a remarkable anticipation of Goethe. "Without a lively pathological interest," he says, "I too have never yet succeeded in elaborating a tragic situation of any kind, and hence I have rather avoided than sought it. Can it perhaps have been still another of the merits of the ancients that the deepest pathos was with them merely æsthetic play, whereas with us the truth of nature must cooperate in order to produce such a work?" We can now answer in the affirmative this latter profound question after our glorious experiences, in which we have found to our astonishment in the case of musical tragedy itself, that the deepest pathos can in reality be merely æsthetic play: and therefore we are justified in believing that now for the first time the proto-phe-nomenon of the tragic can be portrayed with some degree of success. He who now will still persist in talking only of those vicarious effects proceeding from ultra-æs-thetic spheres, and does not feel himself raised above the pathologically-moral process, may be left to despair of his æsthetic nature: for which we recommend to him, by way of innocent equivalent, the interpretation of Shakespeare after the fashion of Gervinus, and the diligent search for poetic justice.

Thus with the re-birth of tragedy the æsthetic hearer is also born anew, in whose place in the theatre a curious *quid pro quo* was wont to sit with half-moral and half-learned pretensions,—the "critic." In his sphere hitherto everything has been artificial and merely glossed over with a semblance of life. The performing artist was in fact at a loss what to do with such a critically comporting hearer, and hence he, as well as the dramatist or operatic composer who inspired him, searched anxiously for the last remains of life in a being so pretentiously barren and incapable of enjoyment. Such "critics," however, have hitherto constituted the public; the student, the schoolboy, yea, even the most harmless womanly creature, were already unwittingly prepared by education and by journals for a similar perception of works of art. The nobler natures among the artists counted upon exciting the moral-religious forces in such a public, and the appeal to a moral order of the world operated vicariously, when in reality some powerful artistic spell should have enraptured the true hearer. Or again, some imposing or at all events exciting tendency of the contemporary political and social world was presented by the dramatist with such vividness that the hearer could forget his critical exhaustion and abandon himself to similar emotions, as, in patriotic or warlike moments, before the tribune of parliament, or at the condemnation of crime and vice:—an estrangement of the true aims of art which could not but lead directly now and then to a cult of tendency. But here there took place what has always taken place in the case of factitious arts, an extraordinary rapid depravation of these tendencies, so that for instance the tendency to employ the theatre as a means for the moral education of the people, which in Schiller's time was taken seriously, is already reckoned among the incredible antiquities of a surmounted culture. While the critic got the upper hand in the theatre and concert-hall, the journalist in the school, and the press in society, art degenerated into a topic of conversation of the most trivial kind, and æsthetic criticism was used as the cement of a vain, distracted, selfish and moreover piteously unoriginal sociality, the significance of which is suggested by the Schopenhauerian parable of the porcupines, so that there has never been so much gossip about art and so little esteem for it. But is it still possible to have intercourse with a man capable of conversing on Beethoven or Shakespeare? Let each answer this question according to his sentiments: he will at any rate show by his answer his conception of "culture," provided he tries at least to answer the question, and has not already grown mute with astonishment.

On the other hand, many a one more nobly and delicately endowed by nature, though he may have gradually become a critical barbarian in the manner described, could tell of the unexpected as well as totally unintelligible effect which a successful performance of *Lohengrin,* for example, exerted on him: except that perhaps every warning and interpreting hand was lacking to guide him; so that the incomprehensibly heterogeneous and altogether incomparable sensation which then affected him also remained isolated and became extinct, like a mysterious star after a brief brilliancy. He then divined what the æsthetic hearer is.

23.

He who wishes to test himself rigorously as to how he is related to the true æsthetic hearer, or whether he belongs rather to the community of the Socrato-critical man, has only to enquire sincerely concerning the sentiment with which he accepts the wonder represented on the stage: whether he feels his historical sense, which insists on strict psychological causality, insulted by it, whether with benevolent concession he as it were admits the wonder as a phenomenon intelligible to childhood, but relinquished by him, or whether he experiences anything else thereby. For he will thus be enabled to determine how far he is on the whole capable of understanding myth, that is to say, the concentrated picture of the world, which, as abbreviature of phenomena, cannot dispense with wonder. It is probable, however, that nearly every one, upon close examination, feels so disintegrated by the critico-historical spirit of our culture, that he can only perhaps make the former existence of myth credible to himself by learned means through intermediary abstractions. Without myth, however, every culture loses its healthy creative natural power: it is only a horizon encompassed with myths which rounds off to unity a social movement. It is only by myth that all the powers of the imagination and of the Apollonian dream are freed from their random rovings. The mythical figures have to be the invisibly omnipresent genii, under the care of which the young soul grows to maturity, by the signs of which the man gives a meaning to his life and struggles: and the state itself knows no more powerful unwritten law than the mythical foundation which vouches for its connection with religion and its growth from mythical ideas.

Let us now place alongside thereof the abstract man proceeding independently of myth, the abstract education, the abstract usage, the abstract right, the abstract state: let us picture to ourselves the lawless roving of the artistic imagination, not bridled by any native myth: let us imagine a culture which has no fixed and sacred primitive seat, but is doomed to exhaust all its possibilities, and has to nourish itself wretchedly from the other cultures—such is the Present, as the result of Socratism, which is bent on the destruction of myth. And now the myth-less man remains eternally hungering among all the bygones, and digs and grubs for roots, though he have to dig for them even among the remotest antiquities. The stupendous historical exigency of the unsatisfied modern culture, the gathering around one of countless other cultures, the consuming desire for knowledge—what does all this point to, if not to the loss of myth, the loss of the mythical home, the mythical source? Let us ask ourselves whether the feverish and so uncanny stirring of this culture is aught but the eager seizing and snatching at food of the hungerer—and who would care to contribute anything more to a culture which cannot be appeased by all it devours, and in contact with which the most vigorous and wholesome nourishment is wont to change into "history and criticism"?

We should also have to regard our German character with despair and sorrow, if it had already become inextricably entangled in, or even identical with this culture, in a similar manner as we can observe it to our horror to be the case in civilised France; and that which for a long time was the great advantage of France and the cause of her vast preponderance, to wit, this very identity of people and culture, might compel us at the sight thereof to congratulate ourselves that this culture of ours, which is so questionable, has hitherto had nothing in common with the noble kernel of the character of our people. All our hopes, on the contrary, stretch out longingly towards the perception that beneath this restlessly palpitating civilised life and educational convulsion there is concealed a glorious, intrinsically healthy, primeval power, which, to be sure, stirs vigorously only at intervals in stupendous moments, and then dreams on again in view of a future awakening. It is from this abyss that the German Reformation came forth: in the choral-hymn of which the future melody of German music first resounded. So deep, courageous, and soul-breathing, so exuberantly good and tender did this chorale of Luther sound,—as the first Dionysian-luring call which breaks forth from dense thickets at the approach of spring. To it responded with emulative echo the solemnly wanton procession of Dionysian revellers, to whom we are indebted for German music—and to whom we shall be indebted for the re-birth of German myth.

I know that I must now lead the sympathising and attentive friend to an elevated position of lonesome contemplation, where he will have but few companions, and I call out encouragingly to him that we must hold fast to our shining guides, the Greeks. For the rectification of our æsthetic knowledge we previously borrowed from them the two divine figures, each of which sways a separate realm of art, and concerning whose mutual contact and exaltation we have acquired a notion through Greek tragedy. Through a remarkable disruption of both these primitive artistic impulses, the ruin of Greek tragedy seemed to be necessarily brought about: with which process a degeneration and a transmutation of the Greek national character was strictly in keeping, summoning us to earnest reflection as to how closely and necessarily art and the people, myth and custom, tragedy and the state, have coalesced in their bases. The ruin of tragedy was at the same time the ruin of myth. Until then the Greeks had been involuntarily compelled immediately to associate all experiences with their myths, indeed they had to comprehend them only through this association: whereby even the most immediate present necessarily appeared to them *sub specie aeterni* and in a certain sense as timeless. Into this current of the timeless, however, the state as well as art plunged in order to find repose from the burden and eagerness of the moment. And a people—for the rest, also a man—is worth just as much only as its ability to impress on its experiences the seal of eternity: for it is thus, as it were, desecularised, and reveals its unconscious inner conviction of the relativity of time and of the true, that is, the metaphysical significance of life. The contrary happens when a people begins to comprehend itself historically and to demolish the mythical bulwarks around it: with which there is usually connected a marked secularisation, a breach with the unconscious metaphysics of its earlier existence, in all ethical consequences. Greek art and especially Greek tragedy delayed above all the annihilation of myth: it was necessary to annihilate these also to be able to live detached from the native soil, unbridled in the wilderness of thought, custom, and action. Even in such circumstances this metaphysical impulse still endeavours to create for itself a form of apotheosis (weakened, no doubt) in the Socratism of science urging to life: but on its lower stage this same impulse led only to a feverish search, which gradually merged into a pandemonium of myths and superstitions accumulated from all quarters: in the midst of which, nevertheless, the Hellene sat with a yearning heart till he contrived, as Græculus, to mask his fever with Greek cheerfulness and Greek levity, or to narcotise himself completely with some gloomy Oriental superstition.

We have approached this condition in the most striking manner since the reawakening of the Alexandro-Roman antiquity in the fifteenth century, after a long, not easily describable, interlude. On the heights there is the same exuberant love of knowledge, the same insatiate happiness of the discoverer, the same stupendous secularisation, and, together with these, a homeless roving about, an eager intrusion at foreign tables, a frivolous deification of the present or a dull senseless estrangement, all *sub speci saeculi,* of the present time: which same symptoms lead one to infer the same defect at the heart of this culture, the annihilation of myth. It seems hardly possible to transplant a foreign myth with permanent success, without dreadfully injuring the tree through this transplantation: which is perhaps occasionally strong enough and sound enough to eliminate the foreign element after a terrible struggle; but must ordinarily consume itself in a languishing and stunted condition or in sickly luxuriance. Our opinion of the pure and vigorous kernel of the German being is such that we venture to expect of it, and only of it, this elimination of forcibly ingrafted foreign elements, and we deem it possible that the German spirit will reflect anew on itself. Perhaps many a one will be of opinion that this spirit must begin its struggle with the elimination of the Romanic element: for which it might recognise an external preparation and encouragement in the victorious bravery and bloody glory of the late war, but must seek the inner constraint in the emulative zeal to be for ever worthy of the sublime protagonists on this path, of Luther as well as our great artists and poets. But let him never think he can fight such battles without his household gods, without his mythical home, without a "restoration" of all German things! And if the German should look timidly around for a guide to lead him back to his long-lost home, the ways and paths of which he knows no longer—let him but listen to the delightfully luring call of the Dionysian bird, which hovers above him, and would fain point out to him the way thither.

24.

Among the peculiar artistic effects of musical tragedy we had to emphasise an Apollonian illusion, through which we are to be saved from immediate oneness with the Dionysian music, while our musical excitement is able to discharge itself on an Apollonian domain and in an interposed visible middle world. It thereby seemed to us that precisely through this discharge the middle world of theatrical procedure, the drama generally, became visible and intelligible from within in a degree unattainable in the other forms of Apollonian art: so that here, where this art was as it were winged and borne aloft by the spirit of music, we had to recognise the highest exaltation of its powers, and consequently in the fraternal union of Apollo and Dionysus the climax of the Apollonian as well as of the Dionysian artistic aims.

Of course, the Apollonian light-picture did not, precisely with this inner illumination through music, attain the peculiar effect of the weaker grades of Apollonian art. What the epos and the animated stone can do—constrain the contemplating eye to calm delight in the world of the *individuatio*—could not be realised here, notwithstanding the greater animation and distinctness. We contemplated the drama and penetrated with piercing glance into its inner agitated world of motives—and yet it seemed as if only a symbolic picture passed before us, the profoundest significance of which we almost believed we had divined, and which we desired to put aside like a curtain in order to behold the original behind it. The greatest distinctness of the picture did not suffice us: for it seemed to reveal as well as veil something; and while it seemed, with its symbolic revelation, to invite the rending of the veil for the disclosure of the mysterious background, this illumined all-conspicuousness itself enthralled the eye and prevented it from penetrating more deeply.

He who has not experienced this,—to have to view, and at the same time to have a longing beyond the viewing,—will hardly be able to conceive how clearly and definitely these two processes coexist in the contemplation of tragic myth and are felt to be conjoined; while the truly æsthetic spectators will confirm my assertion that among the peculiar effects of tragedy this conjunction is the most noteworthy. Now let this phenomenon of the æsthetic spectator be transferred to an analogous process in the tragic artist, and the genesis of tragic myth will have been understood. It shares with the Apollonian sphere of art the full delight in appearance and contemplation, and at the same time it denies this delight and finds a still higher satisfaction in the annihilation of the visible world of appearance. The substance of tragic myth is first of all an epic event involving the glorification of the fighting hero: but whence originates the essentially enigmatical trait, that the suffering in the fate of the hero, the most painful victories, the most agonising contrasts of motives, in short, the exemplification of the wisdom of Silenus, or, æsthetically expressed, the Ugly and Discordant, is always represented anew in such countless forms with such predilection, and precisely in the most youthful and exuberant age of a people, unless there is really a higher delight experienced in all this?

For the fact that things actually take such a tragic course would least of all explain the origin of a form of art; provided that art is not merely an imitation of the reality of nature, but in truth a metaphysical supplement to the reality of nature, placed alongside thereof for its conquest. Tragic myth, in so far as it really belongs to art, also fully participates in this transfiguring metaphysical purpose of art in general: What does it transfigure, however, when it presents the phenomenal world in the guise of the suffering hero? Least of all the "reality" of this phenomenal world, for it says to us: "Look at this! Look carefully! It is your life! It is the hour-hand of your clock of existence!"

And myth has displayed this life, in order thereby to transfigure it to us? If not, how shall we account for the æsthetic pleasure with which we make even these representations pass before us? I am inquiring concerning the æsthetic pleasure, and am well aware that many of these representations may moreover occasionally create even a moral delectation, say under the form of pity or of a moral triumph. But he who would derive the effect of the tragic exclusively from these moral sources, as was usually the case far too long in æsthetics, let him not think that he has done anything for Art thereby; for Art must above all insist on purity in her domain. For the explanation of tragic myth the very first requirement is that the pleasure which characterises it must be sought in the purely æsthetic sphere, without encroaching on the domain of pity, fear, or the morally-sublime. How can the ugly and the discordant, the substance of tragic myth, excite an æsthetic pleasure?

Here it is necessary to raise ourselves with a daring bound into a metaphysics of Art. I repeat, therefore, my former proposition, that it is only as an æsthetic phenomenon that existence and the world appear justified: and in this sense it is precisely the function of tragic myth to convince us that even the Ugly and Discordant is an artistic game which the will, in the eternal fulness of its joy, plays with itself. But this not easily comprehensible proto-phenomenon of Dionysian Art becomes, in a direct way, singularly intelligible, and is immediately apprehended in the wonderful significance of musical dissonance: just as in general it is music alone, placed in contrast to the world, which can give us an idea as to what is meant by the justification of the world as an æsthetic phenomenon. The joy that the tragic myth excites has the same origin as the joyful sensation of dissonance in music. The Dionysian, with its primitive joy experienced in pain itself, is the common source of music and tragic myth.

Is it not possible that by calling to our aid the musical relation of dissonance, the difficult problem of tragic effect may have meanwhile been materially facilitated? For we now understand what it means to wish to view tragedy and at the same time to have a longing beyond the viewing: a frame of mind, which, as regards the artistically employed dissonance, we should simply have to characterise by saying that we desire to hear and at the same time have a longing beyond the hearing. That striving for the infinite, the pinion-flapping of longing accompanying the highest delight in the clearly-perceived reality, remind one that in both states we have to recognise a Dionysian phenomenon, which again and again reveals to us anew the playful upbuilding and demolishing of the world of individuals as the efflux of a primitive delight, in like manner as when Heraclitus the Obscure compares the world-building power to a playing child which places stones here and there and builds sandhills only to overthrow them again.

Hence, in order to form a true estimate of the Dionysian capacity of a people, it would seem that we must think not only of their music, but just as much of their tragic myth, the second witness of this capacity. Considering this most intimate relationship between music and myth, we may now in like manner suppose that a degeneration and depravation of the one involves a deterioration of the other: if it be true at all that the weakening of the myth is generally expressive of a debilitation of the Dionysian capacity. Concerning both, however, a glance at the development of the German genius should not leave us in any doubt; in the opera just as in the abstract character of our mythless existence, in an art sunk to pastime just as in a life guided by concepts, the inartistic as well as life-consuming nature of Socratic optimism had revealed itself to us. Yet there have been indications to console us that nevertheless in some inaccessible abyss the German spirit still rests and dreams, undestroyed, in glorious health, profundity, and Dionysian strength, like a knight sunk in slumber: from which abyss the Dionysian song rises to us to let us know that this German knight even still dreams his primitive Dionysian myth in blissfully earnest visions. Let no one believe that the German spirit has for ever lost its mythical home when it still understands so obviously the voices of the birds which tell of that home. Some day it will find itself awake in all the morning freshness of a deep sleep: then it will slay the dragons, destroy the malignant dwarfs, and waken Brünnhilde—and Wotan's spear itself will be unable to obstruct its course!

My friends, ye who believe in Dionysian music, ye know also what tragedy means to us. There we have tragic myth, born anew from music,—and in this latest birth ye can hope for everything and forget what is most afflicting. What is most afflicting to all of us, however, is—the prolonged degradation in which the German genius has lived estranged from house and home in the service of malignant dwarfs. Ye understand my allusion—as ye will also, in conclusion, understand my hopes.

25.

Music and tragic myth are equally the expression of the Dionysian capacity of a people, and are inseparable from each other. Both originate in an ultra-Apollonian sphere of art; both transfigure a region in the delightful accords of which all dissonance, just like the terrible picture of the world, dies charmingly away; both play with the sting of displeasure, trusting to their most potent magic; both justify thereby the existence even of the "worst world." Here the Dionysian, as compared with the Apollonian, exhibits itself as the eternal and original artistic force, which in general calls into existence the entire world of phenomena: in the midst of which a new transfiguring appearance becomes necessary, in order to keep alive the animated world of individuation. If we could conceive an incarnation of dissonance—and what is man but that?—then, to be able to live this dissonance would require a glorious illusion which would spread a veil of beauty over its peculiar nature. This is the true function of Apollo as deity of art: in whose name we comprise all the countless manifestations of the fair realm of illusion, which each moment render life in general worth living and make one impatient for the experience of the next moment.

At the same time, just as much of this basis of all existence—the Dionysian substratum of the world—is allowed to enter into the consciousness of human beings, as can be surmounted again by the Apollonian transfiguring power, so that these two art-impulses are constrained to develop their powers in strictly mutual proportion, according to the law of eternal justice. When the Dionysian powers rise with such vehemence as we experience at present, there can be no doubt that, veiled in a cloud, Apollo has already descended to us; whose grandest beautifying influences a coming generation will perhaps behold.

That this effect is necessary, however, each one would most surely perceive by intuition, if once he found himself carried back—even in a dream—into an Old-Hellenic existence. In walking under high Ionic colonnades, looking upwards to a horizon defined by clear and noble lines, with reflections of his transfigured form by his side in shining marble, and around him solemnly marching or quietly moving men, with harmoniously sounding voices and rhythmical pantomime, would he not in the presence of this perpetual influx of beauty have to raise his hand to Apollo and exclaim: "Blessed race of Hellenes! How great Dionysus must be among you, when the Delian god deems such charms necessary to cure you of your dithyrambic madness!"—To one in this frame of mind, however, an aged Athenian, looking up to him with the sublime eye of Æschylus, might answer: "Say also this, thou curious stranger: what sufferings this people must have undergone, in order to be able to become thus beautiful! But now follow me to a tragic play, and sacrifice with me in the temple of both the deities!"

[1] *The World as Will and Idea.*

[2] And shall not I, by mightiest desire,
In living shape that sole fair form acquire?
—SWANWICK, trans of *Faust.*
Cf. *GBWW,* Vol. 47, p. 182, ll. 7438-39.

[3] My friend, just this is poet's task:
His dreams to read and to unmask.
Trust me, illusion's truths thrice sealed
In dream to man will be revealed.
All verse-craft and poetisation
Is but soothdream interpretation.

[4] Ye bow in the dust, oh millions?
Thy maker, mortal, dost divine?

[5] Schopenhauer, *The World as Will and Idea.*

[6] "Here sit I, forming mankind
In my image,
A race resembling me,—
To sorrow and to weep,
To taste, to hold, to enjoy,
And not have need of thee,
As I!"

[7] We do not measure with such care:
Woman in thousand steps is there,
But howsoe'er she hasten may,
Man in one leap has cleared the way.
—*Faust,* tr. Bayard Taylor.
Cf. *GBWW,* Vol. 47, p. 97, ll. 3982-85.

[8] This is thy world, and what a world!—*Faust.*

[9] Woe! Woe!
Thou hast it destroyed,
The beautiful world;
With powerful fist;
In ruin 'tis hurled!
—*Faust,* tr. Bayard Taylor.

[10] In me thou seest its benefit,—
To him who hath but little wit,
Through parables to tell the truth.

[11] *See* footnote 2.

[12] In the sea of pleasure's
Billowing roll,
In the ether-waves
Knelling and toll,
In the world-breath's
Wavering whole—
To drown in, go down in—
Lost in swoon—greatest boon!

PICTURE CREDITS

*Key to abbreviations used to indicate location of pictures on page: r.—right; l.—left; t.—top; b.—bottom; c.—center; * —courtesy. Abbreviations are combined to indicate unusual placement.*

—FRONTISPIECE Art Resource **—7** From *Macroevolution: Pattern and Process* by Steven M. Stanley © 1979, W. H. Freeman and Company. All rights reserved. **—10** From *Patterns of Evolution as Illustrated by the Fossil Record,* A. Hallam, ed., Elsevier Scientific Publishing Company, Amsterdam **—12** * American Museum of Natural History **—14** From *Origin and Early Evolution of Angiosperms* by C. G. Beck © 1976, Columbia University Press **—17** * Dr. Lee McAlester, Southern Methodist University **—19** Museum of Comparative Zoology, Harvard University **—22** Gregory S. Paul **—23** * Trustees of the British Museum (Natural History) **—25** From "The Desert Pupfish" by James H. Brown © 1971, Scientific American, Inc. All rights reserved. **—35** From *The Pathology of Development* by H. Grunberg © 1963, John Wiley and Sons, Inc. **—43, 48** From *The New Evolutionary Timetable* by Steven M. Stanley © 1981, Basic Books, Inc. Reprinted by permission. **—185** The Bettmann Archive **—191** UPI **—199** BBC Hulton Library/The Bettmann Archive **—210** Art Resource **—218** (l., r.), **219** BBC Hulton Library/The Bettmann Archive **—227, 229, 233** Art Resource **—241** Culver Pictures **—247** The Granger Collection **—250** * Harper and Row, Publishers **—256** * Random House **—259** * The Viking Press **—262** * Harper and Row, Publishers **—342** Photographie Giraudon **—350** Culver Pictures **—378** Cliché Musées Nationaux **—391** Art Resource **—396** Archive für Kunst und Geschichte

Now there's a way to identify all your fine books with flair and style. As part of our continuing service to you, Britannica Home Library Service, Inc. is proud to be able to offer you the fine quality item shown on the next page.

Booklovers will love the heavy-duty personalized **Ex Libris** embosser. Now you can personalize all your fine books with the mark of distinction, just the way all the fine libraries of the world do.

To order this item, please type or print your name, address and zip code on a plain sheet of paper. (Note special instructions for ordering the embosser). Please send a check or money order only (your money will be refunded in full if you are not delighted) for the full amount of purchase, including postage and handling, to:

Britannica Home Library Service, Inc.
Attn: Yearbook Department
Post Office Box 6137
Chicago, Illinois 60680

(Please make remittance payable to: Britannica Home Library Service, Inc.)